EXPERIMENTAL DESIGN:
PROCEDURES FOR THE
BEHAVIORAL SCIENCES

ROGER E. KIRK

Baylor University

Brooks/Cole Publishing Company
Belmont, California

A division of Wadsworth Publishing Company, Inc.

4 5 6 7 8 9 10   74 73 72

L.C. Cat. Card No.: 68-12958

Printed in the United States of America

PREFACE

Experimental Design is intended to serve both as a text and as a reference book for persons engaged in research. It evolved from lecture notes developed during nine years of teaching a two-semester graduate course in experimental design, and it reflects my belief that there is a need for a book requiring a minimum of mathematical sophistication on the part of the reader but including a detailed coverage of the more complex designs and techniques available to behavioral scientists.

Current books on experimental design generally fall into two categories. One category includes the many excellent books that emphasize the statistical theory underlying experimental design. These books, although comprehensive in coverage, presuppose a mathematical background beyond that of the typical researcher. Furthermore, they are of limited use to him because they contain a minimum of worked examples and frequently leave the development of computing formulas to the reader. The second category includes books that require a minimum of mathematical background. Such books usually cover only the most elementary topics in experimental design and provide the student with little understanding of design principles. The purpose of this book is to fill the gap between these two types of books.

I have tried to provide detailed coverage of those designs and techniques having the greatest potential usefulness to persons engaged in behavioral research. Each experimental design is introduced by a research problem and computational example. Analyses that can be performed in addition to an *F* ratio, such as trend analysis, comparisons among means, estimation of sample size necessary to achieve a specified power, computation of variance components, and measures of strength of association, are described within the context of the research problems. Although mathematical derivations are kept to a minimum, the assumptions underlying each design are explicitly stated. Numerous references to original sources and related literature are provided for the reader who wishes to pursue a particular topic in greater detail.

Several features of the book require special comment. The same numerical data, with minor modifications, are used throughout the book. However, different hypothetical research problems are described in connection with these data. At a time when some reviewers are critical of books using artificial data, the use of only one set of such data requires some justification. Concerning this issue, C. C. Li (1964) has pointed out that one does not first learn to solve quadratic equations by working with *real* data containing such terms as

$$242.9189x^2 - 683.1620x - 1948.5149 = 0$$

but rather with data containing terms like

$$x^2 - 5x - 6 = 0.$$

The use of complicated numerical examples may, in fact, obscure the fundamental principles presented.

Students report that the computational examples in this book are relatively easy to follow. I attribute this, in part, to the fact that the student gains familiarity with one set of numerical data and thus can concentrate on the unique computational procedures associated with each experimental design.

The book presents a simplified computational scheme and a nomenclature for designating experimental designs. The nomenclature consists of a combination of letters and numbers that indicate both the type of design and the number of treatment levels in the design. Besides simplicity, the computational scheme has the added advantage of being easily translated into programs for computer analysis of data. Another feature is the inclusion of selected references to contemporary literature at the end of most chapters. These references illustrate diverse applications of the different experimental designs.

It is assumed that the reader is already familiar with material normally covered in courses in college algebra and basic statistical inference. The text provides material for a two-semester graduate course; suggested chapters for a one-semester graduate course are Chapters 1 through 8 and Chapter 13. If certain sections are deleted, these same chapters with the exception of Chapter 8 are appropriate for a one-semester undergraduate course in experimental design.

It is a pleasure to express my appreciation to B. F. Green, Carnegie-Mellon University; R. Hyman, University of Oregon; H. H. Reynolds, Holloman AFB, N. M.; D. Norton, University of Iowa; and T. A. Ryan, Cornell University, for reading all or a portion of the book, and for their thoughtful comments. I am particularly indebted to S. Korbel, University of Arkansas, and to C. G. Halcomb, Texas Technological College, both of whom used a mimeographed version of this book in their experimental design classes. Their suggestions and the comments of their students were most valuable. Three of my former graduate assistants, L. D. Allen, W. C. Blair, and J. L. Moses, deserve special mention for checking the accuracy of the computational examples and references. Responsibility for any remaining errors belongs, of course, to the author.

I am indebted to the Literary Executor of the late Sir Ronald A. Fisher, F. R. S., Cambridge; to Frank Yates, F. R. S., Rothamsted; and to Oliver and Boyd Ltd., Edinburgh, for permission to reprint Tables D.2, D.4,

D.6, and D.12 from their book *Statistical Tables for Biological, Agricultural and Medical Research.*

I am also indebted to E. S. Pearson and H. O. Hartley, editors of *Biometrika Tables for Statisticians,* vol. 1, and to the *Biometrika* trustees for permission to reprint Tables D.3, D.5, D.7, D.10, and D.14; to D. B. Duncan and the editor of *Biometrics* for permission to reprint Table D.8; to O. J. Dunn and the editor of the *Journal of the American Statistical Association* for permission to reprint Table D.16; to C. W. Dunnett and the editor of the *Journal of the American Statistical Association* for permission to reprint Table D.9 (one-tailed values); to C. W. Dunnett and the editor of *Biometrics* for permission to reprint Table D.9 (two-tailed values); and to H. B. Mann, D. R. Whitney, and the editor of *Annals of Mathematical Statistics* for permission to reprint Table D.15.

CONTENTS

1

2

3

4

COMPLETELY RANDOMIZED DESIGN   99

5

RANDOMIZED BLOCK DESIGN   131

6

LATIN SQUARE AND RELATED DESIGNS   151

7

COMPLETELY RANDOMIZED, HIERARCHAL, AND RANDOMIZED BLOCK FACTORIAL DESIGNS   171

8

SPLIT-PLOT DESIGN — FACTORIAL DESIGN WITH BLOCK-TREATMENT CONFOUNDING   245

9

CONFOUNDED FACTORIAL DESIGNS—FACTORIAL DESIGNS WITH BLOCK–INTERACTION CONFOUNDING *319*

10

FRACTIONAL FACTORIAL DESIGNS—FACTORIAL DESIGNS WITH TREAT-MENT–INTERACTION CONFOUNDING *385*

11

INCOMPLETE BLOCK DESIGNS   *423*

12

ANALYSIS OF COVARIANCE   *455*

13

EXPERIMENTAL DESIGN: PROCEDURES FOR THE BEHAVIORAL SCIENCES

1 / INTRODUCTION TO BASIC CONCEPTS IN EXPERIMENTAL DESIGN

1.1 INTRODUCTION

The term *experimental design* refers to five interrelated activities required in the investigation of scientific or research hypotheses. These activities, listed in the order performed, are as follows:

1. Formulate statistical hypotheses and make plans for the collection and analysis of data to test the hypotheses. A statistical hypothesis is a statement about one or more parameters of a population. Statistical hypotheses are rarely identical to research or scientific hypotheses but are testable formulations of research hypotheses.
2. State decision rules to be followed in testing the statistical hypotheses.
3. Collect data according to plan.
4. Analyze data according to plan.
5. Make decisions concerning the statistical hypotheses based on decision rules and inductive inferences concerning the probable truth or falsity of the research hypotheses.

The term *experimental design* is also used in a more restricted sense to designate a particular type of plan for assigning subjects to experimental conditions and the statistical analysis associated with the plan. The meaning of the term is generally clear from the context in which it is used.

SUBJECT MATTER AND GENERAL ORGANIZATION OF THIS BOOK

The concepts and procedures involved in carrying out steps 1, 2, 4, and 5 above comprise the subject matter of this book. Experimental design is only one of the many facets of scientific research. A carefully conceived and executed design is of no avail if the scientific hypothesis that originally led to the experiment is without merit.

A detailed examination of the logical and statistical aspects of specific experimental designs begins in Chapter 4. The first three chapters provide an overview of experimental designs, a review of basic statistical concepts, and a presentation of statistical *tools* used throughout the remainder of the book. The reader is encouraged to review the introductory chapters *after* reading subsequent chapters.

This book emphasizes those experimental designs that are most useful in the behavioral sciences. Many of the chapters conclude with a selected bibliography of contemporary research, which indicates diverse applications of the designs discussed in the chapter. The reader should consult the bibliographies to gain an over-all view of the way experimental designs are used in research.

The validity of inductive inferences that an experimenter draws from research rests on the fulfillment of certain assumptions. These assumptions are explicitly stated for each design as it is presented. Procedures for determining whether or not the assumptions are tenable in the light of sample data are also described.

A list of advantages and disadvantages for each design is provided to aid an experimenter in the selection of an appropriate design. Subsequent sections of this chapter treat general concepts basic to the selection of the best design for a particular research application.

1.2   DEFINITION OF BASIC TERMS

A number of terms must be defined before concepts basic to the selection of an experimental design can be discussed. It is assumed that the reader already has some familiarity with most of the terms that follow. Therefore, the material in this section is intended only to ensure a common vocabulary for the subsequent discussion. The definitions of some terms are oversimplified, but the assumed mathematical background does not permit rigorous definitions for all terms. Additional definitions are listed in the glossary.

Population.   A collection of all observations identifiable by a set of rules.

Sample.   A subset of observations from a population.

Random Sample.   A sample drawn from a population in such a way that all possible samples of size n have the same probability of being selected.

Parameter.   A measure computed from all observations in a population. Parameters are designated by Greek letters. For example, the symbols for a population mean and standard deviation are μ and σ, respectively.

Statistic.   A measure computed from observations in a sample. Statistics are designated by Latin letters. For example, the symbols for a sample mean and standard deviation are $\bar{X}$ and S, respectively.

Random Variable.   A quantity, say X, which may assume a range of possible values, each having an associated probability, say $p(X)$.

Estimator.   The particular function of observations in a sample that is chosen to estimate a population parameter. For example, the sample mean is used to estimate the population mean. The numerical value obtained is called an estimate.

Expected Value.   The long-run average of a random variable over an indefinite number of samplings. The expected value $[E(X)]$ of a discrete random variable X is given by $E(X) = \Sigma X p(X) = $ mean of X. It should be noted from the above definition that an expected value may be a value that the random variable could not actually have.

Unbiased Estimator.   An estimate of a parameter is said to be unbiased if its expected value is equal to the parameter.

Research Hypothesis.   A tentative theory or supposition provisionally adopted to account for certain facts and to guide in the investigation of others. The terms research hypothesis and scientific hypothesis may be used interchangeably.

Statistical Hypothesis.   A statement about one or more parameters of a population. Null and alternative hypotheses are two forms of a statistical hypothesis.

Null Hypothesis (H_0).   A statement concerning one or more parameters that is subjected to statistical test.

Alternative Hypothesis (H_1).   The hypothesis that remains tenable when the null hypothesis is rejected.

Statistical Test.   A procedure whereby two mutually exclusive statistical hypotheses are evaluated in the light of sample data. The hypothesis that dictates the sampling distribution against which an obtained sample value is compared is said to be the one tested.

Level of Significance (α). Probability of rejecting the null hypothesis when it is true.

Type I Error.   Error that occurs when the experimenter rejects the null hypothesis when it is true. The probability of committing a type I error is determined by the level of significance (α) that the experimenter adopts.

Type II Error.   Error that occurs when the experimenter fails to reject the null hypothesis when it is false. The probability (β) of committing a type II error is determined by the magnitude of the experimental effect, size of sample, magnitude of random error, and level of significance.

Power of Test.   Probability of rejecting the null hypothesis when the alternative hypothesis is true. If β is designated as the probability of committing a type II error, power is equal to $1 - \beta$.

Confidence Interval.   A range of values that, considering all possible samples, has some designated probability of including the true population value.

Confidence Limits.   Upper and lower boundaries of confidence interval.

Critical Region.   A set of outcomes of a statistical test that leads to the rejection of the null hypothesis.

Replication.   The collection of two or more observations under a set of identical experimental conditions.

Degrees of Freedom (df).   The number of independent observations for a source of variation minus the number of independent parameters estimated in computing the variation.

Experimental Error.   Measure that includes all uncontrolled sources of variation affecting a particular score.

Sampling Distribution. A theoretical probability distribution that describes the functional relation between possible values of a statistic based on N cases drawn at random and the probability associated with each value over all possible samples of size N.

Statistical Model. A mathematical statement concerning the sampling distribution of a random variable that is used in evaluating the outcome of an experiment or in predicting the outcome of future replications of an experiment.

Test Statistic. A statistic whose purpose is to provide a test of some statistical hypothesis. Test statistics such as t and F have known sampling distributions that can be employed in determining the probability of an obtained result under the null hypothesis.

Relative Efficiency of a Statistic. Ratio of experimental error of one statistic to that of another statistic.

Statistical Decision Theory. Branch of mathematics concerned with the problem of decision making and the choice of decision rules under uncertain conditions.

1.3 FORMULATION OF PLANS FOR COLLECTION AND ANALYSIS OF DATA

ACCEPTABLE RESEARCH HYPOTHESES

Some questions cannot currently be subjected to experimental investigation. For example, the questions "Can three or more angels sit on the head of a pin?" and "Does life exist in more than one galaxy in the universe?" cannot be answered because no procedures presently exist for observing either angels or other galaxies. Scientists confine their research hypotheses to questions for which procedures can be devised that offer the possibility of arriving at an answer. This does not mean that the question concerning the existence of life on other galaxies can never be investigated. Indeed, with continuing advances in space science it is probable that this question will eventually be answered.

Questions that provide the impetus for experimental research should be statable in the logical form of the general implication. That is, a question should be reducible to the form, *if A, then B.* For example, *if* albino rats are subjected to microwave radiation, *then* their food consumption will decrease. This research hypothesis can be investigated because procedures both for manipulating radiation level and for measuring food consumption of rats are available.

DISTINCTION BETWEEN DEPENDENT AND INDEPENDENT VARIABLES

In the example just cited, the presence or absence of radiation is designated as the *independent variable*—the variable that is under the control of the experimenter. The terms independent variable and treatment will be used interchangeably. The *dependent variable* is the amount of food consumed by the rats. The dependent variable reflects any effects associated with manipulation of the independent variable.

SELECTION OF DEPENDENT VARIABLE

The choice of an appropriate dependent variable may be based on theoretical considerations, although in many investigations the choice is determined by practical considerations. In this example, other dependent variables that could also be measured include

1. Activity level of rat in an activity cage.
2. Body temperature of rat.
3. Emotionality of rat as evidenced by amount of defecation and urination.
4. Problem-solving ability.
5. Weight of rat in grams.
6. Speed of running in a straight-alley maze.
7. Visual discrimination capacity.
8. Frequency of mating behavior.

Several independent variables can be employed in an experiment, but the designs described in this book are limited to the assessment of one dependent variable at a time. If it is necessary to evaluate two or more dependent variables simultaneously, a multivariate analysis of variance design can be used.* Some of these multivariate procedures are so complicated or so tedious that they cannot reasonably be carried out without a digital computer. However, the increasing availability of computer facilities makes the use of multivariate procedures more widespread. Univariate procedures can be appropriately applied to most research problems because it is generally impossible to measure more than a limited number of dependent variables, and those that can be measured are often found to be highly correlated.

The selection of the most fruitful variables to measure should be determined by a consideration of the sensitivity, reliability, distribution, and practicality of the possible dependent variables. From previous experience, an experimenter may know that one dependent variable is more sensitive than another to the effects of a treatment or that one dependent variable is more reliable, that is, gives more consistent results, than another variable. Because behavioral research generally involves a sizable investment in time and material resources, the dependent variable should be reliable and maximally sensitive to the phenomenon under investigation. Choosing a dependent variable that possesses these two characteristics

*A discussion of these designs is beyond the scope of this book. The reader is referred to Anderson (1958), Cooley and Lohnes (1962), Fryer (1966), Morrison (1967), and Rao (1952) for a discussion of multivariate procedures.

may minimize the amount of research effort required to investigate a research hypothesis.

Another important consideration in selecting a dependent variable is whether the observations within each treatment level (or combination of treatment levels in the case of multitreatment experiments) would be normally distributed. The assumption of normality, discussed in Chapter 2, is required for the experimental designs described in Chapters 4 through 12. In some cases it may be possible to *transform* nonnormally distributed observations so that the resultant distributions are normal. This procedure is described in Chapter 2. If theoretical considerations do not dictate the selection of a dependent variable and if several alternative variables are equally sensitive and reliable, in addition to being normally distributed, an experimenter should select the variable that is most easily measured.

SELECTION OF INDEPENDENT VARIABLE

The independent variable was defined earlier as the presence or absence of radiation. Such a treatment is described as having two treatment levels. If the experimenter is interested in the effects of different radiation dosages, he can employ three or more levels of radiation. The levels could consist of 0 microwatts, 20,000 microwatts, 40,000 microwatts, and 60,000 microwatts of radiation. This particular treatment is an example of a *quantitative* independent variable in which different treatment levels constitute different amounts of the independent variable.

In general, when the independent variable is quantitative in character there is little interest in the exact values of the treatment levels used in the experiment. In the radiation example, the research hypothesis could also be investigated, using three other levels of radiation, say, 25,000, 50,000, and 75,000 microwatts in addition to the zero-microwatt control level. The treatment levels should be chosen so as to cover a sufficiently wide range to detect effects of the independent variable if real effects exist. In addition, the number and spacing of the levels should be sufficient to define the shape of the function relating the independent and dependent variables. This is necessary if an experimenter is interested in performing a trend analysis as described in Chapter 4.

Selection of appropriate levels of the independent variable may be based on results of previous experiments or on theoretical considerations. In some research areas, it may be helpful to carry out a small pilot experiment to select treatment levels prior to the main experiment.

Under the conditions described in Chapters 2 and 4, the levels of a quantitative independent variable may be selected randomly from a population of treatment levels. If this procedure is followed, an experimenter can extrapolate from the results of his experiment to treatment levels that are not included in the experiment. If the treatment levels are not randomly sampled, the results of an experiment are applicable only to the specific levels included in the experiment.

Preceding paragraphs described a quantitative independent variable. If the treatment levels consisted of unmodulated radiation, amplitude-modulated radiation, and pulse-modulated radiation, the treatment is designated as a *qualitative* independent variable. The different treatment levels represent different *kinds* rather than different *amounts* of the independent variable. The distinction between quantitative and qualitative treatments is important in connection with trend analysis. The specific levels of a qualitative independent variable employed in an experiment are generally of direct interest to an experimenter. The levels chosen are usually dictated by the nature of the research hypothesis.

CONTROL OF NUISANCE VARIABLES

In addition to independent and dependent variables, all experiments include one or more *nuisance* variables. Nuisance variables are undesired sources of variation in an experiment that may affect the dependent variable. As the name implies, the effects of nuisance variables are of no interest per se. In the radiation example, potential nuisance variables include sex of the rats, variation in weight of the rats prior to the experiment, presence of infectious diseases in one or more cages where the rats are housed, temperature variation among the cages, and differences in previous feeding experiences of the rats. Unless controlled, nuisance variables can bias the outcome of an experiment. For example, if rats in the radiated groups suffer from some undetected disease, differences among the groups would reflect the effects of the disease in addition to radiation effects— if the latter effects exist.

Four approaches can be followed in controlling nuisance variables. One approach is to hold the nuisance variable constant for all subjects. For example, use only male rats of the same weight. Although an experimenter may attempt to hold all nuisance variables constant, the probability is high that some variable will escape his attention. A second approach, one that is used in conjunction with the first, is to assign subjects randomly to the experimental conditions. Then known as well as unsuspected sources of variation or bias are distributed over the entire experiment and thus do not affect just one or a limited number of treatment levels. In this case an experimenter increases the magnitude of random variation among observations in order to minimize systematic effects, that is, the effects of nuisance variables that bias all observations in one or more treatment levels in the same manner. Random variation can be taken into account in evaluating the outcome of an experiment, whereas it is difficult or impossible to account for systematic nuisance effects. A third approach to controlling nuisance variables is to include the variable as one of the *treatments* in the experimental design. This approach is illustrated in Section 1.4 in connection with a Latin square design.

The above three approaches for controlling nuisance variables illustrate the application of *experimental control* as opposed to the fourth approach which is *statistical control*. In some experiments it may be possible —through the use of regression procedures (see Chapter 12)—to remove the effects of a nuisance variable statistically. This use of statistical control is referred to as the analysis of covariance.

CLASSIFICATION OF INDEPENDENT AND NUISANCE VARIABLES

All independent and nuisance variables in behavioral research can be classified in one of three general categories—organismic, environmental, and task variables. In the radiation example, the independent variable of radiation can be classified as an environmental variable. The nuisance variables listed earlier as sex, weight, prior experience, and infectious diseases are examples of organismic variables. The other nuisance variable of temperature variation among the cages is an example of an environmental variable. This radiation experiment does not include a task variable. A task variable could be introduced into the experiment by requiring the rats to perform easy, medium, and difficult visual discriminations before gaining access to food. The effect of the visual discrimination on food consumption represents an additional independent variable that can be classified as a task variable. In the design of experiments, the above classifications may help an experimenter in listing the nuisance variables that should be controlled.

EFFICIENCY AND EXPERIMENTAL DESIGN

An experimenter engaging in research is desirous of arriving at valid conclusions. At the same time he hopes to accomplish this goal as efficiently as possible. Generally several experimental designs can be used in testing a statistical hypothesis. However, alternative designs that are equally valid for testing a hypothesis are rarely equally efficient. Efficiency of alternative research procedures may be defined in different ways. For example, efficiency may be defined in terms of time required to collect data, cost of data collection, ratio of information obtained to cost, and so on. A discussion of relative efficiency by Cochran and Cox (1957, 31) is instructive. A commonly used index for assessing the relative efficiency of two experimental designs is given by the ratio of their respective experimental errors. *Experimental error* refers to all extraneous variation in dependent variable scores that tends to mask the effects of the independent variable. The main sources of experimental error are inherent variability in the behavior of subjects and lack of uniformity in the conduct of the experiment.

A formula that provides insight into factors related to the efficiency of two designs is

$$\text{Efficiency} = \frac{\left(\dfrac{n_2 C_2}{\hat{\sigma}_1^2}\right)\left(\dfrac{df_1 + 1}{df_1 + 3}\right)}{\left(\dfrac{n_1 C_1}{\hat{\sigma}_2^2}\right)\left(\dfrac{df_2 + 1}{df_2 + 3}\right)},$$

where $\hat{\sigma}^2$ = estimate of experimental error per observation, n = number of subjects, C = cost of collecting data per subject, df = experimental error degrees of freedom, and the subscripts designate the two experimental designs (Federer, 1955, 13). If the ratio is less than one, the second design is more efficient than the first. The converse is true if the ratio is greater than one. The formula calls attention to four factors that are related to the efficiency of experimental designs. Unfortunately, an experimental design that is advantageous with respect to one factor may not be advantageous with respect to the others. For example, if a design has the desirable attribute of a small experimental error, it may have a high cost per subject or a small number of degrees of freedom for experimental error, or it may require a large number of subjects. The problem facing an investigator is to select an experimental design that represents the best compromise obtainable within the constraints of his research situation.

DETERMINATION OF SAMPLE SIZE

Once the independent and dependent variables are specified, the number of subjects required for the experiment must be determined. This is one of the more perplexing problems in experimental design. Five factors must be considered in specifying a sample size that is adequate for testing a statistical hypothesis: (1) minimum treatment effects an experimenter is interested in detecting, (2) number of treatment levels, (3) population error variance, (4) probability of making a type I error, and (5) probability of making a type II error. In general, the population error variance is unknown. It may be possible to make a reasonable estimate of the population error variance on the basis of previous experiments or a pilot study. If the above information can be specified, the size of the sample necessary to achieve a given power can be calculated. The power of a research methodology is defined as the probability of rejecting the null hypothesis when the alternative hypothesis is true. Power is equal to $1 - $ (probability of committing a type II error).

The procedure described here for calculating power was developed by Tang (1938). It assumes that the observations are normally distributed with a common error variance $= \sigma_\varepsilon^2$. The parameter ϕ is defined as

$$\phi = \frac{\sqrt{\sum_{1}^{k}(\mu_j - \mu)^2/k}}{\sigma_\varepsilon/\sqrt{n}},$$

where $\mu_j - \mu$ = the minimum treatment effect an experimenter is interested in detecting, k = number of treatment levels, σ_ε = square root of population error variance, and n = size of sample. If estimates of $\mu_j - \mu$ and σ_ε can be made, the size of a sample necessary to achieve a designated power can be determined from Table D.14 by a process of trial-and-error. The probability of type I and type II errors, α and β respectively, that the experimenter is willing to accept must also be specified.

Assume that a treatment has three levels and that the smallest treatment effects of interest to the experimenter are -4, -1, and $+5$. That is,

$$\sum_1^k (\mu_j - \mu)^2 = (-4)^2 + (-1)^2 + (5)^2 = 42.$$

Assume, also, that on the basis of previous research σ_ε is estimated to be six and that the investigator wishes the power of his test $(1 - \beta)$ to equal at least .80 and the probability of a type I error to equal .05. If nine subjects are assigned to each of the three treatment levels, Table D.14 in the appendix can be used to determine if the specified power is achieved. For example,

$$\phi = \frac{\sqrt{\dfrac{(-4)^2 + (-1)^2 + (5)^2}{3}}}{6/\sqrt{9}} = \frac{\sqrt{42/3}}{6/3} = 1.87,$$

with $k - 1 = 2$ and $N - k = 24$ degrees of freedom. The value of $\phi = 1.87$ and $\alpha = .05$ are entered in the table for $k - 1$ degrees of freedom. The curve corresponding to $N - k$ degrees of freedom indicates that the power is equal to .79, which is less than that desired by the experimenter. If the sample size is increased to 30, with ten subjects assigned to each treatment level, the power can be estimated from

$$\phi = \frac{\sqrt{\dfrac{(-4)^2 + (-1)^2 + (5)^2}{3}}}{6/\sqrt{10}} = 1.97,$$

with $k - 1 = 2$ and $N - k = 27$ degrees of freedom. The probability of detecting the specified treatment effects is approximately .83. Thus the required sample size is found to be 30.

If reasonable estimates of the parameters can be made, the required sample size should always be computed before the experiment is begun. If these preliminary calculations indicate that the power of the experimental design is inadequate, the experimenter may choose not to conduct the experiment or may modify it so as to increase its power. The two most common procedures for increasing power are (1) to increase the size of the sample and (2) to employ an experimental design that provides a more precise estimate of treatment effects and a smaller error term. The first procedure was illustrated in this section. The second is described in

Section 1.4. Overall and Dalal (1965) have described a procedure for maximizing the power of a research methodology relative to cost through the optimum allocation of resources to subjects; it requires *a priori* estimates of a number of design parameters. A procedure is described in Section 4.5 for estimating the number of subjects required for an experiment, one that does not necessitate making an estimate of the population error variance.

1.4 OVERVIEW OF TYPES OF EXPERIMENTAL DESIGNS

One of the procedures suggested above for increasing the power of a research methodology was to employ a more *sensitive* experimental design. In this context, the term experimental design refers to the plan by which subjects are assigned to treatment levels and the data analyzed.

An almost bewildering array of kinds of experimental designs exists. Fortunately, most complex experimental designs represent a combination of a relatively small number of basic *building block* designs. For example, most complex designs can be constructed by combining two or more completely randomized, randomized block, or Latin square designs. A simple classification of the experimental designs described in this book is outlined in Table 1.4-1. A more complete classification system appears in Cox (1943); Doxtator, Tolman, Cormany, Bush, and Jensen (1942); and Federer (1955, 6–12).

The category *systematic designs* in the outline is of historical interest only. According to Leonard and Clark (1939), agricultural field research employing systematic designs on a practical scale dates back to 1834. Prior to the work of Fisher, as well as of Neyman and Pearson on the theory of statistical inference, investigators used systematic schemes rather than randomization procedures for assigning treatment levels to plots of land or other suitable experimental units—hence the designation systematic designs for these early field experiments. Impetus for this early experimental research came from a need to improve agricultural techniques. Today the nomenclature of experimental design is replete with terms from agriculture. Systematic designs in which the randomization principle is not followed do not provide a valid estimate of error variance and hence are not subject to powerful tools of statistical analysis, such as analysis of variance.

Modern principles of experimental design, particularly the principle of random assignment of treatment levels to experimental units, received general acceptance as a result of Fisher's work (1922, 1923, 1935). Experimental designs using the randomization principle are called *randomized designs*. Randomized designs can be subdivided into two distinct categories, complete block designs and incomplete block designs, and two pseudo-

TABLE 1.4-1   Outline of Experimental Designs Described in this Book

Experimental Design	Abbreviated Designation
I. Systematic Designs	
II. Randomized Designs	
A. Complete Block Designs	
1. Completely randomized design	CR-k*
2. Randomized block design	RB-k
3. Latin square design	LS-k
4. Graeco-Latin square design	GLS-k
5. Hyper-Graeco-Latin square design	HGLS-k
B. Incomplete Block Designs	
1. Balanced incomplete block design	BIB-t
2. Youden square balanced incomplete block design	YBIB-t
3. Partially balanced incomplete block design	PBIB-t
C. Factorial Experiments	
1. Completely randomized factorial design	CRF-pq
2. Randomized block factorial design	RBF-pq
3. Completely randomized hierarchal design	CRH-$p(q)$
4. Completely randomized partial hierarchal design	CRH-$p(q)r$
5. Split-plot design	SPF-p . q
6. Randomized block completely confounded factorial design	RBCF-p^k
7. Randomized block partially confounded factorial design	RBPF-p^k
8. Latin square completely confounded factorial design	LSCF-p^k
9. Completely randomized fractional factorial design	CRFF-p^k
10. Randomized block fractional factorial design	RBFF-p^k
11. Latin square fractional factorial design	LSFF-p^k
12. Graeco-Latin square fractional factorial design	GLSFF-p^k
D. Analysis of Covariance Experiments	
1. Completely randomized analysis of covariance design	CRAC-k
2. Randomized block analysis of covariance design	RBAC-k
3. Latin square analysis of covariance design	LSAC-k
4. Completely randomized factorial analysis of covariance design	CRFAC-pq
5. Split-plot factorial analysis of covariance design	SPFAC-p . q

*The letter(s) following the dash designates the number and levels of each treatment. Refer to chapters in which the designs are discussed for an explanation of the abbreviated designations.

categories, factorial experiments and analysis of covariance experiments. The former pseudocategory is so designated because a factorial experiment consists of a combination of elementary building block designs. The term factorial experiment refers to the simultaneous evaluation of two or more treatments in one experiment rather than to a distinct kind of experimental design. Analysis of covariance experiments combine building block designs with regression analysis procedures and thus do not represent a distinct type of design. A brief description of some of the simpler designs follows.

COMPLETELY RANDOMIZED DESIGN

The simplest complete block experimental design from the standpoint of assignment of subjects to treatment levels and statistical analysis is the completely randomized design. This design can be used to compare any number of treatment levels. When two treatment levels are used, the statistical test employed in the analysis is equivalent to a test by means of a t ratio for uncorrelated groups. The general features of the design can be illustrated by the microwave radiation example cited earlier. Let b_1, b_2, and b_3 stand for treatment levels 0, 20,000, and 40,000 microwatts of radiation, respectively. Fifteen albino rats are assigned to the three treatment levels by means of a table of numbers. Food consumption of the rats assigned to each treatment level is indicated by X_{ij}, where i designates the ith rat in treatment level j. Table 1.4-2 shows the layout of a completely randomized design. The *average* food consumption of rats in each treatment level is designated by $\bar{X}_{.j}$. The dot in the subscript indicates the variable over which summation has occurred. In this example, treatment means are obtained by summing the scores over the $i = 1$ through 5 rats. The average food consumption for all 15 rats is designated by $\bar{X}_{..}$.

TABLE 1.4-2   Completely Randomized Design

	Treatment Levels	
b_1	b_2	b_3
X_{11}	X_{12}	X_{13}
X_{21}	X_{22}	X_{23}
X_{31}	X_{32}	X_{33}
X_{41}	X_{42}	X_{43}
X_{51}	X_{52}	X_{53}

Treatment means $= \bar{X}_{.1}$ $\bar{X}_{.2}$ $\bar{X}_{.3}$ Grand mean $= \bar{X}_{..}$

Here conclusions concerning the effects of microwave radiation are restricted to the three treatment levels and to the 15 rats included in the experiment. Edgington (1966) recently emphasized that random assignment of subjects to treatment levels is essential if an experimenter wishes to draw statistical inferences concerning treatment effects from non-randomly selected subjects.* Because of the importance of the principle of random assignment, an experimenter should always describe his technique for assigning subjects to treatment levels.

Associated with every experimental design is a mathematical model that purports to include all sources of variability affecting individual scores. To the extent that the model accurately represents these sources of variability, the experimenter can evaluate the effects of a treatment. The linear model for a completely randomized design is

---

*Few experiments in the behavioral sciences are carried out with randomly selected subjects. When a random sample is used, the population sampled is likely to be so specific as to be of little interest.

(1) $$X_{ij} = \mu + \beta_j + \varepsilon_{ij}.$$

According to this model, an individual score is equal to the population mean μ, plus a treatment effect β_j, plus an error effect ε_{ij}, which is unique for each individual subject. In a particular experiment, the parameters μ, β_j, and ε_{ij} are unknown, but sample estimates of these parameters are given by $\hat{\mu}$, $\hat{\beta}_j$, and $\hat{\varepsilon}_{ij}$, respectively. It can be shown by maximum-likelihood methods that unbiased estimates of the required parameters are provided by the statistics

$$\hat{\mu} = \bar{X}.. \qquad \rightarrow \mu$$

$$\hat{\beta}_j = (\bar{X}_{.j} - \bar{X}..) \rightarrow \beta_j$$

$$\hat{\varepsilon}_{ij} = (X_{ij} - \bar{X}_{.j}) \rightarrow \varepsilon_{ij}.$$

The symbol $\rightarrow$ indicates that the term on the left is an estimator of the term on the right. According to the maximum-likelihood method, the best estimate is the one that gives the highest probability of obtaining the observed data. It should be noted that a maximum-likelihood estimator is not necessarily unbiased, although the center of its distribution is generally close to the value of the parameter estimated. Assumptions associated with the mathematical model for a completely randomized design are discussed in Chapter 2 and explicitly stated in connection with the description of each design in subsequent chapters.

The meaning of the term *error effect* is somewhat elusive. An intuitive understanding of this term can be obtained by an examination of Table 1.4-2 and the linear model for the design. It is obvious that the scores for all 5 rats exposed to treatment level b_1 in this table will probably not be identical. Variation among the five scores can be attributed to a variety of sources—experiences of the rats prior to participation in the experiment, unintended variation in administration of the treatment level, lack of reliability in measuring the effect of the treatment level, etc. An error effect is an estimate of all effects *not* attributable to a particular treatment level. This can be seen from the linear model if the terms in equation (1) are rearranged and statistics are substituted for the parameters. The equation can be written

$$\hat{\varepsilon}_{ij} = X_{ij} - \hat{\beta}_j - \hat{\mu}.$$

Thus the error effect is that portion of a score remaining after the treatment effect and grand mean are subtracted from it. An experimenter attempts, by using an appropriate design and experimental controls, to minimize the size of the error effect. Designs described in subsequent paragraphs permit an experimenter to accomplish this by isolating additional sources of variation that affect individual scores.

RANDOMIZED BLOCK DESIGN

A randomized block design is based on the principle of assigning subjects to blocks so that the subjects within each block are more homogeneous than subjects in different blocks. Assume that the 15 albino rats in the previous example were taken from five different litters. Rats from the same litter can be expected to be more homogeneous with respect to genetic characteristics than rats from different litters. In Table 1.4-3 the 3 rats in each row that comprise a block are from the same litter. Differences among the litters can be regarded as a nuisance variable that is experimentally isolated through the use of a randomized block design. The subscripts of X_{ij} designate a particular litter and treatment level, in that order. Differences among the column means reflect treatment effects, whereas differences among the row means reflect litter effects.

TABLE 1.4-3   Randomized Block Design

		Treatment Levels		
	b_1	b_2	b_3	Block means
Block (litter) p_1	X_{11}	X_{12}	X_{13}	$\bar{X}_{1\cdot}$
Block (litter) p_2	X_{21}	X_{22}	X_{23}	$\bar{X}_{2\cdot}$
Block (litter) p_3	X_{31}	X_{32}	X_{33}	$\bar{X}_{3\cdot}$
Block (litter) p_4	X_{41}	X_{42}	X_{43}	$\bar{X}_{4\cdot}$
Block (litter) p_5	X_{51}	X_{52}	X_{53}	$\bar{X}_{5\cdot}$
Treatment means =	$\bar{X}_{\cdot 1}$	$\bar{X}_{\cdot 2}$	$\bar{X}_{\cdot 3}$	Grand mean = $\bar{X}_{\cdot\cdot}$

Assignment of the three treatment levels to the rats is randomized independently for each row. The linear model for this design is

$$X_{ij} = \mu + \beta_j + \pi_i + \varepsilon_{ij}.$$

Unbiased estimates of the parameters are given by the statistics

$$\hat{\mu} = \bar{X}_{\cdot\cdot} \qquad\qquad \to \mu$$

$$\hat{\beta}_j = (\bar{X}_{\cdot j} - \bar{X}_{\cdot\cdot}) \qquad\qquad \to \beta_j$$

$$\hat{\pi}_i = (\bar{X}_{i\cdot} - \bar{X}_{\cdot\cdot}) \qquad\qquad \to \pi_i$$

$$\hat{\varepsilon}_{ij} = (X_{ij} - \bar{X}_{\cdot j} - \bar{X}_{i\cdot} + \bar{X}_{\cdot\cdot}) \to \varepsilon_{ij}.$$

The term π_i represents an effect attributable to the ith block of 3 rats. It can be shown, by regrouping terms in the linear model and substituting statistics for parameters, that the error effect in a randomized block design is equal to

$$\hat{\varepsilon}_{ij} = X_{ij} - \hat{\beta}_j - \hat{\pi}_i - \hat{\mu}.$$

The error effect for a completely randomized design was given earlier as

$$\hat{\varepsilon}_{ij} = X_{ij} - \hat{\beta}_j - \hat{\mu}.$$

Thus the error effect $\hat{\varepsilon}_{ij}$ for a randomized block design is equal to the completely randomized design error effect minus a block effect $\hat{\pi}_i$. It is apparent from this that the error effect for a randomized block design will be smaller than the error effect for a completely randomized design if the block effect $\hat{\pi}_i$ is appreciably greater than zero.

One way of increasing the power of an experimental methodology mentioned in Section 1.3 is to choose an experimental design that provides for a more precise estimate of treatment effects and a smaller error variance. A randomized block design is more powerful than a completely randomized design if the block effects in the former design account for an appreciable portion of the total variance. It should be noted that the increased power of the randomized block design was made possible through the use of matched subjects. In many research situations, the increased experimental effort required to match subjects may not justify the greater power obtainable with a randomized block design.

LATIN SQUARE DESIGN

A Latin square design utilizes the blocking principle to obtain homogeneity with respect to two nuisance variables. The levels of the two nuisance variables are assigned to the rows and columns of a Latin square. Treatment levels are identified within each cell of the Latin square. In the randomized block design example, subjects were equated on the basis of genetic characteristics. It is reasonable to assume that rats in the same litter are also relatively homogeneous in weight. However, because the dependent variable in the radiation example is food consumption, the experimenter might wish to control the extraneous variable of weight. This can be accomplished by assigning the lightest rat in each litter to category b_1, the rat intermediate in weight to category b_2, and the heaviest rat to category b_3. Blocking with respect to both genetic characteristics a_i and weight b_j is shown in Table 1.4-4.

TABLE 1.4-4   Latin Square Design

	Weight Categories of Rats			
	b_1 Lightest	b_2 Intermediate	b_3 Heaviest	Block means
Block (litter) a_1	c_1 X_{111}	c_2 X_{122}	c_3 X_{133}	$\bar{X}_{1..}$
Block (litter) a_2	c_2 X_{212}	c_3 X_{223}	c_1 X_{231}	$\bar{X}_{2..}$
Block (litter) a_3	c_3 X_{313}	c_1 X_{321}	c_2 X_{332}	$\bar{X}_{3..}$
Weight means =	$\bar{X}_{.1.}$	$\bar{X}_{.2.}$	$\bar{X}_{.3.}$	

Grand mean = $\bar{X}...$

Treatment level means: $c_1 = (X_{111} + X_{321} + X_{231})/3 = \bar{X}_{..1}$

$c_2 = (X_{212} + X_{122} + X_{332})/3 = \bar{X}_{..2}$

$c_3 = (X_{313} + X_{223} + X_{133})/3 = \bar{X}_{..3}$

The three subscripts designate a particular block, weight category, and treatment level, in that order. The three treatment levels c_k are randomly assigned to the nine cells with the restriction that each treatment level must occur in any row and any column only once. In order to achieve this balance, a Latin square design must have the same number of rows, columns, and treatment levels. Consequently, only 9 animals can be used in the design shown in Table 1.4-4 instead of the 15 animals used in the two designs described previously.

The linear model for this design is

$$X_{ijk} = \mu + \alpha_i + \beta_j + \gamma_k + \varepsilon_{ijk}.$$

An individual score is equal to the grand mean μ, plus a block effect α_i, plus a column effect β_j, plus a treatment effect γ_k, plus an error effect ε_{ijk}. If the block and column effects, α_i and β_j, in a Latin square design are appreciably greater than zero, the design may be more powerful than either a completely randomized or a randomized block design. This is apparent if the error effect is examined by means of the procedure used for the two designs described previously. The error effect for a Latin square design is equal to

$$\hat{\varepsilon}_{ijk} = X_{ijk} - \hat{\alpha}_i - \hat{\beta}_j - \hat{\gamma}_k - \hat{\mu}.$$

INCOMPLETE BLOCK DESIGN

An incomplete block design is particularly applicable to research situations in which the number of subjects available for each block is less than the number of treatment levels. If, for example, only 2 albino rats from each litter are available, and the experimenter wants to use three treatment levels, an incomplete block design is required. This design is shown in Table 1.4-5.

TABLE 1.4-5   Incomplete Block Design

	Treatment Levels			
	b_1	b_2	b_3	Block means
Block (litter)	X_{11}		X_{13}	$\bar{X}_1.$
Block (litter)		X_{22}	X_{23}	$\bar{X}_2.$
Block (litter)	X_{31}	X_{32}		$\bar{X}_3.$
Treatment means =	$\bar{X}._1$	$\bar{X}._2$	$\bar{X}._3$	Grand mean = $\bar{X}..$

The linear model for this design is

$$X_{ij} = \mu + \beta_j + \pi_i + \varepsilon_{ij}.$$

It should be noted that each block contains the same number of subjects, each treatment level occurs the same number of times, and subjects are assigned to the treatment levels so that each possible pair of treatment levels occurs together within some block an equal number of times. A design having these characteristics is called a *balanced* incomplete block design. *Partially balanced* designs are those in which some pair of treatment levels occur together within the blocks more often than do other pairs.

FACTORIAL EXPERIMENT

A factorial experiment permits an investigator to evaluate the combined effects of two or more treatments in a single experiment. This is accomplished by combining building block designs so that one level from each of two or more treatments is presented simultaneously. The most commonly used building block designs are the completely randomized design and the randomized block design.

In the microwave radiation example, an investigator can, by using a factorial experiment, evaluate the effects of radiation and also the effects of a second treatment, such as room temperature. Assume that there are two levels of ambient room temperature, $a_1 = 80°$ and $a_2 = 65°$, and three levels of radiation, $b_1 = 0$, $b_2 = 20,000$, and $b_3 = 40,000$ microwatts. Tables 1.4-6 and 1.4-7 illustrate the use of two frequently used building block designs in a factorial experiment. In Table 1.4-6 the three subscripts designate a particular temperature level, radiation level, and subject, in that order. The three subscripts in Table 1.4-7 designate a particular temperature level, radiation level, and block, in that order.

In the completely randomized factorial design of Table 1.4-6 it is assumed that 18 albino rats are randomly assigned to the six treatment level combinations. In the randomized block factorial design example shown in Table 1.4-7, the treatment level combinations are randomly assigned within each block of litter mates. The models for the completely randomized and randomized block factorial designs are, respectively,

$$X_{ijm} = \mu + \alpha_i + \beta_j + \alpha\beta_{ij} + \varepsilon_{m(ij)}$$

$$X_{ijm} = \mu + \alpha_i + \beta_j + \pi_m + \alpha\beta_{ij} + \varepsilon_{ijm}.$$

The effect of temperature is designated by α_i, radiation by β_j, interaction of temperature and radiation by $\alpha\beta_{ij}$, experimental error by ε, and litter by π_m. Both designs permit an investigator to determine if radiation dosage has the same effect on food consumption at 80° ambient room temperature as it has at 65° ambient room temperature. It is conceivable that radiation might be more detrimental at a high ambient room temperature than at a low ambient room temperature. If such a result is found, it is called an *interaction effect*.

The error effect for a completely randomized factorial design, using the scheme described previously, can be written

$$\hat{\varepsilon}_{m(ij)} = X_{ijm} - \hat{\alpha}_i - \hat{\beta}_j - \hat{\alpha\beta}_{ij} - \hat{\mu}.$$

If we let τ_{ij} stand for all treatment effects, the error effect can be written

$$\hat{\varepsilon}_{m(ij)} = X_{ijm} - \hat{\tau}_{ij} - \hat{\mu}.$$

In this form the similarity between the error effect for this design and the error effect for a completely randomized design is apparent. This latter error effect was given earlier as

$$\hat{\varepsilon}_{ij} = X_{ij} - \hat{\beta}_j - \hat{\mu}.$$

The similarity between the models for a completely randomized design and a completely randomized factorial design is not surprising in view of the fact that the former design is the *building block* for the latter design.

The error effect for a randomized block factorial design is

$$\hat{\varepsilon}_{ijm} = X_{ijm} - \hat{\alpha}_i - \hat{\beta}_j - \hat{\pi}_m - \widehat{\alpha\beta}_{ij} - \hat{\mu}.$$

TABLE 1.4-6   Completely Randomized Factorial Design

		Radiation Levels		
Temperature Levels	b_1	b_2	b_3	*A treatment means*
a_1	X_{111} X_{112} X_{113}	X_{121} X_{122} X_{123}	X_{131} X_{132} X_{133}	$\bar{X}_{1..}$
a_2	X_{211} X_{212} X_{213}	X_{221} X_{222} X_{223}	X_{231} X_{232} X_{233}	$\bar{X}_{2..}$
B treatment means =	$\bar{X}_{.1.}$	$\bar{X}_{.2.}$	$\bar{X}_{.3.}$	Grand mean = $\bar{X}_{...}$

TABLE 1.4-7   Randomized Block Factorial Design

Temperature Levels	a_1	a_1	a_1	a_2	a_2	a_2	
Radiation Levels	b_1	b_2	b_3	b_1	b_2	b_3	Block mean
Block (litter) p_1	X_{111}	X_{121}	X_{131}	X_{211}	X_{221}	X_{231}	$\bar{X}_{..1}$
Block (litter) p_2	X_{112}	X_{122}	X_{132}	X_{212}	X_{222}	X_{232}	$\bar{X}_{..2}$
Block (litter) p_3	X_{113}	X_{123}	X_{133}	X_{213}	X_{223}	X_{233}	$\bar{X}_{..3}$
Column means	$\bar{X}_{11.}$	$\bar{X}_{12.}$	$\bar{X}_{13.}$	$\bar{X}_{21.}$	$\bar{X}_{22.}$	$\bar{X}_{23.}$	Grand mean = $\bar{X}_{...}$

A_1 treatment mean = $(X_{111} + X_{112} + X_{113} + X_{121} + \cdots + X_{133})/9 = \bar{X}_{1..}$

A_2 treatment mean = $(X_{211} + X_{212} + X_{213} + X_{221} + \cdots + X_{233})/9 = \bar{X}_{2..}$

B_1 treatment mean = $(X_{111} + X_{112} + X_{113} + X_{211} + X_{212} + X_{213})/6 = \bar{X}_{.1.}$

B_2 treatment mean = $(X_{121} + X_{122} + X_{123} + X_{221} + X_{222} + X_{223})/6 = \bar{X}_{.2.}$

B_3 treatment mean = $(X_{131} + X_{132} + X_{133} + X_{231} + X_{232} + X_{233})/6 = \bar{X}_{.3.}$

If treatment effects are designated by τ_{ij}, the error effect can be written

$$\hat{\varepsilon}_{ijm} = X_{ijm} - \hat{\tau}_{ij} - \hat{\pi}_m - \hat{\mu}.$$

It is interesting to note the similarity between this error effect and the error effect for a randomized block design, which is the building block for this factorial design. The error effect for the randomized block design was given earlier as

$$\hat{\varepsilon}_{ij} = X_{ij} - \hat{\beta}_j - \hat{\pi}_i - \hat{\mu}.$$

QUESTIONS TO CONSIDER IN SELECTING AN APPROPRIATE DESIGN

Statisticians have provided an experimenter with a vast array of experimental designs. On what basis should an experimenter decide which design to use? Selection of the *best* experimental design for a particular research problem requires (1) a knowledge of the research area and (2) a knowledge of different experimental designs. To arrive at the best experimental design, an experimenter must consider the following questions:

1. What kinds of data are required to test the statistical hypotheses?
   (a) How many treatment levels should be used?
   (b) Should the treatment levels used in the experiment be selected on an *a priori* basis or by random sampling from a population of treatment levels?
   (c) Should a factorial experiment be used so that interaction effects may be evaluated?
   (d) Are all treatments and treatment levels of equal interest to the experimenter? Experimental designs may be used that sacrifice power in evaluating some treatments in order to gain power in evaluating other treatments.

2. Is the proposed sample of subjects large enough to provide adequate precision in testing the statistical hypotheses?
   (a) Do the available subjects represent a random sample from the population of interest to the experimenter?
   (b) Can the subjects be stratified into homogeneous blocks?
   (c) Does the nature of the experiment permit each subject to be observed under more than one treatment level?
   (d) Will the treatment(s) produce physical or psychological injury to the subjects? The use of potentially injurious treatments precludes the employment of human subjects.

3. Is the power of the proposed experimental design adequate to test the statistical hypotheses?
   (a) What is the size of treatment effects that the experimenter considers to be of practical interest?
   (b) What are the consequences of committing type I and type II errors?

4. Does the proposed experimental design provide maximum efficiency in testing the statistical hypotheses?
   (a) Would efficiency be improved more by using a design employing blocks of homogeneous subjects or by using random assignment of a large number of subjects to the treatment levels?

(b) Can efficiency be increased more by the use of a larger sample size or by exercising additional experimental controls during the conduct of the experiment?

(c) Can efficiency be increased by the measurement of one or more characteristics related to the dependent variable in order to use regression techniques?

(d) Can efficiency be increased more by the use of a complex experimental design that requires considerable time to plan and analyze or by using a simple design but a large number of subjects? If subjects are plentiful and time required to obtain the data is sufficient, a simple design utilizing a large number of subjects may be more efficient than a complex design that involves costly planning and statistical analysis.

It should be apparent that the question "What is the best experimental design to use?" is not easily answered. Statistical as well as nonstatistical factors must be considered. The discussion has emphasized economic factors in the selection of a design because rules can be explicitly stated for increasing the precision and power of an experimental methodology; but, when efficiency is considered, such rules are difficult to formulate.

ROLE OF EXPERIMENTER AND STATISTICIAN

It is the conviction of the author that the selection of the best experimental design for a particular research problem can be most expeditiously accomplished when the roles of experimenter and statistician are performed by the same person. This is essentially the same position taken by Finney (1960, 3), who states, ". . . to write of the 'experimenter' and the 'statistician' as though they are separate persons is often convenient; the one is concerned with undertaking a piece of research comprehensively and accurately yet with reasonable economy of time and materials, the other is to provide technical advice and assistance on quantitative aspects both in planning and in interpretation . . . the statistician can produce good designs only if he understands something of the particular field of research, and the experimenter will receive better help if he knows the general principles of design and statistical analysis. Indeed, the two roles can be combined when an experimenter with a little mathematical knowledge is prepared to learn enough of the theory of design to be able to design his own experiments."

CRITERIA FOR EVALUATING AN EXPERIMENTAL DESIGN

Many different sets of criteria could be given for evaluating an experimental design. The criteria presented by Winer (1962, 47) and Lindquist (1953, 6) are most helpful. The following questions, except for number 5, were selected because they touch on the major points presented in this chapter.

1. Does the design permit an experimenter to calculate a valid estimate of the experimental effects and error effects?
2. Does the data-collection procedure produce reliable results?
3. Does the design provide maximum efficiency within the constraints imposed by the experimental situation?
4. Does the design possess sufficient power to permit an adequate test of the statistical hypotheses?
5. Does the experimental procedure conform to accepted practices and procedures used in the research area? Other things being equal, an experimenter should use procedures that offer an opportunity for comparison of his findings with the results of other investigations.

1.5   A REVIEW OF STATISTICAL INFERENCE

In the previous section an overview of experimental designs was presented. This section is written to accomplish the same goal with respect to procedures involved in statistical inference. It is assumed that the reader is already familiar with basic hypothesis-testing concepts. Hays (1963) presents an excellent introduction to this topic.

A distinguishing characteristic of the scientific method is the formulating and testing of hypotheses. The testing of hypotheses requires the *a priori* formulation of decision rules to guide the decision maker. The problem may be stated: Given two mutually exclusive hypotheses about a population, how does one decide on the basis of sample data which hypothesis is supported? It will be apparent that this question lacks a simple answer.

A statistical hypothesis is a statement about one or more parameters of population distributions; and, as such, it refers to a situation that *might* be true. Such a statement is always made with respect to a population and not to a sample. Distinguishing between statistical hypotheses and research or scientific hypotheses is important. Research hypotheses are normally stated in general terms, at least in the initial stages of an inquiry. In this form they are not amenable to evaluation through the use of the procedures and theory of statistical inference. It may be possible, by means of deductive reasoning, to transform a research hypothesis into a statistical hypothesis that can be subjected to test. Statistical hypotheses refer to population parameters, whereas scientific hypotheses refer to the phenomena of nature and man (Clark, 1963).

In logic, the terms *direct statement* and *indirect statement* are analogous in many ways to statistical and scientific hypotheses. A direct statement is made in reference to limited phenomena that are directly observable; for example, "This rat is running." The truth or falsity of such a direct statement can be determined by observing the rat. An indirect statement refers to phenomena that cannot be directly observed or that are so numerous in time that it is impossible to view them all. For example,

"All rats run under condition X." Such hypotheses can be evaluated by inductive inference only and must be reducible to direct statements. The chain of events required in testing an indirect statement is shown in Figure 1.5-1.

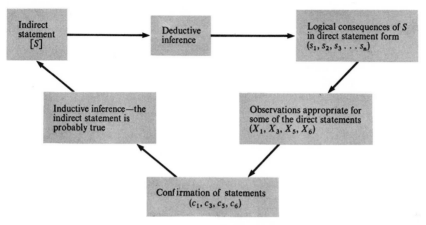

Figure 1.5-1   Test of indirect statement by deductive and inductive inferences.

If, in Figure 1.5-1, the term *scientific hypothesis* is substituted for indirect statement and *statistical hypothesis* for direct statement, the analogy with hypothesis testing is readily apparent. The experimenter has the task of translating his research hypotheses into a dichotomous set of mutually exclusive statistical hypotheses. It should be noted that the chain of deductive reasoning from a *question* concerning nature to a *research hypothesis* to a *statistical hypothesis* and the reverse process of inductive reasoning from the *statistical hypothesis* to the *question* is an exercise in logic rather than statistical inference. If an error occurs in the chain, the statistical hypotheses subjected to test may have no bearing on the original question, or incorrect inferences concerning the question may be made. Grant (1962), Binder (1963), and Edwards (1965) have examined in detail the relation between scientific and statistical hypotheses.

KINDS OF STATISTICAL HYPOTHESES

A null hypothesis (H_0) is the statistical hypothesis that is subjected to a test. The notion that the null hypothesis refers to a parameter value of zero is a simplification; the hypothesis can specify the parameter as having any value, including zero. Less confusion will result if the null hypothesis is considered as the hypothesis that is tested. The hypothesis that remains tenable if the null hypothesis is rejected is called the alternative hypothesis (H_1). Hypothesis testing can be viewed as a procedure whereby an experimenter decides which one of a dichotomous set of mutually exclusive and exhaustive hypotheses is to be rejected and which one is to be accepted at some specified risk of making an incorrect decision (Clark, 1963).

A statistical hypothesis can be either exact or inexact. The hypothesis that the mean (μ) of population j is equal to 40

(1) $$H_0 : \mu_j = 40$$

is an exact hypothesis. The hypothesis

(2) $$H_0 : \mu_j \leq 40$$

is an example of an inexact hypothesis. The alternative (H_1) to the exact null hypothesis above can take any one of several different forms; for example,

$$H_1 : \mu_j = 43 \quad \text{(exact alternative hypothesis)}$$

$$H_1 : \mu_j \neq 40 \quad \text{(inexact two-tailed alternative hypothesis).}$$

The alternative to the inexact null hypothesis above can be written

$$H_1 : \mu_j > 40.$$

If a comparison of the central tendency of two populations j and j' is of interest, the null and alternative hypotheses can take any of the following forms:

$$H_0 : \mu_j - \mu_{j'} = 0$$
$$H_1 : \mu_j - \mu_{j'} \neq 0$$

or

$$H_0 : \mu_j - \mu_{j'} \leq 0$$
$$H_1 : \mu_j - \mu_{j'} > 0$$

or

$$H_0 : \mu_j - \mu_{j'} \geq 0$$
$$H_1 : \mu_j - \mu_{j'} < 0.$$

It should be noted that hypothesis testing in the behavioral sciences usually involves either two inexact hypotheses or one exact and one inexact hypothesis. The distinction between exact and inexact hypotheses is unimportant from a practical standpoint because the same general test procedures are followed in each case. Although we may speak of testing a single hypothesis, in practice we behave as though we were deciding which one of two mutually exclusive and exhaustive hypotheses is supported by our data. The procedure by which we make this decision is called a statistical test.

STATISTICAL TEST

A statistical test is the comparison of two hypotheses in the light of sample data according to a set of decision rules. The null hypothesis leads to a prediction, or anticipated value, and to a hypothetical sampling distribution of anticipated values for a sample statistic. If the sample statistic equals the anticipated value, or falls in a region of the sampling distribution designated as a *probable anticipated value*, a decision is made to accept the null hypothesis. On the other hand, if the sample statistic deviates appreciably from the anticipated value, either a rare and improbable event has occurred or the null hypothesis has led to a poor prediction and should be rejected.

HYPOTHESIS TESTING

Hypothesis testing appears to be a straightforward objective procedure until an attempt is made to define such phrases as "probable anticipated value," "deviates appreciably," and "poor prediction." On what basis does one decide which anticipated values are probable, or when the sample statistic deviates appreciably from the anticipated value, or when a null hypothesis leads to a poor prediction? The answer to these questions in the behavioral sciences is that the experimenter falls back on a set of conventions. A branch of mathematics known as *decision theory* deals with the problem of choosing optimum decision rules. Although hypothesis-testing procedures in the behavioral sciences use many notions from decision theory, the application is incomplete and research is frequently conducted according to rules that are less than optimum for the experimenter's purposes.

STEPS FOLLOWED IN TESTING A HYPOTHESIS

What conventions are currently used in testing a hypothesis? These conventions can be summarized in four steps.

Step 1: State a null hypothesis H_0 and an alternative hypothesis H_1.

Step 2: Decide on an appropriate sample statistic and test statistic. The selection of a test statistic is based on (1) H_0, (2) the chosen sample statistic, and (3) tenable assumptions concerning the population distributions. Assumptions underlying the sampling distributions of χ^2, t, and F test statistics are discussed in Section 2.1.

Step 3: Decide on a level of significance α and a sample size N. α and N, together with the sampling distribution of the test statistic under the null hypothesis, determine the *region for rejecting H_0*.
The *location* and *size* of the region for rejection of the null hypothesis are determined by H_1 and α, respectively. An experimenter attempts to select a level of significance so that the region of rejection contains values of the test statistic that have a low probability of occurrence if H_0 is true but a high probability if H_1 is true.

Step 4: Obtain the sample statistic and compute the test statistic. If the value of the test statistic falls in the region of rejection, H_0 is rejected in favor of H_1. If the test statistic falls outside the region of rejection, the experimenter may either accept H_0 or suspend making a decision concerning it.

These four steps and the conventions they summarize require some amplification. First, the selection of an appropriate sample statistic is determined by the experimenter's interest in a particular parameter or characteristic of a population. If only one population is involved, an experimenter in the behavioral sciences is generally interested in testing a hypothesis with respect to the central tendency of the population. If, as is frequently the case, more than one population is involved, hypotheses concerning differences among the populations in terms either of central tendency or of dispersion may be of interest. The measures most often adopted to describe central tendency and dispersion are the mean and standard deviation, respectively.

Test statistics are similar to sample statistics in that both have sampling distributions; however, unlike sample statistics, test statistics are not used to estimate population parameters. Instead, test statistics provide information in the form of a probability statement, which is used by an experimenter in deciding whether or not to reject a null hypothesis. Conventionally, an experimenter specifies a region of the sampling distribution of the test statistic based on α and H_1 that will lead to rejection of the null hypothesis *prior* to computation of the test statistic. This region is specified in such a way as to contain those values of the test statistic that have a small probability of occurring if the null hypothesis is true but a high probability of occurring if the alternative hypothesis is true. If the test statistic falls in the region for rejection, either an improbable event has occurred or the null hypothesis is false and should be rejected.

Two commonly used test statistics are z and t ratios. For testing a hypothesis concerning a single population mean, z and t ratios have the following form:

$$ z = \frac{\bar{X} - \mu_0}{\sigma/\sqrt{n}} \quad \text{and} \quad t = \frac{\bar{X} - \mu_0}{\hat{\sigma}/\sqrt{n}}, $$

where $\bar{X}$ = sample mean used to estimate the population mean μ, μ_0 = value of population mean specified by null hypothesis, σ = population standard deviation, $\hat{\sigma}$ = unbiased estimate of population standard deviation calculated from a sample, and n = number of observations in the sample. If it can be assumed that the population sampled has a normal distribution, z and t are distributed as the normal curve and t distribution, respectively. That is, a z or t ratio can be computed for each conceivable sample of n independent observations drawn from a normal population with mean = μ. The value of z or t will vary over the different samples from the population. If a plot of the probability-density of each z or t value is made, the resulting distributions will be distributed as the normal distribution and t distribution, respectively. The t distribution, unlike the z distribution, actually is a family of distributions. The exact shape of the t distribution varies, depending on the number of observations in the sample. Probabilities associated with obtaining various values of z or t are given in Tables D.3 and D.4, respectively. It should be noted that the denominator of a z ratio is a constant for any sample of size n because the population parameter σ is a constant. By comparison, the denominator of a t ratio for any sample of size n is a random variable because of sampling variation in estimating the parameter σ. The numerators of both test statistics are subject to sampling variation and hence are random variables.

In practice, the population variance required to compute z is rarely ever known. The ratio

$$\frac{\bar{X} - \mu_0}{\hat{\sigma}/\sqrt{n}}$$

can be treated as a z variable provided that the sample size is large, say around 100, and that the population has a normal distribution. An examination of Appendix Tables D.3 and D.4 reveals that the probabilities associated with values of z and t are quite similar even for samples as small as 30. As the sample size is reduced below 30, the correspondence becomes poorer. Thus, for small samples, the t distribution should be employed if a *sample* standard deviation is used to estimate σ. The t distribution and other useful sampling distributions are discussed in Section 2.1.

EXAMPLE ILLUSTRATING STEPS IN HYPOTHESIS TESTING

An example may help to clarify the concepts and conventions involved in hypothesis testing. Assume that we wish to test the hypothesis that the average performance of some population on a psychological test is greater than 100. An arithmetic mean is chosen as the appropriate measure of central tendency. Two *test statistics* can be suggested for this experiment:

$$z = \frac{\bar{X} - \mu_0}{\sigma/\sqrt{n}} \quad \text{and} \quad t = \frac{\bar{X} - \mu_0}{\hat{\sigma}/\sqrt{n}}.$$

Let us assume in our example that the population is normally distributed and that σ is known to equal 15. Under these conditions, the appropriate test statistic is z. The statistical hypotheses can be stated as follows:

$$H_0 : \mu \leq 100$$

$$H_1 : \mu > 100.$$

We will reject the null hypothesis in favor of the alternative hypothesis only if an observed sample mean is so much larger than 100 that it has a probability of .05 or less of occurring if the population mean really is equal to 100. As written, the null hypothesis is inexact because it states a whole region of possible values for the population mean. However, one exact value is specified, $\mu = 100$. Actually, the hypothesis tested is $\mu = 100$

versus some unspecified alternative greater than 100. If the experimenter can reject the hypothesis that $\mu = 100$ at $\alpha = .05$ level of significance, then he can reject any other hypothesis that $\mu < 100$ at a level of significance $< .05$. The decision rule for this example can be stated as follows: If the test statistic falls among the highest 5 percent of z's in a normal distribution under H_0, reject H_0; otherwise do not reject H_0. If H_0 is rejected, the experimenter, in this example, decides in favor of H_1.

We have stated the null and alternative hypotheses, decided on an appropriate sample statistic and test statistic, and specified the level of significance that will be used in the decision process. The final steps in the hypothesis-testing procedure are to specify the size of the sample that will be observed, obtain the sample, compute the sample statistic and test statistic, and make a decision. Suppose that a random sample of $n = 100$ observations has been obtained from the population and that the mean of this sample is equal to $\bar{X} = 102$. Is the deviation of this sample mean from the predicted mean of 100 large enough to lead the experimenter to reject the null hypothesis? The probability associated with obtaining a sample mean as deviant as 102 if the true mean is 100 can be determined from

$$z = \frac{\bar{X} - \mu_0}{\sigma/\sqrt{n}} = \frac{102 - 100}{15/\sqrt{100}} = \frac{2.0}{1.5} = 1.33$$

and the cumulative normal probability table in Appendix D.3. According to Appendix D.3, the probability associated with obtaining a sample mean of 102 if the true mean is 100 is approximately .09. According to the decision rules outlined above, the null hypothesis is not rejected, because .09 > .05, and therefore z does not fall in the region for rejection of H_0. The regions for rejection or nonrejection of H_0 are illustrated in Figure 1.5-2. If the

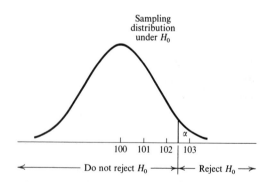

Figure 1.5-2   Regions of the sampling distribution of z that lead to rejection or nonrejection of H_0 according to decision rules specified previously.

sample mean had been 102.5 instead of 102, the decision would have been to reject H_0. This can be demonstrated as follows:

$$z = \frac{\overline{X} - \mu_0}{\sigma/\sqrt{n}} = \frac{102.5 - 100.0}{1.5} = 1.67.$$

According to the normal distribution table in Appendix D.3, the probability of obtaining a sample mean of 102.5 if the true mean is really 100 is less than .05. Thus, either a rare and improbable event has occurred or the true parameter is not 100. This example was fabricated to illustrate the steps involved in testing a statistical hypothesis. In real life most hypotheses are concerned not with a single population but with differences among two or more populations. The steps that have been described in connection with a single population are also applicable to tests involving two or more populations. Procedures and assumptions associated with testing statistical hypotheses with respect to two or more populations are described in Chapters 2 and 3. An excellent survey of hypothesis testing and statistical inference is given by Clark (1963).

TYPE I AND II ERRORS

In carrying out the decision process outlined above, the experimenter may make a correct decision or he may commit an error. If he decides to reject H_0 when the population mean is really equal to 100, he has committed a type I error. On the other hand, if he decides not to reject H_0 when the population mean is really equal to, say, 103, he has committed a type II error. In summary, the two possible errors an experimenter may make are

Type I error. Reject H_0 (tested hypothesis) when it is true. The probability α is the risk of making a type I error.

Type II error. Fail to reject H_0 when it is false. The risk of making a type II error is designated as β.

The regions corresponding to the probability of making a type I error (α) and a type II error (β) are shown in Figure 1.5-3.

It is apparent from Figure 1.5-3 that the probability of making a type I error is determined by an experimenter when he specifies α. This probability can be made as small as an experimenter wishes. It should be noted from the figure that as the area corresponding to α is made smaller, the area designated as β becomes larger. Thus the two types of errors are interrelated. The probability of committing a type II error is determined by α, magnitude of difference between the true parameter and parameter under H_0, size of population error variance, and size of sample (n). If, in the hypothesis-testing example described previously, the statistic is equal to 102, a decision is made not to reject H_0. This decision may be correct or incorrect, depending on the value of the parameter. If

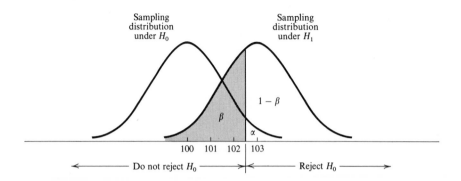

Figure 1.5-3 Regions corresponding to probabilities of making type I error (α) and type II error (β). The region corresponding to a type I error is determined by the experimenter when he specifies α and H_1. If, for a given H_0 and true alternative, α is made smaller, the probability of making a type II error is increased.

the parameter is equal to or less than 100, a correct decision has been made. On the other hand, if the parameter is equal to 103, a type II error has been made.

POWER OF A TEST

If the parameter is equal to 100, the probability of making a correct decision is $1 - \alpha$. If, on the other hand, the parameter is equal to 103, the probability of making a correct decision is $1 - \beta$. This latter probability is called the power of the test. It is simply the probability of deciding that H_0 is wrong, given a decision rule and the true value under H_1. The possible decision outcomes can be categorized as shown in Table 1.5-1.

TABLE 1.5-1   Decision Outcomes Categorized

		True Situation	
		$\mu = 100$	$\mu = 103$
Decision	$\mu = 100$	correct decision $= 1 - \alpha$	type II error $= \beta$
	$\mu = 103$	type I error $= \alpha$	correct decision $= 1 - \beta$

An experimenter attempts to select an experimental design and set of decision rules that will result in the highest power for a given type I error. How can the power of an experimental methodology be increased for a given type I error rate? Two approaches were suggested in Section 1.3. One approach is to increase the size of the sample. A second approach is to use an experimental design that provides for a more precise estimate of treatment effects and a smaller error variance.

If information concerning the true parameter is available, the probability of committing a type II error can be determined. Generally, however, the value of the parameter is unknown. In practice, an experimenter can specify various possible values of the parameter of interest to him and then compute the probability of committing a type II error and $1 - \beta$, given that the specified value of μ is true. Let us assume that the obtained sample statistic is equal to 102.5 and that an experimenter is interested in determining the probability of correctly rejecting H_0 if the population mean is really equal to 103. The probabilities β and $1 - \beta$ can be determined from

$$z = \frac{\bar{X} - \mu}{\sigma/\sqrt{n}} = \frac{102.5 - 103.0}{15/\sqrt{100}} = -.33.$$

According to the normal distribution table in Appendix D.3, the probabilities β and $1 - \beta$ are .37 and .63, respectively. The location of the regions corresponding to β and $1 - \beta$ are shown in Figure 1.5-3. In this example the probability of making a correct decision if $\mu = 103$ is only .63, whereas the corresponding probability if $\mu = 100$ is .95. The probabilities associated with the possible outcomes of our decision rule are summarized in Table 1.5-2.

TABLE 1.5-2   Probabilities Associated with the Decision Process

		True Situation	
		$\mu = 100$	$\mu = 103$
Decision	$\mu = 100$	$1 - \alpha = .95$	type II error $\beta = .37$
	$\mu = 103$	type I error $\alpha = .05$	$1 - \beta = .63$

SELECTION OF A LEVEL FOR α

In the preceding hypothetical example, the probability of a type I error (α) is much lower than the corresponding type II error (β). Experimenters in the behavioral sciences frequently set the type I error rate at .05 or .01. This convention is based primarily on the notion that a type I error is very bad and is to be avoided. In the present example, the decision rule is biased in favor of deciding that the population mean is equal to 100 rather than, say, 103. In many research situations, the cost of a type I error may be large relative to the cost of a type II error. For example, to commit a type I error in concluding that a particular medication arrests the production of cancer cells and therefore can be used in place of other medical procedures is a serious matter. On the other hand, falsely deciding that the medication does not arrest the production of cancer cells (type II error) would result in withholding the medication from the public and would probably lead to further research. In such a context, a type II error is less undesirable than a type I error. However, in another context, concluding that an experimental effect is not significant may result in an experimenter discontinuing a promising line of research whereas a type I error would mean further exploration into a *blind alley*. Faced with these two alternatives, many experimenters might prefer to make a type I rather than a type II error. It is apparent from the foregoing discussion that the *loss function* associated with the two errors must be known before a rational choice concerning α can be made. However, experimenters in the behavioral sciences are generally unable to specify the losses associated with the two errors of inference. Therein lies the problem. The problem is resolved by falling back on accepted conventions. The principal benefit of statistical decision theory—that of using decision rules having optimum properties for a given purpose—is seldom enjoyed by experimenters in the behavioral sciences. A general introduction to the meaning of optimal solutions to problems is given by Ackoff, Gupta, and Minas (1962).

It is hoped that the preceding discussion helps to dispel the magic that seems so inextricably tied to the .05 and .01 levels of significance. The use of the .05 or .01 level of significance in hypothesis testing is a convention. When either level is achieved by a test, it signals that an *improbable* event has occurred or that the hypothesis under test has led to a poor prediction. A test of significance provides information concerning the probability of committing an error in rejecting the null hypothesis. It is one bit of information required in making a decision concerning a research hypothesis. A test of significance embodies no information concerning loss-values associated with the decision, the experimenter's prior personal convictions concerning the hypotheses, or the importance or usefulness of the obtained results. Various problems associated with the uncritical use of significance tests in research have been examined in detail by Bakan (1966). Bayesian statistical theory represents an attempt to incorporate prior information into the decision process, information that is not utilized within the classical theories of Neyman-Pearson and Fisher. A rapprochement involving the best features of classical theory, decision theory, and Bayesian theory is to be hoped for. Binder (1964) in a review mentioned one modification of classical theory that incorporates Bayesian theory. A general introduction to Bayesian theory can be found in Edwards, Lindman, and Savage (1963) and additional references in Binder (1964).

Hypothesis-testing procedures should be viewed as tools that aid an experimenter in interpreting the outcome of research. Such procedures should not be permitted to replace the judicial use of logic by an alert analytic experimenter. In particular, the technique of analysis of variance described in this book should be considered an aid in summarizing data. It should be used to help an experimenter understand what went on in an experiment; it is not an end in itself.

2 / FUNDAMENTAL ASSUMPTIONS IN ANALYSIS OF VARIANCE

2.1 BASIC SAMPLING DISTRIBUTIONS IN ANALYSIS OF VARIANCE

In Chapter 1 we noted that one of the distinguishing characteristics of the scientific method is the formulating and testing of hypotheses concerning population parameters. Tests of statistical hypotheses require the *a priori* formulation of decision rules as well as a knowledge of the sampling distributions of test statistics. The formulation of decision rules was discussed in Section 1.5. Here we shall describe several important theoretical sampling distributions.

The most important sampling distributions in the behavioral sciences are the binomial, normal, t, chi-square, and F distributions. The first three distributions are primarily concerned with drawing inferences about the central tendency of populations. The last two distributions, chi-square and F, are useful in drawing inferences about variability or variance as well as central tendency. The reader is undoubtedly familiar with each of these distributions. Because the analysis of variability is such an important aspect of experimental design, it seems appropriate to review the essential features of the chi-square and F distributions and to examine briefly the interrelations between these distributions and the t distribution. The assumptions required for the mathematical justification of the procedures described in this book are discussed in this chapter. The reader who does not wish to follow the exposition in the subsequent paragraphs will find the essential points summarized at the conclusion of this section. The following material assumes a knowledge of elementary rules of summation and expectations of random variables. All the required principles of summation and expectation are reviewed in Appendixes A and B, respectively.

CHI-SQUARE DISTRIBUTION

In 1876 F. R. Helmert derived the chi-square distribution, but it was Karl Pearson who in 1900 first used it as a means of testing hypotheses. For purposes of illustration, let us assume that there is a population of scores X that has a *normal distribution*. The mean of the distribution of X

is $E(X) = \mu$, where $E(X)$ refers to the expectation or expected value of the random variable X. The expected value of a continuous random variable is simply the long-run average of the variable over an indefinite number of samplings. As noted previously, rules of mathematical expectation are summarized in Appendix B. The variance of the distribution of X is $E(X - \mu)^2 = \sigma^2$, where μ is the population mean. Suppose that a *random sample* of size one is drawn from this normally distributed population. This observation can be expressed in standardized form as

$$z = \frac{X - \mu}{\sigma}.$$

The square of the above formula, that is,

$$z^2 = \frac{(X - \mu)^2}{\sigma^2},$$

is a random variable having a chi-square distribution with one degree of freedom. This squared standardized score z^2 can also be designated $\chi^2_{(1)}$. What does the distribution of $\chi^2_{(1)}$ look like? Because $\chi^2_{(1)}$ is a squared quantity, it can range over only nonnegative real numbers from zero to positive infinity, whereas X and z can range over all real numbers. The distribution of $\chi^2_{(1)}$ is very positively skewed because approximately 68 percent of the sampling distribution lies between zero and one. The remaining 32 percent of the distribution lies between one and positive infinity.

If two random samples of *independent* observations X_1 and X_2 are drawn from the normally distributed population, they can be expressed in standardized form as

$$z_1^2 = \frac{(X_1 - \mu)^2}{\sigma^2} \quad \text{and} \quad z_2^2 = \frac{(X_2 - \mu)^2}{\sigma^2}.$$

Observations are said to be independent if the occurrence of any one observation in no way affects the probability of any other observation. The sum $z_1^2 + z_2^2 = \chi^2_{(2)}$ has a chi-square distribution with two degrees of freedom. The sampling distribution of $\chi^2_{(2)}$ is somewhat less positively skewed than $\chi^2_{(1)}$. For N independent observations drawn at random from a normal distribution, with population mean equal to μ and population variance equal to σ^2,

$$\chi^2_{(N)} = \frac{\sum_1^N (X - \mu)^2}{\sigma^2} = \sum_1^N z^2,$$

with N degrees of freedom. The form of a chi-square distribution depends on the number of independent observations taken at one time. The approximate forms of the chi-square distribution for different degrees of freedom (df) are shown in Figure 2.1-1. It is apparent that as the number of degrees of freedom is increased, the distribution is less positively skewed and approaches the normal form. For df > 2, the mode occurs at df − 2.

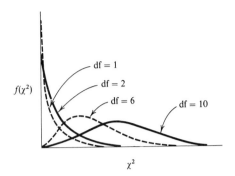

Figure 2.1-1　Forms of the χ^2 distribution for different degrees of freedom.

It can be shown that the mean of a chi-square distribution is equal to df and the variance is equal to 2 df. The distribution of χ^2 is completely specified by one parameter, the degrees of freedom.

It follows from the definition of χ^2 that the sum of two *independent* χ^2's is itself distributed as χ^2 with degrees of freedom equal to $v_1 + v_2$, where v_i designates the respective degrees of freedom. That is,

$$\chi^2_{(v_1)} + \chi^2_{(v_2)} = \chi^2_{(v_1 + v_2)}.$$

In research situations, the value of a sample mean $\bar{X}$ is known or can be determined, but the value of the population mean is unknown. A practical question arises concerning the distribution of $\Sigma_1^N (X - \bar{X})^2/\sigma^2$. That is, what is the form of the distribution if the sample mean is substituted for the population mean? It can be shown that for random samples of N observations from a normally distributed population, $\Sigma_1^N (X - \bar{X})^2/\sigma^2$ has a chi-square distribution but with degrees of freedom equal to $N - 1$ instead of N. To prove this, the following identity can be stated:

$$(X - \mu) = (X - \bar{X}) + (\bar{X} - \mu).$$

Squaring both sides, we have

$$(X - \mu)^2 = [(X - \bar{X}) + (\bar{X} - \mu)]^2$$
$$= (X - \bar{X})^2 + 2(X - \bar{X})(\bar{X} - \mu) + (\bar{X} - \mu)^2.$$

Summing over all of the squared deviations from μ in the sample gives

$$\sum_1^N (X - \mu)^2 = \sum_1^N [(X - \bar{X})^2 + 2(X - \bar{X})(\bar{X} - \mu) + (\bar{X} - \mu)^2]$$

(1)
$$= \sum_1^N (X - \bar{X})^2 + N(\bar{X} - \mu)^2.$$

This follows because the sum over the N observations of the term $(\bar{X} - \mu)^2$ on the right is a constant. According to Rule A.1 in Appendix A, the sum of a constant is equal to N times the constant. In addition, the sum of the product $2(X - \bar{X})(\bar{X} - \mu)$ equals zero because, by Rule A.3, the sum of a variable times a constant is equal to the constant times the sum of the variable. Thus

$$\sum_1^N [2(X - \bar{X})(\bar{X} - \mu)] = 2(\bar{X} - \mu) \sum_1^N (X - \bar{X}),$$

but the sum of the deviations of observations from their mean, $\Sigma_1^N (X - \bar{X})$, is equal to zero. Dividing both sides of equation (1) by the population variance σ^2 gives

(2) $$\frac{\sum_1^N (X - \mu)^2}{\sigma^2} = \frac{\sum_1^N (X - \bar{X})^2}{\sigma^2} + \frac{N(\bar{X} - \mu)^2}{\sigma^2}.$$

The term on the left is based on N randomly sampled observations from a normal population and is thus distributed as $\chi^2_{(N)}$, with $v = N$.

The last term on the right of equation (2) can be rewritten as

$$\frac{N(\bar{X} - \mu)^2}{\sigma^2} = \frac{(\bar{X} - \mu)^2}{\sigma^2/N} = \chi^2_{(1)}.$$

In this form it is apparent that it is also a chi-square random variable, with $v = 1$. This follows because the distribution of $\bar{X}$ for a normal population must be normal with mean equal to μ and variance equal to σ^2/N. We can rewrite equation (2) as

$$\chi^2_{(N)} = \frac{\sum_1^N (X - \bar{X})^2}{\sigma^2} + \chi^2_{(1)}.$$

If the two terms on the right of equation (2) are independent, it follows from the addition property of chi square that $\Sigma_1^N (X - \bar{X})^2/\sigma^2$ must have a chi-square distribution with degrees of freedom equal to $N - 1$. Therefore

(3) $$\chi^2_{(N)} = \chi^2_{(N-1)} + \chi^2_{(1)}.$$

An easily followed proof of the independence of the terms on the right of equation (2) is given by Lindquist (1953, 31–35).

We saw from the foregoing that the term $\Sigma_1^N (X - \bar{X})^2/\sigma^2$, based on the sample mean, must have a chi-square distribution with degrees of freedom equal to $N - 1$. In order to understand the relationship between the chi-square and the F distributions, it is helpful to express $\Sigma_1^N (X - \bar{X})^2/\sigma^2$ as

$$\frac{\sum_1^N (X - \bar{X})^2}{\sigma^2} = \frac{NS^2}{\sigma^2},$$

where S^2 is the sample variance. This follows because

$$S^2 = \frac{\sum_1^N (X - \bar{X})^2}{N}.$$

An unbiased estimate of the population variance $\hat{\sigma}^2$ is given by

$$\hat{\sigma}^2 = \frac{N}{N-1} S^2,$$

from which it can be seen that $(N-1)\hat{\sigma}^2 = NS^2$. If $(N-1)\hat{\sigma}^2$ is substituted for NS^2, we have

$$\frac{NS^2}{\sigma^2} = \frac{(N-1)\hat{\sigma}^2}{\sigma^2} = \chi^2_{(N-1)}.$$

Thus the ratio of $(N-1)\hat{\sigma}^2$ to σ^2 is a random variable that is distributed as chi square with $N-1$ degrees of freedom. The hypothesis

$$H_0 : \sigma_1^2 = \sigma_0^2$$

that concerns a *single* population variance σ_1^2 can be tested by means of the chi-square distribution. The test statistic is $(N-1)\hat{\sigma}_1^2/\sigma_0^2$, where $\hat{\sigma}_1^2$ is an estimate of σ_1^2 computed from a sample and σ_0^2 is the value of the population variance dictated by the null hypothesis. The probability of obtaining a χ^2 as large as that observed in an experiment if the null hypothesis is true can be determined from a table of χ^2 given in Appendix D.

F DISTRIBUTION

The experimental designs described in this book all involve tests concerning *two* population variances rather than a single variance. The sampling distribution that is used for testing a hypothesis about two population variances is the F distribution. The chi-square random variable was described in some detail in previous paragraphs because an F variable can be defined as the ratio of two *independent* chi-square variables, each divided by its degrees of freedom. That is,

$$F = \frac{\chi^2_{(v_1)}/v_1}{\chi^2_{(v_2)}/v_2}.$$

The distribution of this ratio was determined by R. A. Fisher (1924) and given the name F in his honor by G. W. Snedecor (1934).

Let us imagine that there are two populations of scores X_1 and X_2, each having normal distributions. Assume that both populations have the same variance σ^2 but not necessarily the same means. Suppose that two independent random samples of size N_1 and N_2 are drawn from the two populations. Unbiased estimates of σ^2 based on $\hat{\sigma}_1$ and $\hat{\sigma}_2$ are computed for the samples. We know, from the discussion of the chi-square random variable, that

$$\frac{(N-1)\hat{\sigma}_1^2}{\sigma^2} = \chi^2_{(N-1)}.$$

This can be written as

$$\hat{\sigma}_1^2 = \frac{\sigma^2 \chi_{(v_1)}^2}{v_1}$$

for the first population and as

$$\hat{\sigma}_2^2 = \frac{\sigma^2 \chi_{(v_2)}^2}{v_2}$$

for the second population.

The ratio

$$\frac{\hat{\sigma}_1^2}{\hat{\sigma}_2^2} = \frac{\sigma^2 \chi_{(v_1)}^2 / v_1}{\sigma^2 \chi_{(v_2)}^2 / v_2} = \frac{\chi_{(v_1)}^2 / v_1}{\chi_{(v_2)}^2 / v_2}$$

for each possible pair of samples from the two populations is the random variable F. This is true, of course, only if both population variances are equal to σ^2. It follows that an F ratio can be used to test the following kinds of hypotheses:

$$H_0 : \sigma_1^2 = \sigma_2^2$$

$$H_0 : \sigma_1^2 \leq \sigma_2^2$$

$$H_0 : \sigma_1^2 \geq \sigma_2^2.$$

The most common use of an F ratio is in testing hypotheses regarding the equality of three or more population means. The rationale underlying the use of an F ratio in testing hypotheses of the form

$$H_0 : \mu_1 = \mu_2 = \mu_3 = \cdots = \mu_k$$

is discussed in Sections 2.4 and 2.5.

The distribution of F depends on only two parameters, v_1 and v_2. The distribution of F for $v_1 = 9$ and $v_2 = 15$ is shown in Figure 2.1-2. Table D.5 in the appendix provides values of F that cut off the upper proportion α in an F distribution. In analysis of variance, only the upper percentage points of the F distribution are required. This is a consequence of the fact that in practice F is taken as the ratio of $\hat{\sigma}_{larger}^2$ to $\hat{\sigma}_{smaller}^2$. If the lower percentage points of the F distribution are desired, they can be readily computed from

$$F_{1-\alpha; v_1, v_2} = \frac{1}{F_{\alpha; v_2, v_1}}.$$

That is, the value of F in the lower proportion of the F distribution can be found by computing the reciprocal of the corresponding value in the upper proportion, with degrees of freedom for numerator and denominator reversed.

As Figure 2.1-2 shows, the distribution of F for v_1 and v_2 is nonsymmetrical. It approaches normality for very large values of v_1 and v_2. Because an F variable is the ratio of two independent chi-square variables divided by their respective degrees of freedom, it can only range over

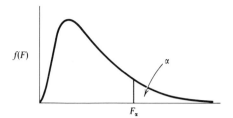

Figure 2.1-2   Form of F distribution for $v_1 = 9$ and $v_2 = 15$.

nonnegative real numbers from zero to positive infinity. The mean and mode of an F distribution are equal to $v_2/(v_2 - 2)$ and $(v_1 v_2 - 2v_2)/(v_1 v_2 + 2v_1)$, respectively. It can be shown that the mean is always greater than unity, whereas the mode is always less than unity. Hence the F distribution is positively skewed.

RELATIONSHIP BETWEEN THE t DISTRIBUTION AND THE χ^2 AND F DISTRIBUTIONS

The exact distribution of the t statistic, or t ratio as it is sometimes called, was derived by W. S. Gosset (1908), who wrote under the pseudonym of Student. Gosset is credited with starting a trend toward the development of exact statistical tests, that is, tests independent of knowledge or assumptions concerning population parameters. This development marked the beginning of the modern era in mathematical statistics. Consider a random sample of scores, X, from a normally distributed population with mean μ and variance σ^2. The mean of this random sample can be expressed in standardized form as

$$z = \frac{\bar{X} - \mu}{\sigma_{\bar{X}}},$$

where $\sigma_{\bar{X}} = \sigma/\sqrt{N}$.

We know that z is normally distributed with mean equal to zero and variance equal to unity. We noted earlier that the quantity $(N - 1)\hat{\sigma}^2/\sigma^2$ has a chi-square distribution, $\chi^2_{(N-1)}$, with degrees of freedom equal to $N - 1$. The t ratio for a single mean can be defined as

$$t = \frac{z}{\sqrt{\chi^2_{(N-1)}/(N - 1)}}.$$

Thus a t statistic is simply the ratio of a standardized normal variable z to the square root of a chi-square variable divided by its degrees of freedom.

The t ratio for a single mean can be written in a form more familiar to the reader.

$$t = \frac{z}{\sqrt{\chi^2_{(N-1)}/(N-1)}} = \frac{\dfrac{\bar{X} - \mu}{\sigma/\sqrt{N}}}{\sqrt{\hat{\sigma}^2/\sigma^2}} = \frac{\dfrac{\bar{X} - \mu}{\sigma/\sqrt{N}}}{\sqrt{S^2 \left(\dfrac{N}{N-1}\right)\Big/\sigma^2}} = \frac{\bar{X} - \mu}{S/\sqrt{N-1}}.$$

It should be noted that the computation of t does not require a knowledge of the population parameter σ^2.

The reader has undoubtedly surmised from the foregoing that t is related to F. What is the relationship between t and F? To answer this question, let us consider the square of the random variable t, with v equal to $N - 1$ degrees of freedom.

$$t^2 = \frac{z^2}{\chi^2_{(N-1)}/(N-1)}.$$

The numerator of this ratio is a chi-square variable, as defined earlier, with one degree of freedom, and the denominator is also a chi-square variable divided by its degrees of freedom, where $v = N - 1$. It can also be shown that the numerator and denominator are independent because $\hat{\sigma}^2$ is independent of $\bar{X}$ for a normal population. It follows from this that t^2 is identical to an F ratio, with 1 and v_2 degrees of freedom. That is $t^2_{(v)} = F_{(1,v_2)}$, where $v = v_2$.

The distribution of t is symmetrical around a mean of zero with variance equal to $v/(v - 2)$. It ranges over values from negative to positive infinity. The distribution of t depends on only one parameter v. Percentage points of Student's t distribution are given in Table D.4. For large values of N, the t distribution approaches the normal distribution. In this connection it should be noted that the normal curve is the *parent* distribution for the t, F, and χ^2 distributions. For $N > 30$, the t distribution may, for most practical purposes, be regarded as normally distributed.

SUMMARY OF BASIC ASSUMPTIONS
ASSOCIATED WITH THE F DISTRIBUTION

The F distribution is the theoretical model against which an F statistic is evaluated. The alternative statistical hypothesis, together with the level of significance discussed in Section 1.5, specifies the region of the F distribution for rejection of the null hypothesis. Hypothesis-testing procedures using the F distribution are based on certain assumptions that are necessary for the mathematical justification of the procedure. The following paragraphs briefly summarize those assumptions that have already been described in connection with the F and χ^2 distributions. We shall see later that even when certain assumptions associated with the F distribution are violated, it may still provide an adequate approximation for purposes of hypothesis testing.

Because F is a random variable formed from the ratio of two independent chi-square variables, each divided by its degrees of freedom, it follows that the assumptions of χ^2 are also assumptions of F. A basic assumption of the chi-square distribution is that the population is normally distributed. It is further assumed that random sampling from this normally distributed population is employed. It follows from the definition of a random sample that the selection of one observation is independent of the selection of another observation. The letters NID are often used as an abbreviation for the assumptions that variables are normally and independently distributed.

In the discussion of the random variable F, it was also assumed that the numerator and denominator of the ratio $\hat{\sigma}_1^2/\hat{\sigma}_2^2$ were independent and that the population variances were equal.

Hypothesis testing based on the F distribution as the theoretical model involves the following assumptions:

1. Observations are drawn from normally distributed populations.
2. Observations represent random samples from populations.
3. Variances of populations are equal.
4. Numerator and denominator of F ratio are independent.

Significance tests for each of the experimental designs described in Chapters 4 through 12 involve the foregoing assumptions. These basic assumptions will be tailored to the particular design being described.

2.2   PARTITION OF TOTAL SUM OF SQUARES

In Section 1.4 the mathematical models for several of the simpler experimental designs were presented. Each score in an experiment represents the effects of one or more sources of variability. For example, a score may include the effects of a treatment that has been administered, effects peculiar to a particular subject, and effects attributable to unknown and uncontrolled variables, such as measurement errors and environmental distractions.

The mathematical model for a design purports to represent all the sources of variability that affect individual scores. The total variability for N scores in an experiment is given by $\Sigma_1^N(X_{ij} - \overline{X}..)^2/N$. The problem, then, is to partition this total variance into its component parts according to the appropriate mathematical model. We shall see that the *breakdown* of the total variance is different for each experimental design. Actually, the partitioning will be done with the total sum of squares given by $\Sigma_1^N(X_{ij} - \overline{X}..)^2$ rather than with the total variance.

It will be shown in this section that, for a completely randomized design, the total sum of squares designated by the letters SS$_{total}$ can be partitioned into two components—sum of squares between groups and sum of squares within groups.

DEFINITION OF AN EFFECT

The model for a completely randomized design was given earlier as

$$X_{ij} = \mu + \beta_j + \varepsilon_{ij}.$$

If sample estimates are substituted for the parameters, the model can be written

$$X_{ij} = \bar{X}.. + \hat{\beta}_j + \hat{\varepsilon}_{ij}.$$

It follows from this model that the deviation of X_{ij} from the grand mean, $\bar{X}..$, is composed of two parts:

(1) $$X_{ij} - \bar{X}.. = \hat{\beta}_j + \hat{\varepsilon}_{ij}.$$

The term $\hat{\beta}_j$ is an estimate of β_j that represents the effect of treatment population j, and $\hat{\varepsilon}_{ij}$ is an estimate of error effect ε_{ij} that represents all effects *not* attributable to treatment j.

The effect of treatment j is defined as the deviation of the mean of population j, μ_j, from the grand population mean μ. The grand mean is simply the mean of all treatment populations under consideration.

$$\text{Effect of treatment } j = \beta_j = (\mu_j - \mu).$$

Treatment population j can be considered as the hypothetical set of all possible observations that might be made under treatment j. If a sample of subjects receive treatment j, the mean of this sample $\bar{X}._j$ is an estimate of the population mean. If samples are obtained from all treatment populations under consideration, the mean of these samples is an estimate of the grand population mean. Thus an estimate of treatment effect β_j for population j is given by

$$\hat{\beta}_j = (\bar{X}._j - \bar{X}..).$$

It follows from formula (1) that an estimate of error effect ε_{ij} for subject i who receives treatment j is given by

$$\hat{\varepsilon}_{ij} = X_{ij} - \bar{X}.. - (\bar{X}._j - \bar{X}..) = (X_{ij} - \bar{X}._j).$$

PARTITION OF TOTAL SUM OF SQUARES INTO BETWEEN- AND WITHIN-GROUPS SUM OF SQUARES

The following material presupposes a knowledge of the rules of summation. These rules are described in Appendix A, and the reader whose statistical background is minimal may wish to review them. The specific summation rules from Appendix A that are used in the following paragraphs are identified by the letter A and the appropriate rule number.

Let us assume that an experiment has been carried out in which 12 subjects are randomly assigned to three levels of a treatment. The data from this hypothetical experiment are shown in Table 2.2-1. In this table there are $k = 3$ levels of treatment B (b_1, b_2, b_3) and $n = 4$ observations per treatment level. Throughout this book, capital letters will be used to identify a treatment. A lower-case letter with a subscript will be used to

TABLE 2.2-1   Data from Hypothetical Experiment

	b_1	b_2	b_3	
	2	3	5	
	1	3	3	
	3	4	4	
	2	2	4	
$\sum_{1}^{n} X_{ij} = 8$		12	16	
$\bar{X}._j = 2$		3	4	$\bar{X}.. = 3$

identify a particular level of the treatment. The deviation of an individual score X_{ij} from the grand mean $\bar{X}..$ in this completely randomized design can be expressed as the sum of two terms: $\hat{\varepsilon}_{ij} + \hat{\beta}_j$, that is

$$(X_{ij} - \bar{X}..) = (X_{ij} - \bar{X}._j) + (\bar{X}._j - \bar{X}..).$$

Consider the score $X_{13} = 5$ in Table 2.2-1. According to the above formula,

$$(5 - 3) = (5 - 4) + (4 - 3)$$
$$2 \quad = \quad 1 \quad + \quad 1.$$

Hence, for a completely randomized design, the deviation of a score from the grand mean, $(X_{ij} - \bar{X}..)$, is equal to the deviation of the score from the treatment mean, $(X_{ij} - \bar{X}._j)$, plus the deviation of the treatment mean from the grand mean, $(\bar{X}._j - \bar{X}..)$. This is true for each of the n scores in the k treatment levels.

As noted previously, our interest is not in partitioning the deviation of a single score from the grand mean but, rather, in partitioning the total sum of squares. The deviation of each of the $kn = N = 12$ scores from the grand mean in Table 2.2-1 can be squared and then summed over the n subjects in each of the k treatment levels. This is written

$$(2) \quad \sum_{1}^{k}\sum_{1}^{n}(X_{ij} - \bar{X}..)^2 = \sum_{1}^{k}\sum_{1}^{n}[(X_{ij} - \bar{X}._j) + (\bar{X}._j - \bar{X}..)]^2$$

$$= \sum_{1}^{k}\sum_{1}^{n}[(X_{ij} - \bar{X}._j)^2 + 2(X_{ij} - \bar{X}._j)(\bar{X}._j - \bar{X}..)$$

$$+ (\bar{X}._j - \bar{X}..)^2].$$

According to Rule A.5 in the appendix, if addition is the only operation to be performed before summation, the summation can be distributed. Thus

$$(3) \quad \sum_{1}^{k}\sum_{1}^{n}(X_{ij} - \bar{X}..)^2 = \sum_{1}^{k}\sum_{1}^{n}[(X_{ij} - \bar{X}.j)^2] + \sum_{1}^{k}\sum_{1}^{n}[2(X_{ij} - \bar{X}.j)(\bar{X}.j - \bar{X}..)]$$

$$+ \sum_{1}^{k}\sum_{1}^{n}[(\bar{X}.j - \bar{X}..)^2].$$

$$(4) \quad \sum_{1}^{k}\sum_{1}^{n}(X_{ij} - \bar{X}..)^2 = \sum_{1}^{k}\sum_{1}^{n}(X_{ij} - \bar{X}.j)^2 + 2\sum_{1}^{k}(\bar{X}.j - \bar{X}..)\left[\sum_{1}^{n}(X_{ij} - \bar{X}.j)\right]$$

$$+ n\sum_{1}^{k}(\bar{X}.j - \bar{X}..)^2.$$

The specific rules used in arriving at each of the terms in equation (4) can be shown as follows:

$$\sum_{1}^{k}\sum_{1}^{n}[(X_{ij} - \bar{X}.j)^2] = \sum_{1}^{k}\sum_{1}^{n}(X_{ij} - \bar{X}.j)^2. \qquad \text{(Rule A.2)}$$

Rule A.2 applies because the *square* of the deviation of the $i = 1, \ldots, n$ scores from their respective treatment means is a variable for each of the $j = 1, \ldots, k$ treatment levels. This is readily apparent from an examination of Table 2.2-1. If the reader has not developed skill in interpretating summation notation, it may be helpful to visualize the summation for a specific set of data, such as that shown in Table 2.2-1.

$$\sum_{1}^{k}\sum_{1}^{n}[2(X_{ij} - \bar{X}.j)(\bar{X}.j - \bar{X}..)] = 2\sum_{1}^{k}(\bar{X}.j - \bar{X}..)\left[\sum_{1}^{n}(X_{ij} - \bar{X}.j)\right].$$

$$\text{(Rules A.3, A.6)}$$

It should be noted that

$$\sum_{1}^{n}(X_{ij} - \bar{X}.j) = 0$$

for each of the j treatment levels. Hence the entire middle term on the right side of equation (4) is equal to zero and disappears when summation is performed. The term on the extreme right of equation (3), $(\bar{X}.j - \bar{X}..)^2$, is a constant with respect to summation $i = 1, \ldots, n$ but a variable with respect to summation $j = 1, \ldots, k$. Thus

$$\sum_{1}^{k}\sum_{1}^{n}[(\bar{X}.j - \bar{X}..)^2] = n\sum_{1}^{k}(\bar{X}.j - \bar{X}..)^2. \qquad \text{(Rules A.1, A.2)}$$

Because the middle cross-product term equals zero, the total sum of squares can be partitioned into two sums of squares.

$$(5) \quad \sum_{1}^{k}\sum_{1}^{n}(X_{ij} - \bar{X}..)^2 = \sum_{1}^{k}\sum_{1}^{n}(X_{ij} - \bar{X}.j)^2 + n\sum_{1}^{k}(\bar{X}.j - \bar{X}..)^2.$$

The term on the left of the equals sign is the *total sum of squares*, and the two terms on the right are referred to as the *within-groups* and *between-groups* sum of squares, respectively.

What purpose does partitioning the total sum of squares serve? We shall see in Sections 2.4 and 2.5 that if the null hypothesis is true, the sum of squares within groups (SS_{WG}) and sum of squares between groups (SS_{BG}), when divided by their respective degrees of freedom (df) provide independent estimates of error variance. If the null hypothesis is false, SS_{BG}/df provides an estimate of treatment effects in addition to error variance. Partitioning of the total sum of squares is central to the analysis of variance because the ratio

$$F = \frac{SS_{BG}/df}{SS_{WG}/df}$$

is used to test the null hypothesis that all treatment effects are equal to zero.

PARTITION OF TOTAL SUM OF SQUARES
FOR MORE COMPLEX DESIGNS

The partition of the total sum of squares as shown in equation (5) is appropriate for a completely randomized design. A different partition is required for more complex designs. For example, in a randomized block design, which is described in Section 1.4, the deviation of an individual score from the grand mean can be expressed as the sum of *three* terms:

$$(X_{ij} - \overline{X}..) = (\overline{X}_{i.} - \overline{X}..) + (\overline{X}_{.j} - \overline{X}..) + (X_{ij} - \overline{X}_{i.} - \overline{X}_{.j} + \overline{X}..).$$

Where $(\overline{X}_{i.} - \overline{X}..)$ is the deviation of a row mean from the grand mean, $(\overline{X}_{.j} - \overline{X}..)$ is the deviation of a treatment mean from the grand mean, and $(X_{ij} - \overline{X}_{i.} - \overline{X}_{.j} + \overline{X}..)$ is a remainder. The derivation of formulas for computing the four sums of squares for a randomized block design follows the procedures that were shown for a completely randomized design.

An examination of the mathematical model for a Latin square design given in Section 1.4 should suggest to the reader that $(X_{ijk} - \overline{X}...)$ can be expressed as the sum of *four* terms. Thus

$$(X_{ijk} - \overline{X}...) = (\overline{X}_{i..} - \overline{X}...) + (\overline{X}_{.j.} - \overline{X}...) + (\overline{X}_{..k} - \overline{X}...)$$
$$+ (X_{ijk} - \overline{X}_{i..} - \overline{X}_{.j.} - \overline{X}_{..k} + 2\overline{X}...),$$

where $(\overline{X}_{.j.} - \overline{X}...)$ and $(\overline{X}_{..k} - \overline{X}...)$ now correspond to the deviation of a column mean and a treatment mean, respectively, from the grand mean. It should be apparent to the reader that more complex designs are formed by partitioning the total sum of squares into a larger number of sources of variation. In complex designs, each sum of squares should represent a source of variation that an experimenter wants either to control or to evaluate.

2.3   DERIVATION OF COMPUTATIONAL FORMULAS

The partition of the total sum of squares as expressed in equation (5), Section 2.2, does not provide formulas that are convenient for computational purposes. These formulas can be rewritten in an alternative form that is more amenable to routine computation.

COMPUTATIONAL FORMULA FOR TOTAL SUM OF SQUARES

The formula for a total sum of squares can be written as follows:

$$\sum_{1}^{k}\sum_{1}^{n}(X_{ij} - \bar{X}..)^2 = \sum_{1}^{k}\sum_{1}^{n}(X_{ij}^2 - 2\bar{X}..X_{ij} + \bar{X}..^2)$$

$$= \sum_{1}^{k}\left(\sum_{1}^{n}X_{ij}^2 - 2\bar{X}..\sum_{1}^{n}X_{ij} + n\bar{X}..^2\right)$$

(Rules A.1, A.2, A.3, A.5)

$$= \sum_{1}^{k}\sum_{1}^{n}X_{ij}^2 - 2\bar{X}..\sum_{1}^{k}\sum_{1}^{n}X_{ij} + kn\bar{X}..^2$$

(Rules A.1, A.2, A.3, A.5)

$$= \sum_{1}^{k}\sum_{1}^{n}X_{ij}^2 - 2\frac{\left(\sum_{1}^{k}\sum_{1}^{n}X_{ij}\right)}{kn}\left(\sum_{1}^{k}\sum_{1}^{n}X_{ij}\right) + kn\frac{\left(\sum_{1}^{k}\sum_{1}^{n}X_{ij}\right)^2}{k^2n^2}$$

because
$$\bar{X}.. = \frac{\sum_{1}^{k}\sum_{1}^{n}X_{ij}}{kn}.$$

(1)
$$\sum_{1}^{k}\sum_{1}^{n}(X_{ij} - \bar{X}..)^2 = \sum_{1}^{k}\sum_{1}^{n}X_{ij}^2 - \frac{\left(\sum_{1}^{k}\sum_{1}^{n}X_{ij}\right)^2}{kn} = \sum_{1}^{N}X_{ij}^2 - \frac{\left(\sum_{1}^{N}X_{ij}\right)^2}{N}.$$

Writing out the above computational formulas for complex designs consumes both space and time. Consequently, abbreviated symbols for the terms are used in this book. In the case of simple designs, these abbreviated symbols offer no particular advantage, but they are very useful for designs described in later chapters. The abbreviated symbols for the terms on the right side of equation (1) are

$$\sum_{1}^{N}X_{ij}^2 = [BS] \quad \text{and} \quad \frac{\left(\sum_{1}^{N}X_{ij}\right)^2}{N} = [X].$$

Thus a total sum of squares can be written, using these symbols, as

$$SS_{total} = [BS] - [X].$$

COMPUTATIONAL FORMULA FOR
BETWEEN-GROUPS SUM OF SQUARES

The formula for a between-groups sum of squares can be written as follows:

$$n\sum_1^k (\bar{X}_{\cdot j} - \bar{X}_{\cdot\cdot})^2 = n\sum_1^k (\bar{X}_{\cdot j}^2 - 2\bar{X}_{\cdot\cdot}\bar{X}_{\cdot j} + \bar{X}_{\cdot\cdot}^2)$$

$$= n(\sum_1^k \bar{X}_{\cdot j}^2 - 2\bar{X}_{\cdot\cdot}\sum_1^k \bar{X}_{\cdot j} + k\bar{X}_{\cdot\cdot}^2)$$

(Rules A.1, A.2, A.3, A.5)

$$= n\sum_1^k \frac{\left(\sum_1^n X_{ij}\right)^2}{n^2} - 2n\frac{\left(\sum_1^k\sum_1^n X_{ij}\right)}{kn}\frac{\left(\sum_1^k\sum_1^n X_{ij}\right)}{n}$$

$$+ kn\frac{\left(\sum_1^k\sum_1^n X_{ij}\right)^2}{k^2 n^2}$$

because $\quad \bar{X}_{\cdot\cdot} = \dfrac{\sum_1^k\sum_1^n X_{ij}}{kn} \quad$ and $\quad \bar{X}_{\cdot j} = \dfrac{\sum_1^n X_{ij}}{n}.$

$$n\sum_1^k (\bar{X}_{\cdot j} - \bar{X}_{\cdot\cdot})^2 = \sum_1^k \frac{\left(\sum_1^n X_{ij}\right)^2}{n} - 2\frac{\left(\sum_1^k\sum_1^n X_{ij}\right)^2}{kn} + \frac{\left(\sum_1^k\sum_1^n X_{ij}\right)^2}{kn}$$

(2) $$\qquad = \sum_1^k \frac{\left(\sum_1^n X_{ij}\right)^2}{n} - \frac{\left(\sum_1^k\sum_1^n X_{ij}\right)^2}{kn}.$$

(3) $\quad n\sum_1^k (\bar{X}_{\cdot j} - \bar{X}_{\cdot\cdot})^2 = \sum_1^k \dfrac{\left(\sum_1^n X_{ij}\right)^2}{n} - \dfrac{\left(\sum_1^N X_{ij}\right)^2}{N}.$

If the numbers of scores in each treatment level are equal, formula (2) is equivalent to formula (3). If the n's are unequal, formula (3) is used for computing the between-groups sum of squares. In terms of abbreviated symbols, $\Sigma_1^k[(\Sigma_1^n X_{ij})^2/n]$ is designated by $[B]$. Thus a between-groups sum of squares can be written

$$SS_{BG} = [B] - [X].$$

COMPUTATIONAL FORMULA FOR
WITHIN-GROUPS SUM OF SQUARES

The formula for a within-groups sum of squares can be written as follows:

$$\sum_{1}^{k}\sum_{1}^{n}(X_{ij} - \bar{X}_{\cdot j})^2 = \sum_{1}^{k}\sum_{1}^{n}(X_{ij}^2 - 2\bar{X}_{\cdot j}X_{ij} + \bar{X}_{\cdot j}^2)$$

$$= \sum_{1}^{k}(\sum_{1}^{n}X_{ij}^2 - 2\bar{X}_{\cdot j}\sum_{1}^{n}X_{ij} + n\bar{X}_{\cdot j}^2),$$

(Rules A.1, A.2, A.3, A.5)

but
$$\sum_{1}^{n}X_{ij} = n\bar{X}_{\cdot j}.$$

$$\sum_{1}^{k}\sum_{1}^{n}(X_{ij} - \bar{X}_{\cdot j})^2 = \sum_{1}^{k}(\sum_{1}^{n}X_{ij}^2 - 2n\bar{X}_{\cdot j}^2 + n\bar{X}_{\cdot j}^2)$$

$$= \sum_{1}^{k}(\sum_{1}^{n}X_{ij}^2 - n\bar{X}_{\cdot j}^2) = \sum_{1}^{k}\left[\sum_{1}^{n}X_{ij}^2 - n\frac{\left(\sum_{1}^{n}X_{ij}\right)^2}{n^2}\right]$$

$$= \sum_{1}^{k}\sum_{1}^{n}X_{ij}^2 - \sum_{1}^{k}\frac{\left(\sum_{1}^{n}X_{ij}\right)^2}{n}$$ (Rules A.2, A.5)

(4)
$$= \sum_{1}^{N}X_{ij}^2 - \sum_{1}^{k}\frac{\left(\sum_{1}^{n}X_{ij}\right)^2}{n}.$$

According to the abbreviated symbols defined earlier, this sum of squares can be written

$$SS_{WG} = [BS] - [B].$$

2.4   EXPECTATION OF SUM OF SQUARES

In Section 2.2 we saw that the total sum of squares for a completely randomized design can be partitioned into between- and within-groups sum of squares. A careful examination of these terms provides an intuitive understanding of the sources of variation which they represent. The within-groups sum of squares is composed of variation due to differences among individual subjects who receive the same treatment level. Some variation among the scores of subjects under identical treatment conditions can always be expected because of individual differences. Since subjects are randomly assigned to the treatment levels, this source represents chance variation. Differences among the scores of subjects who are assigned to different treatment levels reflect chance variation and, in addition, the systematic effects of the particular treatment levels. Therefore the within-groups sum of squares is an estimate of chance variation, whereas the between-groups sum of squares is an estimate of chance variation, plus the effects of treatment levels if such effects are present. A more systematic exposition of these points requires an understanding of the concept of the expected value of a random variable. Before pursuing this further, two models—the fixed-effects and random-effects models—are described.

FIXED-EFFECTS LINEAR MODEL

The partition of the total sum of squares shown in Section 2.2 involved no special assumptions concerning populations or sampling procedures. However, certain assumptions are required if one is to draw inferences concerning population parameters from sample data. General assumptions associated with an F ratio were described in Section 2.1. In addition to these assumptions, special assumptions concerning the mathematical model are necessary. The mathematical model for a completely randomized analysis of variance design is

$$X_{ij} = \mu + \beta_j + \varepsilon_{ij}.$$

The following assumptions are for a *fixed-effects* model. This model is appropriate for experiments in which all treatment levels about which inferences are to be drawn are included in the experiment. If the experiment were replicated, the same treatment levels would be included in the replication. Under these conditions, conclusions drawn from the experiment apply only to the actual k treatment levels in the experiment. If the k treatment levels included in the experiment are a random sample from a much larger population of K levels, the model is a *random-effects* model. Special assumptions appropriate for this model are described later. For the fixed-effects model, β_j is a constant fixed effect for all observations within population j, but it may vary for each of the $j = 1, \ldots, k$ treatment populations. The expected value of the constant β_j is

$$\mathrm{E}(\beta_j) = \beta_j \qquad \text{(Rule B.3)}$$

and

$$\sum_{j=1}^{k} \beta_j = 0,$$

with expected value equal to

$$\mathrm{E}\left(\sum_{j=1}^{k} \beta_j\right) = \mathrm{E}(\beta_1 + \beta_2 + \beta_3 + \cdots + \beta_k) = 0. \qquad \text{(Rule B.3)}$$

Also,

$$E\left(\sum_{j=1}^{k} \beta_j\right)^2 = E(\beta_1 + \beta_2 + \cdots + \beta_k)^2$$

$$= E[\beta_1(\beta_1 + \beta_2 + \cdots + \beta_k) + \beta_2(\beta_1 + \beta_2 + \cdots + \beta_k)$$
$$+ \cdots + \beta_k(\beta_1 + \beta_2 + \cdots + \beta_k)],$$

but

$$(\beta_1 + \beta_2 + \cdots + \beta_k) = 0.$$

Thus

$$E\left(\sum_{j=1}^{k} \beta_j\right)^2 = 0,$$

and

$$E\left(\sum_{j=1}^{k} \beta_j^2\right) = E(\beta_1^2 + \beta_2^2 + \cdots + \beta_k^2)$$

$$= \beta_1^2 + \beta_2^2 + \cdots + \beta_k^2 = \sum_{j=1}^{k} \beta_j^2. \qquad \text{(Rule B.3)}$$

Because both μ and β_j are constant for all observations within population j, the only source of variation among these observations is that due to the experimental error, ε_{ij}. It is assumed that the distribution of ε_{ij} for *each* treatment population is normal, with mean equal to zero and variance equal to σ_ε^2. It is also assumed that the ε_{ij}'s are independent, both within each treatment level and across all treatment levels. If subjects are randomly assigned to treatment levels, the value of ε_{ij} for any observation can be assumed to be independent of the values of ε_{ij}'s for other observations. In summary, it is assumed that ε_{ij} is a random variable that is normally and independently distributed (NID), with mean equal to zero and variance equal to σ_ε^2. The expected value of ε_{ij}, according to the assumptions that have been made, is

$$E(\varepsilon_{ij}) = \mu_{(\varepsilon)} = 0 \qquad \text{(Rule B.1)}$$

and

$$E\left(\sum_{i=1}^{n} \varepsilon_{ij}\right) = n\mu_{(\varepsilon)} = 0 \qquad \text{(Rule B.8)}$$

and

$$E\left(\sum_{i=1}^{n} \varepsilon_{ij}^2\right) = n(\mu_{(\varepsilon)}^2 + \sigma_\varepsilon^2) = n\sigma_\varepsilon^2 \qquad \text{(Rule B.10)}$$

and

$$E\left(\sum_{i=1}^{n} \varepsilon_{ij}\right)^2 = n(n\mu_{(\varepsilon)}^2 + \sigma_\varepsilon^2) = n\sigma_\varepsilon^2. \qquad \text{(Rule B.11)}$$

The expected value of the grand mean μ is

$$E(\mu) = \mu. \tag{Rule B.3}$$

Finally, it is assumed that a score X_{ij} is an estimate of the linear combination of the parameters specified in the mathematical model.

EXPECTATION OF BETWEEN-GROUPS SUM OF SQUARES

The computational formula for a between-groups sum of squares was given in Section 2.3 as

$$(1) \qquad \sum_1^k \frac{\left(\sum_1^n X_{ij} \right)^2}{n} - \frac{\left(\sum_1^k \sum_1^n X_{ij} \right)^2}{kn}.$$

At the beginning of this section we expressed the idea that this sum of squares is an estimate of chance variation, plus treatment effects if the latter are present in an experiment. A more formal exposition of this idea for a fixed-effects linear model involves the concept of an expected value.

It will be shown that the expected value of the between-groups mean square is

$$E(\mathrm{MS_{BG}}) = \sigma_\varepsilon^2 + \frac{n \sum_1^k \beta_j^2}{k - 1}.$$

This final result is obtained by first determining the expected values of the two terms in (1) separately.

The linear model for a completely randomized design was given earlier as

$$X_{ij} = \mu + \beta_j + \varepsilon_{ij}.$$

The terms $(\mu + \beta_j + \varepsilon_{ij})$ can be substituted for X_{ij} in $\Sigma_1^k[(\Sigma_1^n X_{ij})^2/n]$ as follows:

$$E\left[\sum_1^k \frac{\left(\sum_1^n X_{ij} \right)^2}{n} \right] = E\left\{ \sum_1^k \frac{\left[\sum_1^n (\mu + \beta_j + \varepsilon_{ij}) \right]^2}{n} \right\}$$

$$= \frac{1}{n} \sum_1^k E\left\{ \left[\sum_1^n (\mu + \beta_j + \varepsilon_{ij}) \right]^2 \right\} \qquad \text{(Rules B.3, B.6)}$$

$$= \frac{1}{n} \sum_1^k E\left[n\mu + n\beta_j + \sum_1^n \varepsilon_{ij} \right]^2 \qquad \text{(Rules A.1, A.2, A.5)}$$

$$= \frac{1}{n} \sum_1^k E\left[n^2\mu^2 + n^2\beta_j^2 + \left(\sum_1^n \varepsilon_{ij} \right)^2 + 2n^2\mu\beta_j \right]$$

$$\left. + 2n\mu\sum_1^n \varepsilon_{ij} + 2n\beta_j\sum_1^n \varepsilon_{ij}\right]$$

$$= \frac{1}{n}\sum_1^k\left(n^2\mu^2 + n^2\beta_j^2 + n\sigma_\varepsilon^2 + 2n^2\mu\beta_j\right)$$

(Rules B.3, B.4, B.5, B.6, B.8, B.11)

$$= kn\mu^2 + n\sum_1^k\beta_j^2 + k\sigma_\varepsilon^2 + 2n\mu\sum_1^k\beta_j, \quad \text{(Rules A.1, A.3, A.5)}$$

but $\sum_1^k \beta_j = 0$. Thus

$$(2) \qquad E\left[\sum_1^k \frac{\left(\sum_1^n X_{ij}\right)^2}{n}\right] = kn\mu^2 + n\sum_1^k\beta_j^2 + k\sigma_\varepsilon^2.$$

If $(\mu + \beta_j + \varepsilon_{ij})$ is substituted for X_{ij} in $(\Sigma_1^k\Sigma_1^n X_{ij})^2/kn$, following the procedure shown above,

$$E\left[\frac{\left(\sum_1^k\sum_1^n X_{ij}\right)^2}{kn}\right] = E\left\{\frac{\left[\sum_1^k\sum_1^n(\mu + \beta_j + \varepsilon_{ij})\right]^2}{kn}\right\}$$

$$= \frac{1}{kn}E\left[\left(kn\mu + n\sum_1^k\beta_j + \sum_1^k\sum_1^n\varepsilon_{ij}\right)^2\right]$$

(Rules A.1, A.2, A.3, A.5)

$$= \frac{1}{kn}E\left[k^2n^2\mu^2 + n^2\left(\sum_1^k\beta_j\right)^2 + \left(\sum_1^k\sum_1^n\varepsilon_{ij}\right)^2\right.$$

$$\left. + 2kn^2\mu\sum_1^k\beta_j + 2kn\mu\sum_1^k\sum_1^n\varepsilon_{ij} + 2n\sum_1^k\beta_j\sum_1^k\sum_1^n\varepsilon_{ij}\right]$$

$$= \frac{1}{kn}\left(k^2n^2\mu^2 + kn\sigma_\varepsilon^2\right), \quad \text{(Rules B.3, B.4, B.5, B.6, B.8, B.11)}$$

because

$$E\left(\sum_1^k\beta_j\right)^2 = 0, \quad E\left(\sum_1^k\sum_1^n\varepsilon_{ij}\right)^2 = kn(kn\mu_\varepsilon^2 + \sigma_\varepsilon^2) = kn\sigma_\varepsilon^2,$$

$$E\left(\sum_1^k\beta_j\right) = 0, \quad \text{and} \quad E\left(\sum_1^k\sum_1^n\varepsilon_{ij}\right) = kn\mu_\varepsilon = 0.$$

Hence

$$(3) \qquad E\left[\frac{\left(\sum_1^k\sum_1^n X_{ij}\right)^2}{kn}\right] = kn\mu^2 + \sigma_\varepsilon^2.$$

Therefore the expected value of the between-groups sum of squares is equal to

(4) $\quad \mathrm{E}\left[\sum\limits_{1}^{k} \dfrac{\left(\sum\limits_{1}^{n} X_{ij}\right)^2}{n} - \dfrac{\left(\sum\limits_{1}^{k}\sum\limits_{1}^{n} X_{ij}\right)^2}{kn}\right] = \left(kn\mu^2 + n\sum\limits_{1}^{k}\beta_j^2 + k\sigma_\varepsilon^2\right)$

$$- (kn\mu^2 + \sigma_\varepsilon^2) = n\sum\limits_{1}^{k}\beta_j^2 + (k-1)\sigma_\varepsilon^2.$$

A mean square (MS) is obtained by dividing a sum of squares by its degrees of freedom. For an experiment with k treatment levels, the between-treatment degrees of freedom is equal to $k - 1$. The expected value of $\mathrm{MS_{BG}}$ is

$$\mathrm{E(MS_{BG})} = \dfrac{(k-1)\sigma_\varepsilon^2 + n\sum\limits_{1}^{k}\beta_j^2}{k-1} = \sigma_\varepsilon^2 + \dfrac{n\sum\limits_{1}^{k}\beta_j^2}{k-1}.$$

It should be noted at this point that if the null hypothesis stating that $\beta_j = 0$ for all of the j treatment levels is true, then

$$\mathrm{E(MS_{BG})} = \sigma_\varepsilon^2.$$

EXPECTATION OF WITHIN-GROUPS SUM OF SQUARES

The computational formula for a within-groups sum of squares appears in Section 2.3 as

(5) $$\sum\limits_{1}^{k}\sum\limits_{1}^{n} X_{ij}^2 - \sum\limits_{1}^{k} \dfrac{\left(\sum\limits_{1}^{n} X_{ij}\right)^2}{n}.$$

We already saw that

$$\mathrm{E}\left[\sum\limits_{1}^{k} \dfrac{\left(\sum\limits_{1}^{n} X_{ij}\right)^2}{n}\right] = kn\mu^2 + n\sum\limits_{1}^{k}\beta_j^2 + k\sigma_\varepsilon^2.$$

The expectation of the first term of the within-groups sum of squares formula can be determined by substituting $(\mu + \beta_j + \varepsilon_{ij})$ for X_{ij}.

$$\mathrm{E}\left(\sum\limits_{1}^{k}\sum\limits_{1}^{n} X_{ij}^2\right) = \mathrm{E}\left[\sum\limits_{1}^{k}\sum\limits_{1}^{n} (\mu + \beta_j + \varepsilon_{ij})^2\right]$$

$$= \sum\limits_{1}^{k}\mathrm{E}\left[\sum\limits_{1}^{n} (\mu^2 + \beta_j^2 + \varepsilon_{ij}^2 + 2\mu\beta_j + 2\mu\varepsilon_{ij} + 2\beta_j\varepsilon_{ij})\right]$$

$$= \sum_1^k E\left(n\mu^2 + n\beta_j^2 + \sum_1^n \varepsilon_{ij}^2 + 2n\mu\beta_j + 2\mu\sum_1^n \varepsilon_{ij} + 2\beta_j\sum_1^n \varepsilon_{ij}\right)$$

(Rules A.1, A.2, A.3, A.5)

$$= \sum_1^k \left(n\mu^2 + n\beta_j^2 + n\sigma_\varepsilon^2 + 2n\mu\beta_j\right) \qquad \text{(Rules B.3, B.4, B.5, B.8, B.10)}$$

because

$$E\left(\sum_1^n \varepsilon_{ij}^2\right) = n(\mu_\varepsilon^2 + \sigma_\varepsilon^2) = n\sigma_\varepsilon^2 \quad \text{and} \quad E\left(\sum_1^n \varepsilon_{ij}\right) = n\mu_\varepsilon = 0.$$

Thus

$$E\left(\sum_1^k \sum_1^n X_{ij}^2\right) = kn\mu^2 + n\sum_1^k \beta_j^2 + kn\sigma_\varepsilon^2 + 2n\mu\sum_1^k \beta_j,$$

(Rules A.1, A.3, A.5)

but $\sum_1^k \beta_j = 0$, so

$$E\left(\sum_1^k \sum_1^n X_{ij}^2\right) = kn\mu^2 + n\sum_1^k \beta_j^2 + kn\sigma_\varepsilon^2.$$

Hence the expected value of the within-groups sum of squares is equal to

$$E\left[\sum_1^k \sum_1^n X_{ij}^2 - \sum_1^k \frac{\left(\sum_1^n X_{ij}\right)^2}{n}\right] = \left(kn\mu^2 + n\sum_1^k \beta_j^2 + kn\sigma_\varepsilon^2\right)$$

$$- \left(kn\mu^2 + n\sum_1^k \beta_j^2 + k\sigma_\varepsilon^2\right)$$

$$= (kn - k)\sigma_\varepsilon^2.$$

The expectation of the within-groups mean square is equal to the sum of squares divided by its degrees of freedom:

$$E(\mathrm{MS_{WG}}) = \frac{(kn - k)\sigma_\varepsilon^2}{kn - k} = \sigma_\varepsilon^2.$$

Our intuitive understanding of the nature of the within-groups sum of squares has been verified. This source is a pooled estimate of variation due to differences among observations obtained under the same treatment levels.

EXPECTATION OF TOTAL SUM OF SQUARES

The computational formula for a total sum of squares is

$$\sum_1^k \sum_1^n X_{ij}^2 - \frac{\left(\sum_1^k \sum_1^n X_{ij}\right)^2}{kn}.$$

The expected values of the two terms in this formula have already been shown to equal

$$E\left[\sum_1^k\sum_1^n X_{ij}^2 - \frac{\left(\sum_1^k\sum_1^n X_{ij}\right)^2}{kn}\right] = \left(kn\mu^2 + n\sum_1^k\beta_j^2 + kn\sigma_\varepsilon^2\right) - (kn\mu^2 + \sigma_\varepsilon^2)$$

$$= n\sum_1^k\beta_j^2 + (kn - 1)\sigma_\varepsilon^2.$$

The degrees of freedom for SS_{total} are $kn - 1$. The expected value of the total mean square is

$$E(MS_{total}) = \frac{(kn - 1)\sigma_\varepsilon^2 + n\sum_1^k\beta_j^2}{kn - 1} = \sigma_\varepsilon^2 + \frac{n\sum_1^k\beta_j^2}{kn - 1}.$$

Note that if the null hypothesis that $\beta_j = 0$ for all j is true, then

$$E(MS_{total}) = \sigma_\varepsilon^2.$$

Therefore the expectation of the total, between-groups, and within-groups mean squares is σ_ε^2 if the null hypothesis is true. If the null hypothesis is not true, then

$$E(MS_{total}) \quad \text{and} \quad E(MS_{BG}) > \sigma_\varepsilon^2.$$

EXPECTATIONS OF SUM OF SQUARES
FOR RANDOM-EFFECTS MODEL

Earlier we stated the assumptions for a fixed-effects model. One of these assumptions was that all treatment levels about which inferences are to be drawn are included in the experiment. If the k treatment levels included in the experiment are a random sample from a much larger population of K levels, the model is a random-effects model. For this model, the possible values of the treatment effect b_j represent a random variable that is normally distributed with mean equal to zero and variance equal to σ_B^2. A Roman letter b or B (instead of a Greek β) is used to designate random-treatment effects. The values of b_j for the $j = 1, \ldots, k$ treatment levels occurring in the experiment are assumed to be independent of each other and ε_{ij}. The grand mean μ is assumed to be a constant and ε_{ij} is NID, with mean $= 0$ and variance $= \sigma_\varepsilon^2$ as in the fixed-effects model described previously. For this model,

$$E(b_j) = \mu_{(B)} = 0 \quad \text{and} \quad E(b_j^2) = \sigma_B^2.$$

With the procedures employed for the fixed-effects model, it can be shown that

$$E\left(\sum_1^k\sum_1^n X_{ij}^2\right) = kn\mu^2 + kn\sigma_B^2 + kn\sigma_\varepsilon^2$$

$$E\left[\sum_1^k \frac{\left(\sum_1^n X_{ij}\right)^2}{n}\right] = kn\mu^2 + kn\sigma_B^2 + k\sigma_\varepsilon^2$$

$$E\left[\frac{\left(\sum_1^k \sum_1^n X_{ij}\right)^2}{kn}\right] = kn\mu^2 + n\sigma_B^2 + \sigma_\varepsilon^2,$$

and

$$E(SS_{BG}) = (kn\mu^2 + kn\sigma_B^2 + k\sigma_\varepsilon^2) - (kn\mu^2 + n\sigma_B^2 + \sigma_\varepsilon^2)$$

$$= (kn - n)\sigma_B^2 + (k - 1)\sigma_\varepsilon^2$$

$$E(SS_{WG}) = (kn\mu^2 + kn\sigma_B^2 + kn\sigma_\varepsilon^2) - (kn\mu^2 + kn\sigma_B^2 + k\sigma_\varepsilon^2) = (kn - k)\sigma_\varepsilon^2.$$

Dividing the respective sum of squares by their degrees of freedom gives

$$E(MS_{BG}) = \frac{(k - 1)\sigma_\varepsilon^2 + n(k - 1)\sigma_B^2}{k - 1} = \sigma_\varepsilon^2 + n\sigma_B^2$$

and

$$E(MS_{WG}) = \frac{(kn - k)\sigma_\varepsilon^2}{kn - k} = \sigma_\varepsilon^2.$$

Therefore the expected values of the mean squares for the fixed- and random-effects models are very similar for a completely randomized design. This will not be true for more complex experimental designs. The procedure that has been illustrated for determining expected values of mean squares for a completely randomized design can be used to determine the E(MS) for any design. A much simpler set of rules leading to identical E(MS) are described in Section 7.10. The choice of the correct denominator for an F ratio is based on the expected values of the mean squares, a point that will be discussed at length in connection with complex experimental designs.

The expected values of the between-groups mean square for the fixed-effects model is often written, for convenience, as

$$E(MS_{BG}) = \sigma_\varepsilon^2 + n\sigma_\beta^2$$

instead of

$$E(MS_{BG}) = \sigma_\varepsilon^2 + \frac{n\sum_1^k \beta_j^2}{k - 1}.$$

This is satisfactory as long as it is understood that although $\Sigma_1^k \beta_j^2/(k - 1)$ is written as σ_β^2, it is not a variance estimate, for there are only k possible treatment means. Some authors use $\phi(B)$ or θ_B to stand for $\Sigma_{j=1}^k \beta_j^2/(k - 1)$.

2.5   THE *F* RATIO IN ANALYSIS OF VARIANCE

An F ratio in analysis of variance provides a test of the hypothesis that all treatment population means are equal. That is,

$$H_0 : \mu_1 = \mu_2 = \cdots = \mu_k = \mu.$$

This null hypothesis is equivalent to the hypothesis that

$$H_0 : \beta_j = 0 \qquad \text{for all } j.$$

We have seen that when H_0 is true,

$$\mathrm{E(MS_{BG})} = \sigma_\varepsilon^2$$

and

$$\mathrm{E(MS_{WG})} = \sigma_\varepsilon^2.$$

When the null hypothesis is false and the alternative hypothesis that

$$H_1 : \beta_j \neq 0 \qquad \text{for some } j$$

is true,

$$\mathrm{E(MS_{BG})} > \mathrm{E(MS_{WG})}.$$

If the null hypothesis is true, we know from Section 2.1 that the random variables $\mathrm{MS_{BG}}/\sigma_\varepsilon^2$ and $\mathrm{MS_{WG}}/\sigma_\varepsilon^2$ are both distributed as chi-square variables divided by their respective degrees of freedom. Thus, if the null hypothesis is true, if $\mathrm{MS_{BG}}$ and $\mathrm{MS_{WG}}$ are statistically independent, and if the population variances are homogeneous, the ratio

$$\frac{\mathrm{MS_{BG}}}{\mathrm{MS_{WG}}} = \frac{\sigma_\varepsilon^2 \chi_{(v_1)}^2 / v_1}{\sigma_\varepsilon^2 \chi_{(v_2)}^2 / v_2} = F_{(v_1, v_2)}$$

is distributed as the F distribution, with $v_1 = k - 1$ and $v_2 = kn - k$ degrees of freedom. It can be stated without proof that the mean $\overline{X}_j$ and the variance $\hat{\sigma}_j^2$ estimates are statistically independent provided that the population is normally distributed. Hence $\mathrm{MS_{BG}}$ and $\mathrm{MS_{WG}}$ are independent as long as the k samples of observations are independently drawn from normally distributed populations. The probability of obtaining an F as large as that observed in an experiment if the null hypothesis is true can be determined from a table of F given in Appendix D.

An F ratio, as defined above, always provides a one-tailed test of H_0. Ratios less than 1.0 have no meaning with respect to H_0. Such ratios may occur as a result of the operation of chance, for both numerator and denominator are subject to sampling error. Ratios less than 1.0 may also occur because of failure to randomize some important factor properly in the experimental design or because some of the assumptions concerning the linear model for the design are inappropriate. In summary, if two sets of assumptions are tenable—those associated with the derivation of the distribution of F and those associated with the mathematical model for a particular design—the F ratio can be used to test the hypothesis that all treatment population means are equal.

2.6 EFFECTS OF FAILURE TO MEET ASSUMPTIONS IN ANALYSIS OF VARIANCE

The emphasis in the previous sections of this chapter has been on the assumptions necessary for the mathematical justification of hypothesis-testing procedures using the F distribution. What are the consequences of failure to meet these assumptions? Cochran and Cox (1957, 91) stated that failure to meet the assumptions affects both the significance level of a test and the sensitivity of a test. For example, a test performed at the .05 level may actually be made at the .04 or .07 level. Also, a loss in sensitivity results when the assumptions are not fulfilled because it is often possible to construct a more powerful test than that using the F ratio if the correct model can be specified. Fortunately, the F distribution is very robust with respect to violation of many of the assumptions associated with its mathematical derivation. The effects of failure to meet certain assumptions associated with the F distribution and the mathematical model for a design are discussed in the following paragraphs. Cochran (1947) has pointed out that it is impossible to be certain that all required assumptions are exactly satisfied by a set of data. Thus analysis of variance must be regarded as approximate rather than exact. However, it is generally possible, by a careful examination of the data, to detect cases in which a standard analysis will lead to gross errors in interpreting the outcome of an experiment.

ASSUMPTION OF NORMALLY DISTRIBUTED POPULATION

One of the requirements in order for an F ratio to be distributed as the F distribution is that the numerator and denominator of the ratio are independent. If scores are randomly sampled from a normal population, this requirement is satisfied.

An assumption of both the fixed-effects and random-effects models is that the errors ε_{ij} are normally distributed for each treatment population. Because the only source of variation within a treatment population are the errors, the assumption of normally distributed ε_{ij}'s is equivalent to the assumption of normally distributed scores.

A population of scores can depart from the normal distribution in terms of either skewness or kurtosis, or in both skewness and kurtosis.

Studies by Pearson (1931) and Norton, as cited by Lindquist (1953), indicate that the F distribution is relatively unaffected by lack of symmetry of treatment populations. It is also relatively unaffected by kurtosis except in extreme cases of very leptokurtic or platykurtic populations. For the fixed-effects model, an experimenter need not be concerned if the k populations exhibit a moderate departure from the normal distribution provided that the k populations are homogeneous in form, for example, all treatment populations positively skewed and slightly leptokurtic. In general, unless the departure from normality is so extreme that it can be readily detected by visual inspection of the data, the departure will have little effect on the probability associated with the test of significance. It may be possible to transform nonnormally distributed scores so as to achieve normality, under conditions described in Section 2.7.

ASSUMPTION OF HOMOGENEITY OF POPULATION-ERROR VARIANCES

The F distribution is robust with respect to violation of the assumption of homogeneity of population-error variances provided that the number of observations in the samples is equal (Cochran, 1947; Norton as cited by Lindquist, 1953). However, for samples of unequal size, violation of the homogeneity assumption can have a marked effect on the test of significance. According to Box (1953, 1954a), the nature of the bias for this latter case may be positive or negative.

Several statistics are available for testing the homogeneity assumption that

$$H_0 : \sigma_1^2 = \sigma_2^2 = \cdots = \sigma_k^2 = \sigma_\varepsilon^2.$$

The alternative to the above null hypothesis is

$$H_1 : \text{some } \sigma_j^2\text{'s are unequal.}$$

A test statistic proposed by Bartlett (1937) is

$$B = \frac{2.30259}{C} \left[v \log_{10} \text{MS}_{\text{error}} - \sum_{j=1}^{k} (v_j \log_{10} \hat{\sigma}_j^2) \right],$$

where

$$C = 1 + \frac{\sum_{j=1}^{k} \dfrac{1}{v_j} - \dfrac{1}{v}}{3(k-1)},$$

v_j = degrees of freedom for $\hat{\sigma}_j^2$, v = degrees of freedom for MS_{error} equal to $\Sigma_{j=1}^{k} v_j$, $\hat{\sigma}_j^2$ = unbiased estimate of population variance for the jth population given by

$$\hat{\sigma}_j^2 = \left[\sum_1^n X^2 - \frac{\left(\sum_1^n X \right)^2}{n} \right] / (n - 1),$$

$MS_{error} = \sum_{j=1}^k \hat{\sigma}_j^2 / v$, and k = number of variances. For values of $v_j \geq 5$, B is approximately distributed as the χ^2 distribution, with $k - 1$ degrees of freedom. If $v_j < 5$, tables prepared by Merrington and Thompson (1946) may be used.

Two other tests are computationally simpler than Bartlett's test and provide an adequate test of the assumption of homogeneity of variance. The simpler of the two tests, which was proposed by Hartley (1940, 1950), uses the statistic F_{max},

$$F_{max} = \frac{\text{largest of } k \text{ variances}}{\text{smallest of } k \text{ variances}} = \frac{\hat{\sigma}_{j\,largest}^2}{\hat{\sigma}_{j\,smallest}^2},$$

with degrees of freedom equal to k and $n - 1$, where k is the number of variances and n is the number of observations within each treatment level. The distribution of F_{max} is given in Table D.10. The hypothesis of homogeneity of variance is rejected if F_{max} is greater than the tabled value for $F_{max,\alpha}$. If the n's for the treatment levels differ only slightly, the largest of the n's can be used for purposes of determining the degrees of freedom for this test. This procedure leads to a slight positive bias in the test, that is, in rejecting the hypothesis of homogeneity more frequently than it should be rejected.

The other relatively simple test of homogeneity of variance is that proposed by Cochran (1941). This test statistic is given by

$$C = \frac{\hat{\sigma}_{j\,largest}^2}{\sum_{j=1}^k \hat{\sigma}_j^2},$$

where $\hat{\sigma}_{j\,largest}^2$ is the largest of the k treatment variances and $\sum_{j=1}^k \hat{\sigma}_j^2$ is the sum of all of the variances. The degrees of freedom for this test are equal to k and $n - 1$ as defined for the F_{max} test. The sampling distribution of C is given in Table D.11.

Since the F distribution is so robust with respect to violation of the assumption of homogeneity of error variance, it is not customary to test this assumption routinely. Both the Hartley and the Cochran tests have adequate sensitivity for testing the assumption in situations where heterogeneity is suspected. If variances are heterogeneous, a transformation of scores as described in Section 2.7 may produce homogeneity.

It should be noted that all three tests described here are sensitive to departures from normality as well as heterogeneity of variances (Box and Anderson, 1955). For a description of a test that is relatively insensitive to departures from normality, see Odeh and Olds (1959).

ASSUMPTION OF ADDITIVITY OF EFFECTS

A basic assumption of the experimental designs described in this book is that a score is the *sum* of the effects in the linear model. If the assumption of additivity of effects is not tenable, it may be possible to achieve additivity by a suitable transformation of the scores.

References that provide additional discussion of the assumptions in analysis of variance may be found in the papers by Eisenhart (1947) and Cochran (1947).

2.7   TRANSFORMATIONS

A transformation is any systematic alteration in a set of scores whereby certain characteristics of the set are changed and other characteristics remain unchanged. Three major reasons for using transformations in analysis of variance are

1. To achieve homogeneity of error variance.
2. To achieve normality of treatment-level distributions (or within-cell distributions).
3. To obtain additivity of treatment effects.

Because the *F* distribution is relatively unaffected by lack of normality and heterogeneity of variance, the first two reasons for performing a transformation are less compelling than the third. Obtaining additivity of effects is particularly important in designs such as a randomized block design in which a *residual* mean square (abbreviated MS_{res}) is used as an estimate of experimental error. For example, if treatment levels and blocks are not additive, the expected value of the residual mean square is

$$E(MS_{res}) = \sigma_\varepsilon^2 + \sigma_{\beta\pi}^2$$

instead of

$$E(MS_{res}) = \sigma_\varepsilon^2,$$

where $\sigma_{\beta\pi}^2$ refers to the interaction of treatment levels and blocks. Interaction in this context is said to be present when the dependent variable that is measured under the *k* treatment levels behaves differently for different blocks of subjects. The expected value of the treatment mean square for a fixed-effects model is

$$E(MS_B) = \sigma_\varepsilon^2 + n\sigma_\beta^2.$$

If the null hypothesis is true, then, according to Section 2.5, the numerator and denominator of the ratio

$$F = \frac{MS_B}{MS_{res}}$$

should provide independent estimates of the same population error variance, σ_ε^2. It is apparent from an examination of the expected values of the two mean squares that this can occur only if $\sigma_{\beta\pi}^2 = 0$. We shall return to this point in Chapter 5.

Fortunately, a transformation that accomplishes any one of the objectives listed above will usually accomplish the other two objectives. In general, a transformation can be used whenever there is a relationship between the means and variances of the treatment levels and whenever the form of the treatment level distributions is homogeneous. It is not always possible to find an appropriate transformation for a set of data. For example, if any of the following conditions are present, no transformation exists that will make the data more suitable for analysis of variance: (1) means of treatment levels are approximately equal but variances are heterogeneous, (2) means of treatment levels vary independently of variances, or (3) variances are homogeneous but treatment level distributions are heterogeneous in form. If no transformation is appropriate, and if the departures from normality and homogeneity are gross, an experimenter may be able to use one of the nonparametric statistics for k treatment levels described in Chapter 13. Although these statistics require less stringent assumptions than analysis of variance, they are less powerful and provide less information concerning the outcome of an experiment. It should also be noted that the nonparametric procedures described in Chapter 13 provide a test of the hypothesis that $k \geq 2$ population distributions of *unspecified* form are exactly alike. In order to test hypotheses concerning population means, the homogeneity assumptions of analysis of variance must be tenable. This point is discussed in Section 13.1. Another alternative that may be available to the experimenter is to select a different criterion measure. The choice of a dependent variable in the behavioral sciences is often arbitrary; a different choice may fulfill the requirements of additivity, normality, and homogeneity.

A number of procedures exist for determining which transformation is appropriate for a set of data. Several methods are described by Olds, Mattson, and Odeh (1956) and by Tukey (1949b). One procedure is to follow general rules concerning situations in which a given transformation is often successful. This approach will be emphasized in presenting each of the types of transformations. Alternative procedures for selecting a transformation will be described later.

SQUARE-ROOT TRANSFORMATION

For certain types of data, treatment level means and variances tend to be proportional, as in a Poisson distribution, where $\mu = \sigma^2$. This kind of distribution often results when the dependent variable is a frequency count of events having a small probability of occurrence, for example, number of errors at each choice point in a relatively simple multiple T maze. The data can often be normalized for this type of situation by taking the square root of each of the scores. A transformed score X' is given by

$$X' = \sqrt{X}.$$

If any X is less than 10, a more appropriate transformation is given either by

$$X' = \sqrt{X + .5} \quad \text{or} \quad X' = \sqrt{X} + \sqrt{X + 1}.$$

The latter transformation has been recommended by Freeman and Tukey (1950). Tables of $\sqrt{X} + \sqrt{X + 1}$ are reproduced in Mosteller and Bush (1954). The effects of performing a square-root transformation are shown for the data in Table 2.7-1. An examination of the means and variances of the transformed scores shows that they are no longer proportional; additionally, the variances are more homogeneous. These transformed scores are more suitable than the original scores for an analysis of variance.

TABLE 2.7-1 Original and Transformed Scores

	Original Scores			*Transformed Scores* $X' = \sqrt{X + .5}$		
	b_1	b_2	b_3	b_1	b_2	b_3
	3	6	12	1.87	2.55	3.54
	0	4	6	.71	2.12	2.55
	4	2	6	2.12	1.58	2.55
	2	4	10	1.58	2.12	3.24
	2	7	6	1.58	2.74	2.55
$\bar{X} = 2.2$	4.6	8.0	1.57	2.22	2.89
$S^2 = 2.2$	3.4	8.0	.28	.20	.22

LOGARITHMIC TRANSFORMATION

If treatment means and standard deviations tend to be proportional, a logarithmic transformation may be appropriate. A transformed score X' is given by

$$X' = \log_{10} X \quad \text{or} \quad X' = \log_{10}(X + 1).$$

The latter formula is used when some scores are zero or very small. Logarithmic transformations have been found to be useful when the dependent variable is some measure of reaction time and the data are positively skewed.

RECIPROCAL TRANSFORMATION

If the square of treatment means and standard deviations are proportional, a reciprocal transformation may be appropriate. A transformed score X' is given by

$$X' = \frac{1}{X} \quad \text{or} \quad X' = \frac{1}{X + 1}.$$

The latter formula should be used if any scores are equal to zero. A reciprocal transformation may be useful when the dependent variable is reaction time.

ANGULAR OR INVERSE SINE TRANSFORMATION

The angular transformation is given by

$$X' = 2 \arcsin \sqrt{X},$$

where X is expressed as a proportion. It is not necessary to solve for X' in the above formula; a table of values of X from .001 to .999 is given in Table D.13. The transformed values in Table D.13 are in radians. Bartlett (1947) suggests that $\frac{1}{2n}$ or $\frac{1}{4n}$ be substituted for $X = $ zero and $1 - \frac{1}{2n}$ or $1 - \frac{1}{4n}$ be substituted for $X = 1$, where n is the number of observations on which each proportion is based. An angular transformation may be useful when means and variances are proportional and the distribution has a binomial form. This condition may occur when the number of trials is fixed and X is the probability of a correct response that varies from one treatment level to another.

SELECTING A TRANSFORMATION

We have already described situations where particular transformations have been found to be successful. An alternative approach to selecting a transformation uses the fact that means and variances are unrelated for normally distributed treatment populations. The correct transformation to use for a set of data is the one that removes the relationship between the sample means and variances. This can be determined by graphing the means and variances on the x and y axes respectively, for each transformation and selecting the one that appears to remove the dependency relationship best. The correctness of the selected transformation can be verified by inspecting the transformed treatment distributions for normality and homogeneity of variances.

An additional procedure for selecting a transformation is to apply each of the transformations to the largest and smallest score in the treatment levels. The range within each treatment level is then determined and the ratio of the largest to the smallest range is computed. The transformation that produces the smallest ratio is selected as the most appropriate one. This procedure is illustrated in Table 2.7-2 for the data in Table 2.7-1. On the basis of this procedure, a square-root formation would be selected for these data.

Once an appropriate transformation is selected and the data analyzed on the new scale, all inferences regarding treatment effects must be made with respect to the new scale. In most behavioral research situations, inferences based on log X's or $\sqrt{X}$'s, for example, are just as meaningful as inferences based on untransformed scores.

If additivity of treatment effects is the principal concern of an experimenter, the appropriateness of a particular transformation can be determined by a test of nonadditivity that is described in Section 5.3. This test provides a means of determining if treatment effects are additive for the untransformed scores and for any transformations that may be tried. A mathematically sophisticated exposition of general issues involved in the use of transformations is given by Box and Cox (1964).

TABLE 2.7-2   Transformations Applied to Largest and Smallest Scores in Table 2.7-1

	Treatment Levels			$\dfrac{\text{Range}_{\text{largest}}}{\text{Range}_{\text{smallest}}}$
	b_1	b_2	b_3	
Largest score (L)	4	7	12	
Smallest score (S)	0	2	6	
Range =	4	5	6	6/4 = 1.50
$\sqrt{L + .5}$	2.12	2.74	3.54	
$\sqrt{S + .5}$	.71	1.58	2.55	
Range =	1.41	1.16	.99	1.41/.99 = 1.42
log ($L + 1$)	.6990	.9031	1.1139	
log ($S + 1$)	.0000	.4771	.8451	
Range =	.6990	.4260	.2688	.6990/.2688 = 2.60
1/($L + 1$)	.20	.12	.08	
1/($S + 1$)	1.00	.33	.14	
Range =	.80	.21	.06	.80/.06 = 13.33

3 / MULTIPLE COMPARISON TESTS

3.1 INTRODUCTION TO MULTIPLE COMPARISON TESTS

The most common use of analysis of variance in the behavioral sciences is in testing the hypothesis that $k \geq 3$ population means are equal. Other important uses of analysis of variance are described in subsequent chapters. If the over-all hypothesis of equality of means is rejected, the experimenter is still faced with the problem of deciding which pairs or combinations of means are not equal. Thus an over-all test of significance using an F ratio is often merely the first step in analyzing a set of data. A significant F ratio indicates to an experimenter that something has happened in an experiment which has a small probability of happening by chance. The purpose of this chapter is to describe a variety of procedures for determining what it is that has happened. Specifically, we will examine a number of test statistics for determining which comparisons among means in an experiment are significant. The conceptual unit for error rate (significance level) for each of the test statistics will be discussed. Before examining these test statistics, several concepts relevant to the following discussion will be defined.

COMPARISON DEFINED

A *comparison* or *contrast* between two means is the difference between the means, disregarding the algebraic sign. The symbols ψ_i and $\hat{\psi}_i$ are used to designate a comparison and a sample estimate of the comparison, respectively. Thus $\hat{\psi}_i = \bar{X}_j - \bar{X}_{j'}$ is a comparison between sample means for treatment levels j and j', respectively. If an experiment contains $k = 3$ means, $\bar{X}_1$, $\bar{X}_2$, and $\bar{X}_3$, the possible *pairwise* comparisons among these means are

(1) $\hat{\psi}_1 = \bar{X}_1 - \bar{X}_2, \quad \hat{\psi}_2 = \bar{X}_1 - \bar{X}_3, \quad \text{and} \quad \hat{\psi}_3 = \bar{X}_2 - \bar{X}_3.$

A comparison can also involve more than two means; for example,

(2) $\hat{\psi}_4 = \dfrac{\bar{X}_1 + \bar{X}_2}{2} - \bar{X}_3, \quad \hat{\psi}_5 = \dfrac{\bar{X}_1 + \bar{X}_3}{2} - \bar{X}_2,$

and
$$\hat{\psi}_6 = \frac{\overline{X}_2 - \overline{X}_3}{2} - \overline{X}_1.$$

The number of possible pairwise and nonpairwise comparisons among k means increases markedly as the number of means increases.

It can be seen that the comparisons in (1) above have the general form:

$$\hat{\psi}_1 = C_j(\overline{X}_1) + C_{j'}(\overline{X}_2) = 1(\overline{X}_1) - 1(\overline{X}_2)$$
$$\hat{\psi}_2 = C_j(\overline{X}_1) + C_{j'}(\overline{X}_3) = 1(\overline{X}_1) - 1(\overline{X}_3)$$
$$\hat{\psi}_3 = C_j(\overline{X}_2) + C_{j'}(\overline{X}_3) = 1(\overline{X}_2) - 1(\overline{X}_3),$$

where the coefficients C_j and $C_{j'}$ are to equal 1 and -1, respectively. We will define a comparison among means as any linear combination or weighted sum of means in which the weights C_j's are some set of real numbers not all equal to zero. Discussion in this book will be restricted to the case in which the weights sum to zero; that is, $\Sigma_{j=1}^{k} C_j = 0$. If some $C_j \neq 0$ and $\Sigma_{j=1}^{k} C_j = 0$, the comparison is called a *specialized linear function* of the means.

The first comparison involving three means in (2) above can be written

$$\hat{\psi}_4 = C_j(\overline{X}_1) + C_{j'}(\overline{X}_2) + C_{j''}(\overline{X}_3) = \tfrac{1}{2}(\overline{X}_1) + \tfrac{1}{2}(\overline{X}_2) - 1(\overline{X}_3),$$

where $C_j = \tfrac{1}{2}, C_{j'} = \tfrac{1}{2}$, and $C_{j''} = -1$. The coefficients for this comparison also sum to zero, $\Sigma_{j=1}^{k} C_j = \tfrac{1}{2} + \tfrac{1}{2} + (-1) = 0$. Hence this comparison is a specialized linear function of the means. For convenience, coefficients of comparisons are chosen so that the sum of their *absolute value* is equal to two. That is,

$$\sum_{j=1}^{k} |C_j| = 2,$$

where $|C_j|$ indicates that the sign of the coefficient C_j is always taken to be plus. For example, the sum of the absolute value of coefficients $C_j = 1$ and -1 is

$$\sum_{j=1}^{k} |C_j| = 1 + 1 = 2,$$

and for coefficients $C_j = \tfrac{1}{2}, \tfrac{1}{2}$, and -1,

$$\sum_{j=1}^{k} |C_j| = \tfrac{1}{2} + \tfrac{1}{2} + 1 = 2.$$

ORTHOGONAL COMPARISONS

There are obviously a finite number of hypotheses that can be tested for a given set of data if the tests are to be nonredundant, that is, tests involving nonoverlapping pieces of information. As we shall see, an experimenter is often interested in testing hypotheses that involve nonredundant as well as redundant information. In selecting an appropriate test statistic, it is important to distinguish between these two situations.

Two comparisons among k means are said to be orthogonal to each other if they utilize nonoverlapping pieces of information from an experiment. What criterion can an experimenter use to determine if two comparisons are orthogonal and if they utilize nonoverlapping pieces of information? In the following discussion we will use the subscript i to designate a particular comparison. Thus the subscripts of C_{ij} refer to the ith comparison and jth mean, respectively. Whether or not two comparisons are orthogonal can be easily determined by summing the products of their respective coefficients. If the sum

$$\sum_{j=1}^{k} \frac{C_{ij}C_{i'j}}{n_j} = 0 \quad \text{or} \quad \sum_{j=1}^{k} C_{ij}C_{i'j} = 0$$

for the case in which the n's are equal, the two comparisons are orthogonal. If treatment populations are normally distributed, orthogonality of comparisons is equivalent to statistical independence of the comparisons. The application of the rule for determining if two comparisons are orthogonal is as follows. For an experiment with $k = 4$ treatment levels, $k(k-1)/2 = 6$ possible pairwise comparisons can be made among the means. These comparisons are listed in Table 3.1-1.

TABLE 3.1-1   Pairwise Comparisons among Four Means

Comparison	$C_{i1}(\bar{X}_1)$	$C_{i2}(\bar{X}_2)$	$C_{i3}(\bar{X}_3)$	$C_{i4}(\bar{X}_4)$	
$\hat{\psi}_1$	$1(\bar{X}_1)$	$-1(\bar{X}_2)$	$0(\bar{X}_3)$	$0(\bar{X}_4)$	$= \bar{X}_1 - \bar{X}_2$
$\hat{\psi}_2$	$1(\bar{X}_1)$	$0(\bar{X}_2)$	$-1(\bar{X}_3)$	$0(\bar{X}_4)$	$= \bar{X}_1 - \bar{X}_3$
$\hat{\psi}_3$	$1(\bar{X}_1)$	$0(\bar{X}_2)$	$0(\bar{X}_3)$	$-1(\bar{X}_4)$	$= \bar{X}_1 - \bar{X}_4$
$\hat{\psi}_4$	$0(\bar{X}_1)$	$1(\bar{X}_2)$	$-1(\bar{X}_3)$	$0(\bar{X}_4)$	$= \bar{X}_2 - \bar{X}_3$
$\hat{\psi}_5$	$0(\bar{X}_1)$	$1(\bar{X}_2)$	$0(\bar{X}_3)$	$-1(\bar{X}_4)$	$= \bar{X}_2 - \bar{X}_4$
$\hat{\psi}_6$	$0(\bar{X}_1)$	$0(\bar{X}_2)$	$1(\bar{X}_3)$	$-1(\bar{X}_4)$	$= \bar{X}_3 - \bar{X}_4$

In order to determine whether comparisons $\hat{\psi}_1$ and $\hat{\psi}_2$ in the table are orthogonal, the sum of the products of their respective coefficients is obtained.

$$C_{11} \cdots C_{14} = \underline{1 \quad -1 \quad 0 \quad 0}$$

$$C_{21} \cdots C_{24} = \underline{1 \quad 0 \quad -1 \quad 0}$$

$$\sum_{j=1}^{k} C_{1j}C_{2j} = 1 + 0 + 0 + 0 = 1$$

It is evident that comparisons 1 and 2 are not orthogonal. It can be shown that comparisons 1 and 6 are orthogonal.

$$C_{11} \cdots C_{14} = 1 \quad -1 \quad 0 \quad 0$$

$$C_{61} \cdots C_{64} = \underline{0 \quad \quad 0 \quad 1 \quad -1}$$

$$\sum_{j=1}^{k} C_{1j}C_{6j} = 0 + 0 + 0 + 0 = 0$$

Comparison 6 is the only pairwise comparison in Table 3.1-1 that is orthogonal to comparison 1. There is another comparison involving *four* means that is orthogonal to both comparisons 1 and 6. This is the comparison

$$\hat{\psi}_7 = -\tfrac{1}{2}(\bar{X}_1) - \tfrac{1}{2}(\bar{X}_2) + \tfrac{1}{2}(\bar{X}_3) + \tfrac{1}{2}(\bar{X}_4).$$

This comparison involves the average of means one and two versus the average of means three and four. It can be shown that comparison 7 is orthogonal to 1 and 6 as follows:

$$C_{11} \cdots C_{14} = \quad 1 \quad -1 \quad 0 \quad 0$$

$$C_{71} \cdots C_{74} = \underline{-\tfrac{1}{2} \quad -\tfrac{1}{2} \quad \tfrac{1}{2} \quad \tfrac{1}{2}}$$

$$\sum_{j=1}^{k} C_{1j}C_{7j} = -\tfrac{1}{2} + \tfrac{1}{2} + 0 + 0 = 0$$

$$C_{61} \cdots C_{64} = \quad 0 \quad \quad 0 \quad 1 \quad -1$$

$$C_{71} \cdots C_{74} = \underline{-\tfrac{1}{2} \quad -\tfrac{1}{2} \quad \tfrac{1}{2} \quad \tfrac{1}{2}}$$

$$\sum_{j=1}^{k} C_{6j}C_{7j} = \quad 0 + 0 + \tfrac{1}{2} - \tfrac{1}{2} = 0.$$

These three comparisons among the four means exhaust one of the possible sets of orthogonal comparisons. Another set of orthogonal comparisons involves comparisons 2, 5, and 8. The coefficients for comparison 8 are

$$C_{8j} = -\tfrac{1}{2}, \tfrac{1}{2}, -\tfrac{1}{2}, \text{ and } \tfrac{1}{2}.$$

A general principle can be stated. If an experiment contains k treatment levels, only $k - 1$ comparisons among means in any one set of comparisons are orthogonal. Thus comparisons 1, 6, and 7 exhaust the orthogonal comparisons in one set, comparisons 2, 5, and 8 exhaust a second set, and so on. This means that there are always $k - 1$ independent questions that can be answered from the data in an experiment. An experimenter, however, may not be interested in all $k - 1$ questions. For example, he may wish to test the hypothesis that $\mu_1 = \mu_2$ and $\mu_3 = \mu_4$ but not that $(\mu_1 + \mu_2)/2 = (\mu_3 + \mu_4)/2$. This latter hypothesis may have no meaning in terms of the objectives of the experiment. It is also obvious that not all interesting hypotheses involve orthogonal comparisons. In an experiment with, for example, four treatment levels, every one of the six pairwise comparisons among means may be associated with a question that an experimenter seeks to answer. Procedures are described in Sections 3.2 and 3.4 for carrying out planned orthogonal comparisons, planned nonorthogonal comparisons, and unplanned, nonorthogonal comparisons.

In summary, the analysis of variance provides an over-all test of the hypothesis that $\beta_j = 0$ for all j. This test is equivalent to a simultaneous test of the hypothesis that all possible comparisons among means are equal to zero. The degrees of freedom for the treatment mean square MS_{BG} in a completely randomized design is $k - 1$, which is also the number of orthogonal comparisons that can be made among k means. If an over-all test of significance using an F ratio is significant, an experimenter can be certain that some set of orthogonal comparisons contains at least one significant comparison among means. The comparison or comparisons that are significant may or may not be ones that are of interest to an experimenter. An F test in analysis of variance is an *over-all* test that indicates whether or not something has happened. It remains for an experimenter to carry out follow-up tests to determine what has happened.

3.2   *A PRIORI* OR PLANNED COMPARISONS

An investigator, in planning an experiment, often has a specific set of hypotheses that the experiment is designed to test. Tests involving these hypotheses are referred to as *a priori* or *planned* comparisons. This situation may be contrasted with one in which an investigator believes that some treatment effects exist and an experiment is designed to accept or reject this notion. If, in this latter case, an over-all test of significance indicates that some treatment effects are not equal to zero, interest centers on determining which comparisons among means are significant. Techniques that have been developed for *data snooping* following an over-all F test—that is, in evaluating all possible comparisons among means—are referred to as *a posteriori* or *post-hoc* tests.

A PRIORI ORTHOGONAL TESTS USING t RATIO

Comparisons among means that are orthogonal and that fall in the *a priori* category can be carried out by using a t ratio. It is not necessary to perform an over-all test of significance prior to carrying out planned orthogonal t tests. An over-all test using an F ratio simply answers the question, "Did *anything* happen in the experiment?" If an experimenter has a specific set of orthogonal comparisons for which statistical hypotheses have been advanced, he is not interested in answering the *general* question, "Did anything happen in the experiment?" Rather, his interest is in answering a limited number of specific questions from the data. For planned orthogonal comparisons, it is recommended that each comparison be evaluated at α level of significance by means of a t ratio. The conceptual unit for significance level in this case is the individual comparison.

The t statistic for carrying out multiple comparisons among means when the n's in each treatment level are equal is given by

$$t = \frac{C_j(\bar{X}_j) + C_{j'}(\bar{X}_{j'})}{\sqrt{\dfrac{2\mathrm{MS}_{\mathrm{error}}}{n}}}.$$

If the n's are not equal, or if more than two means are involved in the comparison, the respective formulas are

$$t = \frac{C_j(\bar{X}_j) + C_{j'}(\bar{X}_{j'})}{\sqrt{\mathrm{MS}_{\mathrm{error}}\left[\dfrac{(C_j)^2}{n_j} + \dfrac{(C_{j'})^2}{n_{j'}}\right]}} \quad \text{and}$$

$$t = \frac{C_j(\bar{X}_j) + C_{j'}(\bar{X}_{j'}) + \cdots + C_{j''}(\bar{X}_{j''})}{\sqrt{\mathrm{MS}_{\mathrm{error}}\left[\dfrac{(C_j)^2}{n_j} + \dfrac{(C_{j'})^2}{n_{j'}} + \cdots + \dfrac{(C_{j''})^2}{n_{j''}}\right]}}.$$

The symbols in the above formulas are defined as follows: C_j = coefficient for the jth mean, $\bar{X}_j$ = jth treatment mean, $\mathrm{MS}_{\mathrm{error}}$ = unbiased estimate of the population error variance, and n_j = number of scores in the jth treatment level. A prime is used to designate different levels of the treatment. The degrees of freedom for this test is the df associated with $\mathrm{MS}_{\mathrm{error}}$. If the population variances are homogeneous, the respective error variances for each treatment level can be pooled to obtain $\mathrm{MS}_{\mathrm{error}}$. In a completely randomized design an estimate of the common population variance is given by

$$\mathrm{MS}_{\mathrm{WG}} = \left[\sum_1^k \sum_1^n X_{ij}^2 - \sum_1^k \frac{\left(\sum_1^n X_{ij}\right)^2}{n}\right]/(N - k),$$

where $\mathrm{MS}_{\mathrm{WG}}$ refers to the within-groups mean square. The degrees of freedom for this error term is $N - k$. If the population error variances are not homogeneous, procedures described in Section 3.5 can be used to make comparisons among means.

It should be noted that because multiple t ratios use the same denominator, $\mathrm{MS}_{\mathrm{error}}$, the tests of significance are not statistically independent, although the comparisons among means are independent for normally distributed treatment populations. If the number of degrees of freedom for $\mathrm{MS}_{\mathrm{error}}$ is large, the tests of significance can, for all practical purposes, be regarded as independent.

COMPUTATIONAL EXAMPLE OF *A PRIORI* ORTHOGONAL TESTS USING *t* RATIO

The use of multiple t ratios for making comparisons among means will be illustrated for a hypothetical experiment in which 50 subjects have been randomly assigned to five treatment levels. Each treatment level contains 10 subjects. Let us assume that the means for the five treatment levels are

$$\bar{X}_1 = 36.7, \ \bar{X}_2 = 48.7, \ \bar{X}_3 = 43.4, \ \bar{X}_4 = 47.2, \text{ and } \bar{X}_5 = 40.3.$$

Also assume that the treatment populations are normally distributed and that the variances are homogeneous. Because the layout of this experiment corresponds to a completely randomized design, an estimate of the common population-error variance is given by MS_{WG}, which is equal to 28.8. The degrees of freedom for MS_{WG} is equal to $N - k = 50 - 5 = 45$. The experiment has been designed to test the hypotheses shown in Table 3.2-1. The coefficients for each comparison are shown to the right of the

TABLE 3.2-1   Statistical Hypotheses and Associated Orthogonal Coefficients

		Coefficients				
Comparison	*Hypothesis*	C_1	C_2	C_3	C_4	C_5
$\hat{\psi}_1$	$H_0: \mu_2 = \mu_3$ $H_1: \mu_2 \neq \mu_3$	0	1	-1	0	0
$\hat{\psi}_2$	$H_0: \mu_4 = \mu_5$ $H_1: \mu_4 \neq \mu_5$	0	0	0	1	-1
$\hat{\psi}_3$	$H_0: (\mu_2 + \mu_3)/2 = (\mu_4 + \mu_5)/2$ $H_1: (\mu_2 + \mu_3)/2 \neq (\mu_4 + \mu_5)/2$	0	$\frac{1}{2}$	$\frac{1}{2}$	$-\frac{1}{2}$	$-\frac{1}{2}$
$\hat{\psi}_4$	$H_0: \mu_1 = (\mu_2 + \mu_3 + \mu_4 + \mu_5)/4$ $H_1: \mu_1 \neq (\mu_2 + \mu_3 + \mu_4 + \mu_5)/4$	1	$-\frac{1}{4}$	$-\frac{1}{4}$	$-\frac{1}{4}$	$-\frac{1}{4}$

hypotheses. The .05 level of significance is adopted for these comparisons. The reader can easily verify that the preceding comparisons represent one of the sets of $k - 1 = 4$ comparisons among means that are orthogonal. The t ratios for $\hat{\psi}_1$, $\hat{\psi}_2$, $\hat{\psi}_3$, and $\hat{\psi}_4$ are, respectively,

$$t = \frac{1(48.7) - 1(43.4)}{\sqrt{2(28.8)/10}} = \frac{5.3}{2.4} = 2.21, \qquad t = \frac{1(47.2) - 1(40.3)}{\sqrt{2(28.8)/10}} = \frac{6.9}{2.4} = 2.88$$

$$t = \frac{\frac{1}{2}(48.7) + \frac{1}{2}(43.4) - \frac{1}{2}(47.2) - \frac{1}{2}(40.3)}{\sqrt{28.8\left[\frac{(\frac{1}{2})^2}{10} + \frac{(\frac{1}{2})^2}{10} + \frac{(-\frac{1}{2})^2}{10} + \frac{(-\frac{1}{2})^2}{10}\right]}} = \frac{2.3}{1.7} = 1.35$$

$$t = \frac{1(36.7) - \frac{1}{4}(48.7) - \frac{1}{4}(43.4) - \frac{1}{4}(47.2) - \frac{1}{4}(40.3)}{\sqrt{28.8\left[\frac{(1)^2}{10} + \frac{(-\frac{1}{4})^2}{10} + \frac{(-\frac{1}{4})^2}{10} + \frac{(-\frac{1}{4})^2}{10} + \frac{(-\frac{1}{4})^2}{10}\right]}} = \frac{-8.2}{1.9} = -4.32.$$

Percentage points of Student's t distribution are given in Table D.4. For $N - k = 50 - 5 = 45$ degrees of freedom, the tabled value of $t_{.05/2,45} = 2.02$. This is the value of Student's t that cuts off the upper .025 proportion of the distribution for 45 degrees of freedom.

Because Student's distribution is symmetrical, $t_{\alpha/2,v} = -t_{\alpha/2,v}$. If the alternative hypotheses had called for one-tailed tests instead of two-tailed tests, the tabled value would have been designated by $t_{\alpha,v}$. For one-tailed tests, the critical value of t is the value that cuts off the upper α proportion of the distribution. According to the four tests performed, the null hypotheses for ψ_1, ψ_2, and ψ_4 can be rejected at the .05 level of significance. The null hypothesis that $(\mu_2 + \mu_3)/2 = (\mu_4 + \mu_5)/2$ cannot be rejected.

CONFIDENCE INTERVAL FOR DIFFERENCE AMONG PLANNED ORTHOGONAL COMPARISONS

Emphasis in this book is placed on significance tests as opposed to confidence limits. This emphasis is in line with contemporary practice in the behavioral sciences. Many mathematical statisticians, however, prefer confidence procedures, and there is much merit in their position. A majority of the procedures described here can be used to establish $100(1 - \alpha)$ percent confidence limits for the difference between population means.

It is obvious that the difference between two sample means will not ordinarily be equal to the difference between the corresponding population means. An indication of the possible magnitude of the discrepancy can be obtained by computing a *confidence interval*. A confidence interval is an estimated range of values which has a given probability $(1 - \alpha)$ of including the true difference between population means. A confidence interval for the difference between two means is given by

$$\text{prob}(\hat{\psi} - c \leq \psi \leq \hat{\psi} + c) = 1 - \alpha,$$

where
$$c = t_{\alpha/2,v} \sqrt{\text{MS}_{\text{error}} \left[\frac{(C_j)^2}{n_j} + \frac{(C_{j'})^2}{n_{j'}} \right]}$$

$$\hat{\psi} = \overline{X}_j - \overline{X}_{j'}$$

$$\psi = \mu_j - \mu_{j'}.$$

The 95 percent confidence interval for comparison ψ_1 in Table 3.2-1, which involves means μ_2 and μ_3, is given by

$$(48.7 - 43.4) - 4.8 \leq \psi_1 \leq (48.7 - 43.4) + 4.8$$

$$= 5.3 - 4.8 \leq \psi_1 \leq 5.3 + 4.8$$

$$= .5 \leq \psi_1 \leq 10.1,$$

where
$$c = 2.02 \sqrt{28.8 \left[\frac{(1)^2}{10} + \frac{(-1)^2}{10} \right]} = (2.02)(2.4) = 4.8.$$

The two boundaries

$$(\bar{X}_2 - \bar{X}_3) - t_{\alpha/2,\nu} \sqrt{MS_{error} \left[\frac{(C_j)^2}{n_j} + \frac{(C_{j'})^2}{n_{j'}} \right]} = .5$$

and

$$(\bar{X}_2 - \bar{X}_3) + t_{\alpha/2,\nu} \sqrt{MS_{error} \left[\frac{(C_j)^2}{n_j} + \frac{(C_{j'})^2}{n_{j'}} \right]} = 10.1$$

of the confidence interval are called the $100(1 - \alpha)$ percent confidence limits. Over *all possible samples* of size n_j and $n_{j'}$, the probability is approximately .95 that the true difference between μ_2 and μ_3 falls within the interval from .5 to 10.1. The reader should note the qualification that has been added to the probability statement. After the samples are obtained and numerical values of $\bar{X}_j$, $\bar{X}_{j'}$, and MS_{error} are substituted in the formula, it is incorrect to say that the probability is .95 that the difference between the two population means lies between .5 and 10.1. Once the confidence interval is computed, the difference $\mu_2 - \mu_3$ either is or is not in the interval. This point is clarified by realizing that there will be many possible 95 percent confidence intervals over all possible samples. Some of these confidence intervals will include the true difference and others will not. If one confidence interval is sampled at random, the probability is .95 that it will include the true difference.

If, as in the present example, a confidence interval does not include zero, the hypothesis that the two population means are equal is rejected. This same decision was reached earlier using a t ratio. Thus confidence-interval estimation permits an experimenter to reach the same kind of decision as when significance tests are used. In addition, confidence-interval procedures permit an experimenter to consider simultaneously all possible null hypotheses, not just the hypothesis that $\mu_j - \mu_{j'} = 0$. An experimenter, for example, can test any hypothesis he may entertain simply by looking at the confidence interval. If the difference in question lies outside the $100(1 - \alpha)$ percent confidence interval, the hypothesis can be rejected beyond the α level for a two-tailed test. Furthermore, confidence procedures provide information concerning the error variation associated with an estimate, thereby providing an indication of the strength of an inference about any one null hypothesis. The preference of many mathematical statisticians for confidence procedures, as opposed to significance tests, evolves from the fact that, although both procedures involve the same assumptions, the former procedures provide an experimenter with more information than do significance tests. The merits of these two approaches are discussed extensively by Bakan (1966), Binder (1963), Grant (1962), La Forge (1967), Natrella (1960), Nunnally (1960), and Rozeboom (1960).

A PROBLEM INHERENT IN PERFORMING
MULTIPLE COMPARISONS

If an experimenter makes *C independent* comparisons among means, the probability of obtaining at least one significant comparison by chance is given by $1 - (1 - \alpha)^C$, which is approximately equal to $C\alpha$ for small values of α. Therefore, as the number of independent comparisons increases, the probability of at least one spuriously significant result also increases. The corresponding probability for nonindependent comparisons is difficult to ascertain. Harter (1957) and Pearson and Hartley (1942, 1943) have described procedures for computing the type I error associated with nonindependent comparisons. Cochran and Cox (1957, 74) have pointed out that, for the extreme case in which the largest and smallest of $k > 2$ means are compared, a large difference due entirely to chance variation may be observed, as has already been noted. The probability of spurious differences occurring increases with the number of treatment levels. For example, if $k = 3$, the observed value of t for the largest difference will exceed the tabled 5 percent value approximately 13 percent of the time, for $k = 6$ approximately 40 percent, for $k = 10$ approximately 60 percent, and for $k = 20$ treatment levels the figure is 90 percent. Hence, if an experimenter computes enough multiple t ratios, each at α level of significance, he will probably reject one or more null hypotheses even though they are true. The basic question can be raised, "Should the probability of committing a type I error be set at α for each individual comparison or should the probability of an error equal α or less for some larger conceptual unit such as the *collection* of comparisons?" This question, which has been discussed extensively by Ryan (1962) and Wilson (1962), does not have a simple answer. Answers have varied, depending on the nature of the comparisons that are of interest to an experimenter. Multiple comparisons can be classified according to whether they involve (1) planned orthogonal comparisons, (2) planned nonorthogonal comparisons, (3) unplanned nonorthogonal comparisons, or (4) a combination of the above. For planned orthogonal comparisons, contemporary practice in the behavioral sciences favors setting the type I error probability at α for each comparison. For planned and unplanned nonorthogonal comparisons it is suggested that the type I error probability should be set at α for the *collection* of comparisons. As we shall see, mathematical statisticians can tell us how to set the type I error probability equal to or less than α for almost any conceptual unit we choose. However, the behavioral scientist must decide which conceptual unit is most appropriate for his purposes. This issue is reexamined in Section 3.3 after a number of different conceptual units for significance level have been defined.

In the following paragraphs a multiple comparison procedure is described that enables an experimenter to set the probability of making a type I error equal to or less than α for the collection of tests. An experimenter often has in mind a relatively small number of hypotheses he wishes to test. These hypotheses, although few in number, may not be orthogonal. The following test statistic is appropriate for carrying out such tests. If the number of comparisons to be evaluated is large, one of the procedures described in Section 3.4 may have greater power than the procedure described below.

DUNN'S MULTIPLE COMPARISON PROCEDURE

The originator of the procedure described here is unknown. Dunn (1961) has examined the properties of the procedure in detail and has prepared tables that facilitate its use. Consequently, it is referred to as Dunn's procedure. Miller (1966) has used the designation *Bonferroni t statistics* for the same procedure. Dunn's multiple comparison procedure or, alternatively, Bonferroni *t* statistics can be used for making all planned comparisons among means, not simply those that are orthogonal. The procedure, based on Student's *t* distribution, consists of splitting up the level of significance (α) among a set of planned comparisons. This test, like the multiple *t* ratio, does not require a prior significant over-all *F* ratio.

Let us assume that an experimenter is interested in evaluating all pairwise comparisons among the five means shown in Table 3.2-2. These

TABLE 3.2-2   Differences among Means

	$\bar{X}_1$	$\bar{X}_5$	$\bar{X}_3$	$\bar{X}_4$	$\bar{X}_2$
$\bar{X}_1 = 36.7$	–	3.6	6.7	10.5*	12.0*
$\bar{X}_5 = 40.3$		–	3.1	6.9	8.4
$\bar{X}_3 = 43.4$			–	3.8	5.3
$\bar{X}_4 = 47.2$				–	1.5
$\bar{X}_2 = 48.7$					–

*$p < .01$.

are the same data that were used to illustrate the multiple *t* ratio procedure. It should be emphasized that the procedure to be described is also applicable to comparisons involving more than two means. The difference *d* that a comparison must exceed in order to be declared significant according to Dunn's procedure is given by

$$d = t'D_{\alpha/2;C,v} \sqrt{\text{MS}_{\text{error}} \left[\frac{(C_j)^2}{n_j} + \frac{(C_{j'})^2}{n_{j'}} + \cdots + \frac{(C_{j''})^2}{n_{j''}} \right]},$$

where $t'D_{\alpha/2}$ is obtained from Table D.16 for C = number of comparisons that are made among k means and v = degrees of freedom for experimental error. The terms C_j, n_j, and MS_{error} were defined earlier in connection with the multiple *t* ratio procedure.

For the data in Table 3.2-2, an experimenter can make $[k(k-1)]/2 = 10$ pairwise comparisons. If α is set at .01, the critical difference for $C = 10$ comparisons is equal to

$$d = t'D_{.01/2;10,45} \sqrt{28.8 \left[\frac{(1)^2}{10} + \frac{(-1)^2}{10} \right]} = 3.53(2.40) = 8.47,$$

where $\text{MS}_{\text{error}} = 28.8$, $v = 45$, $n_j = 10$, and $n_{j'} = 10$ as specified in connection with the illustration of the multiple t ratio procedure. According to 'Dunn's procedure, two comparisons in Table 3.2-2 are significant. The assumptions associated with this test are the same as those for a t statistic described in Section 2.1.

In the above example, the level of significance (α) was divided evenly among the ten comparisons by the use of Dunn's table (Table D.16). This procedure of dividing α evenly among the C comparisons is appropriate if an experimenter considers the consequences of making a type I error to be equally serious for all comparisons. If this is not true, an experimenter can allocate α unequally among the C comparisons in a manner reflecting his *a priori* concern for type I and II errors. Let us assume that the .05 level of significance is adopted for a collection of $C = 5$ *a priori* comparisons among a set of means. The use of Dunn's table in Appendix D amounts to testing each of the five comparisons at α_i, where $\alpha_i = \alpha/C = .05/5 = .01$ level of significance. The consequences of making a type I error in a given experiment may not be equally serious for all comparisons. If this is true, the experimenter can allocate α_i unequally among the comparisons any way he chooses as long as the sum of α_i for $i = 1, \cdots, C$ is equal to α, the value selected for the collection of comparisons. For example, the five values of α_i could be specified as $\alpha_1 = .02$, $\alpha_2 = .01$, $\alpha_3 = .01$, $\alpha_4 = .005$, and $\alpha_5 = .005$. The level of significance for the collection of the five tests is equal to $.02 + .01 + .01 + .005 + .005 = .05$, which is the same value that would be obtained if α were divided evenly among the five tests. This procedure enables an experimenter to utilize *a priori* information in dividing the critical region unequally, placing the greatest share upon the most important comparisons.

Dunn's procedure can be used to establish confidence intervals. A confidence interval for any comparison ψ_i is constructed by

$$\left[C_j(\bar{X}_j) + C_{j'}(\bar{X}_{j'}) + \cdots + C_{j''}(\bar{X}_{j''}) \right]$$

$$\pm t'D_{\alpha/2;C,\nu} \sqrt{\mathrm{MS}_{\mathrm{error}} \left[\frac{(C_j)^2}{n_j} + \frac{(C_{j'})^2}{n_{j'}} + \cdots + \frac{(C_{j''})^2}{n_{j''}} \right]}.$$

The over-all level of significance for the C intervals is equal to or less than the preassigned value of α. The conceptual unit for significance level using Dunn's procedure is the collection of C comparisons. α is the long-run average number of erroneous statements that an experimenter will make, or, to rephrase, the expected number of errors per experiment. The conceptual unit for significance level when a multiple t ratio is computed is the individual comparison. Thus the interpretation of significance level is different for the two procedures. A general discussion of the distinction between these conceptual units for significance level appears in Section 3.3.

Because Dunn's procedure is not restricted to orthogonal comparisons but is applicable to any number of planned comparisons, the reader may wonder why it has not replaced the multiple t ratio. The answer is to be found in a comparison of the length of the confidence interval for the two procedures. For $C > 1$, a confidence interval based on Dunn's procedure is always longer than the corresponding interval based on the multiple t procedure. Hence the use of Dunn's procedure leads to a higher probability of accepting a false null hypothesis than does the multiple t ratio. The advantage of being able to make all planned comparisons is gained at the expense of an increase in the probability of making a type II error.

Dunn (1961) compared her procedure with *a posteriori* procedures developed by Tukey (1953) and Scheffé (1953). These latter two procedures, which are described in Section 3.4, have been developed for exploring interesting comparisons suggested by an inspection of the data. Dunn has shown that when there are many means in an experiment, and the number of comparisons that an experimenter wants to make among the means is relatively small, her procedure leads to shorter confidence intervals than either of the *a posteriori* procedures. On the other hand, if k is small and C is large, the *a posteriori* procedures lead to shorter confidence intervals. This results partly from the fact that the length of the confidence interval for Dunn's procedure depends on C, the number of comparisons among means, whereas with both *a posteriori* procedures the length depends on k, the number of means. If an experimenter knows in advance that he is interested in making a relatively small number of nonorthogonal comparisons among means, Dunn's *a priori* procedure may be more powerful than the *a posteriori* procedures described in Section 3.4. Procedures are described in Section 3.4 for determining the relative efficiency as well as the relative length of the confidence intervals for any two multiple comparison procedures. For planned comparisons, an experimenter can determine in advance which test procedure would lead to the shortest confidence interval.

A discussion of other procedures for obtaining simultaneous confidence intervals using Student's t distribution is given by Dunn and Massey (1965).

TESTS OF *A PRIORI* ORTHOGONAL
COMPARISONS USING F RATIO

It is often convenient to perform *a priori* orthogonal comparisons by means of an F ratio rather than a t ratio. This may be true, for example, if an electronic computer is used in the analysis. An F ratio for 1 and v degrees of freedom is equivalent to t^2 with v degrees of freedom. The formula for carrying out orthogonal planned comparisons using an F ratio is

$$F = \frac{[C_j(\bar{X}_j) + C_{j'}(\bar{X}_{j'}) + \cdots + C_{j''}(\bar{X}_{j''})]^2}{\mathrm{MS}_{\mathrm{error}} \left[\dfrac{(C_j)^2}{n_j} + \dfrac{(C_{j'})^2}{n_{j'}} + \cdots + \dfrac{(C_{j''})^2}{n_{j''}} \right]}.$$

Each F ratio is tested at α level of significance. Thus the conceptual unit for significance level is the individual comparison.

If the n's in the treatment levels are equal, the sum of the scores in each level, $\Sigma_{i=1}^{n} X_{ij}$, can be substituted for the mean. An F ratio that uses sums rather than means is given by

$$F = \frac{\left[C_j \left(\sum_1^n X_{ij} \right) + C_{j'} \left(\sum_1^n X_{ij'} \right) + \cdots + C_{j''} \left(\sum_1^n X_{ij''} \right) \right]^2}{n\mathrm{MS}_{\mathrm{error}} [(C_j)^2 + (C_{j'})^2 + \cdots + (C_{j''})^2]}.$$

The degrees of freedom for the F ratio is 1 and v, where v is the df for $\mathrm{MS}_{\mathrm{error}}$.

3.3   CONCEPTUAL UNIT FOR ERROR RATE

In testing a hypothesis an experimenter may either make a correct decision or an incorrect decision or he may suspend judgment, that is, neither reject nor accept the null hypothesis. If he makes an incorrect decision, we saw in Section 1.5 that he may commit one of two types of errors. A type I error occurs when the null hypothesis H_0 is falsely rejected. A type II error occurs when the null hypothesis is falsely accepted. Current hypothesis-testing procedures in the behavioral sciences are designed to guard against type I errors rather than type II errors. Some of the reasons for this emphasis were discussed in Section 1.5. Basically the problem stems from our inability to specify the loss function associated with committing either of the two types of errors.

If an experiment contains two treatment levels with one comparison among the means, the probability of committing a type I error if the null hypothesis is true is determined by the significance level adopted. The interpretation of a significance level is unambiguous for experiments with two treatment levels but becomes confusing for multitreatment experiments involving several simultaneous comparisons. The confusion arises in the case of multiple comparisons because a significance level can be specified for a number of different conceptual units. For example, the conceptual unit can be the individual comparison, hypothesis, family of comparisons, or experiment. An *error rate* can be defined for each of these conceptual units.

ERROR RATE PER COMPARISON

An error rate per comparison is defined as the probability that any one of C comparisons will be falsely declared significant.

$$\text{Error rate per comparison} = \frac{\text{no. of comparisons falsely declared significant}}{\text{total no. of comparisons}}$$

This is the error rate that is controlled when a t ratio is used as the test statistic in performing multiple comparisons and α is the level of significance for each comparison. The use of the comparison as the conceptual unit for error rate has been criticized (Ryan, 1959). Consider an experiment containing k treatment levels, where $k > 2$. It is possible to perform $k - 1$ independent tests of significance among the means. The probability that at least one of the comparisons will show spurious significance is equal to

Prob. of one or more significant results, if all H_0 true $= 1 - (1 - \alpha)^C$,

where C is the number of comparisons. For small values of α, this is approximately equal to $C\alpha$. The corresponding probability for nonindependent tests is difficult to compute. Therefore, if an experimenter makes ten independent comparisons among means, each at the .01 level, the probability that at least one will be significant by chance is $10 \, (.01) \simeq .10$. Thus controlling error rate per comparison allows the error rate considered over the entire experiment to vary as a function of the number of comparisons that are made. The larger the number of comparisons performed in an experiment, the greater the probability that one or more of the comparisons will be falsely declared significant.

ERROR RATE PER HYPOTHESIS

Tradition has favored the hypothesis as the proper unit for error rate although many statisticians prefer a larger unit, such as the experiment. If a hypothesis involves a single comparison, error rate per comparison is equivalent to error rate per hypothesis. If, as is typically the case in analysis of variance, a hypothesis involves several comparisons among three or more means, the error rate per comparison differs from the error rate per hypothesis. Error rate per hypothesis is defined as the probability that any one of H hypotheses will be falsely declared significant.

$$\text{Error rate per hypothesis} = \frac{\text{no. of hypotheses falsely declared significant}}{\text{total no. of hypotheses}}$$

A familiar example of the use of the hypothesis as the conceptual unit for error rate is analysis of variance. An F ratio is used to test the hypothesis that $\beta_j = 0$ for all j. The probability of falsely rejecting the hypothesis is equal to α.

It should be noted that the various error rates are all identical for an experiment involving a single comparison. The error rates become more divergent as the number of comparisons and hypotheses evaluated in an experiment are increased.

ERROR RATE PER EXPERIMENT
AND EXPERIMENTWISE

Ryan (1959, 1962) has argued in favor of using the experiment as the conceptual unit for error rate. He defines two error rates as follows:

$$\text{Error rate per experiment} = \frac{\text{no. of comparisons falsely declared significant}}{\text{total no. of experiments}}$$

and

$$\text{Error rate experimentwise} = \frac{\begin{array}{c}\text{no. of experiments with at least one statement}\\ \text{falsely declared significant}\end{array}}{\text{total no. of experiments}}$$

The first error rate is the long-run average number of erroneous statements made per experiment. The error rate experimentwise refers to the probability that one or more erroneous statements will be made in an experiment and is less conservative than the error rate per experiment. The experimentwise error rate is a probability, whereas the error rate per experiment is not a probability but, rather, the expected number of errors per experiment. The error rate per experiment and the error rate experimentwise are often numerically almost identical. The first error rate is used whenever an experimenter wants to control the average number of erroneous statements that are made in an experiment at α. The second error rate is used to guard against making any erroneous statements in an experiment. The use of this latter error rate is based on the premise that it is as serious to make one erroneous statement in an experiment as it is to make, say, five erroneous statements. Because the two error rates are almost identical for small values of α, Miller (1966, 10) observes that a choice between them is essentially a matter of taste.

Error rate per experiment can be set at α for a collection of C comparisons by using Dunn's multiple comparison procedure. In the simplest terms, this procedure is as follows: If an experiment contains k means and C comparisons are to be made, each one is tested at the α/C level of significance. For example, if $C = 10$ and an experimenter wishes the expected number of errors per experiment to be .05, the tabled t value for a two-tailed test for $\alpha = .05/10 = .005$ is used for each comparison. This procedure will often require t values not contained in standard tables. An approximate value for t that cuts off the upper $\alpha/2$ proportion with v degrees of freedom can be determined from the standardized normal distribution by

$$t_{\alpha/2,v} = z + \frac{z^3 + z}{4(v - 2)},$$

where z is the corresponding value in a normal distribution. It should be noted that the procedure of splitting up α evenly or unevenly among a set of comparisons is an extremely versatile technique. It requires only that an experimenter decide which comparisons are of interest, and hence the value of C. If we let α_P and α_{PE} represent per comparison and per experiment error rates, respectively, then for C comparisons

$$\alpha_{PE} = C\alpha_P.$$

A number of *a posteriori* multiple-comparison test statistics have been designed to control the experimentwise error rate. Several of these statistics are described in Section 3.4. The relationship between error rate per comparison and error rate experimentwise can be stated as follows. Let α_P and α_{EW} represent per comparison and experimentwise error rates, respectively; then for C independent comparisons

$$\alpha_{EW} = 1 - (1 - \alpha_P)^C.$$

The relationship for nonindependent comparisons is more complex (Harter, 1957).

ERROR RATE PER FAMILY AND FAMILYWISE

Tukey (1953) has described two types of error rates that are applicable to complex analysis of variance. A family of comparisons corresponds to all comparisons among means associated with a single treatment. For an experiment with one treatment, the family corresponds to the experiment. However, in multitreatment experiments, there are as many families of comparisons as there are F ratios for treatments. In this latter case, the error rate per family and error rate per experiment are not the same. The two error rates associated with families of comparisons in complex analysis of variance are defined as follows:

$$\text{Error rate per family} = \frac{\text{no. of comparisons falsely declared significant}}{\text{total no. of families}}$$

$$\text{Error rate familywise} = \frac{\text{no. of families with at least one statement falsely declared significant}}{\text{total no. of families}}.$$

WHAT IS THE CORRECT CONCEPTUAL UNIT FOR ERROR RATE?

We have seen that the interpretation of significance level is unambiguous for an experiment involving only one comparison. However, the situation is considerably more complex for experiments in which multiple comparisons are made. If orthogonal comparisons have been planned in advance, contemporary practice in the behavioral sciences favors the hypothesis as the conceptual unit for error rate. Under these conditions, each comparison is relevant to a single hypothesis. We noted in Section 3.1 that testing planned orthogonal comparisons is equivalent to partitioning the data so that each test involves nonredundant and nonoverlapping pieces of information about an experiment. The estimate of one comparison is unrelated to the estimate of any other comparison. This is not true for planned and unplanned nonorthogonal comparisons. Many statisticians favor a larger conceptual unit, such as the experiment, for these latter comparisons.

The relative merits of holding constant error rate per comparison, hypothesis, or some larger unit, such as the experiment, have been discussed by Duncan (1955), McHugh and Ellis (1955), Ryan (1959, 1960, 1962), and Wilson (1962). Wilson (1962) has noted that if the error rate per hypothesis is held constant, the error rate per experiment will vary, depending on the size of the experiment and vice versa. It is impossible to conclude, on the basis of purely logical considerations, that either approach is correct. The procedure adopted in this book is to use multiple t ratios for *a priori* orthogonal comparisons. This approach is illustrated by the example presented in Table 3.2-1, which involves four orthogonal comparisons among five means. It is assumed that each of the four comparisons is relevant to a research hypothesis that an experimenter wishes to test. For this situation it seems appropriate to assign an α error rate to each hypothesis rather than to the collection of hypotheses. In this example, each hypothesis involves nonredundant information and is analogous to four separate experiments, which it is assumed an experimenter could and *would* want to carry out. It should be emphasized that it would be unusual for an experimenter to have *a priori* hypotheses that exhaust all $k - 1$ orthogonal comparisons among a set of means.

If an experimenter is interested in evaluating planned nonorthogonal comparisons, Dunn's procedure or one of the *a posteriori* procedures described in Section 3.4 can be used. The choice of procedures can be made on the basis of the relative efficiency of the tests as described in Section 3.4. Some writers recommend the use of multiple t ratios for testing all planned comparisons. In this case, the error rate for each comparison is equal to α. The corresponding error rate per experiment is equal to $C\alpha$; and for C independent comparisons, the error rate experimentwise is equal to $1 - (1 - \alpha)^C$, where α is the error rate per comparison.

If a set of comparisons is *a posteriori* in character, an over-all test of significance based on a range statistic or an F ratio can be computed to determine if there is at least one comparison among means that is not equal to zero. If the over-all test is significant, one of the multiple comparison procedures described in Section 3.4 can be used to determine which comparisons are significant. In the case of *a posteriori* comparisons, the over-all hypothesis associated with, say, each F ratio is the conceptual unit for error rate. If the F ratio is significant, the family of comparisons is assigned the same error rate per family or familywise as that allotted to the F ratio for the over-all hypothesis.

In conclusion, it should be observed that once an experimenter has specified an error rate and has decided on an appropriate conceptual unit for error rate, he can compute the corresponding rate for any other conceptual unit. Basically the problem facing an experimenter is that of choosing, prior to the conduct of an experiment, a test statistic that provides the kind of protection desired. For the benefit of consumers of research reports, the conceptual unit for significance level should be explicitly stated in a report if it is not obvious from a presentation of the experimental results.

3.4   *A POSTERIORI* COMPARISONS

Many experiments are designed to determine if any treatment effects are present. If an over-all test of significance leads to rejection of the null hypothesis, attention is directed to exploring the data in order to find the source of the effects. A number of test statistics have been developed for *data snooping*. Several of these statistics can be used to make all possible comparisons among means. In this section six *a posteriori* multiple comparison tests are described. Two of the test statistics developed by Tukey and Scheffé are also illustrated in subsequent chapters for the designs described in this book.

LEAST SIGNIFICANT DIFFERENCE TEST

The first *a posteriori* test described here is also one of the oldest. In 1935, Fisher (1949, 56–58) described a multiple comparison procedure called the *least significant difference* (LSD) test. This test consists of first performing an over-all test of the hypothesis that $\beta_j = 0$ for all j by means of an F ratio. If the over-all test is significant, a procedure analogous to multiple t ratios is used to make all pairwise comparisons among means. If the over-all F ratio is not significant, no further tests are performed. The error rate per hypothesis is equal to α for the over-all F test. However, if subsequent tests are performed, the conceptual unit for error rate is the individual comparison. Thus the LSD test is not consistent with respect to error rate protection at the two stages of the test. This procedure has been widely used in research but is not generally recommended by statisticians.

If the F ratio is significant, the least significant difference between two means according to the LSD test, is given by

$$LSD = t_{\alpha/2,v} \sqrt{\frac{2MS_{error}}{n}}.$$

$t_{\alpha/2,v}$ is the upper percentage point from Student's t distribution for v degrees of freedom. The degrees of freedom v for this test is the v associated with the denominator of the F ratio. If a difference $|\bar{X}_j - \bar{X}_{j'}|$ exceeds LSD, the difference is declared significant. This procedure is convenient if the n's are equal because LSD need only be computed once for any set of comparisons. If the n's are not equal, comparisons among means can be made using the formula given in Section 3.2 for multiple t ratios.

The use of the LSD test can lead to an anomalous situation in which the over-all F ratio is significant, but none of the pairwise differences among means is significant. This situation can occur because the over-all F ratio is equivalent to a simultaneous test of the hypothesis that all *possible* comparisons among means are equal to zero. For a given set of data, the comparison that is significant may involve some linear combination of means, such as $(1)\mu_1 + (-\frac{1}{2})\mu_2 + (-\frac{1}{2})\mu_3$, rather than $(1)\mu_1 + (-1)\mu_2$.

TUKEY'S HSD TEST

A multiple comparison test similar to the LSD test has been proposed by Tukey (1953). This test, which is called the HSD (honestly significant difference) test or the w procedure, sets the experimentwise error rate at α. The HSD test was designed for making all *pairwise* comparisons among means. The basic assumptions of normality, homogeneity of variance, and so on, described in Section 2.1 in connection with a t ratio are also required for the HSD test. In addition, the n's in each treatment level must be equal or approximately equal.

A comparison involving two means is declared to be significant if it exceeds HSD, which is given by

$$\text{HSD} = q_{\alpha,\nu}\sqrt{\frac{\text{MS}_{\text{error}}}{n}}.$$

The value of q is obtained from the distribution of the studentized range statistic. This distribution is given in Table D.7. The sampling distribution of q is based on the fact that, for random samples, the range tends to be larger as the sample size is increased. In order to enter the table for q, two values are required—the degrees of freedom for MS_{error} and k, the number (range) of treatment levels in the experiment. In a completely randomized design, an estimate of MS_{error} is provided by MS_{WG} with $N - k$ degrees of freedom.

In Section 3.2 a hypothetical set of data was used to illustrate the computation of multiple t ratios. To facilitate a comparison of various multiple comparison procedures, these same data will be used throughout this section. The five means, listed in order of size, are given in Table 3.4-1. The n for each treatment level is ten. The within-groups mean square was given in Section 3.2 as 28.8, with $N - k = 45$ degrees of freedom. For purposes of illustration, the .01 level of significance will be used. The .01 or a higher level of significance, say .005, .001, is adopted whenever an experimenter considers the consequences of making a type I error more undesirable than the consequences of making a type II error. For these data, HSD corresponding to the .01 level of significance for a two-tailed test is equal to

$$\text{HSD} = q_{.01,45}\sqrt{\frac{\text{MS}_{\text{error}}}{n}} = 4.90\sqrt{\frac{28.8}{10}} = 8.33.$$

An over-all test of the hypothesis that $\mu_1 = \mu_2 = \cdots = \mu_k$ is provided by a comparison of the largest pairwise difference between means with the critical value for HSD. This test procedure, which utilizes a range statistic, is an alternative to the F ratio. For most sets of data, the range statistic and the F statistic lead to the same decision concerning the over-all null hypothesis. However, the F statistic generally provides a more powerful test of a false null hypothesis than does the range statistic. According to Table 3.4-1, the difference between the largest and smallest means is equal to 12.0. Because this difference exceeds HSD, the over-all null hypothesis is rejected. An examination of the table indicates that three pairwise comparisons exceed the critical value of 8.33 and hence are declared significant at the .01 level. It should be noted that the tabled values of q in Table D.7 are appropriate for tests of significance in which the *direction* of the difference between means has not been predicted in advance.

TABLE 3.4-1   Differences among Means

	$\bar{X}_1$	$\bar{X}_5$	$\bar{X}_3$	$\bar{X}_4$	$\bar{X}_2$
$\bar{X}_1 = 36.7$	$-$	3.6	6.7	10.5*	12.0*
$\bar{X}_5 = 40.3$		$-$	3.1	6.9	8.4*
$\bar{X}_3 = 43.4$			$-$	3.8	5.3
$\bar{X}_4 = 47.2$				$-$	1.5
$\bar{X}_2 = 48.7$					$-$

*$p < .01$.

The results of Tukey's HSD test can be compared with Dunn's procedure and with the LSD test. The critical difference, according to these latter two tests, is given by

$$\text{LSD} = t_{.01/2,45} \sqrt{\frac{2(\text{MS}_{\text{error}})}{n}} = 2.69 \sqrt{\frac{2(28.8)}{10}} = 6.46$$

and

$$d = t'D_{.01/2;10,45} \sqrt{\frac{2(\text{MS}_{\text{error}})}{n}} = 3.53 \sqrt{\frac{2(28.8)}{10}} = 8.47.$$

The LSD and Dunn tests, as applied to the data in Table 3.4-1, result in five and two significant comparisons, respectively. It is evident that, for this particular example, Dunn's test is the most conservative of the three tests. However, if an experimenter had planned to make only eight instead of all ten pairwise comparisons among means, the critical difference according to Dunn's test would have been

$$d = t'D_{.01/2;8,45} \sqrt{\frac{2(\text{MS}_{\text{error}})}{n}} = 3.46 \sqrt{\frac{2(28.8)}{10}} = 8.20.$$

Dunn's procedure becomes more powerful relative to Tukey's HSD test as the number of comparisons performed among k means is reduced. If an experimenter is interested in testing a relatively small number of planned nonorthogonal comparisons, he should not hesitate to compare Dunn's procedure with some of those described in this section. Doing so will permit him to select the procedure that gives the shortest confidence interval for the kind of protection he desires against a type I error.

If the n's in the treatment levels for Tukey's test are not equal, an approximate HSD test can be computed by substituting $\tilde{n}$ for n. $\tilde{n}$ is given by

$$\tilde{n} = \frac{k}{[(1/n_1) + (1/n_2) + \cdots + (1/n_j)]},$$

where k = number of treatment levels and $n_1, n_2 \ldots n_j$ refer to the respective n's for the treatment levels. This test is not appropriate if there are large differences among the n's.

Tukey's test can be used to establish confidence limits for the difference between two means. The confidence limits are given by

$$(\bar{X}_j - \bar{X}_{j'}) \pm q_{\alpha,v} \sqrt{\frac{\mathrm{MS}_{\mathrm{error}}}{n}}.$$

Tukey's test can also be expressed as a ratio:

$$q = \frac{C_j(\bar{X}_j) + C_{j'}(\bar{X}_{j'})}{\sqrt{\mathrm{MS}_{\mathrm{error}}/n}}.$$

The statistic q can be evaluated by means of Table D.7, which gives the upper percentage points for the studentized range statistic.

A number of multiple comparison procedures have been developed by Tukey. The WSD (wholly significant difference) test merits consideration but is more complex than the HSD test. It is described in a paper by Ryan (1959). Earlier tests by Tukey (1949a) that were designed to locate gaps in adjacent mean differences and to identify stragglers have been supplanted by later tests. Although the HSD test can be extended to nonpairwise comparisons, it is not very sensitive in these cases. The procedure by Scheffé that is described in the following paragraphs is recommended for comparisons involving more than two means.

SCHEFFÉ'S S METHOD

If the over-all F ratio is significant, Scheffé's (1953) S method can be used to make all possible comparisons among means. This procedure is less sensitive than Tukey's HSD test for pairwise comparisons but is more sensitive for complex comparisons. Consequently, it is recommended only for nonpairwise comparisons. Scheffé's method sets the error rate experimentwise equal to α.

Scheffé has shown that the probability is $1 - \alpha$ that all possible contrasts will be captured by a set of intervals given by

$$\hat{\psi} - S \leq \psi \leq \hat{\psi} + S,$$

where ψ and $\hat{\psi}$ refer to a population comparison and an estimate of the comparison, respectively. S is given by

$$S = \sqrt{(k - 1)F_{\alpha;v_1,v_2}} \sqrt{MS_{error}\left[\sum_{j=1}^{k} \frac{(C_j)^2}{n_j}\right]},$$

where $F_{\alpha;v_1,v_2}$ = tabled value of F for v_1 and v_2 degrees of freedom, k = number of treatment levels, C_j = coefficient of the contrast, and n_j = number of scores in the jth treatment level.

In order for a comparison to be significant, it must be larger than S as defined above. This test can be applied to the five means shown in Table 3.4-1. For pairwise comparisons, $\hat{\psi}$ must exceed

$$S = \sqrt{(5 - 1)(3.78)} \sqrt{28.8\left[\frac{(1)^2}{10} + \frac{(-1)^2}{10}\right]} = (3.89)(2.40) = 9.34$$

to be declared significant at the .01 level. The value 3.78 in the above formula is the tabled F value for $k - 1$ and $N - k$ degrees of freedom at the .01 level of significance. According to this criterion, only two of the comparisons in Table 3.4-1 are significant at the .01 level. This method is much more conservative for pairwise comparisons than is the HSD test.

Scheffé's method can also be expressed as a ratio:

$$F = \frac{[C_j(\bar{X}_j) + C_{j'}(\bar{X}_{j'}) + \cdots + C_{j''}(\bar{X}_{j''})]^2}{MS_{error}\left[\frac{(C_j)^2}{n_j} + \frac{(C_{j'})^2}{n_{j'}} + \cdots + \frac{(C_{j''})^2}{n_{j''}}\right]}.$$

In order to be significant, F must exceed F', where $F' = (k - 1)F_{\alpha;v_1,v_2}$.

NEWMAN-KEULS TEST

A different approach to multiple comparisons stems from the work of Student (1927), Newman (1939), and Keuls (1952). The Newman-Keuls test is based on a stairstep or layer approach to significance tests. It provides a protection level lower limit of $1 - \alpha$ for all ordered sets of means regardless of how many steps apart the means are. The critical value for differences between means for this test varies, depending on the number of means in the set. Thus error rate is seen to apply neither on an experimentwise nor on a per comparison basis.

The difference that a comparison must exceed, W_r, for the Newman-Keuls test is given by

$$W_r = q_{r\,\alpha;r,v} \sqrt{\frac{MS_{error}}{n}},$$

where q_r is obtained from the distribution of the studentized range statistic. The subscript r designates the number of steps separating ordered means. Consider the following means:

$\overline{X}_1$	$\overline{X}_5$	$\overline{X}_3$	$\overline{X}_4$	$\overline{X}_2$
36.7	40.3	43.4	47.2	48.7

Mean one is defined as being five steps away from mean two, four steps away from mean four, and so on. Two values are required in order to enter the studentized range table—the degrees of freedom for experimental error and the respective values of r. For $N - k = 45$ degrees of freedom, the respective values of q_r at the .01 level of significance are obtained from Table D.7 in the appendix and are equal to

$$q_2 = 3.80, \; q_3 = 4.35, \; q_4 = 4.68, \text{ and } q_5 = 4.90.$$

The product of

$$q_r \sqrt{\frac{MS_{error}}{n}}$$

for each r is

$$W_2 = 3.80 \sqrt{\frac{28.8}{10}} = 6.46$$

$$W_3 = 4.35 \sqrt{\frac{28.8}{10}} = 7.40$$

$$W_4 = 4.68 \sqrt{\frac{28.8}{10}} = 7.96$$

$$W_5 = 4.90 \sqrt{\frac{28.8}{10}} = 8.33.$$

W_r is the difference that two means, r steps apart, must exceed in order to be declared significant.

There is a prescribed sequence in which tests on the pairwise comparisons must be made. The means must first be arranged in order of increasing size, as shown in Table 3.4-2. The first comparison is made in

TABLE 3.4-2   Differences among Means

	$\overline{X}_1$	$\overline{X}_5$	$\overline{X}_3$	$\overline{X}_4$	$\overline{X}_2$
$\overline{X}_1 = 36.7$	–	3.6	6.7	10.5*	12.0*
$\overline{X}_5 = 40.3$		–	3.1	6.9	8.4*
$\overline{X}_3 = 43.4$			–	3.8	5.3
$\overline{X}_4 = 47.2$				–	1.5
$\overline{X}_2 = 48.7$					–

*$p < .01$.

row one for $\overline{X}_1$ versus $\overline{X}_2$. Because these two means are separated by five steps, the critical difference that this comparison must exceed is 8.33. The difference in Table 3.4-2 exceeds this difference. The next comparison tested is $\overline{X}_1$ versus $\overline{X}_4$ in row one. The critical difference for this comparison is 7.96. This comparison is also significant. This procedure is continued in row one until a nonsignificant comparison is found. In this example, the comparison of $\overline{X}_1$ versus $\overline{X}_3$ is not significant, so no further tests are made in this row or in the following rows to the left of the fourth column. The next test is the comparison of $\overline{X}_2$ versus $\overline{X}_5$ in row two. The critical value for this test is 7.96. This process is repeated for each successive row until a nonsignificant comparison is found or until the point at which tests were stopped in the preceding row is reached. In this example, the Newman-Keuls test leads to three significant pairwise comparisons among the five means. This is the same number of comparisons that was declared significant by the HSD test but one more than that obtained by Scheffé's test.

The Newman-Keuls test cannot be used to construct a confidence interval. The multistage character of this test has no counterpart in confidence procedures.

DUNCAN'S NEW MULTIPLE RANGE TEST

Duncan (1955) has developed a multiple comparison procedure for carrying out all *pairwise* comparisons among means. The error rate for this test is set at α per degree of freedom. The k mean protection level for this test is equal to $(1 - \alpha)^{k-1}$. For five ordered means, and $\alpha = .01$, the protection level is $100(1 - .01)^{5-1} = 96$ percent. This is the minimum probability of finding no erroneous significant pairwise differences among the five means. The k mean protection level decreases as k increases. Duncan (1955) has argued that if $k > 2$ it seems more reasonable to expect that there are some real differences between means than if k is equal to only two. Thus, as k increases, the test should become more powerful, that is, more likely to detect real differences. This increase in power is obtained at the expense of a decrease in protection level. This test, like the Newman-Keuls test, is based on a layer approach to significance tests.

The difference W_r that a comparison must exceed in order to be declared significant according to Duncan's test is given by

$$W_r = q_{r\,\alpha;r,v} \sqrt{\frac{\text{MS}_{\text{error}}}{n}},$$

where q_r is obtained from special tables prepared for this test by Duncan (see Table D.8). The mechanics of this test are identical to those for the Newman-Keuls test. The first step in the analysis is to rank the means in order of size, as was done in Table 3.4-2 Duncan's table of q_r is entered for each value of r and the least significant ranges computed. For the data described in Section 3.2, the critical values are

$$W_2 = 3.80 \sqrt{\frac{28.8}{10}} = 6.46$$

$$W_3 = 3.97 \sqrt{\frac{28.8}{10}} = 6.75$$

$$W_4 = 4.08 \sqrt{\frac{28.8}{10}} = 6.94$$

$$W_5 = 4.16 \sqrt{\frac{28.8}{10}} = 7.07.$$

The sequence in which the tests are carried out is the same as that described for the Newman-Keuls test. An examination of Table 3.4-2 reveals that four of the comparisons are declared significant according to this multiple range test. This is one more significant comparison than was obtained using the HSD and Newman-Keuls tests.

An extension of Duncan's new multiple range test for the case of unequal n's is described by Kramer (1956). Other applications of the test are discussed by Duncan (1957). Duncan's procedure, like the Newman-Keuls test, cannot be used to construct confidence intervals. Scheffé (1959, 78) has criticized the justification originally advanced for Duncan's test.

DUNNETT'S TEST FOR COMPARISONS
INVOLVING A CONTROL MEAN

The object of many experiments is to compare a number of treatment levels with a control condition. Dunnett (1955) has developed a multiple range test for making $k - 1$ comparisons among k means (including the control mean). The conceptual unit for error rate is the collection of $k - 1$ tests; α is the error rate experimentwise.

The difference d' that a comparison must exceed in order to be declared significant according to Dunnett's test is given by

$$d' = tD_{\alpha/2;k,v} \sqrt{\frac{2(\text{MS}_{\text{error}})}{n}},$$

where $tD_{\alpha/2;k,v}$ is the two-tailed value obtained from Dunnett's table (Table D.9 in the appendix). Dunnett's statistic can be used to make both one- and two-tailed tests. The table is entered for $k =$ number of treatment levels, including the control, and $v =$ degrees of freedom associated with MS_{error}. For the data described in Section 3.2, $k = 5$ and $v = 45$. The value of tD according to Table D.9 for a two-tailed test at the .01 level of significance is equal to 3.19. The critical difference d' for a comparison is equal to

$$d' = tD_{.01/2;5,45} \sqrt{\frac{2(28.8)}{10}} = 3.17(2.40) = 7.61.$$

Let us designate $\bar{X}_1 = 36.7$ as the control mean and $\bar{X}_2 = 48.6$, $\bar{X}_3 = 43.4$, $\bar{X}_4 = 47.2$, and $\bar{X}_5 = 40.3$ as the four treatment means, respectively. For these data, the comparisons of $\bar{X}_1$ versus $\bar{X}_2$ and $\bar{X}_1$ versus $\bar{X}_4$ are significant.

      If the number of cases in each treatment level are not equal, the following formula is used:

$$tD = \frac{C_j(\bar{X}_j) + C_{j'}(\bar{X}_{j'})}{\sqrt{MS_{error}\left(\frac{1}{n_j} + \frac{1}{n_{j'}}\right)}}.$$

If the observed $|tD|$ is greater than the tabled value of tD ($|tD_{obs}| > tD_{\alpha/2;k,v}$), the comparison is declared to be significant. The confidence limits for the difference between the control mean and any one of the remaining $k - 1$ means are given by

$$(\bar{X}_j - \bar{X}_{j'}) \pm tD_{\alpha/2;k,v} \sqrt{\frac{2MS_{error}}{n}}.$$

The probability associated with the joint (simultaneous) confidence statements is equal to $1 - \alpha$.

      Dunnett (1964) has described modifications of his procedure that can be used when the variance of the control group is not equal to the variance of the $k - 1$ treatment groups.

COMPARISON OF MULTIPLE COMPARISON PROCEDURES

      A variety of multiple comparison procedures have been described in this chapter. Each procedure has been illustrated for the same example that involved five means. An indication of the power of each test relative to the power of the other tests can be obtained from an examination of Table 3.4-3.

      An inspection of this table shows that procedures recommended for *a priori* orthogonal comparisons are more powerful than procedures recommended for *a priori* nonorthogonal and *a posteriori* comparisons. That is, the former procedures are more likely to detect real differences among means. Also, the various test statistics differ in terms of the error rates they are designed to control. The problem facing an experimenter is to select the most powerful test statistic that provides the desired kind of protection against a type I error. It should be noted that although *a*

TABLE 3.4-3   Comparison of Critical Statistic for Several Multiple Comparison Tests

Test	*Critical Statistic for Test* *No. of steps separating means*				*Sampling Distribution*
	2	3	4	5	
A priori orthogonal multiple *t* ratios	6.46	same	same	same	Student's *t* distribution
LSD test	6.46	same	same	same	Student's *t* distribution
A priori orthogonal multiple *F* ratios	6.46	same	same	same	*F* distribution
Duncan's new multiple range test	6.46	6.75	6.94	7.07	Duncan's q_r distribution
Newman-Keuls test	6.46	7.40	7.96	8.33	Distribution of studentized range
Dunnett's test	7.61 same for comparison of control with $k-1$ means				Dunnett's tD distribution
Tukey's HSD test	8.33	same	same	same	Distribution of studentized range
Dunn's test	8.47	same for $C = 10$	same	same	Dunn's $t'D$ distribution
Scheffé's *S* method	9.34	same	same	same	*F* distribution

posteriori tests such as the HSD and *S* methods are less powerful with respect to any single comparison, they have the advantage over *a priori* orthogonal procedures of enabling an experimenter to test many more hypotheses.

Insight concerning the efficiency of one multiple comparison test relative to another test is given by

$$\text{Relative efficiency} = \frac{(\text{critical statistic for efficient test})^2}{(\text{critical statistic for less efficient test})^2} \times 100.$$

For the example involving five means described in Sections 3.2 and 3.4 the efficiency of the multiple *t* ratio procedure relative to Scheffé's *S* method is given by

$$\text{Relative efficiency} = \frac{c^2}{S^2} \times 100 = \frac{(6.46)^2}{(9.34)^2} \times 100 = 47.8\%,$$

where

$$c = t_{\alpha/2, \nu} \sqrt{\text{MS}_\text{error} \left[\sum_{j=1}^{k} \frac{(C_j)^2}{n_j} \right]} \quad \text{and}$$

$$S = \sqrt{(k-1)F_{\alpha; \nu_1, \nu_2}} \sqrt{\text{MS}_\text{error} \left[\sum_{j=1}^{k} \frac{(C_j)^2}{n_j} \right]}.$$

This indicates that in order to obtain equal precision, approximately 48 percent as many observations are necessary using the multiple *t* ratio procedure as compared with using Scheffé's *S* method. The square root of

$2c^2/2S^2$ provides a measure of the relative length of the confidence interval for the two tests. For this example,

$$\sqrt{2c^2/2S^2} = \sqrt{.478} = .69.$$

Hence the confidence interval for the multiple t ratio procedure is .69 times as long as the corresponding interval for Scheffé's S method.

If several planned orthogonal comparisons are of particular interest to an experimenter, but he also wants to explore the data, both *a priori* and *a posteriori* procedures can be used in the same experiment. Procedures for making both kinds of comparisons are shown in Section 4.6.

3.5   OTHER COMPARISON PROCEDURES

The collection of multiple comparison procedures described earlier are suitable for a wide range of research situations. Several other useful procedures can be briefly mentioned. Bechhofer (1954) and Bechhofer, Dunnett, and Sobel (1954) have developed a test for ordering a set of means with a predetermined probability of being correct. Their procedure can be used to determine the largest mean, next largest mean, and so on.

Another procedure has been proposed by Gabriel (1964). Called the *simultaneous test procedure* (STP), it can be used to test the homogeneity of all sets of means with an experimentwise error rate equal to α.

Ryan (1960) has described a procedure that can be used for making multiple comparisons among means, proportions, variances, and other statistics. His procedure, which is called the *method of adjusted significance levels*, is illustrated in Section 13.2 in connection with nonparametric tests. The method of adjusted significance levels is a layer or stairstep method and was developed to control the experimentwise error rate. Miller (1966) has described a variety of multiple comparison procedures in a book devoted to this topic. This book is a convenient reference source for techniques that are scattered throughout the statistical literature.

Another class of comparison procedures deserves special mention. In Section 2.1 the assumptions underlying the derivation of the sampling distribution of t were described. Although the t statistic does not require a knowledge of the population parameters σ_j^2 and $\sigma_{j'}^2$, it does assume that the parameters as estimated by $\hat{\sigma}_j^2$ and $\hat{\sigma}_{j'}^2$ are homogeneous. If $\sigma_j^2 \neq \sigma_{j'}^2$, the denominator of the statistic

$$t' = \frac{(\bar{X}_j - \bar{X}_{j'}) - (\mu_j - \mu_{j'})}{\sqrt{\dfrac{\hat{\sigma}_j^2}{n_j} + \dfrac{\hat{\sigma}_{j'}^2}{n_{j'}}}}$$

is not distributed as χ^2/ν with ν degrees of freedom. Thus t' does not follow the t distribution. Attempts to derive the exact distribution of t' have met with limited success.

One of the first attempts to solve this problem was made by Behrens and enlarged upon by Fisher (1935). The resulting test, which has remained controversial, is known as the Behrens-Fisher test. Several approximate procedures which do not assume that $\sigma_j^2 = \sigma_{j'}^2$ have come into general usage. One of these procedures is a test proposed by Cochran and Cox (1957, 100). Their test utilizes the t' statistic defined above. The critical value for t' is an average of the tabled values for the two samples, weighted by the two sample variances. That is, the critical value of t' for a one-tailed test is given by

$$t_\alpha' = \frac{(\hat{\sigma}_j^2/n_j)t_{\alpha j} + (\hat{\sigma}_{j'}^2/n_{j'})t_{\alpha j'}}{(\hat{\sigma}_j^2/n_j) + (\hat{\sigma}_{j'}^2/n_{j'})},$$

where $t_{\alpha j}$ and $t_{\alpha j'}$ are the tabled t values at the α level of significance for $n_j - 1$ and $n_{j'} - 1$ degrees of freedom, respectively. The critical value of t' will always fall between the ordinary t values for $n_j - 1$ and $n_{j'} - 1$ degrees of freedom. For a two-tailed test, values of $t_{\alpha/2,j}$ and $t_{\alpha/2,j'}$ are used. If $n_j = n_{j'}$ then $t = t'$, and the conventional t tables can be used with $n_j - 1$ degrees of freedom. This test is conservative in that the value of t' required for significance may be slightly too high.

Another test proposed by Welch (1947) also uses the t' statistic. Tables of the distribution of t' have been prepared by Aspin (1949). An approximation to the critical value for this test is obtained from Student's t distribution with degrees of freedom equal to

$$\mathrm{df} = \frac{(n_j - 1)(n_{j'} - 1)}{(n_{j'} - 1)c^2 + (n_j - 1)(1 - c)^2},$$

where

$$c = \frac{\hat{\sigma}_j^2/n_j}{(\hat{\sigma}_j^2/n_j) + (\hat{\sigma}_{j'}^2/n_{j'})}.$$

A third approximate test has been suggested by Smith (1936) and expanded by Satterthwaite (1946). A similar test is given by Dixon and Massey (1957, 123). In general, there is a close agreement among the approximate tests that have been proposed. The test by Cochran and Cox is probably the best known.

4 / COMPLETELY RANDOMIZED DESIGN

4.1   DESCRIPTION OF DESIGN

Chapters 1, 2, and 3 introduced some of the basic concepts and statistical tools used in experimental design. Chapter 1 presented an over-all view of experimental designs. In the remaining ten chapters those designs that appear to have the greatest potential usefulness to persons engaged in research will be examined in detail.

One of the simplest experimental designs from the standpoint of data analysis and assignment of subjects to treatment levels is the completely randomized design. For convenience, this design is designated as a *type CR-k design*, where k stands for the number of treatment levels. The type CR-k design is appropriate for experiments that meet, in addition to the general assumptions of the analysis of variance model, the following two conditions:

1. One treatment or experimental variable with $k =$ two or more treatment levels. The levels of the treatment can differ either quantitatively or qualitatively. When the experiment consists of only two levels of the treatment, the F test is analogous to a t test for uncorrelated data.

2. Random assignment of subjects to the treatment levels, with each subject designated to receive only one level. If the treatment levels are of equal interest to the investigator, it is advantageous to assign randomly the same number of subjects to each level, although this is not necessary. As a matter of fact, one of the advantages of this particular design is freedom from the restriction of having an equal number of subjects under each level.

It is apparent from the foregoing that the completely randomized design is applicable to a broad range of experimental situations. This design is one of three basic designs that may be used by itself or in combination to form more complex types of experimental designs. The two other designs that may also be used by themselves or as *building blocks* for complex designs are the randomized block design and the Latin square design. The use of these designs as *building blocks* in constructing other designs is described in Chapters 7 through 10.

4.2   LAYOUT OF DESIGN

Let us assume that we are interested in the effects of sleep deprivation on hand steadiness. We have conducted an experiment in which 32
subjects were randomly divided into four groups of 8 subjects each and the
four groups assigned to one of four sleep-deprivation conditions. The
four conditions of sleep deprivation, which will be referred to as *treatment
levels*, are 12, 24, 36, and 48 hours. The letters and subscripts b_1, b_2, b_3,
and b_4 will be used to designate the four treatment levels, respectively.
The original research hypothesis that led to this experiment was based on
the idea that differences in hand steadiness would exist among subjects
assigned to the four treatment levels. A hypothetical set of data for this
experiment is shown in Table 4.2-1. A capital letter $\bar{B}_{\cdot j}$ is used to designate

TABLE 4.2-1   Summary of Sleep-Deprivation Data

	Treatment Levels		
b_1	b_2	b_3	b_4
3	4	7	7
6	5	8	8
3	4	7	9
3	3	6	8
1	2	5	10
2	3	6	10
2	4	5	9
2	3	6	11
$\bar{B}_{\cdot j} = 2.75$	3.50	6.25	9.00
$\hat{\sigma}_j^2 = 2.21$	.86	1.07	1.71

$$\bar{B}_{\cdot j} = \frac{\sum\limits_1^n B_{ij}}{n} \quad \text{and} \quad \hat{\sigma}_j^2 = \frac{\sum\limits_1^n B_{ij}^2 - \dfrac{\left(\sum\limits_1^n B_{ij}\right)^2}{n}}{n-1}$$

the mean of treatment level j. The corresponding Greek letter β_j is used
to designate a treatment effect in the mathematical model shown in Sections 1.4 and 4.4. A lower-case b_j is used to designate specific levels of
treatment B. The sum of scores in treatment level b_j is designated by
$\sum_{i=1}^n B_{ij}$. An unbiased estimate of the variance for treatment population j
is designated by $\hat{\sigma}_j^2$.

It is customary to compute simple descriptive statistics for a set of
data before proceeding with a detailed analysis of the data. If, in an experiment, the variation among the scores within each treatment level appears
to be greater than the variation among the means, there is no need to
proceed with a test of differences among the means. The point is that

decisions concerning the absence of treatment effects can sometimes be made by a simple examination of the data without carrying out an elaborate statistical analysis. It is also customary in research reports to present a brief summary of the data prior to a presentation of tests of significance. This summary generally takes the form of a table of means and variances for the experimental conditions.

An examination of Table 4.2-1 suggests that variation among the means is large enough to warrant further analysis of the data. It should be noted that the dependent variable in this experiment was measured in such a way that hand steadiness is inversely related to the size of the score. In summary, this experiment is concerned with the relationship between hours of sleep deprivation and hand steadiness. The next section restates the research hypothesis concerning sleep deprivation in the form of dichotomous and mutually exclusive statistical hypotheses that can be tested by means of analysis of variance.

4.3 NULL AND ALTERNATIVE HYPOTHESES

The null hypothesis H_0 for the data in Table 4.2-1 can be written as follows:

$$H_0: \mu_1 = \mu_2 = \mu_3 = \mu_4.$$

This hypothesis states that the four population means are equal. The alternative hypothesis takes the form:

H_1: There is some pair of population means μ_j and $\mu_{j'}$ such that

$$\mu_j \neq \mu_{j'}.$$

It is customary, in analysis of variance, to state H_0 and H_1 in terms of treatment effects β_j for Model I and in terms of treatment variances σ_B^2 for Model II. For the fixed-effects model, the following hypotheses are equivalent to those defined above:

$$H_0: \beta_j = 0 \quad \text{for all } j$$
$$H_1: \beta_j \neq 0 \quad \text{for some } j,$$

where $\beta_j = \mu_j - \mu$. If $\beta_j = 0$ for all j, then each of the k population means must equal the grand mean and hence the k populations means are equal. If the treatment levels in the experiment represent a random sample from a population of levels, Model II applies and the hypotheses are stated as follows:

$$H_0: \sigma_B^2 = 0$$
$$H_1: \sigma_B^2 \neq 0.$$

It should be noted that the null hypothesis for the random-effects model applies to the population of levels sampled and not just to the k levels contained in the experiment. It is evident that the variance of the population of treatment effects, σ_B^2, can equal zero only if all of the treatment effects in the population are equal.

The level of significance adopted for the test is $\alpha = .05$. It will be recalled from Section 1.5 that H_0 is the hypothesis subjected to a statistical test and the hypothesis that dictates the sampling distribution against which the obtained treatment effects $\hat{\beta}_j$'s are compared. H_0 is rejected if the observed F ratio exceeds the tabled F value at the designated level of significance, α. If the level of significance adopted by the experimenter is $\alpha = .05$, the probability of erroneously rejecting H_0 when it is true is .05. If H_0 is rejected, it makes tenable the alternative hypothesis H_1—that there is a difference between some pair of population means.

4.4   ASSUMPTIONS OF THE MODEL FOR TYPE CR-k DESIGN

Let X_{ij} be a measure for a randomly selected subject in treatment population j that is normal in form. It is assumed that measurement X_{ij} is equal to the sum of three terms,

$$X_{ij} = \mu + \beta_j + \varepsilon_{i(j)},$$

where $\mu =$ grand mean of treatment populations, which is an unknown constant for all observations.

$\beta_j =$ effect of treatment j, which is a constant for all subjects within treatment population j.

$\varepsilon_{i(j)} =$ experimental error, which is independent of all other ε's and is normally distributed within each treatment population with mean $= 0$ and variance $= \sigma_\varepsilon^2$. The experimental error represents all uncontrolled sources of variation affecting a particular measurement. The use of parentheses for $\varepsilon_{i(j)}$ indicates that subjects are *nested* under the treatment levels. If subjects are assigned to only one level of a treatment, they are said to be nested under that treatment. See Sections 7.10 and 7.15 for a more complete discussion of nesting.

ASSUMPTION OF INDEPENDENCE OF ERRORS

One of the three assumptions of analysis of variance implicit in the model described above is that the experimental errors are independent, both within each treatment level and across all treatment levels. It may be assumed that the ε_{ij}'s are independent if the subjects are randomly assigned to the treatment levels and if variables associated with the conduct of the experiment are also randomized. The assumption of independence of errors would not be tenable, for example, if all subjects in treatment level one are run before subjects in other treatment levels, or if subjects in treatment level one are tested by one experimenter but subjects in other treatment levels are tested by a different experimenter, or if subjects in treatment level one are tested in one experimental location but subjects in other levels are tested in a different location.

ASSUMPTION OF NORMALITY

A second assumption of the model is that the experimental errors ε_{ij}'s are normally distributed within each treatment population. This is equivalent to the statement that X_{ij}'s are normally distributed within each treatment population because the only source of variation among X_{ij}'s is ε. A rough but generally adequate test of the normality assumption can be obtained by making a frequency distribution of the scores in each treatment level. A visual inspection of the distributions will generally reveal any gross departures from normality. This procedure ordinarily is not carried out unless an experimenter has reason to suspect some departure from normality. As discussed in Section 2.6, a moderate departure from normality can be tolerated as long as the treatment distributions are homogeneous with respect to skewness and kurtosis.

ASSUMPTION OF HOMOGENEITY OF VARIANCES

A third assumption of the model is that the variance due to experimental error within each treatment population is homogeneous. That is, $\sigma_1^2 = \sigma_2^2 = \sigma_3^2 = \sigma_4^2$. If an experimenter has reason to suspect that this assumption is not met, a relatively simple test can be made by means of the $F_{\max}$ statistic. $F_{\max} = \hat{\sigma}_{\text{largest}}^2 / \hat{\sigma}_{\text{smallest}}^2$, with k and $n - 1$ degrees of freedom. This test is described in Section 2.6. The variances for each of the treatment levels in Table 4.2-1 were computed by the formula

$$\hat{\sigma}_j^2 = \frac{\sum_1^n B_{ij}^2 - \left(\sum_1^n B_{ij}\right)^2 / n}{n - 1}.$$

An inspection of the variances in Table 4.2-1 indicates that the largest and smallest variances are 2.21 and .86, respectively.

$$F_{\max} = 2.21/.86 = 2.57,$$

with $k = 4$ and $n - 1 = 7$ degrees of freedom.

The tabled value for $F_{\max.05;4,7} = 8.44$, which is greater than the observed value ($F_{\max} = 2.57$). Thus the assumption of homogeneity of variance, that $\sigma_1^2 = \sigma_2^2 = \sigma_3^2 = \sigma_4^2$, is not rejected.

   When the number of subjects in each treatment level is approximately equal, the degrees of freedom for the denominator of the $F_{\max}$ test can be taken as $n - 1$, where n is the size of the largest treatment level. The effect of this procedure is to produce a slight positive bias in the test, that is, rejecting the assumption of homogeneity when it should be accepted. Thus the investigator will err on the conservative side in deciding not to continue with the analysis until an appropriate transformation has been used. Procedures for selecting a transformation are described in Section 2.7. If a transformation that will produce homogeneity of variance cannot be found, nonparametric analysis of variance procedures described in Chapter 13 may be used.

4.5   COMPUTATIONAL PROCEDURES FOR COMPLETELY RANDOMIZED DESIGN

   A preliminary examination of the data and descriptive measures in Table 4.2-1 indicates that further analysis is warranted. The next step in the analysis is to compute sum of squares and mean squares required for a test of significance. A special routine is introduced in Table 4.5-1 for computing sum of squares. The following notation is used in the table:

k levels of treatment (b_j), where $k = 4$.

n levels of subjects (s_i), where $n = 8$.

$$\sum_1^N = \sum_1^k \sum_1^{n\,*}.$$

The BS Summary Table in part (i) of Table 4.5-1 is so designated because variation among the 32 scores reflects the effects of treatment B and subjects (S). Instead of designating individual scores by the letter X, the letter B or letters BS are used, depending on whether one summation, $\sum_{i=1}^n$, or two summations, $\sum_{j=1}^k \sum_{i=1}^n$, are performed on the scores. For example, the equivalent notation for $\sum_{i=1}^n X_{ij}$ and $\sum_{j=1}^k \sum_{i=1}^n X_{ij}$ is

$$\sum_{i=1}^n X_{ij} = \sum_1^n B \quad \text{and} \quad \sum_{j=1}^k \sum_{i=1}^n X_{ij} = \sum_1^k \sum_1^n BS \quad \text{or} \quad \sum_1^N BS.$$

In the summation notation for $\sum_1^n B$ and $\sum_1^k \sum_1^n BS$, the relevant information is contained in the upper limit of summation. It is understood that summation takes place with respect to the subscript that has k or n as its upper limit. In this example, i ranges over $1, \ldots, n$ and j ranges over $1, \ldots, k$.

*Rules of summation are described in Appendix A.

TABLE 4.5-1 Layout of Type CR-4 Design and Computational Procedures

(i) Data:

BS Summary Table

b_1	b_2	b_3	b_4
3	4	7	7
6	5	8	8
3	4	7	9
3	3	6	8
1	2	5	10
2	3	6	10
2	4	5	9
2	3	6	11

$\displaystyle\sum_1^n B = 22$ 28   50   72

$\dfrac{\left(\sum_1^n B\right)^2}{n} = 60.5$ 98.0   312.5   648.0

(ii) Computational symbols:

$$\sum_1^N BS = 3 + 6 + 3 + \cdots + 11 = 172.0$$

$$\sum_1^N BS^2 = [BS] = (3)^2 + (6)^2 + (3)^2 + \cdots + (11)^2 = 1160.0$$

$$\frac{\left(\sum_1^N BS\right)^2}{N} = [X] = \frac{(172.0)^2}{32} = 924.5$$

$$\sum_1^k \frac{\left(\sum_1^n B\right)^2}{n} = [B] = 60.5 + 98.0 + \cdots + 648.0 = 1119.0$$

(iii) Computational formulas:

$$SS_{\text{total}} = [BS] - [X] = 1160.0 - 924.5 = 235.5$$
$$SS_{\text{between groups(BG)}} = [B] - [X] = 1119.0 - 924.5 = 194.5$$
$$SS_{\text{within groups(WG)}} = [BS] - [B] = 1160.0 - 1119.0 = 41.0$$

The computational scheme shown in Table 4.5-1 uses the abbreviated symbols, $[BS]$, $[B]$, and $[X]$, which were described in Section 2.3. This abbreviated notation is particularly useful in presenting the complex designs described in the latter part of this book.

A summary of the analysis is shown in Table 4.5-2. The mean square (MS) value for each row in Table 4.5-2 is obtained by dividing the sum of squares (SS) value by the degrees of freedom (df) in its row. The F ratio is obtained by dividing the mean square in row 1 by the mean square in row

TABLE 4.5-2   Analysis of Variance Table

Source	SS	df	MS	F
1 Between groups (BG)	194.5	$k - 1 = 3$	64.833	$[\frac{1}{2}] = 44.28*$
2 Within groups (WG)	41.0	$N - k = 28$	1.464	
3 Total	235.5	$N - 1 = 31$		

*$p < .01$.

2. This is indicated symbolically by $[\frac{1}{2}]$. The tabled F value at the .05 level of significance according to Table D.5 is 2.95. Since the obtained value exceeds the tabled value, $F_{obs} > F_{.05;3,28}$, the H_0 is rejected. The tabled value of the F distribution for a type CR-k design is written $F_{\alpha;k-1,N-k}$. It is customary in analysis of variance to include in the variance table the approximate probability value associated with the F test. The experimenter should base his decision on his preselected level of significance. The inclusion of the obtained probability value permits the reader to, in effect, set his own level of significance.

In analysis of variance terminology, a *mean square* is an estimate of population variance. The following relationships may help to make the meaning of the terms in Table 4.5-2 clearer:

$$MS = \frac{SS}{df} = \hat{\sigma}^2.$$

Mean squares for between groups and within groups are, respectively,

$$MS_{BG} = \frac{SS_{BG}}{k-1} = \frac{n\sum_1^k (\bar{B}._j - \bar{B}..)^2}{k-1} = \frac{[B] - [X]}{k-1}$$

$$MS_{WG} = \frac{SS_{WG}}{N-k} = \frac{\sum_1^k \sum_1^n (BS_{ji} - \bar{B}._j)^2}{N-k} = \frac{[BS] - [B]}{N-k}.$$

An F ratio is the ratio of two variance estimates; for example,

$$F = \frac{MS_{BG}}{MS_{WG}} = \frac{\hat{\sigma}^2_{larger}}{\hat{\sigma}_{smaller}}.$$

A general expression for degrees of freedom for numerator and denominator of any F ratio is v_1, v_2. The degrees of freedom for the type CR-k design are $k - 1$ and $N - k$. The term *degrees of freedom* refers to the number of independent observations for a source of variation minus the number of independent parameters estimated in computing the variation. For example, the degrees of freedom for SS_{BG} is equal to $4 - 1$. The four means $(\bar{B}._1, \bar{B}._2, \bar{B}._3, \bar{B}._4)$ are the source of variation, and the grand mean $(\bar{B}..)$ is the estimated parameter used in computing a measure of variation. It will be recalled that the formula for computing the variation due to differences between treatments can be written $SS_{BG} = n\Sigma_1^k(\bar{B}._j - \bar{B}..)^2$.

It may be concluded from the above analysis of the sample data that one or more contrasts among the four hand-steadiness population means is significant. The next step in the analysis is to determine which comparisons among means are significant. Procedures for this purpose are described in Section 4.6. Before turning to this topic, we shall describe procedures for computing the power of an F test and specifying a sample size.

POWER OF THE ANALYSIS
OF VARIANCE F TEST

The statistical analysis described in connection with a type CR-k design guarantees that if the null hypothesis is true, $100(1 - \alpha)$ percent of the time this decision will be reached. However, nothing has been said concerning the probability of rejecting the null hypothesis if it is, in fact, false. This is the problem of determining the power $(1 - \beta)$ of the F test in analysis of variance. A general introduction to the concept of power is presented in Section 1.5.

In Section 2.5 we noted that if the hypothesis

$$H_0 : \beta_j = 0 \qquad \text{for all } j$$

is true, the ratio MS_{BG}/MS_{WG} is distributed as the F distribution. In Section 2.1 it was also pointed out that the distribution of F depends on only two parameters, v_1 and v_2. If, however, $\beta_j \neq 0$ for all j, the ratio MS_{BG}/MS_{WG} has a distribution known as *noncentral F*. This latter distribution depends on three parameters: v_1, v_2, and a noncentrality parameter δ, where

$$\delta = \sqrt{\sum_{j=1}^{k} n\beta_j^2/\sigma_\varepsilon^2}.$$

The value of δ depends on the sizes of the squared-treatment effects relative to σ_ε^2. In order to select an appropriate member of the family of noncentral F distributions required in calculating power, it is necessary to know $\Sigma_{j=1}^k n\beta_j^2/\sigma_\varepsilon^2$. Special charts based on a procedure by Tang (1938) simplifying the calculation of power have been prepared. These charts are reproduced in Table D.14. The parameter ϕ is entered in the charts and is given by

$$\phi = \frac{\sqrt{\sum_{j=1}^{k} \beta_j^2/k}}{\sigma_\varepsilon/\sqrt{n}}.$$

In order to use the charts, the following must be specified:

1. α = probability of rejecting the null hypothesis when it is true.

2. $\sum_{j=1}^{k} \beta_j^2$ = sum of squared treatment effects.

3. n = size of the jth sample.

4. σ_ε^2 = error variance.

5. v_1 and v_2 = degrees of freedom for treatment and error effects, respectively.

In practice, the sizes of population treatment effects are unknown. However, one can specify a probability of rejecting H_0, given that ϕ is as large as some critical value, say ϕ'.

The calculation of power will be illustrated for the data summarized in Table 4.5-2. Sample estimates of the parameters required in computing ϕ are obtained from Table 4.5-1. An unbiased estimate of the sum of squared treatment effects is given by

$$\sum_{j=1}^{k} \hat{\beta}_j^2 = \frac{k-1}{n}(\text{MS}_{\text{BG}} - \text{MS}_{\text{WG}}) = \frac{4-1}{8}(64.833 - 1.464) = 23.763.$$

The rationale behind the formula for computing $\Sigma_{j=1}^{k}\hat{\beta}_j^2$ is probably not apparent to the reader. This formula is based on the expected values of the mean squares. In Section 2.4 it was shown that the expected values of MS_{BG} and MS_{WG} are

$$E(\text{MS}_{\text{BG}}) = \sigma_\varepsilon^2 + \frac{n\sum_{j=1}^{k}\beta_j^2}{k-1} \qquad \text{and} \qquad E(\text{MS}_{\text{WG}}) = \sigma_\varepsilon^2.$$

Hence

$$\frac{k-1}{n}(\text{MS}_{\text{BG}} - \text{MS}_{\text{WG}}) = \frac{k-1}{n}\left(\hat{\sigma}_\varepsilon^2 + \frac{n\sum_{j=1}^{k}\hat{\beta}_j^2}{k-1} - \hat{\sigma}_\varepsilon^2\right)$$

$$= \frac{k-1}{n}\left(\frac{n\sum_{j=1}^{k}\hat{\beta}_j^2}{k-1}\right) = \sum_{j=1}^{k}\hat{\beta}_j^2.$$

An unbiased estimate of σ_ε is given by

$$\hat{\sigma}_\varepsilon = \sqrt{\text{MS}_{\text{WG}}} = \sqrt{1.464} = 1.21.$$

For these data,

$$\phi = \frac{\sqrt{23.763/4}}{1.21/2.83} = 5.7.$$

According to Table D.14, a power of approximately .99 is associated with $\phi' = 2.60$, with $v_1 = 3$, and $v_2 = 28$. Unfortunately for purposes of this illustration, the data in Table 4.5-1 yield a value of ϕ outside the range covered by Table D.14. An experimenter can conclude, however, that the probability of rejecting a false null hypothesis is greater than .99.

If the necessary information is available, power calculations should be made before rather than after an experiment is performed. It may be found, for example, that the contemplated sample size is so small that it gives less than a 20 percent chance of detecting treatment effects considered of practical interest. On the other hand, an experimenter may find that the contemplated sample size is wastefully large.

DETERMINATION OF SAMPLE SIZE

Calculation of the power of an F test in analysis of variance provides a basis for deciding on the number of subjects that should be included in an experiment. Instead of solving for ϕ, an experimenter can select a probability of rejecting H_0, given that ϕ is equal to or greater than some critical value ϕ', and solve for n. This general procedure is described in Section 1.3. To the extent that accurate estimates of $\Sigma_{j=1}^k \beta_j$ and σ_ε are available, this procedure is most useful.

If an accurate estimate of σ_ε is not available from previous research or from a pilot study, the procedure described in Section 1.3 for calculating n is not satisfactory. An alternative procedure that does not require a knowledge of σ_ε can be used. According to this procedure, differences among treatment effects, and hence means, of interest to an experimenter are specified in terms of units of σ_ε. For example, an experimenter can determine the size of n necessary to achieve a given power if the largest difference among means is equal to $C\sigma_\varepsilon$, where C is any number greater than zero. Many possible choices of β_j's yield a maximum difference of $C\sigma_\varepsilon$. It can be shown that $\Sigma_{j=1}^k \beta_j^2$ is minimal when two of the treatment effects, say β_j and $\beta_{j'}$ are equal to $-C\sigma_\varepsilon/2$ and $C\sigma_\varepsilon/2$ and all other $k-2$ effects are equal to zero. For this case,

$$\sum_{j=1}^k \beta_j^2 = \left[-\frac{C\sigma_\varepsilon}{2}\right]^2 + \left[\frac{C\sigma_\varepsilon}{2}\right]^2 + 0 + \cdots + 0 = \frac{2C^2\sigma_\varepsilon^2}{4} = \frac{C^2\sigma_\varepsilon^2}{2}.$$

Because power increases with an increase in $\Sigma_{j=1}^k \beta_j^2$, it follows that a choice of values for β_j other than those above will always lead to greater power. Hence, if an experimenter computes the sample size necessary to achieve a given power for the above treatment effects, he can be certain that any other combination of effects for which the maximum difference is $C\sigma_\varepsilon$ will yield a power greater than that specified. The formula for computing n when the size of treatment effects is expressed in units of σ_ε can be written as follows:

$$\phi = \frac{\sqrt{\sum_{j=1}^k \beta_j^2/k}}{\sigma_\varepsilon/\sqrt{n}} = \frac{\sqrt{[C^2\sigma_\varepsilon^2/2]/k}}{\sigma_\varepsilon/\sqrt{n}} = \sqrt{n}\sqrt{C^2/2k}.$$

Let us assume that an experiment contains four treatment levels and that the experimenter is interested in detecting differences among means such that the largest difference is equal to $1\sigma_\varepsilon$. If C, α, $1 - \beta$, and v_1 are specified as 1, .05, .80, and 3, respectively, the value of n can be estimated by trial and error from the formula

$$\phi = \sqrt{n}\sqrt{C^2/2k} = \sqrt{n}\sqrt{(1)^2/2(4)} = \sqrt{n}\,(.353)$$

and from Table D.14. For $n = 20$, Table D.14 can be entered to determine if a power of .80 is associated with $\phi = \sqrt{20}(.353) = 1.58$, $v_1 = 3$, $v_2 = k(n - 1) = 4(20 - 1) = 76$, and $\alpha = .05$. According to Table D.14, the power associated with $n = 20$ falls just short of $1 - \beta = .80$. If $n = 25$, the values of ϕ and v_2 are $\phi = \sqrt{25}(.353) = 1.76$ and $v_2 = 96$. According to Table D.14, the probability of rejecting a false null hypothesis for $n = 25$ is just beyond the .80 level.

The procedure described above for computing n does not require *a priori* information concerning the size of σ_ε. This is an advantage over the procedure described in Section 1.3 because this latter procedure is very sensitive to errors in estimating σ_ε.

4.6   PROCEDURES FOR TESTING DIFFERENCES AMONG MEANS

A PRIORI TESTS

If all orthogonal comparisons among means of interest to the experimenter have been specified prior to collection of the data, t tests may be used to make the comparisons. This class of comparisons is designated as *a priori* orthogonal tests. For these comparisons, the over-all F test for differences among the means does not need to be significant. If the experimenter is interested in knowing whether there is at least one significant comparison among all possible orthogonal sets of comparisons, the over-all F test provides this information.

The procedure for making orthogonal comparisons among means by a t ratio is described more fully in Section 3.2. If $k = 4$ treatment levels, a total of $k(k - 1)/2$, or six comparisons by pairs, can be made among these means. However, no more than $k - 1$, or three comparisons, are orthogonal. If the t ratio is used in making *a priori* tests, only one of the sets of orthogonal comparisons should be tested. Three sets of orthogonal comparisons are shown in Table 4.6-1. The four coefficients in each row define one comparison among the means. The coefficients C_j in the first row are for the comparison between $\bar{B}_1$ and $\bar{B}_2$. Although other sets of orthogonal comparisons could be listed, these three sets include the six possible comparisons involving only two means per comparison. If the experimenter is interested in making all possible comparisons among means,

TABLE 4.6-1   Sets of Orthogonal Comparisons

$\bar{B}_1 = 2.75$ $\bar{B}_2 = 3.50$ $\bar{B}_3 = 6.25$ $\bar{B}_4 = 9.00$	Comparison
$C_j = 1$ $C_{j'} = -1$ $C_{j''} = 0$ $C_{j'''} = 0$	$\bar{B}_1 - \bar{B}_2$
Set 1 $C_j = 0$ $C_{j'} = 0$ $C_{j''} = 1$ $C_{j'''} = -1$	$\bar{B}_3 - \bar{B}_4$
$C_j = -\frac{1}{2}$ $C_{j'} = -\frac{1}{2}$ $C_{j''} = \frac{1}{2}$ $C_{j'''} = \frac{1}{2}$	$[(\bar{B}_3 + \bar{B}_4)/2] - [(\bar{B}_1 + \bar{B}_2)/2]$
$C_j = 1$ $C_{j'} = 0$ $C_{j''} = -1$ $C_{j'''} = 0$	$\bar{B}_1 - \bar{B}_3$
Set 2 $C_j = 0$ $C_{j'} = 1$ $C_{j''} = 0$ $C_{j'''} = -1$	$\bar{B}_2 - \bar{B}_4$
$C_j = -\frac{1}{2}$ $C_{j'} = \frac{1}{2}$ $C_{j''} = -\frac{1}{2}$ $C_{j'''} = \frac{1}{2}$	$[(\bar{B}_2 + \bar{B}_4)/2] - [(\bar{B}_1 + \bar{B}_3)/2]$
$C_j = 1$ $C_{j'} = 0$ $C_{j''} = 0$ $C_{j'''} = -1$	$\bar{B}_1 - \bar{B}_4$
Set 3 $C_j = 0$ $C_{j'} = 1$ $C_{j''} = -1$ $C_{j'''} = 0$	$\bar{B}_2 - \bar{B}_3$
$C_j = -\frac{1}{2}$ $C_{j'} = \frac{1}{2}$ $C_{j''} = \frac{1}{2}$ $C_{j'''} = -\frac{1}{2}$	$[(\bar{B}_2 + \bar{B}_3)/2] - [(\bar{B}_1 + \bar{B}_4)/2]$

and not in just one of the orthogonal sets, he should use an *a posteriori* procedure.

The t test is illustrated below for the first set of comparisons in Table 4.6-1.

(1)
$$t = \frac{C_j(\bar{B}_1) + C_{j'}(\bar{B}_2)}{\sqrt{2MS_{WG}/n}} = \frac{1(2.75) - 1(3.50)}{\sqrt{2(1.464)/8}} = \frac{-.75}{.605} = -1.24$$

$$t = \frac{C_{j'}(\bar{B}_3) + C_{j'''}(\bar{B}_4)}{\sqrt{2MS_{WG}/n}} = \frac{1(6.25) - 1(9.00)}{\sqrt{2(1.464)/8}} = \frac{-2.75}{.605} = -4.55$$

(2)
$$t = \frac{C_j(\bar{B}_1) + C_{j'}(\bar{B}_2) + C_{j''}(\bar{B}_3) + C_{j'''}(\bar{B}_4)}{\sqrt{MS_{WG}\left[\frac{(C_j)^2}{n} + \frac{(C_{j'})^2}{n} + \frac{(C_{j''})^2}{n} + \frac{(C_{j'''})^2}{n}\right]}}$$

$$= \frac{-\frac{1}{2}(2.75) - \frac{1}{2}(3.50) + \frac{1}{2}(6.25) + \frac{1}{2}(9.00)}{\sqrt{1.464\left[\frac{(-\frac{1}{2})^2}{8} + \frac{(-\frac{1}{2})^2}{8} + \frac{(\frac{1}{2})^2}{8} + \frac{(\frac{1}{2})^2}{8}\right]}} = \frac{4.50}{.428} = 10.51.$$

The tabled value for $t_{.05/2,28}$ is 2.05. Since $|t_{obs}| > t_{.05,28}$ for the comparison of $\bar{B}_3$ with $\bar{B}_4$ and $\bar{B}_1 + \bar{B}_2$ with $\bar{B}_3 + \bar{B}_4$, we can conclude that the means forming these comparisons came from different populations. The negative sign of t_{obs} has no significance in this example, for a two-tailed test was employed. The H_0 would also have been rejected had t_{obs} been positive. The algebraic sign of the test is important only when a one-tailed H_1 has been advanced, for example, $\beta_3 > \beta_4$ or $\beta_3 < \beta_4$.

When the n's for the treatment levels are not equal, the t formula becomes

(3)
$$t = \frac{C_j(\bar{B}_j) + C_{j'}(\bar{B}_{j'})}{\sqrt{MS_{WG}\left[\frac{(C_j)^2}{n_j} + \frac{(C_{j'})^2}{n_{j'}}\right]}}.$$

t formulas (1) and (3) are equivalent when the number of scores in each treatment level are equal. For example,

$$t = \frac{1(2.75) - 1(3.50)}{\sqrt{\dfrac{2(1.464)}{8}}} = \frac{1(2.75) - 1(3.50)}{\sqrt{1.464\left[\dfrac{(1)^2}{8} + \dfrac{(-1)^2}{8}\right]}} = -1.24.$$

Dunn's test, which is described in Section 3.2, can be used if an experimenter has advanced a relatively small number of hypotheses that involve nonorthogonal comparisons. The per experiment error rate associated with Dunn's procedure is equal to α. The conceptual unit for error rate for the multiple t ratio procedure described previously is the individual comparison.

A POSTERIORI TESTS

If an experimenter is interested in data snooping, that is, in making tests suggested by an inspection of the data, an *a posteriori* test statistic should be used. A significant over-all test for differences among the means is required before proceeding with *a posteriori* tests.

We shall illustrate two procedures for making *a posteriori* comparisons. The first, developed by Tukey (1953), is useful for making all comparisons among pairs of means. The second procedure, due to Scheffé (1959), can be used to make all possible comparisons among the means, not just those involving two means. Tukey's test statistic is given by

$$(4) \qquad\qquad q = \frac{C_j(\bar{B}_j) + C_{j'}(\bar{B}_{j'})}{\sqrt{\mathrm{MS_{WG}}/n}}.$$

q_{obs} is compared with $q_{\alpha;k,N-k}$, which is the critical value obtained from the Studentized range table shown in Table D.7. If $|q_{\mathrm{obs}}| > q_{\alpha;k,N-k}$, one concludes that the two means were drawn from different populations. Tukey's test statistic will be illustrated for the first two comparisons in Set 1 of Table 4.6-1.

$$q = \frac{C_j(\bar{B}_1) + C_{j'}(\bar{B}_2)}{\sqrt{\mathrm{MS_{WG}}/n}} = \frac{1(2.75) - 1(3.50)}{\sqrt{1.464/8}} = \frac{-.75}{.428} = -1.75$$

$$q = \frac{C_{j''}(\bar{B}_3) - C_{j'''}(\bar{B}_4)}{\sqrt{\mathrm{MS_{WG}}/n}} = \frac{1(6.25) - 1(9.00)}{\sqrt{1.464/8}} = \frac{-2.75}{.428} = -6.43.$$

The critical value for $q_{.05;4,28} = 3.86$. It is apparent that $|q_{\mathrm{obs}}| > q_{.05;4,28}$ for the comparison of $\bar{B}_3$ and $\bar{B}_4$ but not for $\bar{B}_1$ and $\bar{B}_2$.

Using Tukey's test statistic, the experimenter can make all six of the possible *two-mean* comparisons. If he wishes to make comparisons involving more than two means, Scheffé's procedure should be used. Scheffé's test statistic is given by

(5)
$$F = \frac{[C_j(\bar{B}_j) + C_{j'}(\bar{B}_{j'}) + C_{j''}(\bar{B}_{j''}) + \cdots + C_{j'''}(\bar{B}_{j'''})]^2}{\mathrm{MS_{WG}}\left[\dfrac{(C_j)^2}{n_j} + \dfrac{(C_{j'})^2}{n_{j'}} + \dfrac{(C_{j''})^2}{n_{j''}} + \cdots + \dfrac{(C_{j'''})^2}{n_{j'''}}\right]}.$$

For a comparison to be significant it is necessary that $F_{obs} > F'$. F' is defined as $[(k - 1) F_{\alpha;k-1,N-k}]$, where k is the number of treatment levels and $F_{\alpha;k-1,N-k}$ is the tabled value of the F distribution. Scheffé's test statistic will be illustrated for the comparison of $\bar{B}_1$ versus $\bar{B}_2$, $\bar{B}_3$, and $\bar{B}_4$. The coefficients (C_j) for this comparison are $C_j, \ldots, C_{j'''} = 1, -\frac{1}{3}, -\frac{1}{3}$, and $-\frac{1}{3}$.

$$F = \frac{[1(2.75) - \frac{1}{3}(3.50) - \frac{1}{3}(6.25) - \frac{1}{3}(9.00)]^2}{1.464\left[\dfrac{(1)^2}{8} + \dfrac{(-\frac{1}{3})^2}{8} + \dfrac{(-\frac{1}{3})^2}{8} + \dfrac{(-\frac{1}{3})^2}{8}\right]} = \frac{(-3.50)^2}{.244} = 50.20.$$

The value of $F' = (k - 1)F_{.05;3,28} = (3)(2.95) = 8.85$. Since $F_{obs} > F'_{.05;3,28}$, it is concluded that μ_1 is not equal to the average of μ_2, μ_3, and μ_4. The reader may recall that $F = t^2$. The similarity between formulas (2) and (5) is apparent.

THE USE OF *A PRIORI* AND *A POSTERIORI* TESTS IN THE SAME EXPERIMENT

In an experiment $k - 1$ *a priori* orthogonal comparisons can be evaluated. An experimenter may have a particular interest in only one or two of these comparisons. Once the comparisons of interest have been evaluated, he may want to explore the remainder of the data, using *a posteriori* procedures. The combined use of *a priori* and *a posteriori* tests in the same experiment will be illustrated for the data in Table 4.5-1. Let us assume that one comparison, $\hat{\psi} = C_{j'}(\bar{B}_3) + C_{j''}(\bar{B}_4)$, is of particular interest. A t ratio for this comparison is equal to

$$t = \frac{1(6.25) - 1(9.00)}{\sqrt{2(1.464)/8}} = -4.55.$$

A test of this comparison, which is significant beyond the .01 level, accounts for one of the $k - 1 = 3$ degrees of freedom for $\mathrm{SS_{BG}}$. The remaining $k - 1 - 1 = 2$ degrees of freedom can be used in making an over-all test of significance. This test is performed with the sum of squares for $\hat{\psi}$ removed from $\mathrm{SS_{BG}}$ and is given by

$$F = \frac{(\mathrm{SS_{BG}} - \mathrm{SS}_{\hat{\psi}})/(k - 1 - 1)}{\mathrm{MS_{WG}}} = \frac{(194.50 - 30.25)/(4 - 1 - 1)}{1.464}$$

$$= \frac{82.125}{1.464} = 56.10,$$

where

$$SS_{\hat{\psi}} = \frac{[C_{j''}(\bar{B}_3) + C_{j'''}(\bar{B}_4)]^2}{\frac{(C_{j''})^2}{n_{j''}} + \frac{(C_{j'''})^2}{n_{j'''}}} = \frac{[1(6.25) - 1(9.00)]^2}{\frac{(1)^2}{8} + \frac{(-1)^2}{8}} = 30.25.$$

In this example, $F_{obs} > F_{.05;2,28}$. Thus an experimenter can explore all possible remaining comparisons by means of *a posteriori* tests. If the over-all test is insignificant, no *a posteriori* tests are made.

Only one planned comparison was involved in this example. If two planned comparisons had been made, there would have been $k - 1 - 2 = 1$ degree of freedom left for the over-all test. The F ratio for this case would have the form

$$F = \frac{(SS_{BG} - SS_{\hat{\psi}_1} - SS_{\hat{\psi}_2})/(k - 1 - 2)}{MS_{WG}},$$

with $v_1 = 1$ and $v_2 = 28$. The procedure described enables an experimenter to use powerful *a priori* tests for important comparisons and, in addition, to explore all possible remaining comparisons if the over-all F ratio is significant.

The multiple-comparison procedures illustrated in this section are appropriate for a fixed-effects model. If a random-effects model is assumed to be appropriate, an experimenter's principal interest is in testing the hypothesis that the population variance σ_B^2 is equal to zero. Because treatment levels for a random-effects model are randomly sampled from a population of levels, there is little interest in determining which comparisons among the means are not equal to zero.

4.7   TESTS FOR TRENDS IN THE DATA

QUANTITATIVE VERSUS QUALITATIVE
TREATMENT LEVELS

Differences among treatment levels may be either quantitative or qualitative. If the levels represent different amounts of a single common variable, the treatment is referred to as a quantitative treatment. The example involving four levels of sleep deprivation described in Section 4.2 is such a variable. The four treatment levels can obviously be ordered, that is, described in terms of more or less of the variable. If the levels cannot be meaningfully ordered along a single continuum, the treatment is designated as a qualitative treatment.

PURPOSES OF TREND ANALYSIS

An experimenter's principal interest in designs involving a qualitative treatment is in determining whether there are differences among the k means. If the treatment levels differ quantitatively *and* if the sizes of the intervals separating the treatment levels can be specified, the experimenter can turn to more penetrating questions. For example, the experimenter may want to know the nature of the relationship between the independent variable (experimental treatment levels) and the dependent variable (observed performance under each level). If the treatment levels represent a quantitative variable, the following types of questions may be posed.

> *Question 1.* Is there a trend in the data? This question can be rephrased as, Are the means for the dependent variable influenced by changes in the independent variable?

> *Question 2.* Is the trend of the dependent variable means linear or nonlinear?

> *Question 3.* If the trend of the dependent variable means is nonlinear, what higher-degree equation is required to provide a satisfactory fit for the data?

> *Question 4.* Do the means for the dependent variable follow a trend that has been derived from the data? That is, does a particular equation based on the data provide a satisfactory *fit* for the data?

> *Question 5.* Is the trend of means for one treatment the same for different levels of a second treatment?

This last question is not applicable to a completely randomized design, for this design has only one treatment variable. We shall return to this question in Chapter 7, which describes factorial experiments.

TEST FOR PRESENCE OF TREND

An answer to the first question, "Is there a trend in the data?" is provided by $F = \text{MS}_{\text{BG}}/\text{MS}_{\text{WG}}$. If $F_{\text{obs}} > F_{\alpha;v_1,v_2}$, it is concluded that the means for the dependent variable are influenced by changes in the independent variable. If there is no trend, the data will have the appearance shown in Figure 4.7-1 by the squares. A trend is illustrated by the circles.

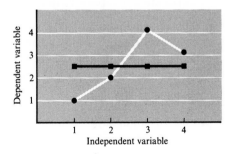

Figure 4.7-1 Squares illustrate lack of trend; circles illustrate presence of trend.

A trend in data is indicated whenever dependent variable means are not equal for different levels of the independent variable.

INTRODUCTION TO TEST FOR
LINEARITY OF TREND

If the F test indicates a trend in the data, the experimenter may want to determine the nature of this trend. In the broadest terms, a trend may be either linear or nonlinear. Procedures for determining the nature of the trend are illustrated in the following paragraphs. The question, "What is the simplest equation that provides a satisfactory description of the data?" can be answered most easily through the use of orthogonal polynomials. A given set of data can often be described by many different equations. A polynomial equation containing one less component than there are treatment levels, $k - 1$ terms, will always provide a fit for the data. The question, "Is a polynomial equation the most appropriate way to fit a set of data?", is outside the scope of this book. An introduction to curve-fitting procedures may be found in Lewis (1960). Orthogonal polynomials are introduced here because they provide a convenient way of determining whether or not the trend of data is linear or nonlinear.

USE OF ORTHOGONAL POLYNOMIALS
IN FITTING A TREND

A polynomial is an algebraic expression containing more than one term. For example, $X = a + bY + cY^2 + dY^3 + eY^4 + \cdots + jY^n$ is an nth degree polynomial containing

$$a = \text{constant}$$
$$bY = \text{linear component}$$
$$cY^2 = \text{quadratic component}$$
$$dY^3 = \text{cubic component}$$
$$eY^4 = \text{quartic component}$$
$$jY^n = n\text{th power component}$$
(where n is a positive integer).

An equation of the form $X = a + bY$ is a first-degree or linear equation, $X = a + bY + cY^2$ is a second-degree or quadratic equation, and $X = a + bY + cY^2 + dY^3$ is a third-degree or cubic equation. These equations, when graphed, have the general forms shown in Figure 4.7-2. The reader may have noted that the symbols X and Y in the figure denote the dependent and independent variables, respectively. This reversal of the conventional use of X and Y is an unhappy consequence of the notation system for analysis of variance used by early writers. Although awkward for discussions of trend analysis, this notation practice will be followed for the sake of consistency.

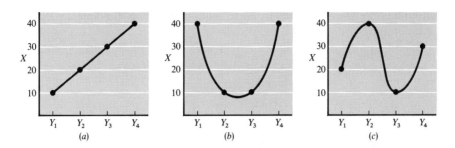

Figure 4.7-2   Illustration of linear (*a*), quadratic (*b*), and cubic (*c*) relations between independent and dependent variable.

Polynomials may be used to approximate curves that are actually exponential or logarithmic in shape. Extensive tables of coefficients that correspond to linear, quadratic, cubic, etc. components are available (Anderson and Houseman, 1942; Fisher and Yates, 1963). A table that contains coefficients for $k = 3$ through 10 is given in Table D.12 in the appendix. In order to use these tables, the treatment levels must be separated by equal intervals. The treatment may represent any continuum, but the difference between any two adjacent treatment levels must be equal. It is also necessary to have an equal number of observations in each treatment level. A procedure for deriving coefficients that negates the equal n and equal interval requirements is described in Appendix C. If an experiment involves treatment levels that are not separated by equal intervals, it is necessary to derive the coefficients for these data.

Orthogonal polynomial coefficients in Table D.12 were derived so that each set represents one and only one trend or form of relationship. It was shown in Section 4.6 that SS_{BG} can be partitioned into $k - 1$ orthogonal comparisons among means. By the same reasoning, the SS_{BG} can be partitioned into $k - 1$ orthogonal trend components. If $k = 4$, the best prediction equation is of no higher degree than $k - 1$. The meaning of these statements can be made clearer by using an example. The coefficients for linear, quadratic, and cubic trends are shown in Table 4.7-1. The X values in Figure 4.7-2a are 10, 20, 30, and 40. If these values are

TABLE 4.7-1   Coefficients for Linear, Quadratic, and Cubic Trends

Treatment Level	Y_1	Y_2	Y_3	Y_4
Linear (c_1)	-3	-1	$+1$	$+3$
Quadratic (c_2)	$+1$	-1	-1	$+1$
Cubic (c_3)	-1	$+3$	-3	$+1$

multiplied by the c_1, c_2, and c_3 coefficients in the table, the following sums are obtained:

$$\sum_1^k [c_1\ X_j] = -3(10)\ -1(20)\ +1(30)\ +3(40) = +100$$

$$\sum_1^k [c_2\ X_j] = +1(10)\ -1(20)\ -1(30)\ +1(40) = 0$$

$$\sum_1^k [c_3\ X_j] = -1(10)\ +3(20)\ -3(30)\ +1(40) = 0.$$

Since the relationship in Figure 4.7-2a is clearly linear, only the linear coefficients are useful in predicting the trend. The products $\sum_1^k [c_2\ X_j]$ and $\sum_1^k [c_3\ X_j]$ sum to zero, which indicates that neither the quadratic nor the cubic coefficients are useful in describing this trend. The X values in Figure 4.7-2b are 40, 10, 10, and 40. Since this trend is quadratic, it may be anticipated that $\sum_1^k [c_1\ X_j]$ and $\sum_1^k [c_3\ X_j]$ will equal zero but $\sum_1^k [c_2\ X_j]$ will be greater than zero. This may be demonstrated as follows:

$$\sum_1^k [c_1\ X_j] = -3(40)\ -1(10)\ +1(10)\ +3(40) = 0$$

$$\sum_1^k [c_2\ X_j] = +1(40)\ -1(10)\ -1(10)\ +1(40) = 60$$

$$\sum_1^k [c_3\ X_j] = -1(40)\ +3(10)\ -3(10)\ +1(40) = 0.$$

Using the same procedure, it can be shown for the data in Figure 4.7-2c that

$$\sum_1^k [c_1\ X_j] \quad \text{and} \quad \sum_1^k [c_2\ X_j] = 0 \quad \text{but} \quad \sum_1^k [c_3\ X_j] > 0.$$

It is apparent from these illustrations that each set of polynomial coefficients has been derived so as to describe one and only one trend or form of relationship. It can also be shown that the $k - 1$ trend components are orthogonal. By definition, $k - 1 = 3$ trend components are orthogonal if the product of their coefficients sum to zero; that is, if $\Sigma c_1 c_2$, $\Sigma c_1 c_3$, and $\Sigma c_2 c_3 = 0$. For example, the product of c_1 and $c_2 = (-3)(+1) + (-1)(-1) + (+1)(-1) + (+3)(+1) = 0$.

COMPUTATIONAL PROCEDURE FOR TESTING LINEARITY OF TREND

Let us turn to computational procedures for answering the second question listed earlier that can be answered by trend analysis. The basic problem confronting an experimenter in trend analysis is in deciding how many functions (trend components) of Y should be used to describe the relationship between X and Y. As a first approximation, an experimenter can determine if a linear equation provides a satisfactory fit to the data. If it does not, quadratic, cubic, or higher-degree equations can be employed. As we shall see, analysis of variance can be used to determine whether or not any particular trend component accounts for a significant portion of the variance of X and thus contributes to the over-all goodness of fit. By employing only those trend components that are found to be significant, an experimenter can write a polynomial equation that represents the simplest possible description of the relationship between the dependent variable (X) and the independent variable (Y).

The use of orthogonal polynomial coefficients in determining whether the trend of the sleep-deprivation data is linear or nonlinear is illustrated in Table 4.7-2. The values $\Sigma B = 22, 28, 50, 72$ in part (i) of

TABLE 4.7-2   Use of Orthogonal Polynomial Coefficients to Test Linearity of Data

	Treatment Levels				
	b_1	b_2	b_3	b_4	

(i)

$$\sum_1^n B = \quad 22 \qquad 28 \qquad 50 \qquad 72$$

$$\text{Linear coefficient } (c_1) = \quad -3 \qquad -1 \qquad +1 \qquad +3 \qquad \sum_1^k c_1^2 = 20 \qquad n\sum_1^k c_1^2 = (8)(20) = 160$$

$$(c_1)\sum_1^n B = \quad -66 \qquad -28 \qquad 50 \qquad 216 \qquad B_1 = \sum_1^k \left(c_1 \sum_1^n B \right) = 172$$

(ii)

$$SS_{lin} = \frac{B_1^2}{n\sum_1^k c_1^2} = \frac{(172)^2}{160} = 184.90 \qquad df = 1$$

$$MS_{lin} = \frac{SS_{lin}}{df} = \frac{184.90}{1} = 184.90$$

$$F = \frac{MS_{lin}}{MS_{WG}} = \frac{184.90}{1.464} = 126.30 \qquad df = 1, N - k$$

$$F_{.05;1,28} = 4.20$$

(iii)

$$SS_{dep\,from\,lin} = SS_{BG} - SS_{lin} = 194.5 - 184.9 = 9.60 \qquad df = k - 2$$

$$MS_{dep\,from\,lin} = \frac{SS_{dep\,from\,lin}}{df} = \frac{9.60}{4-2} = 4.80$$

$$F = \frac{MS_{dep\,from\,lin}}{MS_{WG}} = \frac{4.80}{1.464} = 3.28 \qquad df = k - 2, N - k$$

$$F_{.05;2,28} = 3.34$$

the table are hand-steadiness sums for the four levels of sleep deprivation. The original data appear in Table 4.2-1. The linear coefficients (c_1) are obtained from Table 4.7-1. An F statistic is used to determine if the MS_{lin} makes a significant contribution in describing the trend of the data. This statistic is shown in part (ii) of Table 4.7-2. Since $F_{obs} > F_{.05;1,28}$, it is concluded that the linear component of the trend is significant. The F test procedure described here is appropriate for planned orthogonal trend tests. The conceptual unit for error rate is the individual trend comparison. If an experimenter performs $k - 1 = 3$ trend tests each as $\alpha = .05$, the error rate experimentwise is equal to

$$1 - (1 - .05)^3 = .14.$$

TEST FOR DEPARTURE FROM LINEARITY

If an experimenter has not advanced specific hypotheses with respect to, say, the quadratic and cubic trend components, an over-all test for these higher-order components can be performed. This test is referred to as a test for departure from linearity. Computational procedures for this test are illustrated in Table 4.7-2(iii). Because $F_{obs} < F_{.05;2,28}$, it is concluded that the trend does not depart from linearity. Variability of means from the best-fitting linear equation is assumed to represent nothing more than error variability. If a test for departure from linearity is significant, Scheffé's method or Dunn's procedure can be used to determine which higher-order trend components are significant. This procedure enables an experimenter to assign the same error rate familywise or per family to the collection of tests as that allotted to the F ratio for the over-all hypothesis.

An experimenter may have reason to believe that the linear, quadratic, cubic, etc. trend components all contribute to the over-all trend. In this case he should proceed to test each trend component for which *a priori* hypotheses have been advanced, without first performing an over-all test. Computational procedures for testing quadratic and cubic components are described in the following paragraphs. It should be noted that one or more tests of higher-order trend components may be significant, although the test for departure from linearity is insignificant. This apparent inconsistency may occur if, for example, the individual hypothesis is employed as the conceptual unit for error rate.

COMPUTATIONAL PROCEDURE FOR TESTING
QUADRATIC AND CUBIC TREND COMPONENTS

A third question that can be answered by trend analysis is, "If the trend of dependent variable means is nonlinear, what higher-degree equation is required to provide a satisfactory fit for the data?" Let us assume that *a priori* hypotheses with respect to the presence of linear, quadratic, and cubic trend components have been advanced. The SS_{BG} in the sleep-deprivation example has $k - 1 = 3$ degrees of freedom. It will be shown that this SS_{BG} can be partitioned into linear, quadratic, and cubic trend components with one degree of freedom per component. A general principle is that a SS_{BG} can be partitioned into as many trend components as there are degrees of freedom for treatment levels. Procedures for testing the significance of the quadratic and cubic components are illustrated in Table 4.7-3. Quadratic and cubic orthogonal coefficients are obtained from Table 4.7-1. It is apparent from Table 4.7-3 that $F_{obs} >$

TABLE 4.7-3   **Use of Orthogonal Polynomial Coefficients in Testing Significance of Quadratic and Cubic Components of Trend**

		Treatment Levels			
	b_1	b_2	b_3	b_4	

(i)

$$\sum_1^n B = \quad 22 \qquad 28 \qquad 50 \qquad 72$$

Quadratic coefficient (c_2) =	1	-1	-1	$+1$	$\sum_1^k c_2^2 = 4 \qquad n\sum_1^k c_2^2 = (8)(4) = 32$
Cubic coefficient (c_3) =	-1	$+3$	-3	$+1$	$\sum_1^k c_3^2 = 20 \qquad n\sum_1^k c_3^2 = (8)(20) = 160$

$$(c_2)\sum_1^n B = \quad 22 \qquad -28 \qquad -50 \qquad 72 \qquad B_2 = \sum_1^k \left(c_2 \sum_1^n B\right) = 16$$

$$(c_3)\sum_1^n B = \quad -22 \qquad 84 \qquad -150 \qquad 72 \qquad B_3 = \sum_1^k \left(c_3 \sum_1^n B\right) = -16$$

(ii)

$$SS_{quad} = \frac{B_2^2}{n\sum_1^k c_2^2} = \frac{(16)^2}{32} = 8.0 \qquad df = 1$$

$$MS_{quad} = \frac{SS_{quad}}{df} = \frac{8.0}{1} = 8.0$$

$$SS_{cubic} = \frac{B_3^2}{n\sum_1^k c_3^2} = \frac{(-16)^2}{160} = 1.6 \qquad df = 1$$

$$MS_{cubic} = \frac{SS_{cubic}}{df} = \frac{1.6}{1} = 1.6$$

(iii)

$$F = \frac{MS_{quad}}{MS_{WG}} = \frac{8.0}{1.464} = 5.46 \qquad df = 1, 28$$

$$F = \frac{MS_{cubic}}{MS_{WG}} = \frac{1.6}{1.464} = 1.09 \qquad df = 1, 28$$

$$F_{.05;1,28} = 4.20$$

$F_{.05;1,28}$ for the quadratic component but not for the cubic component. Thus the trend of the data involves some curvature. An inspection of Figure 4.7-3 lends some support to the above conclusion.

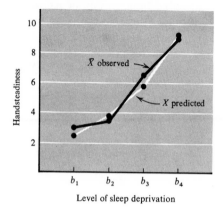

Figure 4.7-3 Trend of data is designated by $\overline{X}$ **observed.**

The sum of the linear, quadratic, and cubic trend component sum of squares is equal to 194.5. This sum is equal to SS_{BG}. Hence it is evident that the SS_{BG} has been partitioned into three orthogonal trend components. Of the 194.5 units of variation due to differences in sleep deprivation, the linear component accounts for 184.9, or 95.1 percent of the variation. The quadratic and cubic components account for 8.0 and 1.6 units, respectively. A summary of the trend analyses that have been performed is shown in Table 4.7-4.

TABLE 4.7-4   Analysis of Variance Table Summarizing Trend Tests

	Source	SS	df	MS	F
1	Between groups	194.5	$k - 1 = 3$	64.833	$\left[\frac{1}{2}\right] = 44.28**$
1a	Linear trend	184.9	1	184.9	$[1a/2] = 126.30**$
1b	Dep from lin trend	9.6	$k - 2 = 2$	4.8	$[1b/2] = 3.28$
1c	Quadratic trend	8.0	1	8.0	$[1c/2] = 5.46*$
1d	Cubic trend	1.6	1	1.6	$[1d/2] = 1.09$
2	Within groups	41.0	$N - k = 28$	1.464	
3	Total	235.5	$N - 1 = 31$		

$*p < .05.$

$**p < .01.$

In experiments involving many treatment levels, it is unlikely that tests of trend components beyond the cubic or quartic degree will add materially to the experimenter's understanding of the data. The usual practice, then, is to test trend components for which there is an *a priori* hypothesis and then pool the remaining components in a test for higher-order trends by $F = MS_{\text{higher-order trends}}/MS_{\text{WG}}$. The $MS_{\text{higher-order trends}}$ is equal to

$$MS_{\text{higher-order trends}} = \frac{SS_{\text{BG}} - SS_{\text{lower-order trends}}}{(k-1) - (df_{\text{lower-order trends}})}.$$

The $SS_{\text{lower-order trends}}$ is the sum of the SS for each trend component not included as one of the higher-order components. The $df_{\text{lower-order trends}}$ is the sum of the df for each of the lower-order sum of squares.

DESCRIBING THE TREND BY A POLYNOMIAL EQUATION

Let us assume that *a priori* hypotheses concerning the linear, quadratic, and cubic trend components have been advanced and that the analyses indicate that hand steadiness is not a simple linear function of amount of sleep deprivation but is a curvilinear function. It is concluded that a polynomial equation of the form $X = a + bY + cY^2$ is adequate to describe the data. This equation includes only those components that were shown to be significant and thus represents the simplest (lowest possible degree) description of the trend. It might be of interest to an experimenter to compare the predicted values with the obtained values or to display the data in graphic form for only the significant components of the trend. Computation of the predicted values for X based on the significant components of the trend is easily accomplished by means of orthogonal polynomials. Computational procedures for this purpose are illustrated below.

For the polynomial case, X can be predicted from Y by $X = a + bY + cY^2 + dY^3 + \cdots jY^n$. For computational purposes, it is more convenient to solve for X, using orthogonal polynomial coefficients.

(1) $$X_j = \bar{X} + b'c_{1j} + c'c_{2j} + d'c_{3j} + \cdots + j'c_{nj}.$$

Definitions of the terms in equation (1) and computational procedures for the sleep-deprivation data are illustrated in Table 4.7-5.

The second-degree equation for predicting X is

$$X = 5.375 + 1.075(c_{1j}) + .500(c_{2j}).$$

In order to predict X for any of the four levels of sleep deprivation, the orthogonal coefficients for this level are substituted in the equation. For example, the linear and quadratic coefficients for level b_2 are -1 and -1, respectively. The equation for determining X for this level of sleep deprivation is

$$X = 5.375 + 1.075(-1) + .500(-1) = 3.800.$$

Although the cubic component was not significant, a third-degree equation provides a better *fit* than does the second-degree equation.

TABLE 4.7-5   Computational Procedures for Polynomial Equations

(i)

$$\overline{X} = \frac{\sum\limits_{1}^{N} BS}{N} = \frac{172}{32} = 5.375$$

$$b' = \frac{B_1}{n\sum\limits_{1}^{k} c_1^2} = \frac{172}{8(20)} = 1.075 \qquad c_{1j} = \text{linear coefficient for treatment}$$
$$\text{level } b_j. \text{ For } b_1, c_{11} = -3$$
$$\text{(see Table 4.7-1).}$$

$$c' = \frac{B_2}{n\sum\limits_{1}^{k} c_2^2} = \frac{16}{8(4)} = .500 \qquad c_{2j} = \text{quadratic coefficient for treatment}$$
$$\text{level } b_j. \text{ For } b_1, c_{21} = +1.$$

$$d' = \frac{B_3}{n\sum\limits_{1}^{k} c_3^2} = \frac{-16}{8(20)} = -.100 \qquad c_{3j} = \text{cubic coefficient for treatment}$$
$$\text{level } b_j. \text{ For } b_1, c_{31} = -1.$$

(ii)

Predicted X for treatment b_1 by linear equation:

$$X_1 = \overline{X} + b'c_{11} = 5.375 + 1.075(-3) = 2.15.$$

Predicted X for treatment b_1 by second-degree equation:

$$X_1 = \overline{X} + b'c_{11} + c'c_{21} = 5.375 + 1.075(-3) + .500(+1) = 2.65.$$

Predicted X for treatment b_1 by third-degree equation:

$$X_1 = \overline{X} + b'c_{11} + c'c_{21} + d'c_{31} = 5.375 + 1.075(-3) + .500(+1)$$
$$-.100(-1) = 2.75.$$

This is of little importance because the best description of a set of data is the *simplest* curve that most nearly fits the points. Any set of k means can be fitted with a curve of, at most, degree $k - 1$. If the reader refers to Table 4.2-1, he will note that the mean for treatment level $b_1 = 2.75$, which is the value predicted by the third-degree equation.

TESTING GOODNESS OF FIT

A fourth question that can be examined by trend-analysis procedures is whether or not the dependent means follow a trend that has been derived from the data. For example, if a second-degree equation has been fitted to the sleep-deprivation data, we can determine if the equation provides a satisfactory fit. Predicted values for treatment levels, $b_1, b_2, b_3,$ and b_4 were computed by means of the equation

$$X_{\text{predicted}} = \overline{X} + b'c_{1j} + c'c_{1j}.$$

A plot of the obtained and predicted values is shown in Figure 4.7-3. It is apparent from this figure that the quadratic equation seems to provide a good fit for the observed data. An F statistic can be used to determine if the predicted values provide a satisfactory fit for the pattern of the obtained values. Computational procedures for an F test for departure from patterns are shown in Table 4.7-6. Because $F_{obs} < F_{.05;1,28}$, it can be concluded that the second-degree equation provides a satisfactory fit for the data. The $F_{\text{departure from linearity}}$ test described earlier is a special case of the more general $F_{\text{departure from pattern}}$ test. When a set of data has been fitted by a linear equation, the two ratios yield identical F values.

TABLE 4.7-6   Computational Procedures for Determining if Patterns of X_{observed} and $X_{\text{predicted}}$ Are Different

	b_j	n_j	$\bar{X}_o$	X_p	$(\bar{X}_o - X_p)^2$	$n_j(\bar{X}_o - X_p)^2$
(i)						
	b_1	8	2.75	2.65	.01	.08
	b_2	8	3.50	3.80	.09	.72
	b_3	8	6.25	5.95	.09	.72
	b_4	8	9.00	9.10	.01	.08
					$\sum\limits_1^k = 1.60$	

(ii)

$$SS_{\text{dep from pattern}} = \sum_1^k n_j(\bar{X}_o - X_p)^2 = 1.60$$

$$MS_{\text{dep from pattern}} = \frac{SS_{\text{dep from pattern}}}{k - c} \qquad \text{where } c = \text{number of constants}$$
$$\text{(e.g., } \bar{X}, b', c') \text{ used to fit equation.}$$

$$= \frac{1.60}{4 - 3} = 1.60$$

$$F = \frac{MS_{\text{dep from pattern}}}{MS_{WG}} = \frac{1.60}{1.464} = 1.09$$

$$F_{.05;1,28} = 4.20$$

A POSTERIORI TREND ANALYSIS PROCEDURES

The trend tests described previously fall in the category of a priori or planned tests. If the experimenter wishes to engage in trend snooping, a test statistic that controls the error rate at α for the collection of trend tests should be used. Either Dunn's procedure, which divides the critical region among the trend tests, or Scheffé's method can be used for this purpose. If Dunn's procedure is used, the observed value of an F ratio is compared with $F_{\alpha/C;v_1,v_2}$, where C is the number of trend comparisons in the family. Before engaging in trend snooping, it must be ascertained that the F ratio for differences between groups is significant. That is, there must be a trend in the data.

4.8   MEASURES OF CORRELATION

In the previous section, procedures for determining if there is a trend in data were described. If a trend is present, an experimenter may want to determine the *strength* of the trend. Several measures of strength of association between independent and dependent variables are described below. If both independent (Y) and dependent (X) variables are numerical, a descriptive index of linear correlation is given by

$$r = \sqrt{\frac{SS_{lin}}{SS_{total}}}.$$

For the sleep-deprivation data summarized in Table 4.7-4, the $SS_{lin} = 184.9$ and $SS_{total} = 235.5$. The linear correlation between sleep deprivation and hand steadiness for the sample data is

$$r = \sqrt{\frac{184.9}{235.5}} = .89.$$

A measure that describes the curvilinear correlation for a sample is given by the correlation ratio

$$\eta = \sqrt{\frac{SS_{BG}}{SS_{total}}}.$$

It was concluded, on the basis of *a priori* testing procedures, that the trend of the sleep-deprivation data is curvilinear. Under these conditions, the correlation ratio provides a better index of relationship than r. The value of η for the data in Table 4.7-4 is

$$\eta = \sqrt{\frac{194.5}{235.5}} = .91.$$

Two useful estimates of strength of association between X and Y for a population are ρI (intraclass correlation) and ω^2 (proportion of variance in X accounted for by Y). Hays (1963, 513) points out that ρI and ω^2 are identical in general meaning. They provide estimates of total strength of association (linear as well as nonlinear) between X and Y when the independent variable is qualitative in character. Both ω^2 and ρI indicate the proportion of variance in X accounted for by specifying the Y treatment-level classification. ρI applies to the random-effects model and ω^2 to the fixed-effects model. (These models are described in Section 4.9.) ρI is given by

$$\hat{\rho I} = \frac{MS_{BG} - MS_{WG}}{MS_{BG} + (n - 1)MS_{WG}}.$$

ρI measures the extent to which observations within the same treatment level tend to be homogeneous relative to observations among different treatment levels. ρI is maximal when scores within each treatment level are identical and the scores differ only from level to level (Haggard, 1958). The computation of ρI is discussed in greater detail in Section 7.8. The measure ω^2, which has been described by Hays (1963, 325), is given by

$$\hat{\omega}^2 = \frac{SS_{BG} - (k - 1)MS_{WG}}{SS_{total} + MS_{WG}}.$$

Examples illustrating the computation of $\hat{\omega}^2$ appear in Sections 5.2 and 7.8.

A significant F ratio for treatment effects in a completely randomized design indicates that there is an association between X and Y. ω^2 and ρI are measures that indicate the strength of the association. This is an important bit of information in evaluating the outcome of an experiment because a *trivial* association among means may achieve statistical significance if the sample is sufficiently large. An alternative method of interpreting the importance of sources of variation is in terms of variance components. This approach is discussed in Section 5.2. It cannot be emphasized too much that an F ratio only provides information concerning the probability that effects are or are not equal to zero. An F ratio does not tell us whether effects are large or small. This latter information is provided by an examination of variance components.

4.9   FIXED-EFFECTS AND RANDOM-EFFECTS MODELS

The structural model underlying the completely randomized design was defined in Section 4.4 as

$$X_{ij} = \mu + \beta_j + \varepsilon_{i(j)}.$$

For both the fixed-effects and the random-effects models, the term μ is a constant for all observations and $\varepsilon_{i(j)}$ is assumed to be normally and independently distributed with mean $= 0$ and variance $= \sigma_\varepsilon^2$. In the fixed-effects model, also called Model I, the k treatment levels are not randomly selected. Thus β_j is a fixed quantity and not a random variable. For this type of experiment, all treatment levels about which inferences are to be made are included in the experiment. If the experimenter were to replicate the experiment, he would include the same treatment levels. Model I is generally more appropriate for type CR-k designs than the model described in the following paragraph.

If the k treatment levels are drawn at random from a population of K levels, where K is large relative to k, the treatment (B) may be regarded as a random variable with mean $= 0$ and variance $= \sigma_B^2$. This case is designated as the random-effects model, or Model II. In the random-effects model, the inclusion or exclusion of a given treatment level in the experiment depends on random sampling. Under these conditions, inferences about the K treatment levels may be made, although only k treatment levels were included in the experiment.

A third model is possible for experimental designs described in later chapters. If the levels of some factors have been randomly selected and those of others have not, the analysis of variance model is referred to as a mixed model, or Model III.

The expected values of the mean square (MS) for Models I and II are shown in Table 4.9-1. The derivation of E(MS) is described in Section 2.4. If k is small relative to K, the coefficient $1 - k/K$ approaches 1.0 and the $\text{E(MS}_{\text{BG}})$ becomes $\sigma_\varepsilon^2 + n\sigma_B^2$. For both models the appropriate test of the hypothesis that the treatment effects equal zero is given by $F = \text{MS}_{\text{BG}}/\text{MS}_{\text{WG}}$. This ratio may be described as

$$F = \frac{\text{MS}_{\text{BG}}}{\text{MS}_{\text{WG}}} = \frac{\text{error term} + \text{treatment effects}}{\text{error term}},$$

in which there are two independent estimates of the error term. For the type CR-k design, the F ratio for both Model I and Model II is composed of the same MS terms. This will not be the case for more complex designs.

TABLE 4.9-1   Comparison of E(MS) for Models I and II

Source	MS	Model I E(MS)	Model II E(MS)
Between groups	MS_{BG}	$\sigma_\varepsilon^2 + n\sigma_\beta^2$	$\sigma_\varepsilon^2 + n(1 - k/K)\sigma_B^2$
Within groups	MS_{WG}	σ_ε^2	σ_ε^2

The above ratio illustrates a basic principle. The numerator of an F ratio should always contain one term in addition to the expected value terms in the denominator. The MS_{BG} is an unbiased estimate of σ_ε^2, the error variance, plus a term that will equal zero only if there are no treatment effects. If the hypothesis of no treatment effects is true, $\text{E(MS}_{\text{BG}}) = \sigma_\varepsilon^2$. If any treatment effect exists, then $\text{E(MS}_{\text{BG}}) > \sigma_\varepsilon^2$. For an elementary discussion of the expected value of a continuous random variable and the derivation of expectations of mean squares, the reader is referred to Edwards (1964) and Hays (1963). If the F ratio is 1.0, it may be concluded that there are no treatment effects. If the ratio exceeds the tabled value for $F_{\alpha;\nu_1,\nu_2}$, it may be concluded that the variability between treatment levels is greater than the pooled variability within treatment levels. Thus at least one of the treatment levels that has been administered to subjects has had a differential effect.

4.10   ADVANTAGES AND DISADVANTAGES OF TYPE CR-k DESIGN

The major advantages of the completely randomized design are

1. Simplicity in layout of the design.

2. Statistical analysis and interpretation of results are straightforward.

3. Does not require the use of equal sample sizes for each treatment level.

4. Allows for the maximum number of degrees of freedom for the error sum of squares.

5. Does not require a subject to participate under more than one treatment level or the use of subjects who have been matched on an appropriate variable.

The major disadvantages of the design are

1. Effects of differences among subjects are *controlled* by random assignment of the subjects to treatment levels. For this to be effective, subjects should be relatively homogeneous or a large number of subjects should be used.

2. When many treatment levels are included in the experiment, the required sample size may be prohibitive.

3. It does not offer the possibility of evaluating interaction effects.

4.11   REPRESENTATIVE APPLICATIONS OF COMPLETELY RANDOMIZED DESIGNS IN THE RESEARCH LITERATURE

In order to comprehend better the way in which completely randomized designs are used in research, the reader should consult the contemporary literature in his field. The following references represent a broad sampling of applications of type CR-k designs.

Adams, Jack A., and Lyle R. Creamer. Anticipatory timing of continuous and discrete responses. *Journal of Experimental Psychology*, 1962, **63**, 84–90. Type CR-3 and CR-4 designs.

Anderson, Richard C. Failure imagery in the fantasy of eighth graders as a function of three conditions of induced arousal. *Journal of Educational Psychology*, 1962, **53**, 293–298. Type CR-3 design.

Hinrichs, John R. The attitudes of research chemists. *Journal of Applied Psychology*, 1964, **48**, 287–293. Type CR-10 design.

McConville, C. B., and J. K. Hemphill. Some effects of communication restraints on problem-solving behavior. *Journal of Social Psychology*, 1966, **69**, 265–276. Type CR-3 design.

Parsons, Oscar A., Harriet I. Maslow, Freda Morris, and J. Peter Denny. Trail-making test performance in relation to certain experimenter, test, and subject variables. *Perceptual and Motor Skills*, 1964, **19**, 199–206. Type CR-4 design.

Rosenthal, Robert, Gordon W. Persinger, Linda Vikan-Kline, and Kermit L. Fode. The effect of early data returns on data subsequently obtained by outcome-biased experimenters. *Sociometry*, 1963, **26**, 487–498. Type CR-3 design.

Sechrest, Lee, and John Wallace. Assimilation and utilization of information in concept attainment under varying conditions of information presentation. *Journal of Educational Psychology*, 1962, **53**, 157–164. Type CR-4 and CR-6 designs.

5 / RANDOMIZED BLOCK DESIGN

5.1 DESCRIPTION OF DESIGN

In behavioral research, variability among subjects may mask or obscure treatment effects of interest to an experimenter. This nuisance variable of individual differences can be minimized by the use of a randomized block design. This design is designated as a *type RB-k design*, where k stands for the number of treatment levels. A randomized block design is appropriate for experiments that meet, in addition to the general assumptions of analysis of variance, the following three conditions:

1. One treatment with k = two or more treatment levels.
2. Assignment of subjects to blocks so that the variability among subjects within any block is less than the variability among the blocks. The number of subjects and observations within each block must be equal.
3. Random assignment of treatment levels to the experimental units within each block. An exception is made to this randomization procedure when a block consists of one subject who receives all treatment levels and when the nature of the treatment precludes randomization of order.

Homogeneity within blocks may be achieved by (1) use of litter mates or identical twins, (2) use of tests to match subjects on relevant variables, and (3) use of a subject as his own control. If blocks are composed of litter mates or identical twins, homogeneity is achieved with respect to genetic characteristics. It can be assumed that the behavior of subjects having identical or similar heredities will be more homogeneous than the behavior of subjects having dissimilar heredities. One alternative is to match subjects on the basis of a variable that correlates with the dependent variable in the investigation. This procedure often requires a relatively large pool of subjects in order to achieve precision in matching. Another alternative is to have each subject participate under all of the treatment levels. The last-named alternative is appropriate if it can be assumed that a subject is the same when each treatment level is presented as he was at previous administrations of the treatment. The use of repeated measures on the same subject is desirable in some research areas, for example, learning and fatigue experiments.

If the variation among experimental units within blocks is appreciably smaller than the variation among blocks, a randomized block design is more powerful than a completely randomized design.

5.2   LAYOUT OF DESIGN

Assume that an experimenter wants to evaluate the relative merits of four versions of an instrument used to display altitude in a helicopter. Eight helicopter pilots with from 500 to 3,000 flight hours are available to serve as subjects. Accuracy in reading the altimeter at low altitudes is of prime importance, so the dependent variable is designated as amount of reading error. It is anticipated that the amount of previous flying time of the pilots may affect their performance with the experimental altimeters. In order to isolate the nuisance variable of previous flying experience, a type RB-4 design with repeated measures is used. Each subject makes 100 readings under simulated flight conditions with each experimental altimeter. The average of each pilot's reading errors comprise the data subjected to statistical analysis. The sequence in which the four altimeters are presented in the experiment is randomized independently for each subject. The following statistical hypotheses are advanced:

$$H_0 : \beta_j = 0 \qquad \text{for all } j$$

$$H_1 : \beta_j \neq 0 \qquad \text{for some } j.$$

The level of significance adopted for this test is .05. The data and analysis procedures appear in Table 5.2-1. The following notation is used in the table:

k levels of treatment (b_j), where $k = 4$.

n levels of blocks (s_i), where $n = 8$.

$$\sum_1^N = \sum_1^k \sum_1^n .$$

The results of the analysis are summarized in Table 5.2-2. It is evident from Table 5.2-2 that differences in reading errors are associated with the four altimeters. Differences among the blocks are not significant. The nonsignificant block mean square indicates that the variability between observations within each block is not appreciably smaller than the variation between blocks. Thus previous flying experience of the pilots does not affect their performance with the experimental altimeters. Under these conditions, little advantage has been gained by isolating that portion of the total variance due to block variation. Expected values of the mean squares for the fixed-effects model appear in the last column of Table 5.2-2. In this example, pilots are not considered to be a random sample from a population of pilots. Therefore conclusions with respect to the four

TABLE 5.2-1   Layout of Type RB-4 Design and Computational Procedures

(i) Data:

BS Summary Table

	b_1	b_2	b_3	b_4	$\sum\limits_1^k S$	$\dfrac{\left(\sum\limits_1^k S\right)^2}{k}$
s_1	3	7	4	7	21	110.25
s_2	6	8	5	8	27	182.25
s_3	3	7	4	9	23	132.25
s_4	3	6	3	8	20	100.00
s_5	1	5	2	10	18	81.00
s_6	2	6	3	10	21	110.25
s_7	2	5	4	9	20	100.00
s_8	2	6	3	11	22	121.00
$\sum\limits_1^n B =$	22	50	28	72		
$\dfrac{\left(\sum\limits_1^n B\right)^2}{n} =$	60.5	312.5	98.0	648.0		

(ii) Computational symbols:

$$\sum_1^N BS = 3 + 6 + 3 + \cdots + 11 = 172.0$$

$$\sum_1^N BS^2 = [BS] = (3)^2 + (6)^2 + (3)^2 + \cdots + (11)^2 = 1160.0$$

$$\frac{\left(\sum\limits_1^N BS\right)^2}{N} = [X] = \frac{(172)^2}{32} = 924.5$$

$$\sum_1^k \frac{\left(\sum\limits_1^n B\right)^2}{n} = [B] = 60.5 + 312.5 + \cdots + 648.0 = 1119.0$$

$$\sum_1^n \frac{\left(\sum\limits_1^k S\right)^2}{k} = [S] = 110.25 + 182.25 + \cdots + 121.00 = 937.0$$

(iii) Computational formulas:

$$SS_{total} = [BS] - [X] = 1160.0 - 924.5 = 235.5$$
$$SS_B = [B] - [X] = 1119.0 - 924.5 = 194.5$$
$$SS_S = [S] - [X] = 937.0 - 924.5 = 12.5$$
$$SS_{res} = [BS] - [B] - [S] + [X] = 1160.0 - 1119.0 - 937.0 + 924.5 = 28.5$$

altimeters are applicable only to the previous flying experiences represented by the eight pilots used in the experiment. In practice, an experimenter would rarely ever employ a fixed-effects model with a randomized block design. The nature of the conclusions that can be drawn when either a mixed or a random-effects model is assumed to be appropriate for the experiment is described in Section 5.3.

TABLE 5.2-2   Analysis of Variance Table

Source	SS	df	MS	F	E(MS) Model I
1 Between treatments (B)	194.5	$k - 1 = 3$	64.833	$[\frac{1}{3}] = 47.78^*$	$\sigma_\varepsilon^2 + n\sigma_\beta^2$
2 Between blocks (S)	12.5	$n - 1 = 7$	1.786	$[\frac{2}{3}] = 1.32$	$\sigma_\varepsilon^2 + k\sigma_\pi^2$
3 Residual	28.5	$(k - 1)(n - 1) = 21$	1.357		σ_ε^2
4 Total	235.5	$N - 1 = 31$			

$^*p < .01$.

POWER OF THE ANALYSIS OF VARIANCE F TEST

Procedures for calculating power and determining the number of subjects necessary to achieve a specified power are described in Sections 1.3, 1.5, and 4.5. These procedures generalize directly to a randomized block design. However, instead of entering Table D.14 with $v_2 = kn - k$, the degrees of freedom are equal to $(k - 1)(n - 1)$.

ESTIMATES OF STRENGTH OF ASSOCIATION AND VARIANCE COMPONENTS

We noted in Section 4.8 that a significant F for treatment effects indicates that there is an association between the independent and dependent variables. An index of strength of association for a fixed-effects model when the independent variable is qualitative in character is given by

$$\hat{\omega}^2 = \frac{SS_B - (k - 1)MS_{res}}{SS_{total} + MS_{res}}.$$

For the data in Table 5.2-2, $\hat{\omega}^2$ equals

$$\hat{\omega}^2 = \frac{194.5 - (4 - 1)1.357}{235.5 + 1.357} = .80.$$

This statistic indicates that the association between independent and dependent variables is very strong. The independent variable (type of altimeter) is estimated to account for 80 percent of the variance in the dependent variable (error in reading altimeter). An alternative approach to evaluating the importance of sources of variation is in terms of variance components. An estimate of σ_β^2, the variance of the means of the four treatment populations, is given by

$$\hat{\sigma}_\beta^2 = \frac{MS_B - MS_{res}}{n} = \frac{64.833 - 1.357}{8} = 7.93.$$

The rationale underlying the above formula for $\hat{\sigma}_\beta^2$ can be understood in terms of the E(MS) for MS_B and MS_{res} shown in Table 5.2-2.

$$\frac{E(MS_B - MS_{res})}{n} = \frac{[(\sigma_\varepsilon^2 + n\sigma_\beta^2) - \sigma_\varepsilon^2]}{n} = \frac{n\sigma_\beta^2}{n} = \sigma_\beta^2.$$

The expected values of the mean squares determine the formula for estimating a variance component. According to the analysis, $\hat{\sigma}_\beta^2$ is approximately six times larger than $\hat{\sigma}_\varepsilon^2 = 1.357$. If an estimate of a variance component is negative, the value is taken to be zero. Variance components cannot be negative, although such estimates may occur as a result of chance sampling error. An estimate of σ_π^2 is given by

$$\hat{\sigma}_\pi^2 = \frac{MS_S - MS_{res}}{k} = \frac{1.786 - 1.357}{4} = .11.$$

The small size of the block variation that represents individual differences is unusual. This can be attributed to the artificial nature of the data. In this example, $\hat{\sigma}_\beta^2$ is 72 times larger than $\hat{\sigma}_\pi^2$.

In Section 4.8 we noted that an F ratio provides no information concerning the size of effects, only whether they are significant. Trivial effects can achieve statistical significance if the sample is sufficiently large. Thus interpretation of research results in terms of $\hat{\omega}^2$ or variance components is an important adjunct to significance tests.

Having determined that the mean square for treatment effects is significant, the next step in the analysis procedure is to determine which contrasts among means are significant. Before describing these procedures, we shall discuss assumptions that underlie the type RB-k design.

5.3   ASSUMPTIONS OF THE MODEL FOR TYPE RB-k DESIGN

Let X_{ij} be a measure for a randomly selected observation in treatment population j and block i. Under the fixed-effects model, it is assumed that measurement X_{ij} is equal to the sum of four terms:

$$X_{ij} = \mu + \beta_j + \pi_i + \varepsilon_{ij},$$

where μ = grand mean of treatment populations, which is a constant for all observations.

β_j = effect of treatment j, which is a constant for all observations within treatment population j, $\Sigma_{j=1}^k \beta_j = 0$.

π_i = a constant associated with block i, $\Sigma_{i=1}^n \pi_i = 0$.

ε_{ij} = experimental error, which is independent of other ε's and is normally distributed within each treatment population with mean = 0 and variance = σ_ε^2.

The F ratios in Table 5.2-2, assuming a fixed-effects model, are distributed as the F distribution under the conditions that (1) the observations in the kn cells constitute random samples of size 1 from each kn population, (2) all kn populations are normally distributed, (3) variances of each of the kn populations are equal, and (4) block and treatment effects are additive; that is, the scores within each block have the same trend with respect to the treatment levels. If this last condition obtains, block and treatment effects are said not to interact. Absence of interaction between block and treatment effects implies that the covariances $(\rho\sigma_{jj'}^2)$ between all pairs of treatment levels are equal. That is,

$$\rho\sigma_{12}^2 = \rho\sigma_{13}^2 = \cdots = \rho\sigma_{k-1,k}^2.$$

It may help, in understanding this point, to refer to Table 5.2-1. Upon reflection it should be evident that if each of the eight scores in Table 5.2-1(i) is changed by X amount from b_1 to b_2, by X' amount from b_2 to b_3, and by X'' amount from b_3 to b_4, the correlation coefficients $(\rho_{jj'}$'s) would be equal and the variances $(\sigma_j^2$'s) would be equal for all pairs of treatment levels. If interaction between block and treatment effects is present, the covariances may be heterogeneous. In summary, a randomized block design requires a highly restrictive assumption, one that was not required for a type CR-k design, namely, that the population covariances for all pairs of treatment levels are homogeneous. This assumption is more likely to be tenable if a block contains q matched subjects rather than q observations on the same subject. Some of the implications of the above assumptions, and procedures for evaluating them, are described in subsequent paragraphs.

F RATIO FOR FIXED-EFFECTS MODEL

For the fixed-effects model, the expected values of mean squares and F ratios are given in Table 5.2-2. Conclusions concerning the treatment effects in this model are restricted to the particular treatment levels and blocks used in the experiment. If the treatment and block effects are not additive, the F tests for treatment effects and block effects are negatively biased. Under this condition, the denominator of the F ratio includes both random error and the interaction of treatment levels with blocks. That is,

$$\mathrm{E}(F) = \frac{\mathrm{E}(MS_B)}{\mathrm{E}(MS_{res})} = \frac{\sigma_\varepsilon^2 + n\sigma_\beta^2}{\sigma_\varepsilon^2 + \sigma_{\beta\pi}^2}, \qquad \mathrm{E}(F) = \frac{\mathrm{E}(MS_S)}{\mathrm{E}(MS_{res})} = \frac{\sigma_\varepsilon^2 + k\sigma_\pi^2}{\sigma_\varepsilon^2 + \sigma_{\beta\pi}^2}.$$

It will be recalled from the discussion in Section 4.9 that the expectation of the numerator MS of an F ratio should contain one more term than the expectation for the denominator MS.

A test of block effects in the randomized block design is rarely of interest because these effects represent a nuisance variable that is to be minimized in the evaluation of the treatment effects.

MIXED AND RANDOM-EFFECTS MODELS

In the altimeter-evaluation example, the eight blocks (previous flying time) did not represent a random sample from a population of blocks. If the subjects (S_i's) comprising the blocks are considered a random sample from a population of subjects, while the treatment levels are fixed, the model is a mixed model. Under these conditions, the random variable s_i is assumed to be normally distributed with mean = 0 and variance = σ_S^2. It is not necessary to assume that the block and treatment effects are additive in order to test the treatment effects in the mixed model. This is apparent from an examination of the expected values of MS_B, MS_S, and MS_{res} shown below. If the block and treatment effects are not additive, the interaction component $\sigma_{\beta S}^2$ appears in both the numerator and denominator of MS_B/MS_{res} but only in the denominator of MS_S/MS_{res}. The F ratios for blocks and treatment effects under the mixed model are given by

$$\mathrm{E}(F) = \frac{\mathrm{E}(MS_S)}{\mathrm{E}(MS_{res})} = \frac{\sigma_\varepsilon^2 + k\sigma_S^2}{\sigma_\varepsilon^2 + \sigma_{\beta S}^2}, \qquad \mathrm{E}(F) = \frac{\mathrm{E}(MS_B)}{\mathrm{E}(MS_{res})} = \frac{\sigma_\varepsilon^2 + \sigma_{\beta S}^2 + n\sigma_\beta^2}{\sigma_\varepsilon^2 + \sigma_{\beta S}^2}.$$

It is evident that the F ratio for treatment effects has the required form. The F test for block effects is negatively biased. If $\sigma_{\beta S} = 0$, the E(MS) for blocks and treatment levels are the same as those shown in Table 5.2-2 for the fixed-effects model. For the mixed model, conclusions can be generalized to the population from which the blocks were sampled.

If the treatment levels also represent a random sample from a population of treatment levels, the model is a random-effects model. Then b_j is also assumed to be normally distributed with mean = 0 and variance = σ_B^2. For this model, the F ratios for block and treatment effects are given by

$$\mathrm{E}(F) = \frac{\mathrm{E}(MS_S)}{\mathrm{E}(MS_{res})} = \frac{\sigma_\varepsilon^2 + \sigma_{BS}^2 + k\sigma_S^2}{\sigma_\varepsilon^2 + \sigma_{BS}^2},$$

$$\mathrm{E}(F) = \frac{\mathrm{E}(MS_B)}{\mathrm{E}(MS_{res})} = \frac{\sigma_\varepsilon^2 + \sigma_{BS}^2 + n\sigma_B^2}{\sigma_\varepsilon^2 + \sigma_{BS}^2}.$$

Conclusions with respect to treatment effects in the random-effects model can be generalized to the populations of treatment levels and blocks. In the fixed-effects and mixed models described previously, conclusions are valid only for the particular treatment levels employed in the experiment.

TEST FOR ADDITIVITY OF BLOCK AND TREATMENT EFFECTS

One of the assumptions of the fixed-effects model described earlier is that the block and treatment effects are additive. That is, the interaction of β and π equals zero. A test developed by Tukey (1949b) provides a means for evaluating this interaction. This test is sensitive to only one source of nonadditivity—the linear by linear component of the interaction. Nevertheless, the test is useful in experiments having one score per cell. In such designs there is no *within-cell* error term, and a residual is used as an estimate of experimental error. If the test for nonadditivity is insignificant, it lends credence to the assumption that MS_{res} is an estimate of σ_{ε}^2 and not of $\sigma_{\varepsilon}^2 + \sigma_{\beta\pi}^2$. Computational procedures for the test of nonadditivity are shown in Table 5.3-1.

It is evident from Table 5.3-1 that the interaction of treatment levels with blocks is significant, in which case a test of differences among treatment levels is negatively biased. If a significant F ratio for treatment effects is obtained, one can be confident that there are differences among the means. If an insignificant F value is obtained, it may be due to (1) the negative bias in the test or (2) the population means may, in fact, be equal.

TABLE 5.3-1 Test for Nonadditivity

(i) Data:

BS Summary Table

	b_1	b_2	b_3	b_4	$\sum_{1}^{k} S_{ij}$	$\bar{S}_i$	$d_i = \bar{S}_i - \overline{BS}$
S_1	3	7	4	7	21	5.25	$-.125$
S_2	6	8	5	8	27	6.75	1.375
S_3	3	7	4	9	23	5.75	.375
S_4	3	6	3	8	20	5.00	$-.375$
S_5	1	5	2	10	18	4.50	$-.875$
S_6	2	6	3	10	21	5.25	$-.125$
S_7	2	5	4	9	20	5.00	$-.375$
S_8	2	6	3	11	22	5.50	.125

$\sum_{1}^{n} B_{ij} =$ 22   50   28   72 $\sum_{1}^{N} BS = 172$

$\bar{B}_j =$ 2.75   6.25   3.50   9.00 $\overline{BS} = \dfrac{172}{32} = 5.375$

$d_j = \bar{B}_j - \overline{BS} =$ -2.625 .875 -1.875 3.625

(ii)

$d_i \times d_j$ Summary Table*

	b_1	b_2	b_3	b_4
S_1	.328125	$-.109375$	.234375	$-.453125$
S_2	-3.609375	1.203125	-2.578125	4.984375
S_3	$-.984375$	.328125	$-.703125$	1.359375
S_4	.984375	$-.328125$	.703125	-1.359375
S_5	2.296875	$-.765625$	1.640625	-3.171875
S_6	.328125	$-.109375$	.234375	$-.453125$
S_7	.984375	$-.328125$	.703125	-1.359375
S_8	$-.328125$	.109375	$-.234375$	.453125

* Entries in this table are product of $d_i \times d_j$; for example, $(d_{.1})(d_{.1}) = (-.125)(-2.625) = .328125$, $(d_{.2})(d_{.1}) = (1.375)(-2.625) = -3.609375$.

TABLE 5.3-1 (continued)

(iii) Computational formulas:

$$SS_{nonadd} = \frac{(\Sigma\Sigma d_{ij}BS_{ji})^2}{(\Sigma d_i^2)(\Sigma d_j^2)} = \frac{[(.328)(3) + (-.109)(7) + \cdots + (.453)(11)]^2}{[(-.125)^2 + \cdots + (.125)^2][(-2.625)^2 + \cdots + (3.625)^2]}$$

$$= \frac{(-24.6875)^2}{(3.1250)(24.3125)} = \frac{609.4727}{75.9766} = 8.02$$

$$SS_{remainder} = SS_{res} - SS_{nonadd} = 28.5 - 8.02 = 20.48$$

$$df_{nonadd} = 1$$

$$df_{rem} = df_{res} - 1 = 21 - 1 = 20$$

$$F_{nonadd} = \frac{SS_{nonadd}/df_{nonadd}}{SS_{rem}/df_{rem}} = \frac{8.02/1}{20.48/20} = \frac{8.02}{1.02} = 7.86$$

$$F_{.25;1,20} = 1.40$$

(iv) Computational checks:

$$\Sigma\Sigma(d_{ij})^2 = (\Sigma d_i^2)(\Sigma d_j^2)$$

$$\Sigma\Sigma(d_{ij})^2 = (.328)^2 + (-3.609)^2 + \cdots + (.453)^2 = 75.9766$$

$$(\Sigma d_i^2)(\Sigma d_j^2) = (3.1250)(24.3125) = 75.9766$$

$$(n)(k)(\Sigma d_i^2)(\Sigma d_j^2) = (SS_S)(SS_B)$$

$$(n)(k)(\Sigma d_i^2)(\Sigma d_j^2) = (8)(4)(3.1250)(24.3125) = 2431.25$$

$$(SS_S)(SS_B) = (12.5)(194.5) = 2431.25$$

The presence of a block × treatment interaction poses an additional interpretation problem for an experimenter. This interaction is a signal to an experimenter that the effects of a treatment cannot be described for n blocks of subjects as a whole but instead must be described individually for each block. In other words, an experimenter cannot draw the same conclusions regarding treatment levels for all blocks.

The level of significance ($\alpha = .25$) adopted for the F_{nonadd} test reflects a willingness to commit a type I error rather than a type II error. The use of a numerically large probability value (low level of significance) will result in an experimenter erring in the direction of rejecting the hypothesis that $\sigma_{\beta\pi}^2 = 0$. When, as in the present example, the interaction of blocks and treatment levels is significant, a transformation that will remove the interaction may be found.

TEST FOR SYMMETRY OF VARIANCE-COVARIANCE MATRIX

One of the assumptions underlying the model for a type RB-k design is that the population covariances ($\rho\sigma_{jj'}^2$) between pairs of treatment levels are constant; that is, $\rho\sigma_{12}^2 = \rho\sigma_{13}^2 = \ldots = \rho\sigma_{k-1,k}^2$. If blocks are composed of matched subjects or litter mates, it is reasonable to assume that the covariances are equal. It is also assumed that the population variances (σ_j^2) for each of the j treatment levels are homogeneous; that is, $\sigma_1^2 = \sigma_2^2 = \cdots = \sigma_k^2$. If these assumptions are true, the data can be described by the following variance-covariance matrix:

$$
\begin{array}{c}
 \\
b_1 \\
b_2 \\
b_3 \\
b_4
\end{array}
\begin{array}{cccc}
b_1 & b_2 & b_3 & b_4
\end{array}
\left[
\begin{array}{cccc}
\sigma_1^2 & \rho\sigma_{12}^2 & \rho\sigma_{13}^2 & \rho\sigma_{14}^2 \\
\rho\sigma_{21}^2 & \sigma_2^2 & \rho\sigma_{23}^2 & \rho\sigma_{24}^2 \\
\rho\sigma_{31}^2 & \rho\sigma_{32}^2 & \sigma_3^2 & \rho\sigma_{34}^2 \\
\rho\sigma_{41}^2 & \rho\sigma_{42}^2 & \rho\sigma_{43}^2 & \sigma_4^2
\end{array}
\right]
$$

in which all σ_j^2's are equal and all $\rho\sigma_{jj'}^2$'s are equal. If, in an experiment, each block is composed of one subject who participates under all treatment levels, it is unlikely that all the covariances will be equal. A test of the assumption that the variance-covariance matrix has the form shown above is described by Box (1950). The formulas for this test are

$$\chi^2 = (1 - E)M$$

$$M = -(n - 1)\ln\frac{|S|}{|S_{\text{ave}}|}$$

$$E = \frac{k(k + 1)^2(2k - 3)}{6(n - 1)(k - 1)(k^2 + k - 4)},$$

where $|S|$ and $|S_{\text{ave}}|$ are the determinants of the S and S_{ave} matrices described below.

Under the assumption that the variance-covariance matrix has the required symmetry, χ^2 is approximately distributed as a chi-square distribution with degrees of freedom equal to

$$\text{df} = \frac{k^2 + k - 4}{2}.$$

The variance-covariance matrix and *average* matrix for the data in Table 5.2-1 appear in Table 5.3-2. The S matrix values in the table were computed by

$$\hat{\sigma}_j^2 = \frac{\sum_1^n B_{ij}^2 - \dfrac{\left(\sum_1^n B_{ij}\right)^2}{n}}{n - 1}$$

$$\rho\hat{\sigma}_{jj'}^2 = \frac{\sum_1^n B_{ij}B_{ij'} - \dfrac{\left(\sum_1^n B_{ij}\right)\left(\sum_1^n B_{ij'}\right)}{n}}{n - 1}.$$

For example,

$$\hat{\sigma}_1^2 = \frac{(3)^2 + (6)^2 + \cdots + (2)^2 - \dfrac{(22)^2}{8}}{8 - 1} = 2.214$$

$$\hat{\rho\sigma}^2_{12} = \frac{(3)(7) + (6)(8) + \cdots + (2)(6) - \dfrac{(22)(50)}{8}}{8 - 1} = 1.357.$$

The values on the main diagonal of the S_{ave} matrix are the average of the four main diagonal values in the S matrix. For example,

$$1.464 = \frac{2.214 + 1.071 + .857 + 1.714}{4}.$$

TABLE 5.3-2   Variance-Covariance Matrices Associated with Data in Table 5.2-1

		S					S_{ave}		
	b_1	b_2	b_3	b_4		b_1	b_2	b_3	b_4
b_1	2.214	1.357	1.143	-1.143	b_1	1.464	.107	.107	.107
b_2	1.357	1.071	.714	$-.714$	b_2	.107	1.464	.107	.107
b_3	1.143	.714	.857	$-.714$	b_3	.107	.107	1.464	.107
b_4	-1.143	$-.714$	$-.714$	1.714	b_4	.107	.107	.107	1.464

The off-diagonal values in the S_{ave} matrix are the average of the off-diagonal values in the S matrix. For example,

$$.107 = \frac{(1.357 + 1.143 + \cdots - .714)}{6}.$$

It should be noted that the six covariances above the main diagonal are duplicated below the main diagonal. The numerical values of the determinants are

$$|S| = .07419 \qquad |S_{ave}| = 4.4604.$$

When the number of treatment levels exceeds five or six, the amount of computation required to arrive at the values of the two determinants by means of a desk calculator becomes prohibitive. The required values are readily obtained with the aid of a computer.* The terms required to test the assumption of symmetry of the variance-covariance matrix are as follows:

$$E = \frac{4(4 + 1)^2 [(2)(4) - 3]}{6(8 - 1)(4 - 1)[(4)^2 + 4 - 4]} = \frac{500}{2016} = .2480$$

$$M = -(8 - 1)\ln\frac{.0742}{4.4604} = -(7)(-2.4889) = 17.4223$$

$$\chi^2 = (1 - .2480)17.4223 = 13.1016$$

---

*A discussion of determinants can be found in most college-algebra textbooks. An elementary introduction to matrices and determinants is given by DuBois (1965) and Searle (1966).

$$df = \frac{(4)^2 + 4 - 4}{2} = 8$$

$$\chi^2_{.05,8} = 15.5.$$

Because $\chi^2_{obs} > \chi^2_{.05,8}$, one concludes that the data depart from the re-quired symmetry.

Computation of MS_{res} by means of formula

$$MS_{res} = \frac{[BS] - [B] - [S] + [X]}{(k - 1)(n - 1)}$$

is convenient. However, this computational procedure does not provide any insight into what is actually pooled in estimating the population-error variance. It can be shown that

(1) $$MS_{res} = \text{ave } \hat{\sigma}^2_j - \text{ave } \hat{\rho\sigma}^2_{jj'}.$$

For example, the value of MS_{res} in Table 5.2-2 is equal to 1.357. The values of ave $\hat{\sigma}^2_j$ and ave $\hat{\rho\sigma}^2_{jj'}$ were computed for Box's test. These values are given in Table 5.3-2 (S_{ave}) and are equal to 1.464 and .107, respectively. According to equation (1),

$$1.357 = 1.464 - .107.$$

Thus MS_{res} is simply the average of the pooled k treatment level variances minus the average of the pooled $k(k - 1)/2$ covariances. This alternative computational formula ($MS_{res} = \text{ave } \hat{\sigma}^2_j - \text{ave } \hat{\rho\sigma}^2_{jj'}$) is inconvenient to use in practice, but it does clarify the nature of the sources that are pooled in estimating the population-error variance.

GEISSER-GREENHOUSE CONSERVATIVE F TEST

The procedures described in this section may be used if the test for symmetry of the variance-covariance matrix is significant. Box (1953) has shown that, for uncorrelated data, the F test is relatively insensitive to violation of the assumption of homogeneity of variance. However, hetero-geneity of both the variances and covariances in a design having repeated measures on the same subjects results in a positive bias in the F test. Using an exact multivariate approach, Box (1954b) found that the true distribution of the univariate F statistic with $(k - 1)$ and $(n - 1)(k - 1)$ degrees of freedom can be approximated by a conventional F statistic with reduced degrees of freedom. The modified degrees of freedom are $\theta(k - 1)$ and $\theta(n - 1)(k - 1)$, where θ is a number that depends on the amount of heterogeneity of the variances and covariances. When the variances are equal and the correlations are constant, the value of θ is one. For this case the univariate F ratio can be used to give the exact significance level of the treatment effects. Geisser and Greenhouse (1958) have shown that as heterogeneity increases, the value of θ decreases. The lowest value that θ can take is $1/(k - 1)$. When there is reason to question the homogeneity assumptions, they recommend a conservative F test in which θ is assumed to be $1/(k - 1)$. For this condition, the degrees of freedom for treatment and error terms are 1 and $n - 1$, respectively. Computational procedures for a conservative F test are identical to those of a conventional F test except that different degrees of freedom are used. If the F test for treatment effects is significant, with θ assumed to equal its lower bound, an experimenter can be certain that an exact test would also be significant. If, however, the conservative test is not significant, the experimenter should determine if a conventional test, in which θ is assumed to equal one, would have been significant. If the conventional test is also insignificant, the experimenter can decide not to reject the null hypothesis.

A problem arises when the conservative F test is insignificant but the conventional test is significant. Under these circumstances an experimenter can attempt to compute a sample estimate of θ or use an exact multivariate test such as Hotelling's T^2 statistic. Lana and Lubin (1963) recommend the latter approach. The procedures that have been described permit the experimenter to bracket the significance level of F with approximately the same amount of computation as required for a conventional F test. Computational procedures for Hotelling's exact multivariate analysis are described below.

HOTELLING'S T^2 TEST FOR EQUALITY OF MEANS

Experiments in which a subject is observed under several levels of a treatment may be analyzed by either univariate or multivariate analysis of variance procedures. If the assumptions of homogeneity of variances and homogeneity of covariances are fulfilled, a univariate analysis is preferable from the standpoint of computational labor. As was pointed out in the previous section, an approximate F test can be made even though the homogeneity assumptions of the univariate model are not fulfilled. However, when the conventional F test is significant but the conservative F test is insignificant, an exact test is required in making a decision regarding the null hypothesis. Hotelling's T^2 statistic provides such a test. This test does not require symmetry of the variance-covariance matrix. It assumes only that the populations have multivariate normal distributions. Hotelling's T^2 statistic is given by

$$T^2 = nB'S^{-1}B,$$

where $n =$ number of blocks.

$$
B = \begin{bmatrix}
\bar{B}._1 - \bar{B}.. \\
\bar{B}._2 - \bar{B}.. \\
\cdot \quad \cdot \\
\cdot \quad \cdot \\
\cdot \quad \cdot \\
\bar{B}._j - \bar{B}..
\end{bmatrix}.
$$

$S^{-1} =$ inverse of the variance-covariance matrix.

$B' =$ transpose of B.

The reader who is not familiar with the matrix operations listed above can find an elementary description in Horst (1963), Morrison (1967), and Searle (1966). The hypothesis of zero-treatment effects is rejected if

$$
T^2_{\text{obs}} > \frac{(n-1)k}{n-k} F_{\alpha;k,n-k}.
$$

Hotelling's test is illustrated for the data in Table 5.2-1.

$$
T^2 = 8[-2.625 + .875 - 1.875 + 3.625]
$$

$$
\begin{bmatrix}
3.2612 & -2.8317 & -1.7784 & .2543 \\
-2.8317 & 4.6164 & -.0620 & .0088 \\
-1.7784 & -.0620 & 3.9527 & .4347 \\
.2543 & .0088 & .4347 & .9378
\end{bmatrix}
\begin{bmatrix}
-2.625 \\
.875 \\
-1.875 \\
3.625
\end{bmatrix}
$$

$$
= 8(37.24) = 297.92.
$$

The value of T^2 that is significant at the .05 level is

$$
\frac{(8-1)4}{8-4}(6.39) = 44.73.
$$

Because $T^2_{\text{obs}} > [(n-1)k/(n-k)]F_{\alpha;k,n-k}$, the experimenter can conclude that at least one contrast among means is significant.

5.4   PROCEDURES FOR TESTING DIFFERENCES AMONG MEANS

Tests of differences among means in a type RB-k design have the same general form as those illustrated in Section 4.6 for a completely randomized design. Comparisons among the means in the two designs employ different error terms. Instead of using MS_{WG} in the denominator of the significance test, a randomized block design uses MS_{res} as the error term.

A priori t tests have the following form:

$$t = \frac{C_j(\bar{B}_j) + C_{j'}(\bar{B}_{j'})}{\sqrt{2MS_{res}/n}} \qquad df = (k - .1)(n - 1).$$

A posteriori tests as described by Tukey (1953) and Scheffé (1959) are given by

$$q = \frac{C_j(\bar{B}_j) + C_{j'}(\bar{B}_{j'})}{\sqrt{MS_{res}/n}} \qquad df = (k - 1)(n - 1)$$

and

$$F = \frac{[C_j(\bar{B}_j) + C_{j'}(\bar{B}_{j'})]^2}{MS_{res}\left[\dfrac{(C_j)^2}{n} + \dfrac{(C_{j'})^2}{n}\right]},$$

respectively. The value of F that is significant in Scheffé's test is

$$F' = (k - 1)F_{\alpha;k-1,(k-1)(n-1)}.$$

5.5   TESTS FOR TRENDS IN THE DATA

If the treatment levels in an experiment differ quantitatively, additional insight concerning the experiment may be obtained by the use of trend analysis. Procedures for carrying out trend analysis were described in Section 4.7 in connection with a completely randomized design. These procedures may be generalized to a randomized block design with one modification. This modification has to do with the choice of an error term. The error terms for testing MS_{lin}, MS_{quad}, and MS_{cubic} are, respectively,

$$MS_{res(lin)} = \frac{SS_{res} + (SS_S - SS_{lin})}{n(k - 1) - 1}$$

$$MS_{res(quad)} = \frac{SS_{res} + (SS_S - SS_{lin} - SS_{quad})}{n(k - 1) - 2}$$

$$MS_{res(cubic)} = \frac{SS_{res} + (SS_S - SS_{lin} - SS_{quad} - SS_{cubic})}{n(k - 1) - 3}.$$

The use of these error terms results in a slight negative bias in the test of significance. A simpler procedure is to use MS_{res} as the error term for all the tests. When the degrees of freedom for MS_{res} exceed 30, the two procedures give almost the same results.

5.6   ESTIMATING MISSING OBSERVATIONS

In the conduct of an experiment, one or more observations may be lost. If the observations are lost for reasons not related to the nature of the treatment used in the experiment, estimation procedures may be used to estimate the lost information. A common reason for losing observations is equipment malfunction. Analysis procedures for a randomized block design require that the number of observations in each block must equal k. Thus when missing data occur, they must be estimated in order to carry out the analysis.

Yates (1933) has described a procedure for estimating a missing observation. The formula is

$$BS_{ji} = \frac{n(\Sigma S_i) + k(\Sigma B_j) - \Sigma BS}{(n-1)(k-1)},$$

where n = number of blocks, k = number of treatment levels, ΣS_i = sum of remaining observations in the block which contains the missing observation, ΣB_j = sum of remaining observations in the treatment level which contains the missing observation, and ΣBS = sum of all available observations. If, for example, observation BS_{27} in Table 5.2-1 were missing, an estimate of the score can be obtained by

$$BS_{27} = \frac{8(15) + 4(45) - 167}{(8-1)(4-1)} = 6.3.$$

The estimate (6.3) is reasonably close to the original score, which is 5. The estimated score should be inserted in the data matrix and the analysis of variance performed according to procedures described in Section 5.2, but with one slight modification. The degrees of freedom for SS_{res} and SS_{total} must be reduced by one.

If more than one observation is missing, an experimenter can *guesstimate* the values for all but one of the missing observations; this one is computed by the above formula. The computed value is inserted in the data matrix, and another of the missing observations that was guesstimated is computed. This iterative process is repeated until the computed values for all the missing observations have become stabilized. Generally, three cycles of the procedure are sufficient for this purpose. For each estimated missing observation, one degree of freedom must be subtracted from the df for SS_{res} and SS_{total}.

Yates (1933) has shown that the use of the missing-score formula results in minimizing the error sum of squares. The analysis of variance is valid if the proportion of missing observations is not large. A slight positive bias is produced in the F test for treatment effects. An exact test may be obtained by procedures described by Federer (1951) and by Yates (1933). A numerical example illustrating a correction for bias is given by Snedecor (1956, 310).

A t ratio for contrasts involving a treatment level with one missing observation is given by

$$t = \frac{C_j(\bar{B}_j) + C_{j'}(\bar{B}_{j'})}{\sqrt{MS_{res}\left[\dfrac{2}{n} + \dfrac{k}{n(n-1)(k-1)}\right]}}.$$

If more than one observation has been estimated, the t ratio is given by

$$t = \frac{C_j(\bar{B}_j) + C_{j'}(\bar{B}_{j'})}{\sqrt{MS_{res}\left(\dfrac{1}{e_j} + \dfrac{1}{e_{j'}}\right)}},$$

where e_j and $e_{j'}$ correspond to the number of *effective* replications in each treatment. According to Taylor (1948), the value of e_j is computed for each block using the following rules:

Assign 1 if block contains a score for both e_j and $e_{j'}$.

Assign $(k-2)/(k-1)$ if block contains a score for e_j but not for $e_{j'}$.

Assign 0 if block does not contain a score for e_j.

Assume, for example, that the values in Table 5.2-1 for BS_{13} and BS_{27} are missing and that estimates for these scores have been made. The values of e_1 and e_2 required for the comparison of $\bar{B}_1$ with $\bar{B}_2$ are, respectively,

$$e_1 = 1 + 1 + 0 + 1 + 1 + 1 + \tfrac{2}{3} + 1 = 6\tfrac{2}{3}$$

$$e_2 = 1 + 1 + \tfrac{2}{3} + 1 + 1 + 1 + 0 + 1 = 6\tfrac{2}{3}.$$

5.7   RELATIVE EFFICIENCY OF RANDOMIZED BLOCK DESIGN

A randomized block design permits an experimenter to minimize the effects of individual differences by isolating that portion of the total variance due to blocks. As a result, the error term for testing the treatment mean square is free of the nuisance variable of individual differences. If the block effects are appreciably greater than zero, a randomized block design is more efficient than a completely randomized design. In the latter design, the error term (MS_{WG}) includes the effects due to individual differences. A measure of the relative efficiency of the two designs, ignoring differences in degrees of freedom, is given by

$$\text{Relative efficiency} = \frac{MS_{WG}}{MS_{res}},$$

where MS_{WG} for a completely randomized design is obtained from a randomized block analysis by

$$MS_{WG} = \frac{(n-1)MS_{blocks} + n(k-1)MS_{res}}{(nk-1)}.$$

For the altimeter example, the efficiency of the randomized block design relative to that of a completely randomized design is

$$MS_{WG} = \frac{(8-1)1.786 + 8(4-1)1.357}{(8)(4)-1} = 1.454$$

$$\text{Relative efficiency} = \frac{1.454}{1.357} \times 100 = 107 \text{ percent}.$$

A ratio greater than 100 percent indicates that the randomized block design is more efficient than the completely randomized design. A correction developed by Fisher (1935) for the smaller error degrees of freedom for a randomized block design is

$$\text{Relative efficiency} = \frac{(nk - n - k + 2)(nk - k + 3)}{(nk - n - k + 4)(nk - k + 1)} \cdot \frac{MS_{WG}}{MS_{res}}.$$

The corrected relative efficiency for the present data is

$$\frac{[(8)(4) - 8 - 4 + 2][(8)(4) - 4 + 3]}{[(8)(4) - 8 - 4 + 4][(8)(4) - 4 + 1]} \cdot \frac{1.454}{1.357} \times 100 = 105 \text{ percent}.$$

In this example, the relative efficiency of the randomized block design is not appreciably greater than that of a completely randomized design. The relative efficiency of a randomized block design depends on the degree to which variation between experimental units within blocks has been reduced relative to variation between blocks.

The number of subjects in a completely randomized design necessary to match the efficiency of a randomized block design is

$$m = (\text{relative efficiency}) \times (n) = 1.05(8) \simeq 9,$$

where m is the required number of subjects in each treatment level of a completely randomized design and n is the number of levels of blocks in a randomized block design.

Partitioning of the total variation and degrees of freedom for the two designs is shown in Figure 5.7-1. It is evident from this figure that the *residual error term* for a randomized block design will be smaller than the *within-groups error term* if the block effects are appreciably greater than zero. If the block effects are equal to zero, $SS_{WG} = SS_{res}$. In this case, the completely randomized design is *more efficient* than a randomized block design because the error term is based on a larger number of degrees of freedom, for example, $N - k$ as opposed to $(k - 1)(n - 1)$. The terms SS_{blocks} and SS_{res} in a type RB-k design can be *pooled* if the block effects are equal to zero. This results in $N - k$ degrees of freedom for the pooled error term. The general question of whether to pool or not to pool is discussed in Section 7.12. It should be apparent from this discussion

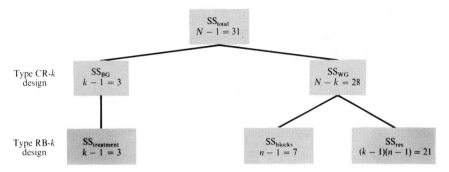

Figure 5.7-1 Schematic comparison of total variation and degrees of freedom for type CR-k and type RB-k designs.

that the block effects in a type RB-k design must account for a sizable portion of the total variance in order to compensate for the loss of $n - 1$ degrees of freedom in the MS_{res} error term. When an experimenter uses a randomized block design, he hopes that he will be compensated for the additional effort required to form homogeneous blocks by obtaining a smaller error term and hence greater power. The question as to whether or not the total experimental effort involved in using blocks of homogeneous subjects is less than the effort required to *run* a larger number of subjects in a completely randomized design should be raised for each proposed research project. Scarcity of subjects makes the use of a randomized block design attractive to experimenters in the behavioral sciences.

5.8   ADVANTAGES AND DISADVANTAGES OF TYPE RB-k DESIGN

The major advantages of the randomized block design are

1. Greater power relative to completely randomized design for many research applications. This design permits an experimenter to minimize the effects of individual differences.

2. Flexibility. Any number of treatment levels and blocks can be used in an experiment.

3. Simplicity in analysis of data.

The major disadvantages of the design are

1. If a large number of treatment levels are included in the experiment, it becomes difficult to form blocks having minimum within-block variability.

2. In the fixed-effects model, a test of treatment effects is negatively biased if $\beta\pi > 0$.

5.9 REPRESENTATIVE APPLICATIONS OF RANDOMIZED BLOCK DESIGNS IN THE RESEARCH LITERATURE

The following references illustrate a variety of applications of type RB-k designs.

Aborn, Murray, and Herbert Rubenstein. Information theory and immediate recall. *Journal of Experimental Psychology*, 1952, **44**, 260–266. Type RB-3 and RB-4 designs.

Barnwell, Franklin H. An angle sense in the orientation of a millipede. *The Biological Bulletin*, 1965, **128**, 33–50. Type RB-9 design.

Biggers, J. D., and R. L. Brinster. Biometrical problems in the study of early mammalian embryos in vitro. *The Journal of Experimental Zoology*, 1965, **158**, 39-47. Type RB-11 design.

Cullinan, Walter L. Stability of adaptation in the oral performance of stutterers. *Journal of Speech and Hearing Research*, 1963, **6**, 70–83. Type RB-3 design.

Rabedeau, Ronald, and Raymond C. Miles. Response decrement in visual exploratory behavior. *Journal of Comparative and Physiological Psychology*, 1959, **52**, 364–367. Type RB-6 design.

Smith, Leon E., and Jim D. Whitley. Faster reaction time through facilitation of neuromuscular junctional transmission in muscles under maximal stretch. *Perceptual and Motor Skills*, 1964, **19**, 503–509. Type RB-5 design.

Warm, Joel S., Lewis F. Greenberg, and C. Stuart Dube II. Stimulus and motivational determinants in temporal perception. *Journal of Psychology*, 1964, **58**, 243–248. Type RB-6 design.

6 / LATIN SQUARE AND RELATED DESIGNS

6.1 DESCRIPTION OF DESIGN

The Latin square design has not been used as extensively in behavioral research as the completely randomized or randomized block designs. Yet for some research applications, the Latin square design is considerably more efficient than the other two designs. For example, the design has been widely employed in agricultural research, and Cochran (1938, 1940b) reported that for a seven-year period the efficiency of this design relative to type CR-k and RB-k designs was 222 and 137 percent, respectively.

The Latin square design derives its name from an ancient puzzle, a puzzle that dealt with the number of different ways Latin letters could be arranged in a square table so that each letter appeared only once in each row and column. If three treatment levels are designated by the letters A, B, and C, one of twelve possible arrangements of a 3×3 Latin square is the following.

A	B	C
B	C	A
C	A	B

Note that each row and each column of the 3×3 square represents a complete replication of the three treatment levels.

A randomized block design permits an experimenter to minimize the effects of one nuisance variable (variation among rows) in evaluating treatment effects. A Latin square design extends this principle to two nuisance variables, variation due to rows and variation due to columns. This design, which is designated as a type LS-k design, is appropriate for experiments that meet, in addition to the general assumptions of the analysis of variance model, the following conditions:

1. One treatment with $p =$ two or more treatment levels. A Latin square design is not practical for $p < 5$ unless more than one observation is

obtained within each cell or unless several squares are combined in a factorial arrangement. This latter procedure is described in Chapters 9 and 10. Latin squares with fewer than five treatment levels are not practical because they provide too few degrees of freedom for experimental error.

2. It must be reasonable to assume that there are no interactions among the rows, columns, and treatment levels of the square. If this assumption is not fulfilled, a test of one or more of the corresponding effects is biased.

3. The number of treatment levels must equal the number of rows and columns. Achieving this balance may be difficult for squares larger than 8 × 8.

4. Random assignment of treatment levels to the experimental units within each row and column with the restriction that each treatment level must appear only once in a row and once in a column.

6.2 CONSTRUCTION AND RANDOMIZATION OF LATIN SQUARES

A discussion of the construction of Latin square designs and extensive tables of designs are given by Fisher and Yates (1963). The purpose of this section is to acquaint the reader with the basic terminology and randomization procedures employed with type LS-k designs.

A Latin square is said to be a *standard square* if the first row and the first column are ordered alphabetically or numerically. The following are examples of standard squares:

$A\ B$	$A\ B\ C$	$A\ B\ C\ D$	$A\ B\ C\ D$	$A\ B\ C\ D$	$A\ B\ C\ D$
$B\ A$	$B\ C\ A$	$B\ A\ D\ C$	$B\ C\ D\ A$	$B\ D\ A\ C$	$B\ A\ D\ C$
	$C\ A\ B$	$C\ D\ B\ A$	$C\ D\ A\ B$	$C\ A\ D\ B$	$C\ D\ A\ B$
		$D\ C\ A\ B$	$D\ A\ B\ C$	$D\ C\ B\ A$	$D\ C\ B\ A$
		(1)	(2)	(3)	(4)

2 × 2   3 × 3   4 × 4

$A\ B\ C\ D\ E$	$A\ B\ C\ D\ E$	$A\ B\ C\ D\ E\ F$
$B\ C\ D\ E\ A$	$B\ A\ E\ C\ D$	$B\ C\ F\ A\ D\ E$
$C\ D\ E\ A\ B$	$C\ D\ A\ E\ B$	$C\ F\ B\ E\ A\ D$
$D\ E\ A\ B\ C$	$D\ E\ B\ A\ C$	$D\ E\ A\ B\ F\ C$
$E\ A\ B\ C\ D$	$E\ C\ D\ B\ A$	$E\ A\ D\ F\ C\ B$
(1)	(2)	$F\ D\ E\ C\ B\ A$

      5 × 5   6 × 6

Two squares are *conjugate* if the rows of one are identical to the columns of another. The conjugate of square 5 × 5(2) is

$$A \quad B \quad C \quad D \quad E$$
$$B \quad A \quad D \quad E \quad C$$
$$C \quad E \quad A \quad B \quad D$$
$$D \quad C \quad E \quad A \quad B$$
$$E \quad D \quad B \quad C \quad A$$

A square is *self-conjugate* if the same square is obtained when the rows and columns are interchanged. For example, squares 2×2, 3×3, $4 \times 4(1, 2, 3, \text{ and } 4)$, and $5 \times 5(1)$ are self-conjugate because the same arrangement of Latin letters results from the interchanging of rows and columns. Squares $5 \times 5(2)$ and 6×6 are not self-conjugate. This is illustrated above for square $5 \times 5(2)$.

Latin squares of any size can be constructed by a *one-step cyclic permutation* of a sequence of letters. This process involves successively moving the first letter in the sequence to the extreme right and simultaneously moving all other letters one position to the left. For example, from the sequence *ABCD* a one-step cyclic permutation gives *BCDA*, a second cyclic permutation *CDAB*, and a third *DABC*. The fourth cyclic permutation gives the original starting sequence *ABCD*. The Latin square constructed from these $p - 1$ one-step cyclic permutations of the letters *ABCD* is

$$A \quad B \quad C \quad D$$
$$B \quad C \quad D \quad A$$
$$C \quad D \quad A \quad B$$
$$D \quad A \quad B \quad C$$

ENUMERATION OF LATIN SQUARES

The letters in a given Latin square can be rearranged so as to produce a total of $k![(k - 1)!]$ Latin squares, including the original square. Enumeration of Latin squares of size 7×7 and smaller has been made by Fisher and Yates (1934), Norton (1939), and Sade (1951). The number of possible arrangements of Latin squares is as follows:

2×2 *Latin square.* One standard square (self-conjugate) and one nonstandard square, which is obtained by interchanging either rows or columns of the standard square. Thus there is a total of two arrangements.

3×3 *Latin square.* One standard square (self-conjugate) and $(3!)(2!) = (3 \cdot 2 \cdot 1)(2 \cdot 1) = 12$ possible arrangements of this standard square.

4×4 *Latin square.* Four standard squares (all self-conjugate) with $(4!)(3!) = 144$ possible arrangements of each standard square. The total number of arrangements is equal to $4(144) = 576$.

5×5 *Latin square.* Twenty-five standard squares and their conjugates, plus 6 self-conjugate squares or 56 standard squares. The total number of possible arrangements is $56(5!)(4!) = 161,280$.

6×6 *Latin square.* 9408 standard squares with $9408(6!)(5!) = 812,851,200$ possible arrangements.

7 × 7 Latin square.   16,942,080 standard squares.

The number of possible standard squares increases sharply as the dimensions of the square increase.

RANDOMIZATION OF LATIN SQUARES

Rules for randomization of Latin squares have been described by Fisher and Yates (1963). Theoretically an experimenter who plans to use a Latin square design should randomly select a square from the population of all possible squares of the proper dimension. However, this is not practical for squares larger than 5 × 5. The following rules, which represent a compromise, are adequate for almost all research applications.

2 × 2 Latin square.   Select one of two arrangements at random.

3 × 3 Latin square.   Randomize the order of rows and columns of the standard square independently.

4 × 4 Latin square.   Select one of four standard squares at random. Randomize the order of rows and columns of the standard square independently.

5 × 5 and higher-order squares.   Arbitrarily select one of 56 standard squares. Randomize the order of rows and columns independently and assign the treatment levels randomly to the letters *A, B, C,* etc.

For example, to select a 4 × 4 Latin square, draw three sets of four random digits (1, 2, 3, 4) from a table of random numbers. Assume that the digits are 2, 1, 3, 4; 3, 1, 2, 4; and 4, 3, 1, 2. Because the first digit is *two,* the second 4 × 4 square shown at the beginning of this section is selected. This square is

	Columns			
	1	2	3	4
1	*A*	*B*	*C*	*D*
2	*B*	*C*	*D*	*A*
Rows 3	*C*	*D*	*A*	*B*
4	*D*	*A*	*B*	*C*

The rows are ordered according to the second set of random digits (3, 1, 2, 4) to yield the following square.

	Columns			
	1	2	3	4
3	*C*	*D*	*A*	*B*
1	*A*	*B*	*C*	*D*
Rows 2	*B*	*C*	*D*	*A*
4	*D*	*A*	*B*	*C*

The final step in the randomization procedure is to order the columns according to the third set of random digits (4, 3, 1, 2). This gives the following square:

Columns

4 3 1 2

	4	3	1	2
3	B	A	C	D
1	D	C	A	B
2	A	D	B	C
4	C	B	D	A

Rows

The randomization procedures for Latin squares described here select a square at random from a set of all squares of the required size for 2×2, 3×3, and 4×4 squares. For 5×5 and higher-order squares, a square is selected at random from a set of squares. Although this procedure does not select higher-order squares from all possible squares, according to Cox (1958) it is suitable for both practical and theoretical purposes. Alternative randomization procedures are described by Federer (1955, 140–142) and Fisher and Yates (1963, 24).

6.3 LAYOUT OF DESIGN

For purposes of illustration, assume that we desire to evaluate automobile tires by means of a road test. The independent variable is four kinds of rubber compounds used in the construction of the tires, and it is designated by c_1, c_2, c_3, and c_4. The dependent variable is thickness of tread remaining on each tire after 10,000 miles of driving. Eight tires of each rubber compound that represent a random sample of production are available for the test. The tires are mounted on four cars according to the scheme shown in Table 6.3-1. The cars are designated by a_1, a_2, a_3, a_4, and the wheel position by b_1 = right front, b_2 = left front, b_3 = right rear, and b_4 = left rear. The road test is repeated using the scheme in Table 6.3-1 so that there are two observations in each cell. An alternative analysis of this experiment is described in Section 10.9. This alternative analysis has the advantage of isolating variation attributable to the repetition of the road test.

An examination of Table 6.3-1 shows that each kind of tire is used equally often on each car and appears the same number of times at each wheel position. By using a type LS-k design, the variation due to differences among automobiles and wheel positions can be isolated while evaluating treatment effects. The Latin square plan in the table is identical to the 4×4 square randomization example in Section 6.2. In order to maintain a consistent notation system, the treatment levels A, B, C, and D are designated by c_1, c_2, c_3, and c_4. Treatment effects for a fixed-effects model are designated by the greek letter γ.

TABLE 6.3-1   Randomization Plan

		Wheel Position			
		b_4	b_3	b_1	b_2
	a_3	c_2	c_1	c_3	c_4
Automobile	a_1	c_4	c_3	c_1	c_2
	a_2	c_1	c_4	c_2	c_3
	a_4	c_3	c_2	c_4	c_1

The following statistical hypotheses are advanced:

$$H_0 : \gamma_k = 0 \qquad \text{for all } k$$

$$H_1 : \gamma_k \neq 0 \qquad \text{for some } k.$$

The level of significance adopted for testing differences among the four rubber compounds is .05. The data and analysis procedures are shown in Table 6.3-2. The following notation is used in the table:

p levels of rows (a_i), where $p = 4$ automobiles.

q levels of columns (b_j), where $q = 4$ wheel positions.

r levels of treatment (c_k), where $r = 4$ rubber compounds.

n levels of observations (s_m) per cell, where $n = 2$.

The results of the analysis are summarized in Table 6.3-3. The first test that should be performed is for the residual mean square. If this test is significant, it indicates that MS_A, or MS_B, or MS_C, or possibly all three MS's estimate, in addition to main effects, some interaction components.

**TABLE 6.3-2   Layout of Type LS-4
Design and Computational Procedures**

(i) Data:

ABCS Summary Table

	b_1	b_2	b_3	b_4
a_1	3	4	7	7
	1	2	5	10
a_2	5	8	8	6
	3	6	10	2
a_3	7	9	3	4
	5	9	2	4
a_4	8	3	3	6
	11	2	3	6

AC Summary Table

	c_1	c_2	c_3	c_4
a_1	4	6	12	17
a_2	8	8	14	18
a_3	5	8	12	18
a_4	5	6	12	19
$\sum\limits_{1}^{p} C =$	22	28	50	72
$\dfrac{\left(\sum\limits_{1}^{p} C\right)^2}{np} =$	60.5	98.0	312.5	648.0

TABLE 6.3-2 (continued)

ABC Summary Table

	b_1	b_2	b_3	b_4	$\sum\limits_1^q A$	$\dfrac{\left(\sum\limits_1^q A\right)^2}{nq}$
a_1	c_1 4	c_2 6	c_3 12	c_4 17	39	190.125
a_2	c_2 8	c_3 14	c_4 18	c_1 8	48	288.000
a_3	c_3 12	c_4 18	c_1 5	c_2 8	43	231.125
a_4	c_4 19	c_1 5	c_2 6	c_3 12	42	220.500

$$\sum\limits_1^p B = 43 \qquad 43 \qquad 41 \qquad 45$$

$$\frac{\left(\sum\limits_1^p B\right)^2}{np} = 231.125 \quad 231.125 \quad 210.125 \quad 253.125$$

(ii) Computational symbols:

$$\sum\limits_1^p\sum\limits_1^q\sum\limits_1^n ABCS = 3 + 1 + 5 + \cdots + 6 = 172$$

$$\sum\limits_1^p\sum\limits_1^q\sum\limits_1^n ABCS^2 = [ABCS] = (3)^2 + (1)^2 + (5)^2 + \cdots + (6)^2 = 1160.000$$

$$\frac{\left(\sum\limits_1^p\sum\limits_1^q\sum\limits_1^n ABCS\right)^2}{np^2} = [X] = \frac{(172)^2}{2(4)^2} = 924.500$$

$$\sum\limits_1^p\sum\limits_1^q \frac{(ABC)^2}{n} = [ABC] = \frac{(4)^2}{2} + \frac{(8)^2}{2} + \cdots + \frac{(12)^2}{2} = 1128.000$$

$$\sum\limits_1^p \frac{\left(\sum\limits_1^q A\right)^2}{nq} = [A] = 190.125 + 288.000 + \cdots + 220.500 = 929.750$$

$$\sum\limits_1^q \frac{\left(\sum\limits_1^p B\right)^2}{np} = [B] = 231.125 + 231.125 + \cdots + 253.125 = 925.500$$

$$\sum\limits_1^r \frac{\left(\sum\limits_1^p C\right)^2}{np} = [C] = 60.5 + 98.0 + \cdots + 648.0 = 1119.000$$

(iii) Computational formulas:

$$SS_{total} = [ABCS] - [X] = 235.500 \qquad\qquad SS_C = [C] - [X] = 194.500$$

$$SS_A = [A] - [X] = 5.250 \qquad\qquad SS_{res} = [ABC] - [A] - [B] - [C] + 2[X] = 2.750$$

$$SS_B = [B] - [X] = 1.000 \qquad SS_{within\ cell} = [ABCS] - [ABC] = 32.000$$

As a result, tests of one or more main effects are positively biased. A test is said to be positively biased if it yields too many significant results. Thus, if a test of, say, MS_C is significant, an experimenter has no way of determining if this is due to treatment C or to a component of the AB or ABC interactions. Because MS_{res} is not significant according to the analysis summarized in Table 6.3-3, it is reasonable to assume that tests of A, B, and C are not positively biased by the presence of interaction components.

According to the analysis in Table 6.3-3, differences among the four tires corresponding to different rubber compounds are significant. In this example, the two nuisance variables, differences among automobiles and differences among wheel positions, were not significant. The effort involved in including these two variables in the experiment has been for naught. Procedures are described in Section 6.5 for determining which differences among the four rubber compounds are significant.

TABLE 6.3-3   Analysis of Variance Table

Source	SS	df	MS	F	E(MS) *Model I*
1 Between A	5.250	$p - 1 = 3$	1.750	$[\frac{1}{5}] = \quad .88$	$\sigma_\varepsilon^2 + np\sigma_\alpha^2$
2 Between B	1.000	$p - 1 = 3$	.333	$[\frac{2}{5}] = \quad .17$	$\sigma_\varepsilon^2 + np\sigma_\beta^2$
3 Between C	194.500	$p - 1 = 3$	64.833	$[\frac{3}{5}] = 32.42*$	$\sigma_\varepsilon^2 + np\sigma_\gamma^2$
4 Residual	2.750	$(p - 1)(p - 2) = 6$	.458	$[\frac{4}{5}] = \quad .23$	$\sigma_\varepsilon^2 + n\sigma_{res}^2$
5 Within cell	32.000	$p^2(n - 1) = 16$	2.000		σ_ε^2
6 Total	235.500	$np^2 - 1 = 31$			

$*p < .01.$

COMPUTATIONAL PROCEDURES FOR $n = 1$

If the road test had not been repeated, there would be no *within-cell* error term. Under these conditions MS_{res} may be used as an error term for testing main effects if it can be assumed that $\sigma_{res}^2 = 0$. The residual term is an estimate of random error plus all nonzero interaction terms (i.e., $\sigma_{\alpha\beta}^2$, $\sigma_{\alpha\gamma}^2$, $\sigma_{\beta\gamma}^2$, and $\sigma_{\alpha\beta\gamma}^2$). If all the interactions are insignificant, MS_{res} provides an estimate of experimental error.

Computational procedures for the case where $n = 1$ are very similar to those shown in Table 6.3-2. In this latter case, the *ABCS* Summary Table is equivalent to an *ABC* Summary Table. The computational symbols should be modified by deleting n wherever it appears.

In Section 6.1 it was pointed out that a Latin square design is not practical for the case in which the dimension of the square is smaller than five unless more than one observation per cell is obtained. This restriction results from the fact that for 2×2, 3×3, and 4×4 Latin squares, the MS_{res} is based on only 0, 2, and 6 degrees of freedom, respectively. A

5×5 square has 12 degrees of freedom. Although marginal, a square with this number of degrees of freedom for experimental error is acceptable.

6.4   ASSUMPTIONS OF THE MODEL
FOR A TYPE LS-k DESIGN

Let X_{ijkm} be a measure for a randomly selected observation m in population ijk. Under the fixed-effects model, it is assumed that measurement X_{ijkm} is equal to the following terms:

$$X_{ijkm} = \mu + \alpha_i + \beta_j + \gamma_k + \text{residual} + \varepsilon_{m(ijk)},$$

where μ = grand mean for treatment populations.

α_i = effect of row i, which is a constant for all observations within population i, $\Sigma_{i=1}^{p}\alpha_i = 0$.

β_j = effect of column j, which is a constant for all observations within population j, $\Sigma_{j=1}^{q}\beta_j = 0$.

γ_k = effect of treatment k, which is a constant for all observations within population k, $\Sigma_{k=1}^{r}\gamma_k = 0$.

residual = all effects due to rows, columns, and treatment levels not predictable from the sum of these effects. If all interactions among these effects = 0, then the mean of residual = 0 with variance = σ_{ε}^2.

$\varepsilon_{m(ijk)}$ = experimental error, which is independent of other ε's and is normally distributed within each cell with mean = 0 and variance = σ_{ε}^2.

The F ratios in Table 6.3-3, assuming a fixed-effects model, are distributed as the F distribution under the conditions that (1) the n experimental units in the k^2 cells represent random samples from the population; (2) all k^2 populations are normal; (3) the variances of the k^2 populations are homogeneous; and (4) the row, column, and treatment effects are additive.

For the case in which $n > 1$, the assumption of homogeneity of variances can be tested by means of an $F_{\max}$ test described in Section 2.6.

When an estimate of $\text{MS}_{\text{within cell}}$ is available, a partial test of the additivity assumption is given by

$$F = \frac{\text{MS}_{\text{res}}}{\text{MS}_{\text{w.cell}}}.$$

If the interactions $\sigma_{\alpha\beta}^2$, $\sigma_{\alpha\gamma}^2$, $\sigma_{\beta\gamma}^2$, and $\sigma_{\alpha\beta\gamma}^2 = 0$, the MS_{res} is an estimate of σ_{ε}^2. Thus, if the numerator and denominator of the ratio $\text{MS}_{\text{res}}/\text{MS}_{\text{w.cell}}$

each have the expected value σ_ε^2, the ratio is equal to one. A discussion of the bias that occurs when a test of significance indicates that interaction effects are not equal to zero appears in Section 10.7.

TUKEY'S TEST FOR NONADDITIVITY

Under the condition that $n = 1$, there is no within-cell term. In order to use MS_{res} as an error term for testing treatment effects, all interactions among rows, columns, and treatment levels must equal zero. A partial test of the additivity assumption when $n = 1$ can be made by means of Tukey's (1955) test for nonadditivity, which was described in Section 5.3 in connection with a type RB-k design. To illustrate, assume that the data in the *ABC* Summary Table of Table 6.3-2 are based on $n = 1$ observation. Computational procedures for Tukey's test are shown in Table 6.4-1. It is apparent from the analysis in this table that the assumption of additivity is tenable. A relatively low level of significance ($\alpha = .10$) was adopted for the F_{nonadd} test. The selection of this level reflects a willingness on the part of the experimenter to commit a type I error rather than a type II error.

If the test of nonadditivity is significant, it means that interaction terms appear in the main effects and residual mean squares. Under these conditions tests of main effects are biased in a complicated manner. For a discussion of this point, see Scheffé (1959, 154-158), Wilk and Kempthorne (1957), and Section 10.7. If, for example, a *BC* interaction is present, the E(MS) for *A* will include this interaction, but the E(MS) for *B* and *C* will be free of this interaction. If $F = MS_{res}/MS_{w.cell}$ or F_{nonadd} is significant, a transformation may be found that will produce additivity.

TABLE 6.4-1 Test for Nonadditivity

(i) Data:

ABC Table

	b_1	b_2	b_3	b_4	$\bar{A}_i$	$d_i = \bar{A}_i - \overline{ABC}$
a_1	c_1 4	c_2 6	c_3 12	c_4 17	9.75	-1.00
a_2	c_2 8	c_3 14	c_4 18	c_1 8	12.00	1.25
a_3	c_3 12	c_4 18	c_1 5	c_2 8	10.75	.00
a_4	c_4 19	c_1 5	c_2 6	c_3 12	10.50	$-.25$

$$\overline{ABC} = \frac{\sum_1^N ABC}{N}$$

$\bar{B}_j = $ 10.75 10.75 10.25 11.25

$d_j = \bar{B}_j - \overline{ABC} = $ .00 .00 $-.50$ .50

$$\overline{ABC} = \frac{172}{16} = 10.75$$

TABLE 6.4-1 (continued)

	C Table						*ABC′ Table*			
	c_1	c_2	c_3	c_4			b_1	b_2	b_3	b_4
	4	6	12	17		a_1	4.50	6.00	11.00	17.50
	8	8	14	18		a_2	8.25	13.75	18.75	7.25
	5	8	12	18		a_3	12.50	18.00	5.00	7.50
	5	6	12	19		a_4	17.75	5.25	6.25	12.75

$$\bar{C}_k = \quad 5.50 \quad 7.00 \quad 12.50 \quad 18.00$$
$$d_k = \bar{C}_k - \overline{ABC} = -5.25 \; -3.75 \quad 1.75 \quad 7.25$$

Values in *ABC′* Table $= \overline{ABC} + d_i + d_j + d_k$. For example,
$$4.50 = 10.75 - 1.00 + .00 - 5.25$$

ABC − ABC′ Table = abc Table

	b_1	b_2	b_3	b_4
a_1	−.50	.00	1.00	−.50
a_2	−.25	.25	−.75	.75
a_3	−.50	.00	.00	.50
a_4	1.25	−.25	−.25	−.75

$(ABC' - \overline{ABC})^2 = x^2$ *Table*

	b_1	b_2	b_3	b_4
a_1	39.0625	22.5625	.0625	45.5625
a_2	6.2500	9.0000	64.0000	12.2500
a_3	3.0625	52.5625	33.0625	10.5625
a_4	49.0000	30.2500	20.2500	4.0000

Values in *abc* Table are obtained by subtracting corresponding entries in Table *ABC′* from *ABC*, e.g., $-.50 = 4 - 4.50$. The sum of each row and column in Table *abc* must equal zero.

Computational check: $\sum\limits_{1}^{p}\sum\limits_{1}^{q} abc^2 = SS_{res} = 5.50$.

(ii) Computational formulas:

$$SS_{nonadd} = \frac{\left[\sum\limits_{1}^{p}\sum\limits_{1}^{q}(abc)(x^2)\right]^2}{SS_{res(x^2\ Table)}} = \frac{[-.50(39.0625) - .25(6.2500) + \cdots + (-.75)(4.000)]^2}{460.3125}$$

$$= \frac{(-31)^2}{460.3125} = 2.088$$

$SS_{res(x^2\ Table)}$ is computed from the x^2 Table by the following formula:

$$[ABC] - [A] - [B] - [C] + 2[X] = 16196.0312 - 10109.4062 - 10394.6406$$
$$- 15381.9531 + 2(10075.1406) = 460.3125$$

$$df_{nonadd} = 1$$
$$SS_{rem} = SS_{res(ABC\ Table)} - SS_{nonadd} = 5.500 - 2.088 = 3.412$$
$$df_{rem} = df_{res(ABC\ Table)} - 1 = 6 - 1 = 5$$
$$F_{nonadd} = \frac{SS_{nonadd}/df_{nonadd}}{SS_{rem}/df_{rem}} = \frac{2.088}{.682} = 3.06$$
$$F_{.10;1,5} = 4.06$$

MIXED AND RANDOM-EFFECTS MODELS

F ratios for random-effects and mixed models have the same form as the fixed-effects model shown in Table 6.3-3 under the condition that all interactions are zero.

6.5   PROCEDURES FOR TESTING DIFFERENCES AMONG MEANS

Tests of differences among means in a type LS-k design have the same general form as those illustrated in Sections 3.2, 3.4, and 4.6. The denominator of the t, q, or F ratio, however, employs the error term used in the analysis of variance, that is, MS_{res} or $MS_{w.cell}$.

6.6   ESTIMATING MISSING OBSERVATIONS

A formula for estimating a missing observation when $n = 1$ has been presented by Allan and Wishart (1930) and Yates (1933). This formula is

$$ABC_{ijk} = \frac{r(\Sigma A_i + \Sigma B_j + \Sigma C_k) - 2\Sigma ABC}{(r - 1)(r - 2)},$$

where $r =$ number of treatment levels, $\Sigma A_i =$ sum of remaining observations in row containing the missing observation, $\Sigma B_j =$ sum of remaining observations in the column, $\Sigma C_k =$ sum of remaining observations in the treatment level, and $\Sigma ABC =$ sum of all available observations. In carrying out the analysis of variance, the estimated score is inserted in the data matrix and one degree of freedom subtracted from the df for MS_{res} and MS_{total}. If an observation is missing in a Latin square design, an estimate is required in order to carry out the computation.

If more than one observation is missing, an experimenter can *guesstimate* the values for all but one of the missing observations; this one is computed by the above formula. The computed value is inserted in the data matrix, and another of the missing observations that was guesstimated is computed. This iterative process is repeated until the computed values for all missing observations have become stabilized. Generally, two or three cycles of the procedure are sufficient for this purpose. One degree of freedom must be subtracted from the df for MS_{res} and MS_{total} for each estimated missing observation.

The above procedure produces a slight positive bias, in that the expectations for row, column, and treatment mean squares are too large. A correction for bias in the treatment mean square when one observation is estimated is given by

$$\text{Correction for bias} = \frac{[\Sigma ABC - \Sigma A_i - \Sigma B_j - (r - 1)\Sigma C_k]^2}{[(r - 1)(r - 2)]^2}.$$

The adjusted treatment sum of squares is given by

$$SS_{C(\text{adj})} = SS_C - \text{correction for bias}.$$

If two or more observations have been estimated, a correction for bias described by Kempthorne (1952, 198) may be made. First, compute SS_{res} for the Latin square design with estimated values in the data matrix. Second, treat the data as a randomized block design, ignoring treatment C, and estimate missing values by the formula appropriate for this design. This procedure is described in Section 5.6. Compute SS_{res} for the randomized block design with the second set of estimated missing observations inserted in the data matrix. The adjusted sum of squares for treatment levels in the Latin square design is given by

$$SS_{C(\text{adj})} = SS_{\text{res(randomized block)}} - SS_{\text{res(Latin square)}}.$$

As noted previously, the degrees of freedom for SS_{res} must be reduced by the number of missing observations.

A t ratio for contrasts involving a treatment level with one missing observation is given by

$$t = \frac{C_j(\bar{C}_j) + C_{j'}(\bar{C}_{j'})}{\sqrt{MS_{\text{res}}\left[\dfrac{2}{r} + \dfrac{1}{(r - 1)(r - 2)}\right]}}.$$

If more than one observation has been estimated, the t ratio is given by

$$t = \frac{C_j(\bar{C}_j) + C_{j'}(\bar{C}_{j'})}{\sqrt{MS_{\text{res}}\left[\dfrac{1}{e_j} + \dfrac{1}{e_{j'}}\right]}},$$

where e_j and $e_{j'}$ correspond to the number of *effective* replications in each treatment. An approximate rule proposed by Yates (1933) assigns a value to e_j and $e_{j'}$ according to the following scheme:

> Assign 1 for treatment level observation if the other observation is present in both the corresponding row and column.
>
> Assign $\frac{2}{3}$ for observation if the other observation is missing in the row or column.
>
> Assign $\frac{1}{3}$ for observation if the other observation is missing in both the row and column.
>
> Assign 0 if the observation itself is missing.

The application of similar rules is illustrated with a numerical example for a randomized block design in Section 5.6.

If missing observations occur in a Latin square design with $n > 1$, an unweighted means analysis procedure, described in Section 7.9, may be used. When one or more rows, columns, or treatment levels are missing, consult Yates (1936a), Yates and Hale (1939), and DeLury (1946).

6.7   RELATIVE EFFICIENCY OF LATIN SQUARE DESIGN WITH $n = 1$

A Latin square design enables an experimenter to minimize the effects of two nuisance variables in evaluating treatment effects. If the row and column effects are appreciably greater than zero, a Latin square design is more powerful than either a completely randomized or randomized block design.

RELATIVE EFFICIENCY OF LATIN SQUARE AND COMPLETELY RANDOMIZED DESIGNS

The relative efficiency of the type CR-k and type LS-k designs, ignoring differences in degrees of freedom, is given by

$$(1) \qquad \text{Relative efficiency} = \frac{\text{MS}_{\text{WG}}}{\text{MS}_{\text{res}}},$$

where MS_{WG} for a completely randomized design is obtained from a Latin square analysis by

$$\text{MS}_{\text{WG}} = \frac{\text{MS}_A + \text{MS}_B + (r - 1)\text{MS}_{\text{res}}}{(r + 1)}.$$

If the data in Table 6.3-2 were based on $n = 1$, the required mean squares for A, B, and residual would be 3.50, .67, and .92, respectively. The value of MS_{WG} required in formula (1) is

$$\text{MS}_{\text{WG}} = \frac{3.50 + .67 + (4 - 1)(.92)}{4 + 1} = 1.39.$$

The relative efficiency is

$$\text{Relative efficiency} = \frac{1.39}{0.92} \times 100 = 151.1 \text{ percent.}$$

Formula (1) does not take into account the fact that MS_{WG} has more degrees of freedom associated with it than does MS_{res}. A correction for difference in degrees of freedom is given by

$$\text{Relative efficiency} = \frac{\text{MS}_{\text{WG}}}{\text{MS}_{\text{res}}} \left[\frac{(r-1)(r-2)+1}{(r-1)(r-2)+3} \right] \left[\frac{r(r-1)+3}{r(r-1)+1} \right]$$

$$= 1.511(.90) \times 100 = 136.0 \text{ percent.}$$

RELATIVE EFFICIENCY OF LATIN SQUARE AND RANDOMIZED BLOCK DESIGNS

The efficiency of a Latin square design relative to a randomized block design may be estimated in two ways, depending on whether the rows or columns of the square are considered as replicates. In the present example, the row variable is automobiles and the column variable is wheel positions. For this example, rows would be considered as replications corresponding to blocks in a randomized block design. The relative efficiency of the two designs, considering rows as replications, is given by

$$\text{Relative efficiency} = \frac{\text{MS}_{\text{res(RB-}k)}}{\text{MS}_{\text{res(LS-}k)}},$$

where $\text{MS}_{\text{res(RB-}k)}$ is estimated from the Latin square analysis by

$$\text{MS}_{\text{res(RB-}k)} = \frac{\text{MS}_B + (r-1)\text{MS}_{\text{res(LS-}k)}}{r}$$

$$= \frac{.67 + (4-1)(.92)}{4} = .86$$

$$\text{Relative efficiency} = \frac{.86}{.92} \times 100 = 93.5 \text{ percent.}$$

A correction for loss of degrees of freedom in the Latin square design, relative to a randomized block design, can be incorporated into the above formula as follows:

$$\text{Relative efficiency} = \frac{\text{MS}_{\text{res(RB-}k)}}{\text{MS}_{\text{res(LS-}k)}} \left[\frac{(r-1)(r-2)+1}{(r-1)(r-2)+3} \right] \left[\frac{(r-1)^2+3}{(r-1)^2+1} \right]$$

$$= \frac{.86}{.92}(.93) \times 100 = 87.0 \text{ percent.}$$

If columns of the Latin square design are considered as replications, $\text{MS}_{\text{res(RB-}k)}$ is estimated by

$$\text{MS}_{\text{res(RB-}k)} = \frac{\text{MS}_A + (r-1)\text{MS}_{\text{res(LS-}k)}}{r} = \frac{3.50 + (4-1)(.92)}{4} = 1.56.$$

The corrected relative efficiency of the Latin square and randomized block designs, with columns of the former design considered as replications, is

$$\text{Relative efficiency} = \frac{1.56}{0.93}(.93) \times 100 = 157.7 \text{ percent.}$$

SCHEMATIC COMPARISON OF TOTAL
VARIATION FOR THREE DESIGNS

At the beginning of this section it was pointed out that a Latin square design is more powerful than either a completely randomized or randomized block design if the row and column effects in the Latin square design are appreciably greater than zero. This point can be made clearer if a stylized comparison of total variation and degrees of freedom is shown for the three designs. Assume that an experiment has four treatment levels, with four observations under each level. Partitioning of total variation and degrees of freedom is presented in Figure 6.7-1.

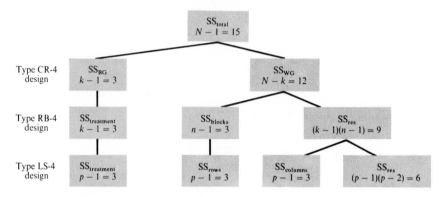

Figure 6.7-1 Schematic comparison of total variation and degrees of freedom for three experimental designs.

If the row and column effects of a Latin square design are not appreciably greater than zero, the design is less powerful than the completely randomized or randomized block designs. This results from the fact that the error term for a type LS-k design is based on fewer degrees of freedom than is the case for the other two designs. A Latin square design is most powerful under the condition that variation within both rows and columns is small relative to variation among the rows and columns. If the reverse condition, of greater variation within as opposed to between the rows and the columns, is true, the Latin square design is much less powerful than a completely randomized design. The latter condition is unlikely to occur unless the average correlation between observations within rows, $\rho_{ii'}$, or columns, $\rho_{jj'}$, is negative.

6.8 GRAECO-LATIN SQUARE DESIGN

Earlier it was pointed out that a Latin square design permits an experimenter to isolate variation due to two nuisance variables in the process of evaluating treatment effects. A Graeco-Latin square design, designated by the letters GLS-k, permits the isolation of three nuisance variables. A type GLS-k design consists of two superimposed orthogonal squares. If, for example, four treatment levels are designated by the Latin letters A, B, C, and D and four levels of a nuisance variable by the Greek letters α, β, γ, and δ, a type GLS-k design has the following form.

| | Columns | | | |
	1	2	3	4
1	$A\alpha$	$B\beta$	$C\gamma$	$D\delta$
2	$B\delta$	$A\gamma$	$D\beta$	$C\alpha$
3	$C\beta$	$D\alpha$	$A\delta$	$B\gamma$
4	$D\gamma$	$C\delta$	$B\alpha$	$A\beta$

(Rows)

Two Latin squares are orthogonal to each other if, when they are superimposed, every letter of one square occurs once and only once with every letter of the other square. An inspection of the above composite square will show that it is composed of two orthogonal squares.

TABLE 6.8-1   Partitioning of Degrees of Freedom and Expectations of Mean Squares for Type GLS-k Design

Source	df	E(MS) *Model I*
Between A (Rows)	$p - 1$	$\sigma_\varepsilon^2 + np\sigma_\alpha^2$
Between B (Columns)	$p - 1$	$\sigma_\varepsilon^2 + np\sigma_\beta^2$
Between C (Latin letters)	$p - 1$	$\sigma_\varepsilon^2 + np\sigma_\gamma^2$
Between D (Greek letters)	$p - 1$	$\sigma_\varepsilon^2 + np\sigma_\delta^2$
Residual	$(p - 1)(p - 3)$	$\sigma_\varepsilon^2 + n\sigma_{res}^2$
Within cell	$p^2(n - 1)$	σ_ε^2
Total	$np^2 - 1$	

Partitioning of the degrees of freedom for a type GLS-k design is shown in Table 6.8-1. Expectations of the mean squares for the fixed-effects model under the assumption of zero-interaction effects also appear. Computational procedures for a type GLS-k design are almost identical to procedures shown in Table 6.3-2 for a type LS-k design. Of course, an additional table, D Summary Table, is required. The computational formula for sum of squares for u levels of D is

$$SS_D = [D] - [X],$$

where

$$[D] = \sum_1^p \frac{\left(\sum_1^u D\right)^2}{nu}.$$

The formula for SS_{res} is given by

$$SS_{res} = [ABCD] - [A] - [B] - [C] - [D] + 3[X].$$

The symbol $[ABCD]$ replaces the symbol $[ABC]$ in the residual formula because the corresponding table includes the effects of four sources of variation instead of only three.

Complete sets of orthogonal Latin squares of size 3, 4, 5, 7, 8, 9, and 10 are given by Fisher and Yates (1963, 25, 86-89). It has been shown (Fisher and Yates, 1934) that no orthogonal pair of 6×6 Latin squares exists. Orthogonal squares are known to exist for all prime numbers and powers of primes. Bose, Shrikhande, and Parker (1960) proved that orthogonal squares exist for squares of the size $4s + 2$, where $s > 1$.

Graeco-Latin square designs have not proven very useful in the behavioral sciences for several reasons. First, interaction among variables is common in behavioral research. Consequently, it is difficult to find four variables that do not interact. Zero interactions are required in type GLS-k designs in order for tests of the main effects to be valid. A second reason for this design's lack of popularity is the restriction that each of the four variables must have the same number of levels. It is difficult to achieve this balance for four variables. Graeco-Latin squares are most useful as parts of more inclusive designs. These designs, which permit the isolation of certain interactions among variables, are described in Chapter 10.

6.9   HYPER-GRAECO-LATIN SQUARE DESIGNS

If another orthogonal Latin square is superimposed on a Graeco-Latin square, it is called a hyper-Graeco-Latin square. The number of orthogonal Latin squares that can be combined in forming hyper-squares is limited. For example, no more than three orthogonal 4×4 squares can be combined. This is evident if the $p^2 - 1$ degrees of freedom for total sum of squares (disregarding within-cell degrees of freedom) are analyzed. In the case of a 4×4 square, each mode of classification has $p - 1 = 3$ degrees of freedom. Thus the five modes of classification—rows, columns, Latin letters, Greek letters, and Hebrew letters—account for the $(4)^2 - 1 = 15$ degrees of freedom for total sum of squares. For a 5×5 square, the $p^2 - 1 = 24$ degrees of freedom are accounted for by rows, columns, Latin letters, Greek letters, Hebrew letters, and German letters. Hence, no more than four orthogonal 5×5 squares can be combined. The degrees of freedom and computational formulas for SS_{res} for hyper-Graeco-Latin square designs with five and six modes of classification are, respectively,

$$df = (p - 1)(p - 4) \qquad SS_{res} = [ABCDE] - [A] - [B] - [C]$$
$$- [D] - [E] + 4[X]$$

$$\mathrm{df} = (p-1)(p-5) \qquad \mathrm{SS_{res}} = [ABCDEF] - [A] - [B] - [C]$$
$$- [D] - [E] - [F] + 5[X].$$

The sum of squares formulas for rows, columns, etc. have the same general pattern as the corresponding formulas in a Latin square design. For a discussion of hyper-Graeco-Latin squares, see Federer (1955, Chapter 15).

6.10   ADVANTAGES AND DISADVANTAGES OF TYPE LS-*k* DESIGN

The major advantages of the Latin square design are

1. Greater power relative to completely randomized and randomized block designs for many research applications. This design permits an experimenter to partially isolate variation attributable to two nuisance variables.

2. Simplicity in analysis of data.

The major disadvantages of the design are

1. The number of treatment levels, rows, and columns must be the same. As a result of this requirement, Latin squares larger than 8×8 are seldom used.

2. Unless more than one observation per cell is obtained, squares smaller than 5×5 are not practical because of the small number of degrees of freedom for experimental error.

3. The design is not appropriate for research problems involving interactions among the variables unless several squares are combined. The use of a Latin square as a building block for complex designs is described in Chapters 9 and 10.

4. Randomization is relatively complex.

A list of representative applications of Latin square designs is given at the conclusion of Chapters 9 and 10.

7 / COMPLETELY RANDOMIZED, HIERARCHAL, AND RANDOMIZED BLOCK FACTORIAL DESIGNS

7.1 INTRODUCTION TO FACTORIAL EXPERIMENTS

A factorial design is constructed from basic *building block* designs described in Chapters 4, 5, and 6. It is the most widely used design in the behavioral sciences, as an examination of recent volumes of behavioral science journals will verify. The term *factorial experiment* refers to the simultaneous evaluation of two or more treatments in one experiment rather than to a distinct kind of experimental design. The design of factorial experiments utilizing completely randomized or randomized block designs is described in this chapter. In Chapter 8 factorial experiments that combine both type CR-k and RB-k designs in the same experiment are described. These designs are referred to as split-plot designs. Two additional variations of factorial experiments, a confounded factorial design and a fractional factorial design, are described in Chapters 9 and 10, respectively.

One assumption that has guided the writing of this and subsequent chapters is that *complex designs* appear less *complex* when they are perceived as consisting of elementary building block designs.

7.2 DESCRIPTION OF COMPLETELY RANDOMIZED FACTORIAL DESIGN

The simplest factorial experiment, from the standpoint of data analysis and assignment of subjects to treatment levels, is the completely randomized factorial design. This design is appropriate for experiments that meet, in addition to the assumptions of a completely randomized design described in Chapter 4, the following conditions:

1. Two or more treatments, with each treatment having two or more levels. If there are p levels of one treatment and q levels of another treatment, the experiment consists of pq treatment combinations.

2. Random assignment of subjects to the pq treatment combinations, with each subject receiving only one combination.

TREATMENT DESIGNATION SCHEME

A completely randomized factorial design with two treatments is designated as a type CRF-pq design. If the experiment includes three treatments, the designation is a type CRF-pqr design. At this point it is desirable to describe in some detail the system of designating treatments that is used in this and subsequent chapters. Treatments are designated by capital letters A through G. A particular but unspecified *level* of a treatment is designated by lower-case letters a through g and a lower-case subscript, for example, a_i, b_j, and so on. If two unspecified levels of a treatment must be differentiated, a prime is used after one of the subscripts. For example, two levels of treatment B are b_j and $b_{j'}$. Specific levels of a treatment are designated by number subscripts, for example, b_1, b_2, and so on. Besides specifying a particular treatment level, it is also necessary in experimental design notation to indicate the number of levels of a treatment. Seven lower-case letters are used for this purpose. The complete designation scheme is shown below.

$$p \text{ levels of } a_i$$

$$q \text{ levels of } b_j$$

$$r \text{ levels of } c_k$$

$$u \text{ levels of } d_l$$

$$v \text{ levels of } e_o$$

$$w \text{ levels of } f_h$$

$$z \text{ levels of } g_t.$$

The letter S is used in the notation scheme to designate a subject or a group of subjects. The letters s_m refer to a particular but unspecified subject or group of subjects. There are n levels of s_m. The above designation scheme uses 24 letters of the alphabet. The remaining two letters of the alphabet, X and Y, are used to designate individual scores.

According to this treatment designation scheme, a completely randomized factorial design with four treatments is a type CRF-$pqru$ design. If the number of levels of $pqru$ is 4, 3, 6, and 5, respectively, the design is a type CRF-4365 design. If any treatment has more than nine levels, commas are used to separate the levels for this treatment from other levels. For example, if treatment B has 11 levels, the designation is a type CRF-4,11,65 design.

ASSIGNMENT OF SUBJECTS
TO TREATMENT COMBINATIONS

A block diagram of a type CRF-23 design appears in Figure 7.2-1. It is assumed in a completely randomized factorial design that a random

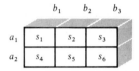

Figure 7.2-1 Block diagram of type CRF-23 design.

sample of npq subjects from a population is available. The sample is randomly subdivided into pq samples of size n. The pq samples are then randomly assigned to the pq treatment combinations of the factorial experiment. In Figure 7.2-1 the letters $s_1 \ldots s_6$ refer to the $pq = 6$ samples of n subjects. The minimum number of subjects required for a type CRF-23 design is equal to $n(2)(3) = 6$, where $n = 1$. It is desirable in factorial experiments to have more than one observation in each of the pq cells. If $n = 1$, it is not possible to compute a within-cell estimate of experimental error. In this case, an interaction must be used as an estimate of experimental error under the assumption that the interaction effects are insignificant. If $n = 5$, the above experiment would require $(5)(2)(3) = 30$ subjects. As the number of levels of a treatment increases, the number of subjects required increases markedly. For example, if treatment A had three instead of two levels, the number of subjects that would be required is $(5)(3)(3) = 45$ subjects.

It will be recalled that the number of subjects assigned to each treatment level of a type CR-k design does not have to be equal. This is also true for type CRF-pq designs if a particular proportionality exists among treatment level n's. Analysis of experiments with unequal n's is discussed in Section 7.9.

7.3 LAYOUT AND COMPUTATIONAL
PROCEDURES FOR TYPE CRF-pq DESIGN

The layout of a type CRF-24 design is shown in Table 7.3-1. For purposes of presentation, let us assume that an experimenter is interested in the effects of social deprivation (treatment B) and magnitude of reinforcement (treatment A) on children's motor behavior. The task performed by the children consisted of taking marbles from a bin, one at a time, and inserting them in a hole in a box. The dependent variable was designated as the number of marbles inserted during a four-minute period. Social reinforcement was administered by an adult experimenter for ten minutes, during which time each child learned to perform the task. Two levels of social reinforcement were employed: level a_1 consisted of smiles, nods, and praise statements by the experimenter; level a_2 consisted of smiles and nods by the experimenter but no praise statements. Prior to performing the task, the children were subjected to one of four levels of social deprivation. The deprivation consisted of being left alone in a waiting room for $b_1 = 20$ minutes, $b_2 = 40$ minutes, $b_3 = 60$ minutes, and $b_4 = 80$ minutes. The waiting room contained numerous toys with which the children could amuse themselves. However, during the deprivation period the children were isolated from contact with adults and with other children.

The research hypotheses leading to this experiment can be evaluated by means of statistical tests of the following null hypotheses:

$$H_0: \quad \alpha_i = 0 \qquad \text{for all } i$$
$$H_1: \quad \alpha_i \neq 0 \qquad \text{for some } i$$

$$H_0: \quad \beta_j = 0 \qquad \text{for all } j$$
$$H_1: \quad \beta_j \neq 0 \qquad \text{for some } j$$

$$H_0: \alpha\beta_{ij} = 0 \qquad \text{for all } ij$$
$$H_1: \alpha\beta_{ij} \neq 0 \qquad \text{for some } ij.$$

The first two null hypotheses are the familiar hypotheses which state that no differences exist among the respective population means. The third null hypothesis, that $\alpha\beta_{ij} = 0$ for all ij, is unique to factorial experiments, and it states that the interaction between treatments A and B is equal to zero. The interpretation of a significant interaction between two treatments is illustrated graphically in Figures 7.3-1 and 7.3-2 and discussed in the accompanying text. The mathematical model for a type CRF-pq design is given in Sections 1.4 and 7.5. The level of significance adopted for all tests is .05.

A total of 32 subjects was obtained by random sampling from a population. The subjects are randomly divided into eight sub-samples of four subjects each. The sub-samples are randomly assigned to the eight treatment combinations of the type CRF-24 design. Assume that all treatment levels of interest to the experimenter are included in the experiment. Thus a fixed-effects model, Model I (described in Sections 2.4, 4.9, and 7.5), applies to the experiment. The data that are subjected to statistical analysis consist of the square root of the number of marbles dropped into the box. A square-root transformation is often helpful in achieving normality for this kind of data. A discussion of the selection of an appropriate transformation appears in Section 2.7.

The layout of the type CRF-24 design, computational tables, and formulas are shown in Table 7.3-1, where the following notation is used:

$$p \text{ levels of } a_i, \text{ where } p = 2$$

$$q \text{ levels of } b_j, \text{ where } q = 4$$

$$n \text{ levels of } s_m, \text{ where } n = 4$$

$$\sum_1^N = \sum_1^p \sum_1^q \sum_1^n.$$

**TABLE 7.3-1　Layout of Type CRF-24
Design and Computational Procedures**

(i) Data:

ABS Summary Table　　　　　　　　　　　　　*AB Summary Table*

a_1	a_1	a_1	a_1	a_2	a_2	a_2	a_2
b_1	b_2	b_3	b_4	b_1	b_2	b_3	b_4
3	4	7	7	1	2	5	10
6	5	8	8	2	3	6	10
3	4	7	9	2	4	5	9
3	3	6	8	2	3	6	11

	b_1	b_2	b_3	b_4	$\sum_1^q A$	$\dfrac{\left(\sum_1^q A\right)^2}{nq}$
	$n = 4$					
a_1	15	16	28	32	91	517.5625
a_2	7	12	22	40	81	410.0625

$$\sum_1^p B = 22 \quad 28 \quad 50 \quad 72$$

$$\frac{\left(\sum_1^p B\right)^2}{np} = 60.5 \ \ 98.0 \ 312.5 \ 648.0$$

(ii) Computational symbols:

$$\sum_1^N ABS = 3 + 6 + 3 + \cdots + 11 = 172$$

$$\sum_1^N (ABS)^2 = [ABS] = (3)^2 + (6)^2 + (3)^2 + \cdots + (11)^2 = 1160.000$$

$$\frac{\left(\sum_1^N ABS\right)^2}{npq} = [X] = \frac{(172)^2}{(4)(2)(4)} = 924.500$$

$$\sum_1^p \frac{\left(\sum_1^q A\right)^2}{nq} = [A] = 517.5625 + 410.0625 = 927.625$$

$$\sum_1^q \frac{\left(\sum_1^p B\right)^2}{np} = [B] = 60.5 + 98.0 + \cdots + 648.0 = 1119.000$$

$$\sum_1^p \sum_1^q \frac{(AB)^2}{n} = [AB] = \frac{(15)^2}{4} + \frac{(16)^2}{4} + \cdots + \frac{(40)^2}{4} = 1141.500$$

(iii) Computational formulas:

$$SS_{total} = [ABS] - [X] = 235.500 \qquad SS_{AB} = [AB] - [A] - [B] + [X] = 19.375$$

$$SS_A = [A] - [X] = 3.125 \qquad SS_{w.cell} = [ABS] - [AB] = 18.500$$

$$SS_B = [B] - [X] = 194.500$$

The labels for the *AB* and *ABS* Summary Tables represent a convenient way of designating the sources of variation represented by scores in these tables. The *n* scores corresponding to *S*(subjects) in the *ABS* Summary Table were summed in constructing the *AB* Summary Table. Both tables provide information concerning treatments *A* and *B*, but information concerning variation among *S*(subjects) cannot be obtained from the *AB* Summary Table. In order to partition the total sum of squares in a factorial design, it is convenient for computational purposes to begin by constructing a summary table that represents all sources of variation that the design is supposed to estimate. This summary table can be collapsed into smaller summary tables by summing scores over one or more sources of variation, a procedure that is continued until summary tables have been constructed from which all of the sums of squares in the design can be computed. An excellent discussion of acceptable design symbolizations and procedures for arriving at a design model has been given by Lee (1966).

The analysis of variance is summarized in Table 7.3-2. The degrees

TABLE 7.3-2   Analysis of Variance Table for Type CRF-24 Design

Source	SS	df	MS	F	E(MS) Model I
1 *A*	3.125	$p - 1 = 1$	3.125	$\left[\frac{1}{4}\right] = 4.05$	$\sigma_\varepsilon^2 + nq\sigma_\alpha^2$
2 *B*	194.500	$q - 1 = 3$	64.833	$\left[\frac{2}{4}\right] = 84.09^*$	$\sigma_\varepsilon^2 + np\sigma_\beta^2$
3 *AB*	19.375	$(p - 1)(q - 1) = 3$	6.458	$\left[\frac{3}{4}\right] = 8.38^*$	$\sigma_\varepsilon^2 + n\sigma_{\alpha\beta}^2$
4 W.cell	18.500	$pq(n - 1) = 24$	.771		σ_ε^2
5 Total	235.500	$npq - 1 = 31$			

*$p < .01$.

of freedom for each sum of squares, as well as the expected values of the mean squares for Model I, are indicated in the table. Tests of the *A*, *B*, and *AB a priori* orthogonal comparisons in Table 7.3-2 are each performed at $\alpha = .05$ level of significance. The conceptual unit for error rate in this example is the individual hypothesis. The probability of falsely rejecting one or more hypotheses (error rate experimentwise) is equal to $1 - (1 - .05)^3 = .14$. The relative merits of holding constant error rate per hypothesis or per some larger conceptual unit, such as the experiment, have been widely debated. This issue is discussed in Section 3.3. The practice adopted in this book is to make the hypothesis the conceptual unit for error rate if, as in Table 7.3-2, the hypotheses involve *a priori* orthogonal comparisons. Indeed, a type CRF-*pq* design can be regarded as a set of type CR-*k* designs with prespecified families of comparisons, that is, *A*, *B*, and *AB*, each of which is tested at α level of significance.

GRAPHIC REPRESENTATION OF INTERACTION

According to the analysis in Table 7.3-2, the null hypothesis for treatment B and the interaction of $A \times B$ (read A by B) are rejected. Whenever an interaction is significant, interpretation of tests of main effects must be qualified. This point requires further clarification. A graphic representation of the interaction of treatments A and B is shown in Figure 7.3-1. It is evident from this figure that high reinforcement is associated

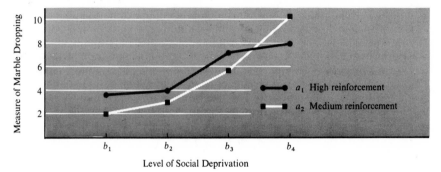

Figure 7.3-1   Illustration of interaction between treatments A and B.

with more marbles being dropped in the box than is medium reinforcement when a child has experienced a low or medium level of social deprivation (b_1, b_2, and b_3). This situation is reversed when a child has a high level of social deprivation (b_4). The variables of reinforcement and social deprivation are described as interacting with each other. The term *interaction* means that one treatment behaves differently under different levels of the other treatment. Two other examples illustrating interaction are shown in Figure 7.3-2a and b. Example (c) in Figure 7.3-2 illustrates two treatments that do not interact.

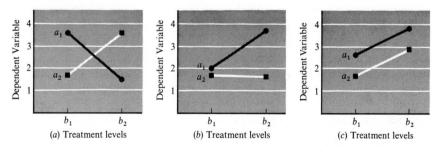

Figure 7.3-2 Examples (a) and (b) illustrate interaction between the two treatments. Example (c) illustrates two treatments that do not interact.

Whenever a significant interaction occurs, it is a signal to an experimenter that interpretation of tests of main effects must be qualified. There is usually little interest in comparisons among means for main effects, if the interaction is significant. One reason for this becomes evident upon an examination of Figure 7.3-2a. In this figure, comparisons of $\bar{A}_1$ versus $\bar{A}_2$ and $\bar{B}_1$ versus $\bar{B}_2$ are equal to zero. For example,

$$\bar{A}_1 = \frac{3.7 + 1.5}{2} = 2.6$$

$$\bar{A}_2 = \frac{1.5 + 3.7}{2} = 2.6.$$

However, comparisons of $\bar{A}_1$ versus $\bar{A}_2$ at either level of treatment B, as well as comparisons of $\bar{B}_1$ versus $\bar{B}_2$ at either level of A, are not equal to zero. For example,

$$\bar{A}_1 \text{ at } b_1 = 3.7$$

$$\bar{A}_2 \text{ at } b_1 = 1.5.$$

If an experimenter only evaluated main-effects means, he would draw the erroneous conclusion that there were no differences among the means. Thus, although MS_A and MS_B may be insignificant, a significant MS_{AB} is a signal to look for differences among means at specific levels of the other treatment.

Figure 7.3-2b illustrates a related point concerning the meaning of interaction. It is probable that the comparison of main-effects means $\bar{A}_1$ versus $\bar{A}_2$, for example, would be significant. An examination of Figure 7.3-2b indicates, however, that although the comparison $\bar{A}_1$ versus $\bar{A}_2$ is appreciably different from zero at level b_2, this is not true at level b_1. Again the point is emphasized that the presence of interaction always calls for some qualification of tests of main effects and, in addition, a further examination of the data. One final point should be made. The presence of an interaction between two treatments may be important in and of itself. For instance, because of the nature of an experimenter's research hypothesis, his principal interest may not be in testing main effects but in determining whether two treatments interact.

POWER OF THE ANALYSIS OF VARIANCE *F* TESTS

General procedures for calculating power and determining the number of subjects necessary to achieve a specified power are described in Sections 1.3, 1.5, and 4.5. These procedures generalize to factorial experiments. Formulas for computing the power of tests of treatments A and B and the AB interaction in a type CRF-pq design are, respectively,

$$\phi = \frac{\sqrt{\sum\limits_{i=1}^{p} \alpha_i^2 / p}}{\sigma_\varepsilon / \sqrt{nq}} \qquad \begin{aligned} v_1 &= p - 1, \\ v_2 &= pq(n - 1) \end{aligned}$$

$$\phi = \frac{\sqrt{\sum\limits_{j=1}^{q} \beta_j^2 / q}}{\sigma_\varepsilon / \sqrt{np}} \qquad \begin{aligned} v_1 &= q - 1, \\ v_2 &= pq(n - 1) \end{aligned}$$

$$\phi = \frac{\sqrt{\sum\limits_{i=1}^{p}\sum\limits_{j=1}^{q} (\alpha\beta_{ij})^2 / [(p - 1)(q - 1) + 1]}}{\sigma_\varepsilon / \sqrt{n}} \qquad \begin{aligned} v_1 &= (p - 1)(q - 1), \\ v_2 &= pq(n - 1). \end{aligned}$$

It should be noted that the denominator of $\Sigma_{i=1}^{p}\alpha_i^2$, $\Sigma_{j=1}^{q}\beta_j^2$, and $\Sigma_{i=1}^{p}\Sigma_{j=1}^{q}(\alpha\beta_{ij})^2$ is the degrees of freedom for the respective effects *plus one*.

7.4 TESTS OF SIMPLE MAIN EFFECTS IN TYPE CRF-*pq* DESIGN

In the example of the effects of social deprivation and reinforcement on children's motor behavior, the two independent variables were found to interact. This is a cue to the experimenter that additional insight concerning the results of the experiment can be obtained by computing tests of *simple main effects*. These tests are designed to evaluate the following null hypotheses:

$$H_0: \alpha_i = 0 \qquad \text{for all } i \text{ at level } b_1$$
$$H_0: \alpha_i = 0 \qquad \text{for all } i \text{ at level } b_2$$
$$H_0: \alpha_i = 0 \qquad \text{for all } i \text{ at level } b_3$$
$$H_0: \alpha_i = 0 \qquad \text{for all } i \text{ at level } b_4$$
$$H_0: \beta_j = 0 \qquad \text{for all } j \text{ at level } a_1$$
$$H_0: \beta_j = 0 \qquad \text{for all } j \text{ at level } a_2.$$

It can be shown that

$$\sum_{1}^{q} SS_A \text{ for } b_j = SS_A + SS_{AB}$$

and

$$\sum_{1}^{p} SS_B \text{ for } a_i = SS_B + SS_{AB}.$$

In other words, the sum of simple main-effects sums of squares is equal to the main-effects sum of squares plus the corresponding interaction. Each sum of squares for simple main effects contains a portion of the corresponding interaction. The important point is that, instead of testing the hypothesis that $\alpha_i = 0$ over all levels of b_j, tests of the hypothesis are performed at each level of treatment B. Procedures for carrying out these tests are illustrated in Table 7.4-1 and the results summarized in Table 7.4-2.

TABLE 7.4-1   Computational Procedures for Simple Main-Effects Sum of Squares

(i)

AB Summary Table

	b_1	b_2	b_3	b_4	$\sum_1^q A$
a_1	15	16	28	32	91
a_2	7	12	22	40	81
$\sum_1^p B = $	22	28	50	72	

(ii)

$$\text{SS}_A \text{ at } b_1 = \sum_1^p \frac{(AB_{i1})^2}{n} - \frac{\left(\sum_1^p B_{i1}\right)^2}{np} = \frac{(15)^2}{4} + \frac{(7)^2}{4} - \frac{(22)^2}{8} = 8.0$$

$$\text{SS}_A \text{ at } b_2 = \sum_1^p \frac{(AB_{i2})^2}{n} - \frac{\left(\sum_1^p B_{i2}\right)^2}{np} = \frac{(16)^2}{4} + \frac{(12)^2}{4} - \frac{(28)^2}{8} = 2.0$$

$$\text{SS}_A \text{ at } b_3 = \sum_1^p \frac{(AB_{i3})^2}{n} - \frac{\left(\sum_1^p B_{i3}\right)^2}{np} = \frac{(28)^2}{4} + \frac{(22)^2}{4} - \frac{(50)^2}{8} = 4.5$$

$$\text{SS}_A \text{ at } b_4 = \sum_1^p \frac{(AB_{i4})^2}{n} - \frac{\left(\sum_1^p B_{i4}\right)^2}{np} = \frac{(32)^2}{4} + \frac{(40)^2}{4} - \frac{(72)^2}{8} = 8.0$$

As a computational check $\sum_1^q \text{SS}_A$ for $b_j = \text{SS}_A + \text{SS}_{AB} = 22.5$.

(iii)

$$\text{SS}_B \text{ at } a_1 = \sum_1^q \frac{(AB_{1j})^2}{n} - \frac{\left(\sum_1^q A_{1j}\right)^2}{nq} = \frac{(15)^2}{4} + \frac{(16)^2}{4} + \cdots + \frac{(32)^2}{4} - \frac{(91)^2}{16} = 54.6875$$

$$\text{SS}_B \text{ at } a_2 = \sum_1^q \frac{(AB_{2j})^2}{n} - \frac{\left(\sum_1^q A_{2j}\right)^2}{nq} = \frac{(7)^2}{4} + \frac{(12)^2}{4} + \cdots + \frac{(40)^2}{4} - \frac{(81)^2}{16} = 159.1875$$

As a computational check $\sum_1^p \text{SS}_B$ for $a_i = \text{SS}_B + \text{SS}_{AB} = 213.875$.

TABLE 7.4-2   Analysis of Variance Table

Source	SS	df	MS	F
1 A	3.1250	$p - 1 = 1$	3.125	$\left[\frac{1}{10}\right] = 4.05$
2 A at b_1	8.0000	$p - 1 = 1$	8.000	$\left[\frac{2}{10}\right] = 10.38*$
3 A at b_2	2.0000	$p - 1 = 1$	2.000	$\left[\frac{3}{10}\right] = 2.59$
4 A at b_3	4.5000	$p - 1 = 1$	4.500	$\left[\frac{4}{10}\right] = 5.84$
5 A at b_4	8.0000	$p - 1 = 1$	8.000	$\left[\frac{5}{10}\right] = 10.38*$
6 B	194.5000	$q - 1 = 3$	64.833	$\left[\frac{6}{10}\right] = 84.09**$
7 B at a_1	54.6875	$q - 1 = 3$	18.229	$\left[\frac{7}{10}\right] = 23.64**$
8 B at a_2	159.1875	$q - 1 = 3$	53.062	$\left[\frac{8}{10}\right] = 68.82**$
9 AB	19.3750	$(p - 1)(q - 1) = 3$	6.458	$\left[\frac{9}{10}\right] = 8.38**$
10 W.cell	18.5000	$pq(n - 1) = 24$	.771	
11 Total	235.5000	$npq - 1 = 31$		

$*p < .02.$

$**p < .01.$

A decision to compute simple main-effects tests is usually made following an examination and statistical analysis of the data. The procedure recommended for such tests is to assign the same per family error rate to the simple main-effects tests as that allotted to the over-all F ratio. This can be accomplished by testing each of the simple main-effects ratios for treatments A and B at $\alpha/q = .05/4 = .0125$ and $\alpha/p = .05/2 = .025$ levels of significance, respectively. This procedure divides the over-all α for a main-effects test evenly among the *collection* of simple main-effects tests. If this procedure is followed, the critical values for $\alpha = .05$ for tests involving A and B are $F_{.0125;1,24} \simeq 7.47$ and $F_{.025;3,24} = 3.72$, respectively. According to the analysis summarized in Table 7.4-2, the null hypothesis that $\alpha_i = 0$ for all i can be rejected at levels b_1 and b_4. It can be concluded that a difference in the number of marbles placed in the box exists between the medium and high levels of reinforcement but only at two of the four levels of social deprivation. The null hypothesis that $\beta_j = 0$ for all j can be rejected at both levels of reinforcement (treatment A).

An examination of contemporary research practices as described in the scientific literature clearly shows that many experimenters prefer to adopt the individual simple main-effects hypothesis as the conceptual unit for error rate. If this procedure is followed, the critical values for tests involving treatments A and B are the tabled values of $F_{\alpha;v_1,v_2}$, which are $F_{.05;1,24} = 4.26$ and $F_{.05;3,24} = 3.01$, respectively. Although the error rate for each simple main-effects hypothesis is equal to α, the error rate per family of tests is $(4)(.05) = .20$ for treatment A and $(2)(.05) = .10$ for treatment B.

If one or more tests of simple main effects are significant, an experimenter may be interested in making comparisons among means for these simple main effects. These comparisons have the form

$$\text{Comparison of } \bar{A}_1 \text{ with } \bar{A}_2 \text{ at level } b_1 = \overline{AB}_{11} - \overline{AB}_{21}$$

$$\text{Comparison of } \bar{A}_1 \text{ with } \bar{A}_2 \text{ at level } b_4 = \overline{AB}_{14} - \overline{AB}_{24}$$

$$\text{Comparison of } \bar{B}_1 \text{ with } \bar{B}_2 \text{ at level } a_1 = \overline{AB}_{11} - \overline{AB}_{12}$$

$$\text{Comparison of } \bar{B}_1 \text{ with } \bar{B}_3 \text{ at level } a_1 = \overline{AB}_{11} - \overline{AB}_{13}$$

$$\text{Comparison of } \bar{B}_3 \text{ with } \bar{B}_4 \text{ at level } a_2 = \overline{AB}_{23} - \overline{AB}_{24}.$$

Procedures for testing *a priori* and *a posteriori* hypotheses for simple main-effects means follow those described in Sections 3.2, 3.4, and 7.6.

7.5 ASSUMPTIONS OF THE MODEL FOR TYPE CRF-*pq* DESIGN

Let X_{ijm} be a measure for a randomly selected subject in treatment population ab_{ij}. Under the fixed-effects linear model,

$$X_{ijm} = \mu + \alpha_i + \beta_j + \alpha\beta_{ij} + \varepsilon_{m(ij)},$$

where μ = grand mean of treatment populations.

α_i = effect of treatment i, which is a constant for all subjects within treatment population i, $\Sigma_{i=1}^{p}\alpha_i = 0$.

β_j = effect of treatment j, which is a constant for all subjects within treatment population j, $\Sigma_{j=1}^{q}\beta_j = 0$.

$\alpha\beta_{ij}$ = effect that represents nonadditivity of effects α_i and β_j, $\Sigma_{i=1}^{p}\alpha\beta_{ij}$ $= 0$, $\Sigma_{j=1}^{q}\alpha\beta_{ij} = 0$.

$\varepsilon_{m(ij)}$ = experimental error, which is normally and independently distributed (NID), with mean = 0 and variance = σ_ε^2.

The F ratios in Table 7.3-2 are distributed as the F distribution under the conditions that (1) the n subjects in the pq cells constitute random samples from a common population, (2) treatments A and B represent fixed effects, (3) each of the pq populations is normal, and (4) the variances of the pq populations are equal.

ASSUMPTION OF HOMOGENEITY
OF EXPERIMENTAL ERROR

The variance for population ij is estimated from cell ij of a type CRF-pq design by

$$\hat{\sigma}_{ij}^2 = \frac{\sum\limits_{1}^{n} S_{ijm}^2 - \dfrac{\left(\sum\limits_{1}^{n} S_{ijm}\right)^2}{n}}{n-1}.$$

$\hat{\sigma}_{ij}^2$ is rarely equal to zero in behavioral research. The n independent observations within cell ij are all obtained under the same treatment combination. Thus $\hat{\sigma}_{ij}^2$ is free of effects attributable to the treatments because they remain constant for that cell. To what can the variation among the n observations within cell ij be attributed? Several sources of variation can be suggested. One major source is differences among the experimental units (subjects) that existed prior to the experiment. This source is commonly referred to as *individual differences*. Other sources of variation among the observations within a cell include lack of consistency in measuring the dependent variable, variation in administration of the treatments to the n experimental units, and interaction between the experimental units and the treatments. These and other unidentified sources of variation are referred to as *experimental error* or *error variance*. It can be shown by maximum-likelihood methods that the variance ($\hat{\sigma}_{ij}^2$) of n units representing a random sample from a population of N units provides an unbiased estimate of the population variance σ_{ij}^2. The model underlying a completely randomized design requires that the population variance (experimental error) be constant for each of the pq populations. This assumption of homogeneity of experimental error can be restated as

$$\sigma_{11}^2 = \sigma_{12}^2 = \cdots = \sigma_{ij}^2 \qquad \text{for all } ij\text{'s.}$$

Let us denote the variance due to experimental error within any ij population by σ_ε^2.

The best estimate of σ_ε^2, if the homogeneity assumption is met, is obtained by pooling $\hat{\sigma}_{ij}^2$ over the pq treatment levels. The estimate of σ_ε^2 obtained by this procedure is called $MS_{\text{within cell}}$. Thus

$$\hat{\sigma}_{\text{pooled}}^2 = \frac{\sum\limits_{1}^{p}\sum\limits_{1}^{q} \hat{\sigma}_{ij}^2}{pq} = MS_{\text{within cell}}.$$

A test of the hypothesis that $\sigma_{11}^2 = \sigma_{12}^2 = \cdots = \sigma_{ij}^2$ can be made by the $F_{\max}$ ratio with pq and $n-1$ degrees of freedom. The $F_{\max}$ ratio, which is described in Section 2.6, is given by

$$F_{\max} = \frac{\text{largest } \hat{\sigma}_{ij}^2}{\text{smallest } \hat{\sigma}_{ij}^2}.$$

For the data in Table 7.3-1, F_{max} equals

$$F_{max} = \frac{2.25}{0.25} = 9.00$$

$$F_{max.05;8,3} = 83.5.$$

On the basis of this test, the hypothesis of homogeneity of variance is not rejected. If F_{max} had been significant, homogeneity of variance might be achieved by an appropriate transformation of the data as described in Section 2.7. An alternate but less desirable procedure is described by Box (1954b). It should be noted that a moderate departure from homogeneity of variances does not seriously affect significance tests using the F statistic. This is true only when the number of observations within each cell is equal. This point is discussed in Section 2.6.

EXPECTED VALUES OF MEAN SQUARES
FOR FIXED-EFFECTS, MIXED, AND
RANDOM-EFFECTS MODELS

Random sampling was not used to determine the levels of treatments included in the experiment described in Section 7.3. Instead, the particular levels were included because they covered the levels of interest to the experimenter. If, as discussed in Section 4.9, the levels for all treatments are selected on a nonrandom basis, the model for the experiment is a fixed-effects model. The E(MS) shown in Table 7.3-2 are appropriate for this model, which is sometimes referred to as Model I (Eisenhart, 1947). If the levels for one or more, but not all, of the treatments are selected at random from a population of levels, the model is a mixed model. The expected values of mean squares for the mixed model differ from those for the fixed-effects model. If the levels for all treatments employed in the experiment are drawn at random from a population of levels, the model is a random-effects model. It is possible for the sample of levels to include all levels of the treatments in the population. In that case Model I applies. The random-effects and mixed models are sometimes referred to as Model II and Model III, respectively. Not all writers follow this designation scheme, but it will be adhered to in this book. An excellent discussion of these models may be found in Hays (1963, Chapters 12 and 13).

Much confusion concerning the correct error term to use in testing main effects and interactions has arisen because of failure to distinguish among the preceding three cases of the finite model in analysis of variance. A comparison of E(MS) for the fixed-effects, mixed, and random-effects models is shown in Table 7.5-1. Fixed effects are designated by Greek letters α and β; random effects by light italic Roman letters A and B. It is apparent that $MS_{w.cell}$ is the proper error term for testing treatment mean squares for Model I but not for Model II. It will be recalled from

TABLE 7.5-1   Expected Values of Mean Squares for Type CRF-pq Design

Mean square	Model I A Fixed B Fixed	Model II A Random B Random	Model III A Fixed B Random	Model III A Random B Fixed
1 A	$\sigma_\varepsilon^2 + nq\sigma_\alpha^2$	$\sigma_\varepsilon^2 + n\sigma_{AB}^2 + nq\sigma_A^2$	$\sigma_\varepsilon^2 + n\sigma_{\alpha B}^2 + nq\sigma_\alpha^2$	$\sigma_\varepsilon^2 + nq\sigma_A^2$
2 B	$\sigma_\varepsilon^2 + np\sigma_\beta^2$	$\sigma_\varepsilon^2 + n\sigma_{AB}^2 + np\sigma_B^2$	$\sigma_\varepsilon^2 + np\sigma_B^2$	$\sigma_\varepsilon^2 + n\sigma_{A\beta}^2 + np\sigma_\beta^2$
3 AB	$\sigma_\varepsilon^2 + n\sigma_{\alpha\beta}^2$	$\sigma_\varepsilon^2 + n\sigma_{AB}^2$	$\sigma_\varepsilon^2 + n\sigma_{\alpha B}^2$	$\sigma_\varepsilon^2 + n\sigma_{A\beta}^2$
4 W.cell	σ_ε^2	σ_ε^2	σ_ε^2	σ_ε^2

Section 4.9 that the numerator of an F ratio should contain, in addition to the expected value terms in the denominator, one additional term. It might be helpful at this point to review several concepts introduced in Chapter 1. A test of the null hypothesis in the fixed-effects model is a test of the hypothesis that all treatment effects are equal to zero. The effect of treatment $i(\alpha_i)$ is defined as the deviation of the mean of population $i(\mu_i)$ from the grand population mean (μ),

$$\alpha_i = \mu_i - \mu.$$

In the fixed-effects model, the mean of the p treatment population means is the grand mean. The null hypothesis is written

$$H_0: \alpha_i = 0 \qquad \text{for all } i.$$

If $\alpha_i = 0$ for all i, this is equivalent to the statement that

$$\mu_1 = \mu_2 = \cdots = \mu_i = \mu.$$

It should be apparent that if the population means are all equal, the variance of the treatment effects (σ_α^2) will be equal to zero. That is, if $\mu_1 = \mu_2 = \cdots = \mu_i = \mu$ or, equivalently, if $\alpha_1 = \alpha_2 = \cdots = \alpha_i$,

$$\sigma_\alpha^2 = 0.$$

On the other hand, if the p treatment effects are not all equal,

$$\sigma_\alpha^2 > 0.$$

A test of the hypothesis that $\sigma_\alpha^2 = 0$ as opposed to the alternative that $\sigma_\alpha^2 > 0$ is made by means of an F ratio. The F ratio is constructed so that $E(MS_{\text{numerator}})$ equals $E(MS_{\text{denominator}})$ under the condition that $\sigma_\alpha^2 = 0$. An F ratio with the required form for testing MS_A, assuming a fixed-effects model, is

$$E(F) = \frac{E(MS_A)}{E(MS_{\text{w.cell}})} = \frac{\sigma_\varepsilon^2 + nq\sigma_\alpha^2}{\sigma_\varepsilon^2}.$$

Under the random-effects model, the F ratio for testing MS_A has the form

$$E(F) = \frac{E(MS_A)}{E(MS_{AB})} = \frac{\sigma_\varepsilon^2 + n\sigma_{AB}^2 + nq\sigma_A^2}{\sigma_\varepsilon^2 + n\sigma_{AB}^2}.$$

It should be noted that procedures for computing SS_A, SS_B, etc. are identical for all three models. The form of the tests of significance, however, depends on the procedures used in selecting the treatment levels included in the experiment.

ASSUMPTIONS OF RANDOM-EFFECTS AND MIXED MODELS

Under the random-effects linear model,

$$X_{ijm} = \mu + a_i + b_j + ab_{ij} + \varepsilon_{m(ij)}.$$

The assumptions underlying the random-effects model are (1) the possible values of a_i represent a random variable that is normally and independently distributed (NID), with mean = zero and variance = σ_A^2, (2) the possible values of b_j represent a random variable that is NID, with mean = zero and variance = σ_B^2, (3) the values of ab_{ij} represent a random variable that is NID, with mean = zero and variance = σ_{AB}^2, and (4) the values of the random variable $\varepsilon_{m(ij)}$ are NID, with mean = zero and variance = σ_ε^2. In stating the assumptions of the random-effects model, the convention of using roman letters (a_i, b_j) to designate random treatment effects and Greek letters (α_i, β_j) to designate fixed effects has been followed. This convention was followed in Section 4.9 but it is generally unnecessary. The distinction between random and fixed treatment effects is usually clear from the context.

The assumption of independence is particularly important in the random-effects model. That is, the p values of the random variable a_i, for example, which occur in the experiment must be independent of each other. Also, the effects a_i must be independent of b_j, ab_{ij}, and $\varepsilon_{m(ij)}$. Dependency among ε's occurs most frequently when repeated observations are obtained on subjects as in learning experiments. In such situations there is customarily a serial trend in the scores and in the associated ε's. In tracking tasks the occurrence of an error affects the likelihood of the occurrence of another error of the same magnitude or direction. This also results in statistical dependence.

The pq interaction effects are tied to the levels of treatments A and B included in the experiment. It is assumed, however, that, in the population, the average of the interaction effects over all levels of one treatment is independent of the main effects of the other treatment. That is, $\overline{AB}_{i.}$ is independent of $\overline{A}_i$ and $\overline{AB}_{.j}$ is independent of $\overline{B}_j$.

The random-effects model involves two sampling procedures. The levels of treatments included in the experiment are randomly sampled. In addition, the experimental units assigned to each treatment level are randomly sampled.

The null hypothesis for the fixed-effects model was stated earlier as

$$H_0: \alpha_i = 0 \qquad \text{for } p \text{ levels of } i.$$

The null hypothesis for the random-effects model is stated with respect to the treatment levels included in the experiment as well as all possible levels in the population sampled. If $a_i = 0$ for all possible i, then $\sigma_A^2 = 0$. The statistical hypotheses for a type CRF-pq design under Model II are usually stated as follows:

$$H_0: \sigma_A^2 = 0$$
$$H_1: \sigma_A^2 \neq 0$$

$$H_0: \sigma_B^2 = 0$$
$$H_1: \sigma_B^2 \neq 0$$

$$H_0: \sigma_{AB}^2 = 0$$
$$H_1: \sigma_{AB}^2 \neq 0.$$

Although computational procedures for the fixed-effects and random-effects models are identical, the inferences that can be drawn from the two models are quite different. Inferences under the fixed-effects model are made with respect to the treatment levels actually included in the experiment. Under the random-effects model, inferences are made with respect to the *population* of treatment levels sampled.

The assumptions underlying a mixed model, where α_i represents a fixed effect and b_j a random variable can be summarized as follows: (1) α_i represents a fixed effect, $\Sigma_{i=1}^p \alpha_i = 0$, (2) the possible values of b_j and αb_{ij} are jointly normal, with means $= 0$ and variance $= \sigma_B^2$ and $\sigma_{\alpha B}^2$, respectively, $\Sigma_{i=1}^p \alpha B_{ij} = 0$, $\Sigma_{j=1}^q \alpha B_{ij} \neq 0$, and (3) the values of the random variable $\varepsilon_{m(ij)}$ are NID, with mean $= 0$ and variance $= \sigma_\varepsilon^2$. Two variables are *jointly normal* if each set of variables is itself normal, but some of the variables are correlated. The statistical hypotheses for a type CRF-pq design in which treatments A and B represent fixed and random effects, respectively, are

$$H_0: \alpha_i = 0 \qquad \text{for all } i$$
$$H_1: \alpha_i \neq 0 \qquad \text{for some } i$$

$$H_0: \sigma_B^2 = 0$$
$$H_1: \sigma_B^2 \neq 0$$

$$H_0: \sigma_{\alpha B}^2 = 0$$
$$H_1: \sigma_{\alpha B}^2 \neq 0.$$

7.6   PROCEDURES FOR TESTING DIFFERENCES AMONG MEANS IN TYPE CRF-pq DESIGN

A PRIORI TESTS

If all orthogonal comparisons among means have been specified prior to collection of the data, t ratios may be used to make the comparisons. This procedure is described in Section 3.2. Comparisons among levels of treatment A are given by

$$t = \frac{C_j(\bar{A}_i) + C_{j'}(\bar{A}_{i'})}{\sqrt{2\text{MS}_{\text{w.cell}}/nq}} \qquad \text{df} = pq(n-1).$$

Comparisons among levels of treatment B are given by

$$t = \frac{C_j(\bar{B}_j) + C_{j'}(\bar{B}_{j'})}{\sqrt{2\text{MS}_{\text{w.cell}}/np}} \qquad \text{df} = pq(n-1).$$

When, as in the present example, the AB interaction is significant, tests of differences among means for main effects are generally of little interest to an experimenter. Under this condition, interest shifts to comparisons among means for simple main effects. If *a priori* hypotheses concerning simple main-effects means have been advanced, orthogonal comparisons among these means can be made by the t ratio. Two computational examples appear below.

Comparison of $\bar{A}_1$ with $\bar{A}_2$ at level b_1

$$t = \frac{C_j(\overline{AB}_{11}) + C_{j'}(\overline{AB}_{21})}{\sqrt{2\text{MS}_{\text{w.cell}}/n}} = \frac{1(3.75) - 1(1.75)}{\sqrt{2(.771)/4}} = \frac{2.00}{.62} = 3.23$$

$$\text{df} = pq(n-1) = 24.$$

Comparison of $\bar{B}_1$ with $\bar{B}_2$ at level a_1

$$t = \frac{C_j(\overline{AB}_{11}) + C_{j'}(\overline{AB}_{12})}{\sqrt{2\text{MS}_{\text{w.cell}}/n}} = \frac{1(3.75) - 1(4.00)}{\sqrt{2(.771)/4}} = \frac{-.25}{.62} = -.40$$

$$\text{df} = pq(n-1) = 24$$

$$t_{.05/2,24} = 2.06.$$

A POSTERIORI TESTS

A posteriori comparison procedures for Tukey's and Scheffé's tests are described in Section 3.4.

Comparisons among means by Tukey's test have the following form:

Comparison of $\bar{A}_i$ with $\bar{A}_{i'}$

$$q = \frac{C_j(\bar{A}_i) + C_j(\bar{A}_{i'})}{\sqrt{MS_{w.cell}/nq}} \qquad df = pq(n-1).$$

Comparison of $\bar{B}_j$ with $\bar{B}_{j'}$

$$q = \frac{C_j(\bar{B}_j) + C_j(\bar{B}_{j'})}{\sqrt{MS_{w.cell}/np}} \qquad df = pq(n-1).$$

Comparison of $\overline{AB}_{ij}$ with $\overline{AB}_{i'j}$ at level b_j

$$q = \frac{C_j(\overline{AB}_{ij}) + C_{j'}(\overline{AB}_{i'j})}{\sqrt{MS_{w.cell}/n}} \qquad df = pq(n-1).$$

Comparisons among means by Scheffé's test:

Comparisons of $\bar{A}_i$ with $\bar{A}_{i'}$

$$F = \frac{[C_j(\bar{A}_i) + C_{j'}(\bar{A}_{i'})]^2}{MS_{w.cell}\left[\dfrac{(C_j)^2}{nq} + \dfrac{(C_{j'})^2}{nq}\right]} \qquad df = p-1,\ pq(n-1).$$

Comparison of $\bar{B}_j$ with $\bar{B}_{j'}$ and $\bar{B}_{j''}$

$$F = \frac{[C_j(\bar{B}_j) + C_{j'}(\bar{B}_{j'}) + C_{j''}(\bar{B}_{j''})]^2}{MS_{w.cell}\left[\dfrac{(C_j)^2}{np} + \dfrac{(C_{j'})^2}{np} + \dfrac{(C_{j''})^2}{np}\right]} \qquad df = q-1,\ pq(n-1).$$

Comparison of $\overline{AB}_{ij}$ with $\overline{AB}_{ij'}$ and $\overline{AB}_{ij''}$ at level a_i

$$F = \frac{[C_j(\overline{AB}_{ij}) + C_{j'}(\overline{AB}_{ij'}) + C_{j''}(\overline{AB}_{ij''})]^2}{MS_{w.cell}\left[\dfrac{(C_j)^2}{n} + \dfrac{(C_{j'})^2}{n} + \dfrac{(C_{j''})^2}{n}\right]} \qquad df = q-1,\ pq(n-1).$$

The value of F that is significant is given by

$$(k-1)F_{\alpha;\nu_1,\nu_2},$$

where k designates the total number of means, from which specific comparisons are formed.

7.7   TESTS FOR TRENDS IN TYPE CRF-*pq* DESIGN

Analysis of variance is a convenient way to summarize the data obtained in an experiment. By analysis of variance, information from an experiment can be separated into nonoverlapping portions and decisions can be made with respect to the significance of each portion. If one or more of the treatments represent a quantitative variable, additional insight concerning the experiment may be obtained by partitioning the data into nonoverlapping trend components. The general rationale for trend analysis is described in Section 4.7.

The data presented in Table 7.3-1 can be subjected to trend analysis because treatment B represents a quantitative variable. The four levels of social deprivation correspond to successively longer periods of isolation. Although treatment A is referred to as *magnitude of reinforcement*, it is probably more realistic to assume that the two levels differ qualitatively.

TEST FOR PRESENCE OF TREND

A test of the hypothesis of *no trend* in the data for treatment B is provided by

$$F = \frac{\text{MS}_B}{\text{MS}_{\text{w.cell}}}.$$

If the F ratio is significant, it indicates that the dependent variable means are related in some manner to the independent variable of social deprivation. According to the analysis in Table 7.3-2, MS_B is significant. Thus there is a trend in the data. A graph of this trend is shown in Figure 7.7-1. If the over-all test for presence of a trend is not significant, further tests for trends with respect to treatment B should not be made unless an experimenter has advanced *a priori* hypotheses concerning specific trends. *A posteriori* procedures should be used for trend snooping, whereas *a priori* procedures can be used to carry out planned trend tests.

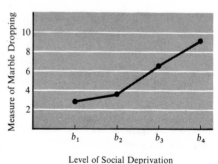

Figure 7.7-1   Over-all trend of data for levels of treatment B.

A test of the hypothesis of *no trend* for treatment A is provided by

$$F = \frac{\text{MS}_A}{\text{MS}_{\text{w.cell}}}.$$

In the present example, treatment A is not considered to represent a quantitative variable and therefore is not suitable for trend tests.

A factorial experiment enables an experimenter to make a trend test not previously described. This test provides an answer to the question,

"Is the trend of means for one treatment the same for different levels of a second treatment?" This test has the form

$$F = \frac{MS_{AB}}{MS_{w.cell}}.$$

According to the analysis of the data presented in Table 7.3-2, the AB interaction is significant. A graph illustrating the difference in trends for treatment B at the two levels of treatment A appears in Figure 7.3-1.

PARTITION OF TREATMENTS AND INTERACTION INTO TREND COMPONENTS

We noted in Section 4.7 that SS_{BG} in a completely randomized design can be partitioned into $k - 1$ trend components. Similarly, if both treatments of, say, a type CRF-34 design represent quantitative variables, the data can be partitioned into trend components as shown below. The

Source		df	Source		df
A		2	AB		6
	Linear	1		Linear × linear	1
	Quadratic	1		Linear × quadratic	1
B		3		Linear × cubic	1
	Linear	1		Quadratic × linear	1
	Quadratic	1		Quadratic × quadratic	1
	Cubic	1		Quadratic × cubic	1

reader may have difficulty visualizing the meaning of linear × linear, quadratic × cubic, etc. trend components. A response surface for a set of data is shown in Figure 7.7-2. These same data, with the exception of treatment level a_3, are presented in Table 7.3-1. Level a_3 is added to the figure for illustrative purposes. If, in a type CRF-34 design, the AB interaction is significant, it indicates that the profiles for treatment A at q levels of B are not parallel and that the profiles for B at p levels of A are not parallel.

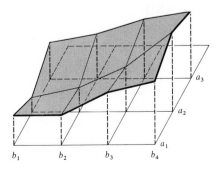

Figure 7.7-2 Response surface for data in Table 7.3-1. Treatment level a_3 added for illustrative purposes.

An examination of Figure 7.7-2 suggests that the profiles for treatment A are predominantly quadratic in form, whereas those for treatment B are linear or perhaps quadratic. Hence an experimenter might expect to find that the quadratic × linear and quadratic × quadratic interaction components are significant for these data. This type of analysis of the AB interaction provides the experimenter with an indication of the fit of differently shaped surfaces to the data.

If the AB interaction is significant, an experimenter may be interested in determining which of the trend components account for differences in the profiles of treatment A at q levels of B and which account for differences in the profiles of treatment B at p levels of A.

For the data in Table 7.3-1, it is assumed that treatment A is a qualitative variable and B is a quantitative variable. For these data, the following partition of the data into trend components is appropriate.

Source	df	
A	1	
B	3	
Linear		1
Quadratic		1
Cubic		1
AB	3	
Difference in linear trend		1
Difference in quadratic trend		1
Difference in cubic trend		1

Profiles for treatment B at the two levels of A are shown in Figure 7.3-1. The question that the analysis outlined above attempts to answer is which trend components account for the differences in the profiles.

Procedures for carrying out the trend analyses described above are presented in the following sections.

TESTS OF SIGNIFICANCE OF LINEAR AND HIGHER-ORDER TREND COMPONENTS FOR TREATMENTS

Although the AB interaction for the data presented in Table 7.3-1 is significant, an experimenter might want to know how much of the variation in the dependent variable is accounted for by the linear, quadratic, and cubic trend components. It is assumed that an experimenter has advanced *a priori* hypotheses with respect to each of the three trend components.

Alternatively, an experimenter might simply want to determine if the trend is linear or curvilinear. Tests for linearity and departure from linearity, which are described in Section 4.7, can be used to answer this question. Procedures for testing the significance of the linear, quadratic, and cubic trend components will be illustrated for treatment B. The levels of treatment B in this example are separated by equal intervals. This simplifies the computation because tables of orthogonal coefficients used in the analysis are available for the equal interval case. Procedures for deriving coefficients when treatment levels are not separated by equal intervals are described in Appendix C. Computational procedures for testing the linear, quadratic, and cubic trend components are illustrated in Table 7.7-1.

TABLE 7.7-1   Procedures for Testing Trend Components for Treatment B

		Treatment Levels			
		b_1	b_2	b_3	b_4

(i)

$$\sum_1^p B = \quad 22 \quad 28 \quad 50 \quad 72$$

Linear coefficient $(c_1) = \quad -3 \quad -1 \quad 1 \quad 3 \qquad \sum_1^q c_1^2 = 20 \quad np\sum_1^q c_1^2 = (8)(20) = 160$

Quadratic coefficient $(c_2) = \quad 1 \quad -1 \quad -1 \quad 1 \qquad \sum_1^q c_2^2 = 4 \quad np\sum_1^q c_2^2 = (8)(4) = 32$

Cubic coefficient $(c_3) = \quad -1 \quad 3 \quad -3 \quad 1 \qquad \sum_1^q c_3^2 = 20 \quad np\sum_1^q c_3^2 = (8)(20) = 160$

$(c_1)\sum_1^p B = \quad -66 \quad -28 \quad 50 \quad 216 \qquad B_1 = \sum_1^q \left(c_1 \sum_1^p B \right) = 172$

$(c_2)\sum_1^p B = \quad 22 \quad -28 \quad -50 \quad 72 \qquad B_2 = \sum_1^q \left(c_2 \sum_1^p B \right) = 16$

$(c_3)\sum_1^p B = \quad -22 \quad 84 \quad -150 \quad 72 \qquad B_3 = \sum_1^q \left(c_3 \sum_1^p B \right) = -16$

(ii)

$$\text{SS}_{\text{lin}} = \frac{B_1^2}{np\sum_1^q c_1^2} = \frac{(172)^2}{160} = 184.900 \qquad\qquad \text{MS}_{\text{lin}} = \frac{\text{SS}_{\text{lin}}}{df} = \frac{184.900}{1} = 184.900$$

$$df = 1$$

$$F = \frac{\text{MS}_{\text{lin}}}{\text{MS}_{\text{w.cell}}} = \frac{184.900}{.771} = 239.82$$

$$\text{SS}_{\text{quad}} = \frac{B_2^2}{np\sum_1^q c_2^2} = \frac{(16)^2}{32} = 8.000 \qquad\qquad \text{MS}_{\text{quad}} = \frac{\text{SS}_{\text{quad}}}{df} = \frac{8.000}{1} = 8.000$$

$$df = 1$$

$$F = \frac{\text{MS}_{\text{quad}}}{\text{MS}_{\text{w.cell}}} = \frac{8.000}{.771} = 10.38$$

TABLE 7.7-1 (continued)

$$SS_{cubic} = \frac{B_3^2}{np\sum\limits_{1}^{q} c_3^2} = \frac{(-16)^2}{160} = 1.600 \qquad MS_{cubic} = \frac{SS_{cubic}}{df} = \frac{1.600}{1} = 1.600$$

$$df = 1$$

$$F = \frac{MS_{cubic}}{MS_{w.cell}} = \frac{1.600}{.771} = 2.08$$

$$F_{.05;1,24} = 4.26$$

It is apparent from the analysis in Table 7.7-1 that the linear and quadratic trend components are significant, but the cubic component is not. Therefore the curve in Figure 7.7-1, which depicts the over-all trend with respect to treatment B, can be described by an equation of the form

$$X = a + bY + cY^2.$$

Procedures for fitting a polynomial equation to the curve shown in Figure 7.7-1 are described in Section 4.7. A visual inspection of this curve suggests that the linear component of the trend accounts for more of the variation than does the quadratic component. This is easily verified by the following calculations:

$$\frac{SS_{lin}}{SS_B} = \frac{184.9}{194.5} \times 100 = 95.1 \text{ percent}$$

$$\frac{SS_{quad}}{SS_B} = \frac{8.0}{194.5} \times 100 = 4.1 \text{ percent.}$$

Thus the linear component accounts for 95.1 percent of the variation, whereas the quadratic component accounts for only 4.1 percent of the variation.

The partition of the data into trend components with respect to treatment A follows the same computational procedures as those shown in Table 7.7-1. This process will not be illustrated because treatment A has only two levels, the over-all test for trends was insignificant, and, in addition, this treatment is not considered to represent a quantitative variable.

TESTS OF SIGNIFICANCE OF TREND COMPONENTS FOR *AB* INTERACTION

If, in a type CRF-24 design, the two treatments represent quantitative variables, the three degrees of freedom for interaction can be partitioned into lin × lin, lin × quad, and lin × cubic components. To illustrate, assume that both treatments for the data presented in Table 7.3-1 are quantitative variables. The orthogonal coefficients for treatments A and B are

	Treatment A		*Treatment B*			
Linear coefficient (c_1) = 1 − 1		Linear coefficient (c_1) =	−3	−1	1	3
		Quadratic coefficient (c_2) =	1	−1	−1	1
		Cubic coefficient (c_3) =	−1	3	−3	1

The products of the coefficients for treatments A and B are

A lin × B lin	*A lin × B quad*	*A lin × B cubic*
$d_{11} =$ 1 × −3 = −3	$d_{11} =$ 1 × 1 = 1	$d_{11} =$ 1 × −1 = −1
$d_{12} =$ 1 × −1 = −1	$d_{12} =$ 1 × −1 = −1	$d_{12} =$ 1 × 3 = 3
$d_{13} =$ 1 × 1 = 1	$d_{13} =$ 1 × −1 = −1	$d_{13} =$ 1 × −3 = −3
$d_{14} =$ 1 × 3 = 3	$d_{14} =$ 1 × 1 = 1	$d_{14} =$ 1 × 1 = 1
$d_{21} =$ −1 × −3 = 3	$d_{21} =$ −1 × 1 = −1	$d_{21} =$ −1 × −1 = 1
$d_{22} =$ −1 × −1 = 1	$d_{22} =$ −1 × −1 = 1	$d_{22} =$ −1 × 3 = −3
$d_{23} =$ −1 × 1 = −1	$d_{23} =$ −1 × −1 = 1	$d_{23} =$ −1 × −3 = 3
$d_{24} =$ −1 × 3 = −3	$d_{24} =$ −1 × 1 = −1	$d_{24} =$ −1 × 1 = −1

Computation of the AB interaction trend components, using the foregoing d_{ij} coefficients, is illustrated in Table 7.7-2. According to the analysis in Table 7.7-2, the lin × lin trend component accounts for $(13.225/19.375) \times 100 = 68.3$ percent of the variation due to the AB interaction.

SIGNIFICANCE OF DIFFERENCES FOR TREND COMPONENTS

An over-all test of the hypothesis that the trend for one treatment is the same at all levels of a second treatment is given by $F = \mathrm{MS}_{AB}/\mathrm{MS}_{\mathrm{w.cell}}$. If this test is significant, it may be of interest to determine whether the interaction is due to *differences* in the linear trend, the quadratic trend, the cubic trend, or several of the trends. Procedures for testing the significance of differences for trend components are illustrated in Table 7.7-3.

According to the analysis in Table 7.7-3, a major part of the variation associated with the AB interaction (68.3 percent) can be attributed to a difference in the linear trends. The reader may have noted that when one treatment has only two levels, $\mathrm{SS}_{\mathrm{lin \times lin}} = \mathrm{SS}_{AB \text{ diff in lin trend}}$.

A POSTERIORI TREND ANALYSIS PROCEDURES

The probability of rejecting one or more null hypotheses in trend analysis, even though all are true, is given by $1 - (1 - \alpha)^C$, where α is

TABLE 7.7-2   Procedures for Testing Significance of Interaction Trend Components

(i)

Treatment level combination AB_{1j} =	15	16	28	32
Treatment level combination AB_{2j} =	7	12	22	40

(ii)

$$d_{1j(\text{lin} \times \text{lin})} = \quad -3 \quad -1 \quad 1 \quad 3$$

$$d_{2j(\text{lin} \times \text{lin})} = \quad 3 \quad 1 \quad -1 \quad -3$$

$$d_{1j(\text{lin} \times \text{quad})} = \quad 1 \quad -1 \quad -1 \quad 1$$

$$d_{2j(\text{lin} \times \text{quad})} = \quad -1 \quad 1 \quad 1 \quad -1$$

$$d_{1j(\text{lin} \times \text{cubic})} = \quad -1 \quad 3 \quad -3 \quad 1$$

$$d_{2j(\text{lin} \times \text{cubic})} = \quad 1 \quad -3 \quad 3 \quad -1$$

(iii)

$$SS_{\text{lin} \times \text{lin}} = \frac{\left[\sum_1^p \sum_1^q d_{ij(\text{lin} \times \text{lin})}(AB_{ij})\right]^2}{n\left[\sum_1^p \sum_1^q d_{ij(\text{lin} \times \text{lin})}^2\right]} = \frac{[(-3)(15) + (-1)(16) + \cdots + (-3)(40)]^2}{4[(-3)^2 + (-1)^2 + \cdots + (-3)^2]}$$

$$= \frac{(46)^2}{4(40)} = 13.225$$

$$df = 1$$

$$F = \frac{MS_{\text{lin} \times \text{lin}}}{MS_{\text{w.cell}}} = \frac{13.225}{.771} = 17.15$$

$$SS_{\text{lin} \times \text{quad}} = \frac{\left[\sum_1^p \sum_1^q d_{ij(\text{lin} \times \text{quad})}(AB_{ij})\right]^2}{n\left[\sum_1^p \sum_1^q d_{ij(\text{lin} \times \text{quad})}^2\right]} = \frac{[(1)(15) + (-1)(16) + \cdots + (-1)(40)]^2}{4[(1)^2 + (-1)^2 + \cdots + (-1)^2]}$$

$$= \frac{(10)^2}{4(8)} = 3.125$$

$$F = \frac{MS_{\text{lin} \times \text{quad}}}{MS_{\text{w.cell}}} = \frac{3.125}{.771} = 4.05$$

$$SS_{\text{lin} \times \text{cubic}} = \frac{\left[\sum_1^p \sum_1^q d_{ij(\text{lin} \times \text{cub})}(AB_{ij})\right]^2}{n\left[\sum_1^p \sum_1^q d_{ij(\text{lin} \times \text{cub})}^2\right]} = \frac{[(-1)(15) + (3)(16) + \cdots + (-1)(40)]^2}{4[(-1)^2 + (3)^2 + \cdots + (-1)^2]}$$

$$= \frac{(22)^2}{4(40)} = 3.025$$

$$F = \frac{MS_{\text{lin} \times \text{cubic}}}{MS_{\text{w.cell}}} = \frac{3.025}{.771} = 3.92$$

$$F_{.05;1,24} = 4.26$$

the level of significance adopted for each test and C is the number of trend tests performed. The error rate familywise for the data in Tables 7.7-1, 7.7-2, and 7.7-3 is equal to $1 - (1 - .95)^3 \simeq .14$. If an experimenter has not advanced specific hypotheses concerning trends prior to an analysis of the data, he can use Dunn's or Scheffé's procedures to assign the same error rate per family or familywise as that allotted to tests of main effects or interaction F ratios. The computational formulas for trend analysis are unchanged. The value that F_{obs} must exceed in order to be declared significant for Dunn's procedure is equal to $F_{\alpha/C;\nu_1,\nu_2}$, where C is the number of trend tests performed.

TABLE 7.7-3 Procedures for Testing Significance of Differences for Trend Components

(i)

Treatment level combination AB_{1j} = 15   16   28   32

Treatment level combination AB_{2j} = 7   12   22   40

(ii)

$$\text{Linear coefficient } (c_1) = \quad -3 \quad -1 \quad 1 \quad 3 \qquad \sum_1^q c_1^2 = 20$$

$$\text{Quadratic coefficient } (c_2) = \quad 1 \quad -1 \quad -1 \quad 1 \qquad \sum_1^q c_2^2 = 4$$

$$\text{Cubic coefficient } (c_3) = \quad -1 \quad 3 \quad -3 \quad 1 \qquad \sum_1^q c_3^2 = 20$$

(iii)

$$\sum_1^q (c_k)(AB_{ij})$$

$$(c_1)(AB_{1j}) = \quad -45 \quad -16 \quad 28 \quad 96 = \quad 63$$

$$(c_1)(AB_{2j}) = \quad -21 \quad -12 \quad 22 \quad 120 = \quad 109$$

$$(c_2)(AB_{1j}) = \quad 15 \quad -16 \quad -28 \quad 32 = \quad 3$$

$$(c_2)(AB_{2j}) = \quad 7 \quad -12 \quad -22 \quad 40 = \quad 13$$

$$(c_3)(AB_{1j}) = \quad -15 \quad 48 \quad -84 \quad 32 = \quad -19$$

$$(c_3)(AB_{2j}) = \quad -7 \quad 36 \quad -66 \quad 40 = \quad 3$$

(iv)

$$SS_{AB \text{ diff in lin trend}} = \frac{\sum\limits_1^p \left[\sum\limits_1^q (c_1)(AB_{ij}) \right]^2}{n \sum\limits_1^q c_1^2} - \frac{\left[\sum\limits_1^p \sum\limits_1^q (c_1)(AB_{ij}) \right]^2}{np \sum\limits_1^q c_1^2} = \frac{(63)^2}{4(20)} + \frac{(109)^2}{4(20)}$$

$$- \frac{(172)^2}{(4)(2)(20)} = 13.225$$

$$df = 1$$

$$F = \frac{MS_{AB \text{ diff in lin trend}}}{MS_{w.cell}} = \frac{13.225}{.771} = 17.15$$

$$SS_{AB \text{ diff in quad trend}} = \frac{\sum\limits_1^p \left[\sum\limits_1^q (c_2)(AB_{ij}) \right]^2}{n \sum\limits_1^q c_2^2} - \frac{\left[\sum\limits_1^p \sum\limits_1^q (c_2)(AB_{ij}) \right]^2}{np \sum\limits_1^q c_2^2} = \frac{(3)^2}{4(4)} + \frac{(13)^2}{4(4)}$$

$$- \frac{(16)^2}{(4)(2)(4)} = 3.125$$

$$F = \frac{MS_{AB \text{ diff in quad trend}}}{MS_{w.cell}} = \frac{3.125}{.771} = 4.05$$

TABLE 7.7-3 (continued)

$$SS_{AB \text{ diff in cubic trend}} = \frac{\sum\limits_{1}^{p}\left[\sum\limits_{1}^{q}(c_3)(AB_{ij})\right]^2}{n\sum\limits_{1}^{q}c_3^2} - \frac{\left[\sum\limits_{1}^{p}\sum\limits_{1}^{q}(c_3)(AB_{ij})\right]^2}{np\sum\limits_{1}^{q}c_3^2} = \frac{(-19)^2}{4(20)} + \frac{(3)^2}{4(20)}$$

$$- \frac{(-16)^2}{(4)(2)(20)} = 3.025$$

$$F = \frac{MS_{AB \text{ diff in cubic trend}}}{MS_{\text{w.cell}}} = \frac{3.025}{.771} = 3.92 \qquad F_{.05;1,24} = 4.26$$

7.8   ESTIMATING STRENGTH OF ASSOCIATION IN TYPE CRF-*pq* DESIGN

A significant F ratio for treatment effects in a type CRF-pq design indicates that some relationship exists between the dependent variable and the treatment levels. Although this information is useful, it provides no information concerning the strength of the association. An estimate of strength of association for a fixed-effects model when the *numerical value* of the dependent variable and the treatment *levels* of the independent variable are specified is given by ω^2. The three measures of association for the data in Table 7.3-2 are

$$\hat{\omega}^2_{X|A} = \frac{SS_A - (p - 1)\,MS_{\text{w.cell}}}{SS_{\text{total}} + MS_{\text{w.cell}}} = \frac{3.125 - (2 - 1)(.771)}{235.500 + .771} = .01$$

$$\hat{\omega}^2_{X|B} = \frac{SS_B - (q - 1)\,MS_{\text{w.cell}}}{SS_{\text{total}} + MS_{\text{w.cell}}} = \frac{194.500 - (4 - 1)(.771)}{235.500 + .771} = .81$$

$$\hat{\omega}^2_{X|AB} = \frac{SS_{AB} - (p - 1)(q - 1)\,MS_{\text{w.cell}}}{SS_{\text{total}} + MS_{\text{w.cell}}}$$

$$= \frac{19.375 - (2 - 1)(4 - 1)(.771)}{235.500 + .771} = .07.$$

According to the above analysis, treatment B (level of social deprivation) accounts for an appreciable proportion of the variance in the dependent variable ($\omega^2_{X|B} = .81$), while treatment A (magnitude of reinforcement) accounts for a negligible portion of the variance ($\omega^2_{X|A} = .01$). It is interesting to note that specifying the treatment combination for both A and B accounts for an additional 7 percent of the variance. If the computed value of $\hat{\omega}^2$ is negative, $\hat{\omega}^2$ is set equal to zero. If the F ratio for the treatment of interest is significant, the value of $\hat{\omega}^2$ will be positive. Information concerning the proportion of variance in the dependent variable accounted for by the treatments is most useful to an experimenter in interpreting the outcome of research. It cannot be emphasized enough that a *trivial* association may achieve statistical significance if the sample is made sufficiently large.

A comparable measure of strength of association for a random-effects model is the intraclass correlation (ρI). For treatment A, the intraclass correlation is equal to

$$\rho I_{X|A} = \frac{\sigma_A^2}{\sigma_A^2 + \sigma_B^2 + \sigma_{AB}^2 + \sigma_\varepsilon^2}.$$

Estimates of the different variance components required to compute ρI can be obtained from the analysis of variance. E(MS) for the random-effects model are given in Table 7.5-1. According to this table, the expected values of the mean squares are

$$\text{E(MS}_A) = \sigma_\varepsilon^2 + n\sigma_{AB}^2 + nq\sigma_A^2$$

$$\text{E(MS}_B) = \sigma_\varepsilon^2 + n\sigma_{AB}^2 + np\sigma_B^2$$

$$\text{E(MS}_{AB}) = \sigma_\varepsilon^2 + n\sigma_{AB}^2$$

$$\text{E(MS}_{\text{w.cell}}) = \sigma_\varepsilon^2.$$

Thus estimates of the variance components can be obtained by the following formulas:

$$\hat{\sigma}_A^2 = \frac{\text{MS}_A - \text{MS}_{AB}}{nq}$$

$$\hat{\sigma}_B^2 = \frac{\text{MS}_B - \text{MS}_{AB}}{np}$$

$$\hat{\sigma}_{AB}^2 = \frac{\text{MS}_{AB} - \text{MS}_{\text{w.cell}}}{n}$$

$$\hat{\sigma}_\varepsilon^2 = \text{MS}_{\text{w.cell}}.$$

If any of the preceding component estimates are negative in sign, the component is estimated to be zero. Formulas for estimating the intraclass correlation for treatment B and interaction AB are, respectively,

$$\hat{\rho} I_{X|B} = \frac{\hat{\sigma}_B^2}{\hat{\sigma}_A^2 + \hat{\sigma}_B^2 + \hat{\sigma}_{AB}^2 + \hat{\sigma}_\varepsilon^2}$$

$$\hat{\rho} I_{X|AB} = \frac{\hat{\sigma}_{AB}^2}{\hat{\sigma}_A^2 + \hat{\sigma}_B^2 + \hat{\sigma}_{AB}^2 + \hat{\sigma}_\varepsilon^2}.$$

The magnitude of treatment effects can be interpreted directly in terms of variance components. This alternative approach to analyzing the outcome of research is described in Section 5.2. Additional applications of variance components are discussed by Bross (1950), Hays (1963; 422–424, 437–438, 446–447), Scheffé (1959, 231–235), and Tukey (1953).

7.9   THE PROBLEM OF UNEQUAL CELL n's

Although it is desirable to have equal n's in each cell of a completely randomized factorial design, this is not always possible. Three general reasons for unequal n's and the appropriate analysis procedures for each situation are presented in this section.

CONVENTIONAL ANALYSIS FOR UNEQUAL CELL n's

In some research situations the experimenter may choose, for convenience, to obtain a different number of observations for the treatment combinations. This might occur if the treatment levels require different kinds of equipment that are in limited supply and if the levels are to be administered to all subjects at the same time. If, for example, 20 units of equipment associated with treatment level a_2 are available but only 12 units associated with level a_1, an experimenter might decide to assign 32 subjects to the two levels so as to utilize all available equipment. In this example, 12 subjects would be assigned to level a_1 and 20 subjects to level a_2. In order for the analysis to be valid, it must be assumed that the availability of equipment is not related to the nature of the independent variables in the experiment. As long as a particular proportionality exists among the treatment combination n's, a conventional analysis is appropriate. Three examples illustrating this proportionality are shown in Table 7.9-1. For example, the n's for the AB Summary Table (c) are $1:3 =$

TABLE 7.9-1   Examples Illustrating Proportionality Among Cell n's

(i)

AB Summary Table (a)

	b_1	b_2	b_3	b_4	n_i
a_1	$n = 3$	$n = 3$	$n = 3$	$n = 3$	12
a_2	$n = 5$	$n = 5$	$n = 5$	$n = 5$	20
$n_j = $	8	8	8	8	

AB Summary Table (b)

	b_1	b_2	b_3	b_4	n_i
a_1	$n = 3$	$n = 4$	$n = 4$	$n = 5$	16
a_2	$n = 3$	$n = 4$	$n = 4$	$n = 5$	16
$n_j = $	6	8	8	10	

AB Summary Table (c)

	b_1	b_2	b_3	b_4	n_i
a_1	$n = 1$	$n = 1$	$n = 2$	$n = 4$	8
a_2	$n = 3$	$n = 3$	$n = 6$	$n = 12$	24
$n_j = $	4	4	8	16	

TABLE 7.9-1 (continued)

(ii)

Modified computational symbols required when n's are proportional:

$$[A] = \sum_1^p \frac{\left(\sum_1^q A\right)^2}{n_i} \qquad [B] = \sum_1^q \frac{\left(\sum_1^p B\right)^2}{n_j} \qquad [AB] = \sum_1^p \sum_1^q \frac{(AB)^2}{n_{ij}}$$

$1:3 = 2:6 = 4:12$ and $1:1:2:4 = 3:3:6:12$. Modification of the computational symbols required for a *conventional analysis* is shown in part (ii) of Table 7.9-1.

TABLE 7.9-2   Unweighted Means Analysis for Type CRF-24 Design

(i) Data:

ABS Summary Table

a_1	a_1	a_1	a_1	a_2	a_2	a_2	a_2
b_1	b_2	b_3	b_4	b_1	b_2	b_3	b_4
3	3	7	6	1	2	5	10
6	4	8	7	2	3	6	10
3	5	7	8	2	4	5	9
	4		9	2	3	6	11
	3		8				
$\sum_1^n AB = 12$	19	22	38	7	12	22	40

$\overline{AB}$ Summary Table

	b_1	b_2	b_3	b_4	$\sum_1^q \overline{A}$	$\dfrac{\left(\sum_1^q \overline{A}\right)^2}{q}$
a_1	$n = 3$ 4.00	$n = 5$ 3.80	$n = 3$ 7.33	$n = 5$ 7.60	22.73	129.16
a_2	$n = 4$ 1.75	$n = 4$ 3.00	$n = 4$ 5.50	$n = 4$ 10.00	20.25	102.52
$\sum_1^p \overline{B} =$	5.75	6.80	12.83	17.60		
$\dfrac{\left(\sum_1^p \overline{B}\right)^2}{p} =$	16.53	23.12	82.30	154.88		

Note: Entries in $\overline{AB}$ Summary Table are cell means, e.g.,

$\overline{AB}_{11} = \frac{12}{3} = 4.00$.

TABLE 7.9-2 (continued)

(ii) Computational symbols:

$$\sum_1^N (ABS)^2 = [ABS] = (3)^2 + (6)^2 + \cdots + (11)^2 = 1160.00$$

$$\sum_1^p \sum_1^q \frac{\left(\sum_1^n AB\right)^2}{n_{ij}} = [AB] = \frac{(12)^2}{3} + \frac{(19)^2}{5} + \cdots + \frac{(40)^2}{4} = 1139.58$$

$$\sum_1^p \sum_1^q \overline{AB} = 4.00 + 3.80 + \cdots + 10.00 = 42.98$$

$$\sum_1^p \sum_1^q (\overline{AB})^2 = [\overline{AB}] = (4.00)^2 + (3.80)^2 + \cdots + (10.00)^2 = 284.24$$

$$\frac{\left(\sum_1^p \sum_1^q \overline{AB}\right)^2}{pq} = [\overline{X}] = \frac{(42.98)^2}{(2)(4)} = 230.91$$

$$\sum_1^p \frac{\left(\sum_1^q \overline{A}\right)^2}{q} = [\overline{A}] = 129.16 + 102.52 = 231.68$$

$$\sum_1^q \frac{\left(\sum_1^p \overline{B}\right)^2}{p} = [\overline{B}] = 16.53 + 23.12 + \cdots + 154.88 = 276.83$$

$$\tilde{n} = \frac{pq}{1/n_{ij} + 1/n_{ij} + \cdots + 1/n_{ij}} = \frac{(2)(4)}{\frac{1}{3} + \frac{1}{5} + \cdots + \frac{1}{4}} = 3.87$$

(iii) Computational formulas:

$$SS_A = \tilde{n}([\overline{A}] - [\overline{X}]) = \quad 2.98 \qquad SS_{AB} = \tilde{n}([\overline{AB}] - [\overline{A}] - [\overline{B}] + [\overline{X}]) = 25.70$$

$$SS_B = \tilde{n}([\overline{B}] - [\overline{X}]) = 177.71 \qquad SS_{w.cell} = [ABS] - [AB] = 20.42$$

UNWEIGHTED MEANS ANALYSIS

An experimenter may plan to have equal n's in each treatment combination; but, for reasons unrelated to the nature of the treatments, data for some subjects are not obtained. One common reason for *losing* data is equipment failure. Unequal n's may also result from the unavailability of subjects during the experiment. Subjects may be unavailable because they have forgotten their appointments, are ill, or, in the case of animal subjects, have died. If unequal n's occur for reasons not related to the nature of the particular treatments used in the experiment, and the cell n's do not have the proportionality shown in Table 7.9-1, an unweighted means analysis may be used. Procedures for carrying out this analysis are shown in Table 7.9-2. The results of this analysis are summarized in Table 7.9-3. Note that the *total sum of squares* is not included in the table. It is not included because in an unweighted means analysis the sum of squares for A, B, AB, and within cell do not add up to the total sum of squares. The

TABLE 7.9-3   Analysis of Variance Table for Unweighted Means Analysis

Source	SS	df	MS	F
1 A	2.98	$p - 1 = 1$	2.98	$[\frac{1}{4}] = 3.51$
2 B	177.71	$q - 1 = 3$	59.24	$[\frac{2}{4}] = 69.69*$
3 AB	25.70	$(p - 1)(q - 1) = 3$	8.57	$[\frac{3}{4}] = 10.08*$
4 W.cell	20.42	$N - pq = 24$	.85	

$*p < .01.$

analysis shown in Table 7.9-3 gives equal weight to the data in each cell, although some cells contain more data than others. Computation of the sum of squares for treatments A and B and the interaction is based on the $\overline{AB}$ Summary Table, which contains cell means. If n's for each cell are equal, the unweighted means analysis and a conventional analysis give identical results. Comparisons among means follow the procedures outlined in Section 7.6. A test for comparing means based on unequal n's has the form

$$t = \frac{C_j(\overline{A}_i) + C_{j'}(\overline{A}_{i'})}{\sqrt{\mathrm{MS}_{\mathrm{w.cell}}\left[\dfrac{1}{n_i} + \dfrac{1}{n_{i'}}\right]}}.$$

Tukey's test for comparisons involving unequal n's has the following form:

$$q = \frac{C_j(\overline{A}_i) + C_{j'}(\overline{A}_{i'})}{\sqrt{\mathrm{MS}_{\mathrm{w.cell}}/\tilde{n}}}.$$

This formula is appropriate if the n's are not too different.

The unweighted means analysis uses available data in each cell to provide an estimate of a cell mean. If all observations within a cell are missing, an estimate of the cell mean must be obtained from data in other cells. No completely satisfactory method exists for estimating a cell mean when all data within the cell are missing. A discussion of methods and problems involved in estimating a missing cell mean is given by Federer (1955; 124–127, 133–134).

A relatively simple procedure for obtaining an estimate of a cell mean uses the following formula:

$$\overline{AB}'_{ij} = \overline{A}_i + \overline{B}_j - \overline{ABS},$$

where $\overline{AB}'_{ij}$ = estimate of missing cell mean.

$\overline{A}_i$ = mean of observations in treatment level a_i that contains missing cell.

$\overline{B}_j$ = mean of observations in treatment level b_j that contains missing cell.

$\overline{ABS}$ = mean of available observations.

To illustrate, assume that cell AB_{23} in the AB Summary Table of Table 7.3-1 is missing. An estimate of this cell mean is

$$\overline{AB}_{23}' = \bar{A}_2 + \bar{B}_3 - \overline{ABS} = 4.92 + 7.00 - 5.36 = 6.56.$$

This estimate can be substituted in the data matrix and an unweighted means analysis performed. The degrees of freedom for interaction should be reduced by the number of missing cells that have been estimated. The procedure described above does not take into account interaction among the treatments. There is no completely satisfactory procedure for estimating the mean of a missing cell in the absence of knowledge concerning the interaction.

LEAST-SQUARES ANALYSIS

A third general class of situations that result in unequal n's is described in this section. If an experimenter intends to have equal cell n's but unequal n's are present for reasons related to the nature of the treatments, a least-squares solution should be used. In the example of the effects of social deprivation and magnitude of reinforcement, some of the children in the 20-minute deprivation group might refuse to play the marble game because of their low need for adult approval. In this example, missing data are related to the nature of the treatment levels used in the experiment.

Computational procedures for a least-squares solution are more complex than for an unweighted means analysis. The rationale underlying a least-squares analysis for unequal n's has been presented by Kempthorne (1952, 79). The general nature of a least-squares analysis is as follows. It was shown in Section 1.4 that the error effect for a completely randomized factorial design can be written

$$\varepsilon_{m(ij)} = X_{ijm} - \alpha_i - \beta_j - \alpha\beta_{ij} - \mu.$$

The method of least-squares is a mathematical technique involving differential calculus for finding values of the estimators $\hat{\alpha}_i$, $\hat{\beta}_j$, $\widehat{\alpha\beta}_{ij}$, and $\hat{\mu}$ such that

$$\sum_1^p\sum_1^q\sum_1^n \hat{\varepsilon}_{m(ij)}^2 = \sum_1^p\sum_1^q\sum_1^n (X_{ijm} - \hat{\alpha}_i - \hat{\beta}_j - \widehat{\alpha\beta}_{ij} - \hat{\mu})^2 = \text{minimum}.$$

According to the least-squares principle, the appropriate estimates of α_i, β_j, $\alpha\beta_{ij}$, and μ are those values that make the error sum of squares as small as possible. It can be shown that if $\varepsilon_{m(ij)}$ is normally and independently distributed, the method yields essentially the same estimates as the more complex method of maximum likelihood.

The computational procedures illustrated in Table 7.9-4 for obtaining an *adjusted* sum of squares for treatment B is known as the Dwyer square-root algorithm (Dwyer, 1951). The analysis is summarized in Table 7.9-5.

**TABLE 7.9-4   Least-Squares Solution by Dwyer
Square-Root Algorithm**

(i)

AB Summary Table

	b_1	b_2	b_3	b_4	$\sum_1^q A_{ij}$
a_1	$n_{11} = 3$	$n_{12} = 5$	$n_{13} = 3$	$n_{14} = 5$	$\Sigma n_{1j} = 16$
	12	19	22	38	91
a_2	$n_{21} = 4$	$n_{22} = 4$	$n_{23} = 4$	$n_{24} = 4$	$\Sigma n_{2j} = 16$
	7	12	22	40	81
$\sum_1^p n_{ij} = 7$	9	7	9		
$\sum_1^p B_{ij} = 19$	31	44	78		

(ii)

	n_1'	n_2'	n_3'	n_4'	$n_5' = B_j'$
n_1'	5.4375	-1.9375	-1.5625	-1.9375	-18.3125
n_2'		6.4375	-1.9375	-2.5625	-17.6875
n_3'			5.4375	-1.9375	6.6875
n_4'				6.4375	29.3125

$$n_{11}' = \Sigma n_{i1} - \frac{n_{11}^2}{\Sigma n_{1j}} - \frac{n_{21}^2}{\Sigma n_{2j}} = 7 - \frac{(3)^2}{16} - \frac{(4)^2}{16} = 5.4375$$

$$n_{12}' = -\left[\frac{n_{11}n_{12}}{\Sigma n_{1j}} + \frac{n_{21}n_{22}}{\Sigma n_{2j}}\right] = -\left[\frac{(3)(5)}{16} + \frac{(4)(4)}{16}\right] = -1.9375$$

$$n_{13}' = -\left[\frac{n_{11}n_{13}}{\Sigma n_{1j}} + \frac{n_{21}n_{23}}{\Sigma n_{2j}}\right] = -\left[\frac{(3)(3)}{16} + \frac{(4)(4)}{16}\right] = -1.5625$$

.   .   .   .
.   .   .   .
.   .   .   .

$$n_{22}' = \Sigma n_{i2} - \frac{n_{12}^2}{\Sigma n_{1j}} - \frac{n_{22}^2}{\Sigma n_{2j}} = 9 - \frac{(5)^2}{16} - \frac{(4)^2}{16} = 6.4375$$

$$n_{23}' = -\left[\frac{n_{12}n_{13}}{\Sigma n_{1j}} + \frac{n_{22}n_{23}}{\Sigma n_{2j}}\right] = -\left[\frac{(5)(3)}{16} + \frac{(4)(4)}{16}\right] = -1.9375$$

$$n_{24}' = -\left[\frac{n_{12}n_{14}}{\Sigma n_{1j}} + \frac{n_{22}n_{24}}{\Sigma n_{2j}}\right] = -\left[\frac{(5)(5)}{16} + \frac{(4)(4)}{16}\right] = -2.5625$$

$$n_{33}' = \Sigma n_{i3} - \frac{n_{13}^2}{\Sigma n_{1j}} - \frac{n_{23}^2}{\Sigma n_{2j}} = 7 - \frac{(3)^2}{16} - \frac{(4)^2}{16} = 5.4375$$

.   .   .   .
.   .   .   .

TABLE 7.9-4 (continued)

$$B'_1 = \sum_1^p B_{i1} - \left[\frac{n_{11}\sum_1^q A_{1j}}{\sum n_{1j}} + \frac{n_{21}\sum_1^q A_{2j}}{\sum n_{2j}}\right] = 19 - \left[\frac{3(91)}{16} + \frac{4(81)}{16}\right] = -18.3125$$

$$B'_2 = \sum_1^p B_{i2} - \left[\frac{n_{12}\sum_1^q A_{1j}}{\sum n_{1j}} + \frac{n_{22}\sum_1^q A_{2j}}{\sum n_{2j}}\right] = 31 - \left[\frac{5(91)}{16} + \frac{4(81)}{16}\right] = -17.6875$$

$$B'_3 = \sum_1^p B_{i3} - \left[\frac{n_{13}\sum_1^q A_{1j}}{\sum n_{1j}} + \frac{n_{23}\sum_1^q A_{2j}}{\sum n_{2j}}\right] = 44 - \left[\frac{3(91)}{16} + \frac{4(81)}{16}\right] = 6.6875$$

$$B'_4 = \sum_1^p B_{i4} - \left[\frac{n_{14}\sum_1^q A_{1j}}{\sum n_{1j}} + \frac{n_{24}\sum_1^q A_{2j}}{\sum n_{2j}}\right] = 78 - \left[\frac{5(91)}{16} + \frac{4(81)}{16}\right] = 29.3125$$

Computational check $\sum_{j=1}^q n'_{ij} = 0$; e.g., $\sum_{j=1}^q n'_{3j} = -1.5625 - 1.9375 + 5.4375 - 1.9375 = 0$.

(iii)

	n''_1	n''_2	n''_3	n''_4	$n''_5 = B''_j$
n''_1	2.3318	−.8309	−.6701	−.8309	−7.8534
n''_2		2.3974	−1.0405	−1.3569	−10.1001
n''_3			1.9763	−1.9765	−4.5966

$$n''_{11} = \sqrt{n'_{11}} = \sqrt{5.4375} = 2.3318$$

$$n''_{1j} = \frac{n'_{1j}}{n''_{11}}, \qquad j > 1$$

$$n''_{12} = \frac{n'_{12}}{n''_{11}} = \frac{-1.9375}{2.3318} = -.8309$$

$$n''_{13} = \frac{n'_{13}}{n''_{11}} = \frac{-1.5625}{2.3318} = -.6701$$

$$\begin{matrix} . & . & . & . \\ . & . & . & . \\ . & . & . & . \end{matrix}$$

$$n''_{15} = \frac{n'_{15}}{n''_{11}} = \frac{-18.3125}{2.3318} = -7.8534$$

$$n''_{22} = \sqrt{n'_{22} - n''^2_{12}} = \sqrt{6.4375 - (-.8309)^2} = 2.3973$$

$$n''_{2j} = \frac{n'_{2j} - n''_{12}n''_{1j}}{n''_{22}}, \qquad j > 2$$

$$n''_{23} = \frac{n'_{23} - n''_{12}n''_{13}}{n''_{22}} = \frac{-1.9375 - (-.8309)(-.6701)}{2.3974} = -1.0405$$

$$\begin{matrix} . & . & . & . \\ . & . & . & . \\ . & . & . & . \end{matrix}$$

TABLE 7.9-4 (continued)

$$n''_{25} = \frac{n'_{25} - n''_{12}n''_{15}}{n''_{22}} = \frac{-17.6875 - (-.8309)(-7.8534)}{2.3974} = -10.1001$$

$$n''_{33} = \sqrt{n'_{33} - n''^2_{13} - n''^2_{23}} = \sqrt{5.4375 - (-.6701)^2 - (-1.0405)^2} = 1.9763$$

$$n''_{3j} = \frac{n'_{3j} - n''_{13}n''_{1j} - n''_{23}n''_{2j}}{n''_{33}}, \qquad j > 3$$

$$.$$
$$.$$
$$.$$

$$n''_{35} = \frac{n'_{35} - n''_{13}n''_{15} - n''_{23}n''_{25}}{n''_{33}} = \frac{6.6875 - (-.6701)(-7.8534) - (-1.0405)(-10.1001)}{1.9763}$$

$$= -4.5966$$

In general, $n''_{ii} = \sqrt{n'_{ii} - \sum_{1}^{r} n''_{ki}}$, where $k = 1, 2, \ldots, i - 1$.

$$n''_{ij} = \frac{n'_{ij} - \sum_{1}^{r} n''_{ki}n''_{kj}}{n''_{ii}}, \text{ where } k = 1, 2, \ldots, i - 1 \text{ and } j > i.$$

Algorithm terminates after $q - 1$ rows are complete.

Computational check $\sum_{j=1}^{q} n''_{ij} = 0$, for $j \geq i$; e.g., $\sum_{j=1}^{q} n''_{2j} = 2.3974 - 1.0405 - 1.3569 = 0$

$\mathrm{SS}_{B(\mathrm{adj})} = B''^2_1 + B''^2_2 + B''^2_3 = 184.8166.$

(iv) Computational symbols:

$$\sum_{1}^{N} ABS = 3 + 6 + \cdots + 11 = 172.000 \qquad \text{(from } ABS \text{ Summary Table 7.9-2)}$$

$$\sum_{1}^{N} (ABS)^2 = [ABS] = (3)^2 + (6)^2 + \cdots + (11)^2 = 1160.0000$$

(from ABS Summary Table 7.9-2)

$$\frac{\left(\sum_{1}^{N} ABS\right)^2}{N} = [X] = \frac{(172)^2}{32} = 924.5000 \qquad \text{(from } ABS \text{ Summary Table 7.9-2)}$$

$$\sum_{1}^{p} \frac{\left(\sum_{1}^{q} A\right)^2}{\sum_{1}^{q} n_{ij}} = [A] = \frac{(91)^2}{16} + \frac{(81)^2}{16} = 927.6250 \qquad \text{(from } ABS \text{ Summary Table 7.9-2)}$$

$$\sum_{1}^{q} \frac{\left(\sum_{1}^{p} B\right)^2}{\sum_{1}^{p} n_{ij}} = [B] = \frac{(12 + 7)^2}{7} + \frac{(19 + 12)^2}{9} + \cdots + \frac{(38 + 40)^2}{9} = 1110.9205$$

(from ABS Summary Table 7.9-2)

$$\sum_{1}^{p} \sum_{1}^{q} \frac{\left(\sum_{1}^{n} AB\right)^2}{n_{ij}} = [AB] = \frac{(12)^2}{3} + \frac{(19)^2}{5} + \cdots + \frac{(40)^2}{4} = 1139.5833$$

(from ABS Summary Table 7.9-2)

TABLE 7.9-4 (continued)

(v) Computational formulas:

$\text{SS}_{\text{between cell}} = [AB] - [X] = 215.0833$ $\text{SS}_{A(\text{adj})} = \text{SS}_A + \text{SS}_{B(\text{adj})} - \text{SS}_B = 1.5211$

$\quad\quad \text{SS}_A = [A] - [X] = 3.1250$ $\quad\quad\quad = \text{SS}_{\text{between cell}} - \text{SS}_{AB(\text{adj})} - \text{SS}_B = 1.5211$

$\quad\quad \text{SS}_B = [B] - [X] = 186.4205$ $\quad \text{SS}_{B(\text{adj})} = B_1''^2 + B_2''^2 + B_3''^2 = 184.8166$

$\quad \text{SS}_{\text{w.cell}} = [ABS] - [AB] = 20.4167$ $\text{SS}_{AB(\text{adj})} = \text{SS}_{\text{between cell}} - \text{SS}_A - \text{SS}_{B(\text{adj})} = 27.1417$

TABLE 7.9-5   Analysis of Variance Table for Least-Squares Solution

Source	SS	df	MS	F
1 A(adj)	1.5211	$p - 1 = 1$	1.52	$\left[\frac{1}{4}\right] = 1.79$
2 B(adj)	184.8166	$q - 1 = 3$	61.61	$\left[\frac{2}{4}\right] = 72.48^*$
3 AB(adj)	27.1417	$(p-1)(q-1) = 3$	9.05	$\left[\frac{3}{4}\right] = 10.65^*$
4 W.cell	20.4167	$N - pq = 24$	.85	

$^*p < .01.$

In a least-squares solution, only one adjusted sum of squares has to be computed. The other required adjusted terms can be obtained by subtraction, as shown in Table 7.9-4. If one of the treatments has only two levels, a simpler computation scheme is described by Rao (1952, 95). Another more widely known procedure for obtaining an adjusted sum of squares is the abbreviated Doolittle algorithm. This procedure, which requires more computation than the Dwyer square-root algorithm, is illustrated by Anderson and Bancroft (1952, 197) and by Winer (1962, 294).

7.10   RULES FOR DERIVING EXPECTED VALUES OF MEAN SQUARES

An experimenter may find it necessary to derive E(MS) for a complex design in order to determine the proper denominators for F ratios. A laborious procedure for deriving expected values of mean squares was presented in Section 2.4. A simpler set of rules are described in this section that lead to the same E(MS) as the procedure used earlier. Rules similar to those presented here have been described by Bennett and Franklin (1954, 413) and by Cornfield and Tukey (1956).

For purposes of illustration, expected values of mean squares will be derived for a type CRF-pq design.

TABLE 7.10-1   Expected Values of Mean Squares for Type CRF-pq Design

(i)	(ii)			(iii)
	i	j	m	
Effects	p	q	n	E(MS)
1 α_i	$1 - \dfrac{p}{P}$	q	n	$\sigma_\varepsilon^2 + n\left(1 - \dfrac{q}{Q}\right)\sigma_{\alpha\beta}^2 + nq\sigma_\alpha^2$
2 β_j	p	$1 - \dfrac{q}{Q}$	n	$\sigma_\varepsilon^2 + n\left(1 - \dfrac{p}{P}\right)\sigma_{\alpha\beta}^2 + np\sigma_\beta^2$
3 $\alpha\beta_{ij}$	$1 - \dfrac{p}{P}$	$1 - \dfrac{q}{Q}$	n	$\sigma_\varepsilon^2 + n\sigma_{\alpha\beta}^2$
4 $\varepsilon_{m(ij)}$	1	1	$1 - \dfrac{n}{N}$	σ_ε^2

Rule 1.   Write the linear model for the design.

$$X_{ijm} = \mu + \alpha_i + \beta_j + \alpha\beta_{ij} + \varepsilon_{m(ij)}$$

Rule 2.   Construct a two-way table. See Table 7.10-1 for details of the layout.
(a) Column headings in part (ii) of the table consist of the subscripts of the terms in the linear model, e.g., i, j, and m. Below each subscript in the table, indicate the levels over which summation takes place, e.g., p, q, and n. The number of columns must equal the number of different subscripts in the model.
(b) Row headings in part (i) of the table consist of the terms on the right side of the linear model with the exception of the grand mean. The number of rows must equal the number of terms on the right of the linear model that have subscripts.

Rule 3.   Entries below each column heading of part (ii) are determined as follows:
(a) If the column heading (part ii) appears as a subscript of a row term (part i), but not in parentheses, enter the sampling fraction appropriate for that column $1 - (p/P)$, $1 - (q/Q)$, $1 - (n/N)$, etc. in the row. The sampling fraction must correspond to the levels of the effects. For column i, the proper sampling fraction is $1 - (p/P)$.
(b) If the column heading does not appear as a subscript of a row term, enter the appropriate letter for that column, e.g., p, q, n, etc. in the row.
(c) If the column heading appears in the subscript of a row term, but in parentheses, enter the number 1 in that row.

Rule 4.   For each row in part (iii), list the variances of the linear model terms that contain *all* the subscript(s) of that row term. No distinction is made between subscripts in parentheses and those not in parentheses for this listing. For example, the subscript in row one is i. Variances of terms in the linear model that contain the subscript i are σ_ε^2, $\sigma_{\alpha\beta}^2$, and σ_α^2.

Rule 5.   Coefficients of the variances in part (iii) are obtained by covering up columns (part ii) headed by subscripts that appear in the row (part i), but not including subscripts in parentheses, and multiplying each row variance (part iii) by the remaining terms in part (ii) of the table. For example, the coefficients in the first row for σ_α^2 are n and q, which are found in part (ii) of row one. The coefficients for $\sigma_{\alpha\beta}^2$ in the first row are n and $1 - (q/Q)$, which are found in part (ii) of row three. The coefficients for σ_ε^2 in row one are 1 and $1 - (n/N)$, which are found in part (ii) of row four. The expected value of a mean square for any main effects is thus a weighted sum of all the variance components that contain the subscripts of the main effects.

Rule 6. Sampling fractions in part (iii) equal 0 if the corresponding terms in the linear model represent fixed effects and 1 if the corresponding terms are random effects. Values between 0 and 1 may be appropriate for the sampling fraction, but these two values are most often used in practice.

(a) Experimental error is considered a random variable; thus $1 - (n/N)$ is equal to 1.

Once the table is completed, expected values of mean squares for the fixed-effects, random-effects, and mixed models can be readily obtained. For example, if treatments A and B represent fixed effects, their respective sampling fractions, $1 - (p/P)$ and $1 - (q/Q)$, are both equal to zero. For this case, the expected values of mean squares and F ratios are shown below.

1 $\qquad E(MS_A) = \sigma_\varepsilon^2 + nq\sigma_\alpha^2 \qquad E(F) = \left[\frac{1}{4}\right]$

2 $\qquad E(MS_B) = \sigma_\varepsilon^2 + np\sigma_\beta^2 \qquad E(F) = \left[\frac{2}{4}\right]$

3 $\qquad E(MS_{AB}) = \sigma_\varepsilon^2 + n\sigma_{\alpha\beta}^2 \qquad E(F) = \left[\frac{3}{4}\right]$

4 $\qquad E(MS_{w.cell}) = \sigma_\varepsilon^2.$

Let treatment A be a fixed effect and treatment B a random effect. Then the sampling fraction $1 - (p/P) = 0$, but $1 - (q/Q) = 1$. The expected values of mean squares and F ratios are as follows:

1 $\qquad E(MS_A) = \sigma_\varepsilon^2 + n\sigma_{\alpha\beta}^2 + nq\sigma_\alpha^2 \qquad E(F) = \left[\frac{1}{3}\right]$

2 $\qquad E(MS_B) = \sigma_\varepsilon^2 + np\sigma_\beta^2 \qquad E(F) = \left[\frac{2}{4}\right]$

3 $\qquad E(MS_{AB}) = \sigma_\varepsilon^2 + n\sigma_{\alpha\beta}^2 \qquad E(F) = \left[\frac{3}{4}\right]$

4 $\qquad E(MS_{w.cell}) = \sigma_\varepsilon^2.$

A second example showing the application of the six rules appears in Table 7.10-2 for a type CRF-pqr design, which is described in Section 7.13. This example has three treatments. The linear model for this design is

$$X_{ijkm} = \mu + \alpha_i + \beta_j + \gamma_k + \alpha\beta_{ij} + \alpha\gamma_{ik} + \beta\gamma_{jk} + \alpha\beta\gamma_{ijk} + \varepsilon_{m(ijk)}.$$

Table 7.10-2 can be constructed following the rules given in this section. If treatments A, B, and C are random variables, the expected values of mean squares and F ratios for a type CRF-pqr design are given below. For this random-effects model, $1 - (p/P)$, $1 - (q/Q)$, and $1 - (r/R)$ equal one.

1    $E(MS_A) = \sigma_\varepsilon^2 + n\sigma_{\alpha\beta\gamma}^2 + nq\sigma_{\alpha\gamma}^2 + nr\sigma_{\alpha\beta}^2 + nqr\sigma_\alpha^2$ $E(F) = [?]$

2    $E(MS_B) = \sigma_\varepsilon^2 + n\sigma_{\alpha\beta\gamma}^2 + np\sigma_{\beta\gamma}^2 + nr\sigma_{\alpha\beta}^2 + npr\sigma_\beta^2$ $E(F) = [?]$

3    $E(MS_C) = \sigma_\varepsilon^2 + n\sigma_{\alpha\beta\gamma}^2 + np\sigma_{\beta\gamma}^2 + nq\sigma_{\alpha\gamma}^2 + npq\sigma_\gamma^2$ $E(F) = [?]$

4    $E(MS_{AB}) = \sigma_\varepsilon^2 + n\sigma_{\alpha\beta\gamma}^2 + nr\sigma_{\alpha\beta}^2$ $E(F) = [\frac{4}{7}]$

5    $E(MS_{AC}) = \sigma_\varepsilon^2 + n\sigma_{\alpha\beta\gamma}^2 + nq\sigma_{\alpha\gamma}^2$ $E(F) = [\frac{5}{7}]$

6    $E(MS_{BC}) = \sigma_\varepsilon^2 + n\sigma_{\alpha\beta\gamma}^2 + np\sigma_{\beta\gamma}^2$ $E(F) = [\frac{6}{7}]$

7    $E(MS_{ABC}) = \sigma_\varepsilon^2 + n\sigma_{\alpha\beta\gamma}^2$ $E(F) = [\frac{7}{8}]$

8    $E(MS_{\text{w.cell}}) = \sigma_\varepsilon^2.$

An examination of the E(MS) for this design indicates that the model does not provide an error term for testing the three main effects. For example, the error term for MS_A should contain the following components:

$$\sigma_\varepsilon^2 + n\sigma_{\alpha\beta\gamma}^2 + nq\sigma_{\alpha\gamma}^2 + nr\sigma_{\alpha\beta}^2.$$

TABLE 7.10-2   Expected Values of Mean Squares for Type CRF-*pqr* Design

(i)	(ii)				(iii)
Effects	i p	j q	k r	m n	E(MS)
α_i	$1 - \frac{p}{P}$	q	r	n	$\sigma_\varepsilon^2 + n\left(1 - \frac{q}{Q}\right)\left(1 - \frac{r}{R}\right)\sigma_{\alpha\beta\gamma}^2$ $+ nq\left(1 - \frac{r}{R}\right)\sigma_{\alpha\gamma}^2 + n\left(1 - \frac{q}{Q}\right)r\sigma_{\alpha\beta}^2 + nqr\sigma_\alpha^2$
β_j	p	$1 - \frac{q}{Q}$	r	n	$\sigma_\varepsilon^2 + n\left(1 - \frac{p}{P}\right)\left(1 - \frac{r}{R}\right)\sigma_{\alpha\beta\gamma}^2$ $+ np\left(1 - \frac{r}{R}\right)\sigma_{\beta\gamma}^2 + n\left(1 - \frac{p}{P}\right)r\sigma_{\alpha\beta}^2 + npr\sigma_\beta^2$
γ_k	p	q	$1 - \frac{r}{R}$	n	$\sigma_\varepsilon^2 + n\left(1 - \frac{p}{P}\right)\left(1 - \frac{q}{Q}\right)\sigma_{\alpha\beta\gamma}^2$ $+ np\left(1 - \frac{q}{Q}\right)\sigma_{\beta\gamma}^2 + n\left(1 - \frac{p}{P}\right)q\sigma_{\alpha\gamma}^2 + npq\sigma_\gamma^2$
$\alpha\beta_{ij}$	$1 - \frac{p}{P}$	$1 - \frac{q}{Q}$	r	n	$\sigma_\varepsilon^2 + n\left(1 - \frac{r}{R}\right)\sigma_{\alpha\beta\gamma}^2 + nr\sigma_{\alpha\beta}^2$
$\alpha\gamma_{ik}$	$1 - \frac{p}{P}$	q	$1 - \frac{r}{R}$	n	$\sigma_\varepsilon^2 + n\left(1 - \frac{q}{Q}\right)\sigma_{\alpha\beta\gamma}^2 + nq\sigma_{\alpha\gamma}^2$
$\beta\gamma_{jk}$	p	$1 - \frac{q}{Q}$	$1 - \frac{r}{R}$	n	$\sigma_\varepsilon^2 + n\left(1 - \frac{p}{P}\right)\sigma_{\alpha\beta\gamma}^2 + np\sigma_{\beta\gamma}^2$
$\alpha\beta\gamma_{ijk}$	$1 - \frac{p}{P}$	$1 - \frac{q}{Q}$	$1 - \frac{r}{R}$	n	$\sigma_\varepsilon^2 + n\sigma_{\alpha\beta\gamma}^2$
$\varepsilon_{m(ijk)}$	1	1	1	$1 - \frac{n}{N}$	σ_ε^2

This problem can be approached from several different points of view. If any of the interactions among treatments are significant, an experimenter would not ordinarily be interested in tests of main effects for those treatments. On the other hand, if, for example, the ratio

$$F = \frac{\mathrm{MS}_{AB}}{\mathrm{MS}_{ABC}}$$

is not significant, the inclusion of the component $nr\sigma_{\alpha\beta}^2$ in the E(MS) for treatment A is open to question. If it can be concluded that $nr\sigma_{\alpha\beta}^2 = 0$, the proper error term for testing treatment A is MS_{AC}. A general discussion of preliminary tests on the model and pooling procedures appears in Section 7.12. If the model does not include mean squares with the proper expected values, it may be possible by combining terms to *piece together* an error term. This procedure is described in Section 7.11.

The linear models for some of the designs that have been presented included subscripts in parentheses. This information was used (Rule 3) in completing the two-way table for deriving the E(MS). The use of parentheses around a subscript indicates that certain effects are *nested*. Effects that are restricted to a single level of a treatment are said to be nested within that treatment. The symbol $\varepsilon_{m(ij)}$ indicates that the error effects are nested within the AB treatment combinations. An examination of Table 7.3-1 shows that n different subjects appear in each cell of the table. Thus a particular sample of subjects is restricted to a single treatment combination. Treatments A and B are not nested in the design in Table 7.3-1 because every level of treatment A appears in combination with every level of treatment B.

7.11 QUASI *F* RATIOS

We noted in the previous section that mean squares having appropriate expected values for constructing F ratios are not always present in an experiment. Under these conditions, an error term that does have the appropriate expected values can be *pieced together*. F ratios formed in this manner are called *quasi ratios* and are designated by the symbols F' or F''.

The error term for testing MS_A in a type CRF-pqr design, assuming a random-effects model, is

$$\sigma_\varepsilon^2 + n\sigma_{\alpha\beta\gamma}^2 + nq\sigma_{\alpha\gamma}^2 + nr\sigma_{\alpha\beta}^2.$$

A composite mean square having these expected values can be pieced together, following the procedure suggested by Satterthwaite (1946), by combining the following mean squares:

$$\mathrm{MS}_{AC} + \mathrm{MS}_{AB} - \mathrm{MS}_{ABC}.$$

It can be shown that the above combination of mean squares leads to the appropriate error term for testing MS_A.

$$E(MS_{AB}) = \sigma_\varepsilon^2 + n\sigma_{\alpha\beta\gamma}^2 \qquad\qquad + nr\sigma_{\alpha\beta}^2$$
$$+ E(MS_{AC}) = \sigma_\varepsilon^2 + n\sigma_{\alpha\beta\gamma}^2 + nq\sigma_{\alpha\gamma}^2$$
$$\underline{- E(MS_{ABC}) = -\sigma_\varepsilon^2 - n\sigma_{\alpha\beta\gamma}^2}$$
$$E(MS_{AB}) + E(MS_{AC}) - E(MS_{ABC}) = \sigma_\varepsilon^2 + n\sigma_{\alpha\beta\gamma}^2 + nq\sigma_{\alpha\gamma}^2 + nr\sigma_{\alpha\beta}^2.$$

Thus a test of the main effects of treatment A is given by the quasi F' ratio

$$F' = \frac{MS_A}{MS_{AB} + MS_{AC} - MS_{ABC}}.$$

The F' ratio has the general form

$$F' = \frac{MS_1}{MS_2 + MS_3 - MS_4}.$$

The degrees of freedom for the denominator of this ratio is the nearest integral value of

$$df = \frac{(MS_2 + MS_3 - MS_4)^2}{MS_2^2/df_2 + MS_3^2/df_3 + MS_4^2/df_4},$$

where df_2, df_3, and df_4 correspond to the degrees of freedom for the respective mean squares. The degrees of freedom for the numerator of the F' ratio is the regular df for MS_1.

One problem inherent in the F' ratio is that of obtaining a negative denominator. Cochran (1951) proposed that Satterthwaite's method be modified by adding mean squares to the numerator rather than subtracting them from the denominator. This ratio, which is designated as an F'' ratio, has the general form

$$F'' = \frac{MS_1 + MS_2}{MS_3 + MS_4}.$$

The degrees of freedom for numerator and denominator are equal to the nearest integral values, respectively, of

$$\frac{(MS_1 + MS_2)^2}{(MS_1^2/df_1) + (MS_2^2/df_2)} \quad \text{and} \quad \frac{(MS_3 + MS_4)^2}{(MS_3^2/df_3) + (MS_4^2/df_4)}.$$

A quasi F'' ratio for the main effects of treatment A for the design described above is given by

$$F'' = \frac{MS_A + MS_{ABC}}{MS_{AC} + MS_{AB}}.$$

It can be shown that this quasi ratio has the required form in terms of expected values of mean squares.

$$E(F'') = \frac{2\sigma_\varepsilon^2 + 2n\sigma_{\alpha\beta\gamma}^2 + nq\sigma_{\alpha\gamma}^2 + nr\sigma_{\alpha\beta}^2 + nqr\sigma_\alpha^2}{2\sigma_\varepsilon^2 + 2n\sigma_{\alpha\beta\gamma}^2 + nq\sigma_{\alpha\gamma}^2 + nr\sigma_{\alpha\beta}^2}.$$

Quasi F ratios for tests of treatments B and C in the type CRF-pqr design, assuming a random-effects model, have the following forms:

$$F' = \frac{\text{MS}_B}{\text{MS}_{AB} + \text{MS}_{BC} - \text{MS}_{ABC}} \qquad F'' = \frac{\text{MS}_B + \text{MS}_{ABC}}{\text{MS}_{AB} + \text{MS}_{BC}}$$

$$F' = \frac{\text{MS}_C}{\text{MS}_{AC} + \text{MS}_{BC} - \text{MS}_{ABC}} \qquad F'' = \frac{\text{MS}_C + \text{MS}_{ABC}}{\text{MS}_{AC} + \text{MS}_{BC}}.$$

7.12   PRELIMINARY TESTS ON THE MODEL AND POOLING PROCEDURES

The selection of an experimental design and associated linear model is largely based on an experimenter's subject-matter knowledge. Other factors influencing the selection of a design are discussed in Section 1.4. The model selected should include all sources of variation that an experimenter is interested in and that are expected to contribute significantly to the total variation. In reality, all sources of variation not specifically included in the model as treatment effects become a part of the experimental error.

A factorial design is often employed because an experimenter expects that interaction terms are an important source of variation. Procedures discussed in this section are concerned with using data·obtained in an experiment to make preliminary tests on the appropriateness of a particular linear model. Mathematical statisticians disagree on whether to adhere to the model specified at the beginning of the experiment, even though the data suggest that it is incorrect, or whether it is permissible or desirable to modify the model along lines suggested by the data. The procedures recommended here represent a middle-of-the-road position with respect to the issue of preliminary tests and pooling. This position is similar to that adopted by Green and Tukey (1960) and by Bozivich, Bancroft, and Hartley (1956).

Assume that a random-effects model type CRF-pqr design has been used in an experiment. The linear model for this design is

$$X_{ijkm} = \mu + \alpha_i + \beta_j + \gamma_k + \alpha\beta_{ij} + \alpha\gamma_{ik} + \beta\gamma_{jk} + \alpha\beta\gamma_{ijk} + \varepsilon_{m(ijk)}.$$

The expected values of mean squares and the linear model determine the form of the tests of hypotheses. If there is any question about whether interaction terms *should* appear in the model, preliminary tests can be performed. Such tests are designed to revise or confirm the specification of parameters included in the model. The first component that should be tested is the triple interaction ($\sigma_{\alpha\beta\gamma}^2$). According to the expected values of the mean square for this design in Section 7.11, the F ratio for the test of $\sigma_{\alpha\beta\gamma}^2$ has the form

$$F = \frac{\text{MS}_{ABC}}{\text{MS}_{\text{w.cell}}}.$$

A type II error—accepting the hypothesis that $\sigma_{\alpha\beta\gamma}^2 = 0$ when it is false—should be avoided in preliminary tests. The probability of a type II error can be made relatively small by adopting a numerically large value of α ($\alpha = .25$). If the test of MS_{ABC} is insignificant at the .25 level, and an experimenter has no *a priori* reason for including this component in the model, it can be dropped. The revised model is

$$X_{ijkm} = \mu + \alpha_i + \beta_j + \gamma_k + \alpha\beta_{ij} + \alpha\gamma_{ik} + \beta\gamma_{jk} + \varepsilon.$$

According to the revised model, $\sigma_{\alpha\beta\gamma}^2$ is assumed to equal zero. MS_{ABC} is thus an independent estimate of experimental error and can be combined with $\text{MS}_{\text{w.cell}}$ to form a pooled error term:

$$\text{MS}_{\text{res}} = \frac{\text{SS}_{\text{w.cell}} + \text{SS}_{ABC}}{pqr(n - 1) + (p - 1)(q - 1)(r - 1)}$$

with df $= pqr(n - 1) + (p - 1)(q - 1)(r - 1)$.

The expected values of mean squares for the revised model are shown in Table 7.12-1.

TABLE 7.12-1   Expected Values of Mean Squares
for Revised Model

Source of Variation	E(MS)
MS_A	$\sigma_\varepsilon^2 + nq\sigma_{\alpha\gamma}^2 + nr\sigma_{\alpha\beta}^2 + nqr\sigma_\alpha^2$
MS_B	$\sigma_\varepsilon^2 + np\sigma_{\beta\gamma}^2 + nr\sigma_{\alpha\beta}^2 + npr\sigma_\beta^2$
MS_C	$\sigma_\varepsilon^2 + np\sigma_{\beta\gamma}^2 + nq\sigma_{\alpha\gamma}^2 + npq\sigma_\gamma^2$
MS_{AB}	$\sigma_\varepsilon^2 + nr\sigma_{\alpha\beta}^2$
MS_{AC}	$\sigma_\varepsilon^2 + nq\sigma_{\alpha\gamma}^2$
MS_{BC}	$\sigma_\varepsilon^2 + np\sigma_{\beta\gamma}^2$
$\left.\begin{array}{l}\text{MS}_{ABC}\\ \text{MS}_{\text{w.cell}}\end{array}\right\}$ residual	σ_ε^2

The next step in the preliminary test of the model is to determine if the three first-order interactions should be retained. According to Table 7.12-1, the appropriate F ratios have the form

$$F = \frac{\text{MS}_{AB}}{\text{MS}_{\text{res}}}, \quad F = \frac{\text{MS}_{AC}}{\text{MS}_{\text{res}}}, \quad F = \frac{\text{MS}_{BC}}{\text{MS}_{\text{res}}}.$$

Assume that tests of MS_{AB} and MS_{BC} are insignificant at the .25 level but MS_{AC} is significant. The revised model, under these conditions, can be written

$$X_{ijkm} = \mu + \alpha_i + \beta_j + \gamma_k + \alpha\gamma_{ik} + \varepsilon.$$

The expected values of mean squares for this revised model and F ratios are shown in Table 7.12-2. The pooled error term for testing MS_B and MS_{AC} is given by

$$MS_{res} = \frac{SS_{AB} + SS_{BC} + SS_{ABC} + SS_{w.cell}}{(p-1)(q-1) + (q-1)(r-1) + (p-1)(q-1)(r-1) + pqr(n-1)}.$$

TABLE 7.12-2   Expected Values of Mean Squares for Revised Model and F Ratios

Source of Variation	E(MS)	F
1 MS_A	$\sigma_\varepsilon^2 + nq\sigma_{\alpha\gamma}^2 + nqr\sigma_\alpha^2$	$[\frac{1}{4}]$
2 MS_B	$\sigma_\varepsilon^2 + npr\sigma_\beta^2$	$[\frac{2}{5}]$
3 MS_C	$\sigma_\varepsilon^2 + nq\sigma_{\alpha\gamma}^2 + npq\sigma_\gamma^2$	$[\frac{3}{4}]$
4 MS_{AC}	$\sigma_\varepsilon^2 + nq\sigma_{\alpha\gamma}^2$	$[\frac{4}{5}]$
5 $\left.\begin{array}{l} MS_{AB} \\ MS_{BC} \\ MS_{ABC} \\ MS_{w.cell} \end{array}\right\}$ residual	σ_ε^2	

Alternative rules for carrying out preliminary tests and pooling have been described by Paull (1950) and by Bozivich, Bancroft, and Hartley (1956). Green and Tukey (1960) present a detailed example of the application of Paull's rule.

One advantage of carrying out preliminary tests and pooling is readily apparent. If interaction components can be deleted from the linear model, the pooled error term will have more degrees of freedom. However, the disadvantages associated with carrying out preliminary tests and pooling may outweigh the advantages if an error term in the original model is based on an adequate number of degrees of freedom (df = 25 − 30). The principal disadvantage of preliminary tests and pooling is that subsequent tests are carried out as if no preliminary tests had preceded them. The sampling distributions of statistics used in tests that are preceded by preliminary tests differ from sampling distributions for tests that are not preceded by preliminary tests. In general, the appropriate sampling distribution of the statistic at each stage of preliminary testing of the model is not available to the experimenter. The use of a sampling distribution that is not appropriate for sequential decisions probably introduces a slight positive bias, that is, too often rejecting H_0 when it should not be rejected. Thus pooling introduces contingencies that are difficult to evaluate statistically. Adherence to the original model eliminates this problem, although tests associated with an incorrect model may be less powerful than tests based on a revised model.

An experimenter can take three positions with respect to conducting preliminary tests and pooling. These positions are (1) never pool, (2) always pool, and (3) pool only when evidence indicates that the initial model is incorrect. Both the first and third rules have much to recommend them. The author favors the third. For other discussions of this point, see Bennett and Franklin (1954, 392), Bozivich, Bancroft, and Hartley (1956), Paull (1950), and Scheffé (1959, 126).

7.13 COMPUTATIONAL PROCEDURES FOR TYPE CRF-*pqr* DESIGN

INTRODUCTION TO TYPE CRF-*pqr* DESIGN

The analysis procedures described in Section 7.3 for a two-treatment factorial experiment can easily be extended to experiments having three or more treatments. A numerical example of a three-treatment type CRF-*pqr* design is given in this section. Procedures for expanding this design to any number of treatments are also described.

A block diagram of a type CRF-*pqr* design appears in Figure 7.13-1.

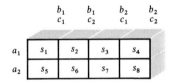

Figure 7.13-1   Block diagram of type CRF-222 design.

The linear model underlying this design is

$$X_{ijkm} = \mu + \alpha_i + \beta_j + \gamma_k + \alpha\beta_{ij} + \alpha\gamma_{ik} + \beta\gamma_{jk} + \alpha\beta\gamma_{ijk} + \varepsilon_{m(ijk)}.$$

For purposes of illustration assume that the experiment described in Section 7.3 on the effects of social deprivation and magnitude of reinforcement on children's motor behavior has been modified and a third treatment added to the experiment. It is hypothesized that the sex of the adult (treatment C) who administers reinforcement will interact with the other two treatments. Treatment C consists of two levels: c_1 = reinforcement administered by man, c_2 = reinforcement administered by women. Treatment B has been modified by reducing the number of treatment levels to two: b_1 = 40 minutes of isolation, b_2 = 80 minutes of isolation. Treatment A is not changed.

The three treatments have *pqr* = 8 treatment combinations. Assume that a total of 32 subjects has been obtained by random sampling from a population. The subjects are randomly divided into eight subsamples of four subjects each and randomly assigned to the eight treatment combinations. For any type CRF-*pqr* design, a total of *npqr* subjects is required.

This three-treatment design permits an experimenter to evaluate four interactions. General procedures for enumerating interactions in a factorial design are described in the following section.

ENUMERATION OF INTERACTIONS
FOR ANY TYPE CRF DESIGN

The interaction terms associated with an experiment can be readily determined by writing down all combinations of treatment letters, ignoring order of the letters. For example, treatments A, B, and C can be combined to form the following combinations:

$$AB$$
$$AC$$
$$BC$$
$$ABC.$$

Interactions involving two letters are called first-order interactions, two-factor interactions, or double interactions. If three letters are involved, the interaction is a second-order or triple interaction, and so on. Four treatment letters ($ABCD$) can be combined to form the following combinations:

$$
\begin{array}{ll}
AB & \\
AC & ABC \\
AD & ABD \\
BC & ACD \\
BD & BCD \\
CD & ABCD.
\end{array}
$$

A four-treatment experiment that is based on a completely randomized building block design is designated by the letters CRF-$pqru$.

In general, the number of first, second, third, etc. order interactions is given by

$$c_n^k = \frac{k!}{n!(k-n)!},$$

where k = number of treatments and n = number of letters in interaction. For example, a four-treatment experiment has six two-factor interactions,

$$c_2^4 = \frac{4!}{2!(4-2)!} = \frac{4 \cdot 3 \cdot 2 \cdot 1}{2 \cdot 1(2 \cdot 1)} = \frac{24}{4} = 6,$$

four three-factor interactions,

$$c_3^4 = \frac{4!}{3!(4-3)!} = \frac{4\cdot 3\cdot 2\cdot 1}{3\cdot 2\cdot 1(1)} = \frac{24}{6} = 4,$$

and one four-factor interaction,

$$c_4^4 = \frac{4!}{4!(4-4)!*} = \frac{4\cdot 3\cdot 2\cdot 1}{4\cdot 3\cdot 2\cdot 1(1)} = \frac{24}{24} = 1.$$

LAYOUT AND COMPUTATIONAL PROCEDURES FOR TYPE CRF-*pqr* DESIGN

The layout of the type CRF-222 design, computational tables, and formulas are shown in Table 7.13-1. The analysis of variance is summarized in Table 7.13-2. The following notation system is used in the tables:

$$p \text{ levels of } a_i, \text{ where } p = 2$$

$$q \text{ levels of } b_j, \text{ where } q = 2$$

$$r \text{ levels of } c_k, \text{ where } r = 2$$

$$n \text{ levels of } s_m, \text{ where } n = 4$$

$$\sum_1^N = \sum_1^p \sum_1^q \sum_1^r \sum_1^n .$$

TABLE 7.13-1 Layout of Type CRF-222 Design and Computational Procedures

(i) Data:

ABCS Summary Table

a_1	a_1	a_1	a_1	a_2	a_2	a_2	a_2
b_1	b_1	b_2	b_2	b_1	b_1	b_2	b_2
c_1	c_2	c_1	c_2	c_1	c_2	c_1	c_2
3	4	7	7	1	2	5	10
6	5	8	8	2	3	6	10
3	4	7	9	2	4	5	9
3	3	6	8	2	3	6	11

ABC Summary Table

	b_1	b_1	b_2	b_2
	c_1	c_2	c_1	c_2
a_1 ($n=4$)	15	16	28	32
a_2	7	12	22	40

*Note: 0! ≈ 1.

TABLE 7.13-1 (continued)

		AB Summary Table				*AC Summary Table*			*BC Summary Table*	
	b_1	b_2	$\sum\limits_1^q A$	$\dfrac{\left(\sum\limits_1^q A\right)^2}{nqr}$		c_1	c_2		c_1	c_2
a_1	$nr = 8$ 31	60	91	517.5625	a_1	$nq = 8$ 43	48	b_1	$np = 8$ 22	28
a_2	19	62	81	410.0625	a_2	29	52	b_2	50	72

$$\sum_1^p B = \quad 50 \quad\quad 122$$

$$\frac{\left(\sum\limits_1^p B\right)^2}{npr} = 156.25 \quad 930.25$$

$$\sum_1^p C = \quad 72 \quad\quad 100$$

$$\frac{\left(\sum\limits_1^p C\right)^2}{npq} = 324.00 \quad 625.00$$

(ii) Computational symbols:

$$\sum_1^N ABCS = 3 + 6 + 3 + \cdots + 11 = 172.000$$

$$\sum_1^N (ABCS)^2 = [ABCS] = (3)^2 + (6)^2 + (3)^2 + \cdots + (11)^2 = 1160.000$$

$$\frac{\left(\sum\limits_1^N ABCS\right)^2}{npqr} = [X] = \frac{(172.000)^2}{(4)(2)(2)(2)} = 924.500$$

$$\sum_1^p \frac{\left(\sum\limits_1^q A\right)^2}{nqr} = [A] = 517.5625 + 410.0625 = 927.625$$

$$\sum_1^q \frac{\left(\sum\limits_1^p B\right)^2}{npr} = [B] = 156.25 + 930.25 = 1086.500$$

$$\sum_1^r \frac{\left(\sum\limits_1^p C\right)^2}{npq} = [C] = 324.00 + 625.00 = 949.00$$

$$\sum_1^p\sum_1^q \frac{(AB)^2}{nr} = [AB] = \frac{(31)^2}{(4)(2)} + \cdots + \frac{(62)^2}{(4)(2)} = 1095.750$$

$$\sum_1^p\sum_1^r \frac{(AC)^2}{nq} = [AC] = \frac{(43)^2}{(4)(2)} + \cdots + \frac{(52)^2}{(4)(2)} = 962.250$$

$$\sum_1^q\sum_1^r \frac{(BC)^2}{np} = [BC] = \frac{(22)^2}{(4)(2)} + \cdots + \frac{(72)^2}{(4)(2)} = 1119.000$$

$$\sum_1^p\sum_1^q\sum_1^r \frac{(ABC)^2}{n} = [ABC] = \frac{(15)^2}{4} + \cdots + \frac{(40)^2}{4} = 1141.500$$

TABLE 7.13-1 (continued)

(iii) Computational formulas:

$$SS_{total} = [ABCS] - [X] = 235.500$$
$$SS_A = [A] - [X] = 3.125$$
$$SS_B = [B] - [X] = 162.000$$
$$SS_C = [C] - [X] = 24.500$$
$$SS_{AB} = [AB] - [A] - [B] + [X] = 6.125$$
$$SS_{AC} = [AC] - [A] - [C] + [X] = 10.125$$
$$SS_{BC} = [BC] - [B] - [C] + [X] = 8.000$$
$$SS_{ABC} = [ABC] - [AB] - [AC] - [BC] + [A] + [B] + [C] - [X] = 3.125$$
$$SS_{w.cell} = [ABCS] - [ABC] = 18.500$$

TABLE 7.13-2   Analysis of Variance Table

Source	SS	df	MS	F	E(MS) Model I
1 A	3.125	$p - 1 = 1$	3.125	$\left[\frac{1}{8}\right] = \quad 4.05$	$\sigma_\varepsilon^2 + nqr\sigma_\alpha^2$
2 B	162.000	$q - 1 = 1$	162.000	$\left[\frac{2}{8}\right] = 210.12*$	$\sigma_\varepsilon^2 + npr\sigma_\beta^2$
3 C	24.500	$r - 1 = 1$	24.500	$\left[\frac{3}{8}\right] = \quad 31.78*$	$\sigma_\varepsilon^2 + npq\sigma_\gamma^2$
4 AB	6.125	$(p - 1)(q - 1) = 1$	6.125	$\left[\frac{4}{8}\right] = \quad 7.94*$	$\sigma_\varepsilon^2 + nr\sigma_{\alpha\beta}^2$
5 AC	10.125	$(p - 1)(r - 1) = 1$	10.125	$\left[\frac{5}{8}\right] = \quad 13.13*$	$\sigma_\varepsilon^2 + nq\sigma_{\alpha\gamma}^2$
6 BC	8.000	$(q - 1)(r - 1) = 1$	8.000	$\left[\frac{6}{8}\right] = \quad 10.38*$	$\sigma_\varepsilon^2 + np\sigma_{\beta\gamma}^2$
7 ABC	3.125	$(p - 1)(q - 1)(r - 1) = 1$	3.125	$\left[\frac{7}{8}\right] = \quad 4.05$	$\sigma_\varepsilon^2 + n\sigma_{\alpha\beta\gamma}^2$
8 W.cell	18.500	$pqr(n - 1) = 24$	.771		σ_ε^2
9 Total	235.500	$npqr - 1 = 31$			

*$p < .01$.

All the first-order interactions in Table 7.13-2 are significant. Under these conditions, attention is directed to tests of simple main effects. These tests follow the pattern described in Section 7.4. The *AB*, *AC*, and *BC* Summary Tables in Table 7.13-1 are used in carrying out these tests. Computational formulas for simple main effects of *A* at b_j and *B* at a_i are shown in Table 7.4-1. The same pattern is followed for tests of *B* at c_k, *C* at b_j, *A* at c_k, and *C* at a_i.

COMPUTATIONAL PROCEDURES FOR SIMPLE SIMPLE MAIN EFFECTS AND SIMPLE INTERACTION EFFECTS SUMS OF SQUARES

If the three-factor interaction in Table 7.13-2 had been significant, tests of *simple simple main* effects and *simple interaction* effects could provide additional insight concerning the experiment. Mean squares for *simple simple main* effects are used in testing the following kinds of hypotheses:

$$H_0 : \alpha_i = 0 \qquad \text{for all } i \text{ at level } bc_{jk}$$

$$H_0 : \beta_j = 0 \qquad \text{for all } j \text{ at level } ac_{ik}$$

$$H_0 : \gamma_k = 0 \qquad \text{for all } k \text{ at level } ab_{ij}.$$

Mean squares for *simple interaction* effects are used in testing the following kinds of hypotheses:

$$H_0 : \alpha\beta_{ij} = 0 \qquad \text{for all } ij \text{ at level } c_k$$

$$H_0 : \alpha\gamma_{ik} = 0 \qquad \text{for all } ik \text{ at level } b_j$$

$$H_0 : \beta\gamma_{jk} = 0 \qquad \text{for all } jk \text{ at level } a_i.$$

Thus the hypothesis that $\alpha = 0$ for all levels of i is evaluated at each of the qr combinations of treatments B and C. Similarly, the hypothesis that $\alpha\beta_{ij} = 0$ for all levels of ij is evaluated at each level of treatment C. Procedures for computing sum of squares required for testing the above hypotheses are illustrated in Table 7.13-3.

TABLE 7.13-3   Procedures for Computing SS's for Simple Simple Main Effects and Simple Interaction Effects

(i)

ABC Summary Table

		b_1	b_1	b_2	b_2
		c_1	c_2	c_1	c_2
a_1	$n = 4$	15	16	28	32
a_2		7	12	22	40
	$BC_{jk} = 22$	28	50	72	

TABLE 7.13-3 (continued)

(ii)

$$\text{SS}_A \text{ at } bc_{11} = \sum_1^p \frac{(ABC_{i11})^2}{n} - \frac{(BC_{11})^2}{np} = \frac{(15)^2}{4} + \frac{(7)^2}{4} - \frac{(22)^2}{(4)(2)} = 8.000$$

$$\text{SS}_A \text{ at } bc_{12} = \sum_1^p \frac{(ABC_{i12})^2}{n} - \frac{(BC_{12})^2}{np} = \frac{(16)^2}{4} + \frac{(12)^2}{4} - \frac{(28)^2}{(4)(2)} = 2.000$$

$$\text{SS}_A \text{ at } bc_{21} = \sum_1^p \frac{(ABC_{i21})^2}{n} - \frac{(BC_{21})^2}{np} = \frac{(28)^2}{4} + \frac{(22)^2}{4} - \frac{(50)^2}{(4)(2)} = 4.500$$

$$\text{SS}_A \text{ at } bc_{22} = \sum_1^p \frac{(ABC_{i22})^2}{n} - \frac{(BC_{22})^2}{np} = \frac{(32)^2}{4} + \frac{(40)^2}{4} - \frac{(72)^2}{(4)(2)} = 8.000$$

Computational check $\sum_1^q \sum_1^r \text{SS}_A$ for $bc_{jk} = \text{SS}_A + \text{SS}_{AB} + \text{SS}_{AC} + \text{SS}_{ABC} = 22.5.$

$$\text{SS}_B \text{ at } ac_{11} = \sum_1^q \frac{(ABC_{1j1})^2}{n} - \frac{(AC_{11})^2}{nq} = \frac{(15)^2}{4} + \frac{(28)^2}{4} - \frac{(43)^2}{(4)(2)} = 21.125$$

$$\text{SS}_B \text{ at } ac_{22} = \sum_1^q \frac{(ABC_{2j2})^2}{n} - \frac{(AC_{22})^2}{nq} = \frac{(12)^2}{4} + \frac{(40)^2}{4} - \frac{(52)^2}{(4)(2)} = 98.000$$

Computational check $\sum_1^p \sum_1^r \text{SS}_B$ for $ac_{ik} = \text{SS}_B + \text{SS}_{AB} + \text{SS}_{BC} + \text{SS}_{ABC}.$

$$\text{SS}_C \text{ at } ab_{11} = \sum_1^r \frac{(ABC_{11k})^2}{n} - \frac{(AB_{11})^2}{nr} = \frac{(15)^2}{4} + \frac{(16)^2}{4} - \frac{(31)^2}{(4)(2)} = .125$$

$$\text{SS}_C \text{ at } ab_{22} = \sum_1^r \frac{(ABC_{22k})}{n} - \frac{(AB_{22})}{nr} = \frac{(22)}{4} + \frac{(40)}{4} - \frac{(62)}{(4)(2)} = 40.500$$

Computational check $\sum_1^p \sum_1^q \text{SS}_C$ for $ab_{ij} = \text{SS}_C + \text{SS}_{AC} + \text{SS}_{BC} + \text{SS}_{ABC}.$

(iii)

$$\text{SS}_{AB} \text{ at } c_1 = \left[\sum_1^p \sum_1^q \frac{(ABC_{ij1})^2}{n} - \frac{\left(\sum_1^p C_{i1}\right)^2}{npq} \right] - \text{SS}_A \text{ at } c_1 - \text{SS}_B \text{ at } c_1$$

$$= \left[\frac{(15)^2}{4} + \frac{(28)^2}{4} + \cdots + \frac{(22)^2}{4} - \frac{(72)^2}{(4)(2)(2)} \right] - 12.250 - 49.000 = .2500$$

Computational check $\sum_1^r \text{SS}_{AB}$ for $c_k = \text{SS}_{AB} + \text{SS}_{ABC}.$

$$\text{SS}_{AC} \text{ at } b_1 = \left[\sum_1^p \sum_1^r \frac{(ABC_{i1k})^2}{n} - \frac{\left(\sum_1^p B_{i1}\right)^2}{npr} \right] - \text{SS}_A \text{ at } b_1 - \text{SS}_C \text{ at } b_1$$

$$= \left[\frac{(15)^2}{4} + \frac{(16)^2}{4} + \cdots + \frac{(12)^2}{4} - \frac{(50)^2}{(4)(2)(2)} \right] - 9.000 - 2.250 = 1.0000$$

Computational check $\sum_1^q \text{SS}_{AC}$ for $b_j = \text{SS}_{AC} + \text{SS}_{ABC}.$

$$\text{SS}_{BC} \text{ at } a_1 = \left[\sum_1^q \sum_1^r \frac{(ABC_{1jk})^2}{n} - \frac{\left(\sum_1^q A_{1j}\right)^2}{nqr} \right] - \text{SS}_B \text{ at } a_1 - \text{SS}_C \text{ at } a_1$$

TABLE 7.13-3 (continued)

$$= \left[\frac{(15)^2}{4} + \frac{(16)^2}{4} + \cdots + \frac{(32)^2}{4} - \frac{(91)^2}{(4)(2)(2)} \right] - 52.5625 - 1.5625 = .5625$$

Computational check $\sum_{1}^{p} SS_{BC}$ for $a_i = SS_{BC} + SS_{ABC}$.

GENERAL PATTERN UNDERLYING COMPUTATIONAL FORMULAS FOR TYPE CRF DESIGNS

A pattern that underlies the computational formulas may be evident to the reader. Sum of squares formulas for main effects have the general form

$$SS_A = [A] - [X]$$
$$SS_B = [B] - [X]$$

$$SS_G = [G] - [X].$$

First-order interaction sum of squares formulas have the form

$$SS_{AB} = [AB] - [A] - [B] + [X]$$
$$SS_{AC} = [AC] - [A] - [C] + [X]$$

$$SS_{FG} = [FG] - [F] - [G] + [X].$$

Second- and third-order interaction sum of squares formulas have the form

$$SS_{ABC} = [ABC] - [AB] - [AC] - [BC] + [A] + [B] + [C] - [X]$$
$$SS_{ABCD} = [ABCD] - [ABC] - [ABD] - [ACD] - [BCD] + [AB]$$
$$+ [AC] + [AD] + [BC] + [BD] + [CD] - [A]$$
$$- [B] - [C] - [D] + [X].$$

In general, an interaction involving k terms (letters) is given by

$$k \text{ terms interaction} = [k \text{ terms}] - \Sigma[\text{all combinations of } k - 1 \text{ terms}]$$
$$+ \Sigma[\text{all combinations of } k - 2 \text{ terms}]$$
$$- \Sigma[\text{all combinations of } k - 3 \text{ terms}]$$
$$+ \cdots \pm \Sigma[\text{all } k - (k - 1) \text{ terms}] \pm [X].$$

If k is an even number, the sign of $[X]$ is plus; if k is an odd number, the sign is negative. This is evident because the sign changes for each group of terms. Construction of interaction formulas for any factorial design can be accomplished by following the foregoing general rule.

The rationale underlying the computational formulas is relatively simple. A term such as $[AB]$ in a type CRF-*pq* design is given by

$$[AB] = \sum_{1}^{p}\sum_{1}^{q} \frac{(AB)^2}{n}.$$

The *correction term* $[X]$ is given by

$$[X] = \frac{\left(\sum_{1}^{N} ABS\right)^2}{npq}.$$

If the correction term $[X]$ is subtracted from $[A]$, $[B]$, $[AB]$, $[ABS]$, etc., a sum of squares is obtained. Thus

$$[A] - [X] = \text{sum of squares for treatment } A$$
$$[B] - [X] = \text{sum of squares for treatment } B$$
$$[AB] - [X] = \text{sum of squares for treatments } A \text{ and } B$$
$$\text{and the } AB \text{ interaction.}$$

$[AB]$ may be thought of as including variation due to main effects of A, B, and the AB interaction. In order to obtain the AB interaction sum of squares, it is necessary to subtract SS_A and SS_B from $([AB] - [X])$.

$$SS_{AB} = ([AB] - [X]) - ([A] - [X]) - ([B] - [X])$$
$$= [AB] - [A] - [B] + [X].$$

The term $[ABS]$ is given by

$$[ABS] = \sum_{1}^{N} \frac{(ABS)^2}{1}$$

and may be thought of as composed of variation due to treatments A and B, the AB interaction, and subjects (S). The reader may wonder why $[ABS]$ includes variation due to the AB interaction but not variation due to the AS and BS interactions. This can be explained by the fact that treatments A and B are *crossed*, but subjects are *nested* within both treatments. (See Section 7.15 for a discussion of crossed and nested treatments.) If the correction term $[X]$ is subtracted from $[ABS]$, the total sum of squares is obtained. It should be obvious that the variation due to subjects ($SS_{\text{within cell}}$) is given by

$$SS_{\text{w.cell}} = [ABS] - [AB] = \text{sum of squares due to subjects.}$$

If sources of variation within a summary table are correctly identified, for example, $[ABS]$, $[AB]$, etc., the reader should have no difficulty in writing out the computational formulas for factorial designs.

KINDS OF COMPUTATIONAL FORMULAS
USED IN ANALYSIS OF VARIANCE

The reader may feel that a bewildering array of computational formulas are used in analysis of variance. At first glance this appears to be true, but it can be shown that actually only *four* kinds of formulas are used in computing the various sums of squares. These formulas can be classified as (1) between, (2) within, (3) interaction, or (4) total formulas. To illustrate, *between* sum of squares formulas for the designs described previously have the following form:

type CR-k design	$[B] - [X]$
type RB-k design	$[B] - [X]$, $[S] - [X]$
type LS-k design	$[A] - [X]$, $[B] - [X]$, $[C] - [X]$
type CRF-pq design	$[A] - [X]$, $[B] - [X]$
type CRF-pqr design	$[A] - [X]$, $[B] - [X]$, $[C] - [X]$.

All between formulas have the same form regardless of whether the formula is for variation between groups, blocks, columns, or treatments.

The pattern for *within* sum of squares formulas is as follows:

type CR-k design	$[BS] - [B]$
type RB-k design	no within sum of squares
type LS-k design	$[ABCS] - [ABC]$ for $n > 1$
type CRF-pq design	$[ABS] - [AB]$
type CRF-pqr design	$[ABCS] - [ABC]$.

Again, the pattern underlying all within formulas is the same.

The third kind of formula, the one for computing *interaction* sum of squares, has the following general form:

type CR-k design	no interaction sum of squares
type RB-k design	$[BS] - [B] - [S] + [X]$
type LS-k design	$[ABC] - [A] - [B] - [C] + 2[X]$
type CRF-pq design	$[AB] - [A] - [B] + [X]$.

In some designs, such as a randomized block design, the interaction formula is referred to as a *residual* formula. This designation is often used whenever an interaction mean square is used in lieu of a within-groups mean square to estimate experimental error.

The final kind of formula is a *total* sum of squares formula. This formula has the general form illustrated by the following examples:

type CR-k design	$[BS] - [X]$
type RB-k design	$[BS] - [X]$
type LS-k design	$[ABCS] - [X]$
type CRF-pq design	$[ABS] - [X]$.

Complex designs described in subsequent chapters should appear less complex when it is realized that all designs involve at most only four kinds of formulas and hence four kinds of variation.

7.14 COMPLETELY RANDOMIZED FACTORIAL DESIGN WITH $n = 1$

Experimenters in the behavioral sciences are often interested in conducting research that involves many treatments, each with many levels. A type CRF-354 design that is not an unusually large experiment by current standards has 60 treatment combinations. In order to compute a within-cell sum of squares, a minimum of 120 subjects is required. Yet a sample of this size may not be available. Considerations such as time or cost may also preclude the use of such a large sample of subjects. Under these conditions several design alternatives are available to an experimenter. One alternative, which is described in this section, is to assign only one subject to each treatment combination. If this approach is followed, the highest-order interaction, instead of the within-cell error term, is used as an estimate of experimental error. Additional design alternatives are described in Chapters 8, 9, and 10; these designs permit an experimenter, by careful planning, to carry out multitreatment experiments with a minimum of subjects.

Consider the following models for a two-treatment factorial experiment:

$$X_{ijm} = \mu + \alpha_i + \beta_j + \alpha\beta_{ij} + \varepsilon_{m(ij)}$$

$$X_{ijm} = \mu + \alpha_i + \beta_j + \varepsilon_{m(ij)}.$$

The first model includes a first-order interaction, the second does not. If the second model provides an adequate description of the sources of variation in the experiment, MS_{AB}, as well as $MS_{w.cell}$, is an estimate of experimental error. For experiments in which $n = 1$, a *mean square within-cell* term cannot be computed. If the second model above is appropriate,

MS_{AB} may be used in place of $MS_{w.cell}$. The basic question to be answered is; "Which model is appropriate for the experiment?"

    Tukey's test for additivity described in Section 5.3 is helpful in deciding between the two models. The model in which

$$MS_{AB} \rightarrow \sigma_\varepsilon^2 + \sigma_{\alpha\beta}^2$$

is called a nonadditivity model, while

$$MS_{AB} \rightarrow \sigma_\varepsilon^2$$

is called an additivity model. Computational procedures for Tukey's test for a randomized block design are shown in Table 5.3-1. These computational procedures generalize with slight modification to factorial experiments. A test for nonadditivity for a type CRF-pq design requires the substitution in Table 5.2-1 of an AB Summary Table in place of the BS Summary Table. The computational formulas are

$$SS_{nonadd} = \frac{\left(\sum_1^p \sum_1^q d_{ij} AB_{ij}\right)^2}{\left(\sum_1^p d_i^2\right)\left(\sum_1^q d_j^2\right)}$$

$$SS_{remainder} = SS_{AB} - SS_{nonadd}$$

$$df_{nonadd} = 1$$

$$df_{rem} = df_{(AB)} - 1$$

$$F_{nonadd} = \frac{MS_{nonadd}}{MS_{rem}}.$$

If F_{nonadd} is not significant at a numerically high level of significance ($\alpha = .10 - .25$), it lends credence to the assumption that

$$MS_{AB} \rightarrow \sigma_\varepsilon^2.$$

Under this condition with $n = 1$ and a fixed-effects model, MS_{AB} is used as the error term for testing treatments A and B. If F_{nonadd} is significant, a transformation that will eliminate the AB interaction may be found. For a discussion of Tukey's test and the effects of various transformations on nonadditivity, see Harter and Lum (1962).

    A nonadditivity test for a type CRF-pqr design also follows the procedures illustrated in Table 5.3-1. An ABC Summary Table must be substituted for the BS Summary Table. A $d_i \times d_j \times d_k$ Summary Table must be substituted for the $d_i \times d_j$ Summary Table. The required computational formulas are

$$SS_{nonadd} = \frac{\left(\sum_1^p \sum_1^q \sum_1^r d_{ijk} ABC_{ijk}\right)^2}{\left(\sum_1^p d_i^2\right)\left(\sum_1^q d_j^2\right)\left(\sum_1^r d_k^2\right)}$$

$$SS_{rem} = SS_{ABC} - SS_{nonadd}$$

$$df_{nonadd} = 1$$

$$df_{rem} = df_{(ABC)} - 1$$

$$F_{nonadd} = \frac{MS_{nonadd}}{MS_{rem}}.$$

If F_{nonadd} is insignificant at the .25 level, the nonadditivity model is rejected in favor of the additivity model, in which

$$MS_{ABC} \rightarrow \sigma_\varepsilon^2.$$

7.15 INTRODUCTION TO HIERARCHAL EXPERIMENT

The factorial experiments presented in previous sections of this chapter can be described as *crossed treatment* (classification) experiments. Their distinguishing characteristic is that all possible combinations of levels of two or more treatments occur together in an experiment. However, in some research situations it may not be possible or convenient to design an experiment so that treatments are crossed. A *hierarchal experiment* may be appropriate for such situations. One or more of the treatments in a hierarchal experiment are *nested* instead of being crossed. Treatment B is said to be nested within A if each level of B appears with only one level of treatment A. The difference between crossed and nested treatments is shown in Figure 7.15-1. It is apparent from part (b) that treatment B

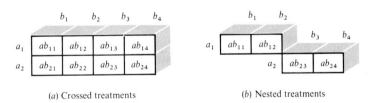

(a) Crossed treatments   (b) Nested treatments

Figure 7.15-1 Comparison of crossed and nested treatments.

is *nested* within treatment A. That is, levels b_1 and b_2 occur with a_1, but different levels of treatment B occur with level a_2, namely, levels b_3 and b_4. This kind of design is designated by the letters CRH-$p(q)$. The letter in parentheses indicates that treatment B is a nested treatment. Although B is called a nested treatment, in most designs it is more aptly referred to as a nuisance variable. In the following two illustrations, it is included in the design in order to isolate a source of variation that affects scores.

The following examples may help to clarify the distinction between crossed and nested treatments and to indicate the general character of nested treatments. Assume that two types of programmed instruction materials are to be evaluated and that four sixth-grade classes are available for the experiment. Each type of programmed material is randomly assigned to two classes. For administrative reasons, all children in a particular class must use the same type of programmed material. The two treatment classifications consist of two types of programmed materials (a_1 and a_2) and four classrooms (b_1, b_2, b_3, and b_4). This hierarchal experiment is analogous to the design illustrated in Figure 7.15-1b. Levels of treatment B are nested within levels of treatment A. The linear model for this experiment is

$$X_{ijm} = \mu + \alpha_i + \beta_{j(i)} + \varepsilon_{m(ij)},$$

where the symbol $\beta_{j(i)}$ indicates nesting of treatment B within treatment A. Note that the interaction of treatments A and B does not appear in the model. The term $\beta_{j(i)}$ is actually the pooled simple main effects of treatment B at each level of treatment A. The reader may recall from Table 7.4-1 that

$$\sum_1^p SS_B \text{ for } a_i = SS_B + SS_{AB}.$$

Thus $SS_{B_{j(i)}}$ in a hierarchal experiment is equivalent to $SS_B + SS_{AB}$ in a corresponding factorial experiment. A common error in the analysis of experiments similar to that just described is to treat the design as if it were a type CR-k design with $nq_{(i)}$ subjects in each level of treatment A. In this case a test of the ratio $MS_{\text{between } A}/MS_{\text{WG}}$ in a completely randomized design may be biased because of variation associated with the different classrooms. An examination of the E(MS) in Table 7.15-2 reveals that if the nested treatment is a random variable, σ_β^2 appears in the E(MS) for treatment A. The correct error term for evaluating treatment A is $MS_{B\text{w.}A}$, not MS_{WG}. If the design is analyzed as a type CR-k design, the only error term available is MS_{WG}.

A nested treatment may occur in animal research when it is necessary to administer the same treatment level to all animals within the same cage or housing compound. For example, an experiment is designed to evaluate the effects of positive and negative ionization of air molecules (treatment levels a_1 and a_2, respectively) on the activity of rats. The subjects are radiated continuously for a three-week period, after which their activity level is measured in an open field situation. Thirty-two rats are housed in eight cages (treatment levels b_1, b_2, ..., b_8) with four rats per cage. Each cage is equipped with ionizing equipment for producing the required condition within the cage. A table of random numbers is used to assign half the cages to the positive ionization condition, while the other half receives the negative ionization condition. In this example, cages are nested under ionization conditions. The activity level of rat X_{ijm} assigned to ionization condition a_i and cage b_j can be attributed to the ionization condition received as well as to the particular cage in which it is housed. It is possible for systematic differences to develop among rats in the cages receiving level a_i due to differences in dispersion of ionized air within the cages, undetected infectious diseases in some cages, presence of neurotic rats in certain cages, and so on. The use of a hierarchal design in this example takes cognizance of the fact that cages per se may contribute significantly to the total variation among rats' activity level. It would be incorrect to use a type CR-2 design to evaluate the effects of ionization because this design does not take into account the effects of cages, which are a part of the physical conduct of the experiment.

The presence of nested treatments in an experiment is not always as obvious as in the preceding two examples. Hicks (1965, 165) and Snedecor (1956, 267) present several such examples. Some experiments include both crossed and nested treatments and are called partial hierarchal experiments. Analysis procedures for experiments involving nested treatments are described in subsequent paragraphs.

LAYOUT AND COMPUTATIONAL PROCEDURES
FOR TYPE CRH-$p(q)$ DESIGN

The layout of a type CRH-2(8) design and computational formulas are shown in Table 7.15-1. Assume that the data are from the ionization experiment described above. The analysis of variance is summarized in Table 7.15-2, where the following notation is used:

p levels of a_i, where $p = 2$

q levels of b_j, where $q = 8$

$q_{(i)}$ levels of b_j nested within A, where $q_{(i)} = 4$

n levels of s_m, where $n = 4$

$$\sum_1^N = \sum_1^p \sum_1^{q_{(i)}} \sum_1^n.$$

It is assumed, for the analysis summarized in Table 7.15-2, that treatment A is fixed and treatment B is random. The eight cages used in the experiment can be considered to represent a random sample from a hypothetical population of cages of interest to the experimenter. In a hierarchal design, $\beta_{j(i)}$ is generally considered a random variable, just as $\varepsilon_{i(j)}$ is a random variable in a type CR-k design. The sampling fraction $1 - (q/Q)$ in the E(MS) column for the random variable is assigned the value of one. The F ratios for tests of treatments A and B have the following forms, respectively,

$$E(F) = \frac{E(MS_A)}{E(MS_{B\,w.\,A})} = \frac{\sigma_\varepsilon^2 + n\sigma_B^2 + nq\sigma_\alpha^2}{\sigma_\varepsilon^2 + n\sigma_B^2},$$

$$E(F) = \frac{E(MS_{B\,w.\,A})}{E(MS_{w.cell})} = \frac{\sigma_\varepsilon^2 + n\sigma_B^2}{\sigma_\varepsilon^2}.$$

TABLE 7.15-1   Layout of Type CRH-2(8) Design and Computational Procedures

(i) Data:

ABS Summary Table

a_1	a_1	a_1	a_1	a_2	a_2	a_2	a_2
b_1	b_2	b_3	b_4	b_5	b_6	b_7	b_8
3	4	7	7	1	2	5	10
6	5	8	8	2	3	6	10
3	4	7	9	2	4	5	9
3	3	6	8	2	3	6	11

AB Summary Table

	b_1	b_2	b_3	b_4	b_5	b_6	b_7	b_8	$\sum_1^q A$	$\dfrac{\left(\sum_1^q A\right)^2}{nq_{(i)}}$
a_1	$n = 4$ 15	16	28	32					91	517.5625
a_2					7	12	22	40	81	410.0625

(ii) Computational symbols:

$$\sum_1^N ABS = 3 + 6 + 3 + \cdots + 11 = 172.000$$

$$\sum_1^N (ABS)^2 = [ABS] = (3)^2 + (6)^2 + (3)^2 + \cdots + (11)^2 = 1160.00$$

$$\frac{\left(\sum_1^N ABS\right)^2}{npq_{(i)}} = [X] = \frac{(172)^2}{4(2)(4)} = 924.500$$

$$\sum_1^p \frac{\left(\sum_1^q A\right)^2}{nq_{(i)}} = [A] = 517.5625 + 410.0625 = 927.625$$

$$\sum_1^p \sum_1^q \frac{(AB)^2}{n} = [AB] = \frac{(15)^2}{4} + \frac{(16)^2}{4} + \cdots + \frac{(40)^2}{4} = 1141.500$$

(iii) Computational formulas:

$$SS_{total} = [ABS] - [X] = 235.500 \qquad SS_{B\,w.\,A} = [AB] - [A] = 213.875$$

$$SS_A = [A] - [X] = 3.125 \qquad SS_{w.cell} = [ABS] - [AB] = 18.500$$

**TABLE 7.15-2 Analysis of Variance Table
for Type CRH-2(8) Design**

Source	SS	df	MS	F(Model III)	E(MS)
1 A	3.125	$p - 1 = 1$	3.125	$[\frac{1}{2}] = $ N.S.	$\sigma_\varepsilon^2 + n\left(1 - \dfrac{q}{Q}\right)\sigma_\beta^2 + nq\sigma_\alpha^2$
2 B w. A	213.875	$p(q_{(i)} - 1) = 6$	35.646	$[\frac{2}{3}] = 46.23*$	$\sigma_\varepsilon^2 + n\sigma_\beta^2$
3 W.cell	18.500	$pq_{(i)}(n - 1) = 24$	.771		σ_ε^2
4 Total	235.500	$N - 1 = 31$			

*$p < .01$.

In order for these ratios to follow the F distribution, the assumptions of a completely randomized design (described in Section 4.4) must be met. A special comment should be made with respect to the use of $MS_{B\,w.\,A}$ as a denominator of an F ratio. We noted earlier that $SS_{B\,w.\,A}$ represents a pooled sum of squares

$$
\begin{array}{cc}
 & \text{df} \\
B\,w.\,a_1 & q_{(i)} - 1 \\
\cdot & \cdot \\
\cdot & \cdot \\
\cdot & \cdot \\
B\,w.\,a_p & q_{(i)} - 1 \\
\Sigma = \overline{B\,w.\,A} & \overline{p(q_{(i)} - 1)}.
\end{array}
$$

This pooled error term must represent homogeneous sources of variation. Procedures for partitioning $SS_{B\,w.\,A}$ into p sources of variation for carrying out tests of homogeneity of variance are described in Section 7.4. If $SS_{B\,w.\,A}$ is based on less than 25 to 30 degrees of freedom, preliminary tests on the model and pooling of $MS_{B\,w.\,A}$ with $MS_{w.cell}$, following procedures described in Section 7.12, may provide a more adequate error term. One of the problems involved in using a hierarchal design is that, typically, $MS_{B\,w.\,A}$ is based on a relatively small number of degrees of freedom.

If unequal n's are assigned to the levels of treatments, the test of treatment A for Models II and III, in which treatment B is a random variable, is not exact. This results from the fact that the coefficients of σ_B^2 for the numerator and denominator of the F ratio are not the same. Thus even though the numerator and denominator of the F ratio have the following expected values, where $\sigma_\alpha^2 = 0$, the ratio will not equal one.

$$
E(F) = \frac{E(MS_A)}{E(MS_{B\,w.\,A})} = \frac{\sigma_\varepsilon^2 + n_1\sigma_B^2 + n_2q\sigma_\alpha^2}{\sigma_\varepsilon^2 + n_3\sigma_B^2}.
$$

Snedecor (1956, 271) discusses the problems resulting from unequal n's.

According to the summary in Table 7.15-2, we can conclude that $\sigma_B^2 \neq 0$ for one or both levels of treatment A. Presumably there is little interest in a test of this hypothesis, for the choice of a hierarchal design is based on the belief that differences are likely to exist among population means for the nested treatment. The analysis in Table 7.15-2 illustrates a not uncommon situation. The $MS_{Bw.A}$ is greater than MS_A. Under these conditions, one suspects that a design is not randomized with respect to some important factor or that sampling variation has either decreased the estimate of treatment A or increased the estimate of treatment B relative to their respective population values. The use of the contrived data in this example permits the point to be made that the nested treatment is the pooled simple main effects of treatment B at each level of treatment A. These same data are also analyzed as if the design were a type CRF-24 design. A summary of this analysis is presented in Table 7.4-2. A comparison of this analysis with that summarized in Table 7.15-2 reveals that

$$SS_{Bw.A} = \sum_{1}^{p} SS_B \text{ for } a_i = SS_B + SS_{AB}$$

$$213.875 = 54.6875 + 159.1875 = 194.500 + 19.375.$$

DESCRIPTION AND COMPUTATIONAL FORMULAS FOR A TYPE CRH-$p(q)(r)$ DESIGN

A hierarchal experiment in which treatment B is nested under treatment A and treatment C is nested under B is designated as a type CRH-$p(q)(r)$ design. The linear model for this design is

$$X_{ijkm} = \mu + \alpha_i + \beta_{j(i)} + \gamma_{k(ij)} + \varepsilon_{m(ijk)}.$$

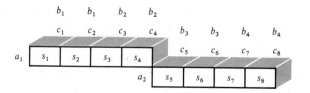

Figure 7.15-2   Block design of type CRH-2(4)(8) design.

In this design, treatment C is nested under B, which is nested under A (C w. B w. A). It can be shown that $SS_{Cw.Bw.A}$ corresponds to

$$SS_{Cw.Bw.A} = SS_C + SS_{AC} + SS_{BC} + SS_{ABC}$$

in a factorial experiment. $SS_{Bw.A}$ and $SS_{Cw.Bw.A}$ represent pooled simple main effects and pooled simple simple main effects, respectively. The sources of variation that are pooled to form these sums of squares must be homogeneous in order for them to serve as denominators of F ratios.

A block diagram of a type CRH-2(4)(8) design is shown in Figure 7.15-2. Computational formulas, degrees of freedom, and E(MS) appear in Table 7.15-3. The following notation is appropriate for the type CRH-2(4)(8) design, which is diagramed in Figure 7.15-2:

p levels of a_i, where $p = 2$

$q_{(i)}$ levels of b_j nested within A, where $q_{(i)} = 2$

$r_{(j)}$ levels of c_k nested within B, where $r_{(j)} = 2$

n levels of s_m.

TABLE 7.15-3   Computational Formulas, Degrees of Freedom, and Expected Values of Mean Squares for Type CRH-$p(q)(r)$ Design

Source	Formula	df	E(MS)
1 A	$[A] - [X]$	$p - 1$	$\sigma_\varepsilon^2 + n\left(1 - \dfrac{r}{R}\right)\sigma_\gamma^2$ $\quad\quad + n\left(1 - \dfrac{q}{Q}\right)r\sigma_\beta^2 + nqr\sigma_\alpha^2$
2 B w. A	$[AB] - [A]$	$p(q_{(i)} - 1)$	$\sigma_\varepsilon^2 + n\left(1 - \dfrac{r}{R}\right)\sigma_\gamma^2 + nr\sigma_\beta^2$
3 C w. B w. A	$[ABC] - [AB]$	$pq_{(i)}(r_{(j)} - 1)$	$\sigma_\varepsilon^2 + n\sigma_\gamma^2$
4 W.cell	$[ABCS] - [ABC]$	$pq_{(i)}r_{(j)}(n - 1)$	σ_ε^2
5 Total	$[ABCS] - [X]$	$npq_{(i)}r_{(j)} - 1$	

DESCRIPTION AND COMPUTATIONAL FORMULAS FOR A TYPE CRPH-$p(q)r$ DESIGN

As mentioned earlier, some research situations call for both crossed and nested treatments in the same experiment. This kind of design is called a partial hierarchal design. If treatment B is nested within treatment A, but treatment C is crossed with treatments B and A, the design can be diagramed as shown in Figure 7.15-3.

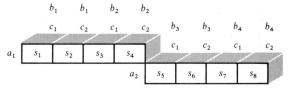

Figure 7.15-3   Block diagram of type CRPH-2(4)2 design.

The linear model for this type CRPH-$p(q)r$ design is

$$X_{ijkm} = \mu + \alpha_i + \beta_{j(i)} + \gamma_k + \alpha\gamma_{ik} + \beta\gamma_{j(i)k} + \varepsilon_{m(ijk)}.$$

If A and B are crossed treatments, but C is nested under B, the design is designated as a type CRPH-$pq(r)$ design. The linear model for this latter design is

$$X_{ijkm} = \mu + \alpha_i + \beta_j + \gamma_{k(j)} + \alpha\beta_{ij} + \alpha\gamma_{ik(j)} + \varepsilon_{m(ijk)}.$$

It is apparent from the above linear models that a partial hierarchal experiment includes interactions between all crossed treatments. Computational formulas, degrees of freedom, and expected values of mean squares for a type CRPH-$p(q)r$ design are shown in Table 7.15-4. Analysis procedures for this design require the construction of $ABCS$, ABC, AB, and AC Summary Tables. Harter and Lum (1955) have prepared extensive tables of E(MS) for type CRPH designs involving up to four treatments.

TABLE 7.15-4 Computational Formulas, Degrees of Freedom, and Expected Values of Mean Squares for Type CRPH-$p(q)r$ Design

Source	Formula	df	E(MS)
1 A	$[A] - [X]$	$p - 1$	$\sigma_\varepsilon^2 + n\left(1 - \dfrac{q}{Q}\right)\left(1 - \dfrac{r}{R}\right)\sigma_{\beta\gamma}^2$ $+ nq\left(1 - \dfrac{r}{R}\right)\sigma_{\alpha\gamma}^2$ $+ nr\left(1 - \dfrac{q}{Q}\right)\sigma_\beta^2 + nqr\sigma_\alpha^2$
2 B w. A	$[AB] - [A]$	$p(q_{(i)} - 1)$	$\sigma_\varepsilon^2 + n\left(1 - \dfrac{r}{R}\right)\sigma_{\beta\gamma}^2 + nr\sigma_\beta^2$
3 C	$[C] - [X]$	$r - 1$	$\sigma_\varepsilon^2 + n\left(1 - \dfrac{q}{Q}\right)\sigma_{\beta\gamma}^2$ $+ nq\left(1 - \dfrac{p}{P}\right)\sigma_{\alpha\gamma}^2 + npq\sigma_\gamma^2$
4 AC	$[AC] - [A]$ $- [C] + [X]$	$(p - 1)(r - 1)$	$\sigma_\varepsilon^2 + n\left(1 - \dfrac{q}{Q}\right)\sigma_{\beta\gamma}^2 + nq\sigma_{\alpha\gamma}^2$
5 B w. $A \times C$	$[ABC] - [AB]$ $- [AC] + [A]$	$P(q_{(i)} - 1)(r - 1)$	$\sigma_\varepsilon^2 + n\sigma_{\beta\gamma}^2$
6 W.cell	$[ABCS] - [ABC]$	$pq_{(i)}r(n - 1)$	σ_ε^2
7 Total	$[ABCS] - [X]$	$npq_{(i)}r - 1$	

7.16   INTRODUCTION TO RANDOMIZED BLOCK FACTORIAL DESIGN

If each subject or each set of matched subjects receives *all ab* treatment combinations in an experiment, the design is called a type RBF-*pq* design. The building block for this factorial experiment is a randomized block design. A comparison of a type CRF-23 design with a RBF-23 design is shown in Figure 7.16-1. If repeated measures are obtained

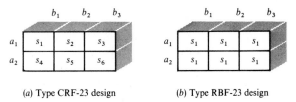

(a) Type CRF-23 design   (b) Type RBF-23 design

Figure 7.16-1   Comparison of type CRF-23 and type RBF-23 designs.

on subjects, s_1 in part (b) represents a set of subjects who receive all *ab* treatment combinations. The order of administration of the *pq* combinations is randomized independently for each subject. If sets of matched subjects are used, one subject from each set is randomly assigned to each *ab* treatment combination. General considerations with respect to the use of matched subjects or repeated measures on the same subjects are discussed in Section 5.1 for a randomized block design. These considerations also apply to a type RBF-*pq* design. If the number of treatment combinations is large, it may not be possible to observe each subject under all *pq* combinations or to secure *pq* sets of matched subjects. Then a split-plot design, described in Chapter 8, may be used. This latter design requires a subject to participate under only *q* of the *pq* treatment combinations. If sets of matched subjects are used, a set consists of *q* subjects instead of the *pq* subjects required in a type RBF-*pq* design. Another alternative design that achieves a reduction in the number of treatment combinations to which subjects must be assigned is a confounded factorial design, described in Chapter 9.

ASSUMPTIONS OF THE MODEL FOR TYPE RBF-*pq* DESIGN

The fixed-effects linear model for a type RBF-*pq* design is

$$X_{ijm} = \mu + \alpha_i + \beta_j + \alpha\beta_{ij} + \pi_m + \varepsilon_{ijm},$$

where μ = grand mean of treatment populations.

α_i = effect of treatment i, which is a constant for all subjects within treatment population i, $\Sigma_{i=1}^{p} \alpha_i = 0$.

β_j = effect of treatment j, which is a constant for all subjects within treatment population j, $\Sigma_{j=1}^{q} \beta_j = 0$.

$\alpha\beta_{ij}$ = effect, which represents nonadditivity of effects α_i and β_j, $\Sigma_{i=1}^{p} \alpha\beta_{ij} = 0$, $\Sigma_{j=1}^{q} \alpha\beta_{ij} = 0$.

π_m = a constant associated with block m, $\Sigma_{m=1}^{n} \pi_m = 0$.

ε_{ijm} = experimental error, which is NID with mean = 0 and variance = σ_{ε}^2.

A residual mean square is used in a randomized block factorial design as an estimate of experimental error if it can be assumed that the treatments × blocks interactions are zero, that is, if $\alpha\pi$, $\beta\pi$, and $\alpha\beta\pi = 0$. A test of the hypothesis of zero interaction between blocks and treatments can be made by Tukey's test described in Section 5.3. If the interactions are not equal to zero, $MS_{A \times blocks}$, $MS_{B \times blocks}$, and $MS_{AB \times blocks}$ may be used as error terms. The choice of error terms for testing main effects depends on the expected values of the mean squares, which, in turn, depend on the model that is appropriate for the experiment.

In this design, as in a randomized block design, it is assumed that the $pq \times pq$ variance-covariance matrix has the symmetry described in Section 5.3. If individual error terms, instead of the MS_{res}, are used to test main effects, the $p \times p$, $q \times q$, and $pq \times pq$ matrices should each have the proper symmetry. Procedures for determining if the variance-covariance matrices have the required symmetry are described in Section 5.3. This test, as well as Tukey's test mentioned above, is not normally made unless an experimenter has reason to question the respective assumptions.

LAYOUT AND COMPUTATIONAL PROCEDURES
FOR TYPE RBF-24 DESIGN

In Section 7.3 a completely randomized factorial design was used in evaluating the effects of magnitude of reinforcement and social deprivation on children's motor behavior. A "marble dropping game" was employed to assess motor behavior. Thirty-two children in the experiment were randomly assigned to $pq = 8$ subsamples, with four subjects per subsample. Let us alter the situation slightly by assuming that data for a game "pick up the sticks" are available for a large sample of children. Assume, also, that children's scores on the game "pick up the sticks" are positively correlated with their scores on the marble dropping game. Data for the "sticks" game are used to form four sets (blocks) of $pq = 8$ matched subjects. It is hoped that by this matching procedure variability in marble dropping performance among subjects within any block will be less than the variability among blocks. The research hypotheses for this experiment are identical to those for a type CRF-24 design in Section 7.3.

The layout of the type RBF-24 design, computational tables, and formulas are shown in Table 7.16-1. The analysis of variance is summarized in Table 7.16-2, where the following notation is used:

$$p \text{ levels of } a_i, \text{ where } p = 2$$

$$q \text{ levels of } b_j, \text{ where } q = 4$$

$$n \text{ levels of } s_m, \text{ where } n = 4$$

$$\sum_1^N = \sum_1^p \sum_1^q \sum_1^n.$$

TABLE 7.16-1　Layout of Type RBF-24 Design and Computational Procedures

(i) Data:

ABS Summary Table

	a_1 b_1	a_1 b_2	a_1 b_3	a_1 b_4	a_2 b_1	a_2 b_2	a_2 b_3	a_2 b_4	$\sum_1^p\sum_1^q S$	$\dfrac{\left(\sum_1^p\sum_1^q S\right)^2}{pq}$
s_1	3	4	7	7	1	2	5	10	39	190.125
s_2	6	5	8	8	2	3	6	10	48	288.000
s_3	3	4	7	9	2	4	5	9	43	231.125
s_4	3	3	6	8	2	3	6	11	42	220.500

AB Summary Table

	b_1	b_2	b_3	b_4	$\sum_1^q A$	$\dfrac{\left(\sum_1^q A\right)^2}{nq}$
a_1	$n = 4$ 15	16	28	32	91	517.5625
a_2	7	12	22	40	81	410.0625
$\sum_1^p B =$	22	28	50	72		
$\dfrac{\left(\sum_1^p B\right)^2}{np} =$	60.5	98.0	312.5	648.0		

(ii) Computational symbols:

$$\sum_1^N ABS = 3 + 6 + 3 + \cdots + 11 = 172.000$$

$$\sum_1^N (ABS)^2 = [ABS] = (3)^2 + (6)^2 + (3)^2 + \cdots + (11)^2 = 1160.000$$

TABLE 7.16-1 (continued)

$$\frac{\left(\sum_{1}^{N} ABS\right)^2}{N} = [X] = \frac{(172)^2}{32} = 924.500$$

$$\sum_{1}^{n} \frac{\left(\sum_{1}^{p} \sum_{1}^{q} S\right)^2}{pq} = [S] = 190.125 + 288.000 + \cdots + 220.500 = 929.750$$

$$\sum_{1}^{p} \frac{\left(\sum_{1}^{q} A\right)^2}{nq} = [A] = 517.625 + 410.0625 = 927.625$$

$$\sum_{1}^{q} \frac{\left(\sum_{1}^{p} B\right)^2}{np} = [B] = 60.5 + 98.0 + \cdots + 648.0 = 1119.000$$

$$\sum_{1}^{p} \sum_{1}^{q} \frac{(AB)^2}{n} = [AB] = \frac{(15)^2}{4} + \frac{(16)^2}{4} + \cdots + \frac{(40)^2}{4} = 1141.500$$

(iii) Computational formulas:

$$SS_{total} = [ABS] - [X] = 235.500 \qquad SS_B = [B] - [X] = 194.500$$
$$SS_{blocks} = [S] - [X] = 5.250 \qquad SS_{AB} = [AB] - [A] - [B] + [X] = 19.375$$
$$SS_{treats} = [AB] - [X] = 217.000 \qquad SS_{res} = [ABS] - [S] - [AB] + [X] = 13.250$$
$$SS_A = [A] - [X] = 3.125$$

TABLE 7.16-2   Analysis of Variance Table
for Type RBF-24 Design

Source	SS	df	MS	F(Model I)
1 Blocks	5.250	$n - 1 = 3$	1.750	$[\frac{1}{6}] = \quad 2.77$
2 Treatments	217.000	$pq - 1 = 7$		
3 A	3.125	$p - 1 = 1$	3.125	$[\frac{3}{6}] = \quad 4.95*$
4 B	194.500	$q - 1 = 3$	64.833	$[\frac{4}{6}] = 102.75**$
5 AB	19.375	$(p - 1)(q - 1) = 3$	6.458	$[\frac{5}{6}] = \quad 10.23**$
6 Residual	13.250	$(n - 1)(pq - 1) = 21$	.631	
7 Total	235.500	$npq - 1 = 31$		

*$p < .05$.

**$p < .01$.

According to the analysis in Table 7.16-2, the AB interaction is significant. Consequently, tests of main effects are of little interest, and attention is directed to tests of simple main effects. Computational procedures for these tests appear in Table 7.4-1. The error term $MS_{residual}$ should be used for these simple main effects tests.

A randomized block factorial design is more powerful than a completely randomized factorial design if the block effects in the former design are appreciably greater than zero. The reason for this is obvious if the two designs are compared with respect to the way in which the total variation is partitioned into the underlying sums of squares. This comparison is presented in Figure 7.16-2. In choosing between these two designs, one should consider not only their relative power but also the cost of using matched subjects versus random assignment of subjects to treatments.

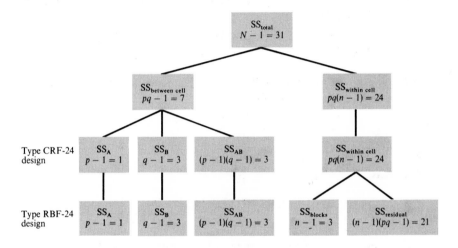

Figure 7.16-2 Schematic comparison of total variation and degrees of freedom for two factorial experiments.

EXPECTED VALUES OF MEAN SQUARES

The expected values of mean squares for Models I, II, and III can be obtained from Table 7.16-3. The terms $1 - (p/P)$ and $1 - (q/Q)$ in the table become zero if the corresponding terms A and B represent fixed effects and one if the corresponding terms are random.

TABLE 7.16-3 Procedures for Determining E(MS) for Type RBF-pq Design

Source	E(MS)
Blocks	$\sigma_\varepsilon^2 + pq\sigma_\pi^2$
A	$\sigma_\varepsilon^2 + \left(1 - \dfrac{q}{Q}\right)n\sigma_{\alpha\beta}^2 + nq\sigma_\alpha^2$
B	$\sigma_\varepsilon^2 + \left(1 - \dfrac{p}{P}\right)n\sigma_{\alpha\beta}^2 + np\sigma_\beta^2$
AB	$\sigma_\varepsilon^2 + n\sigma_{\alpha\beta}^2$
Residual	σ_ε^2

The residual mean square is a composite term that estimates σ_ε^2, $\sigma_{\alpha\pi}^2$, $\sigma_{\beta\pi}^2$, and $\sigma_{\alpha\beta\pi}^2$. If the last three components are not equal to zero, the use of MS_{res} in testing main effects leads to negatively biased tests. One solution to this problem is to partition MS_{res} into its component interactions. Computational formulas for this purpose appear below. The expected values of the mean squares for the situation in which treatments $\times$ blocks interactions are not zero can be readily determined by procedures described in Section 7.10. If A and B are fixed effects and blocks are random (Model III), F ratios for testing treatments A and B and the AB interaction have the following form:

$$F = \frac{MS_A}{MS_{A \times blocks}}, \quad F = \frac{MS_B}{MS_{B \times blocks}}, \quad F = \frac{MS_{AB}}{MS_{AB \times blocks}}.$$

Computational formulas used in computing denominator mean squares for the above ratios have the form

$$MS_{A \times blocks} = \frac{[AS] - [A] - [S] + [X]}{(p - 1)(n - 1)}$$

$$MS_{B \times blocks} = \frac{[BS] - [B] - [S] + [X]}{(q - 1)(n - 1)}$$

$$MS_{AB \times blocks} = \frac{[ABS] - [AB] - [AS] - [BS] + [A] + [B] + [S] - [X]}{(p - 1)(q - 1)(n - 1)}.$$

A disadvantage of using the above error terms rather than MS_{res} in evaluating treatment effects for Model III is that the individual error terms are often based on a relatively small number of degrees of freedom. An alternative solution to using individual error terms is to select a dependent variable for which the treatments $\times$ blocks interactions are zero or to use a transformation that eliminates the interactions.

From a casual inspection of the SS_{res} formula, it is not evident that this formula is composed of three interaction formulas. This can be easily demonstrated, however, by adding together the computational formulas for $SS_{A \times blocks}$, $SS_{B \times blocks}$, and $SS_{AB \times blocks}$. For example,

$$([AS] - [A] - [S] + [X]) + ([BS] - [B] - [S] + [X])$$

$$+ ([ABS] - [AB] - [AS] - [BS] + [A] + [B] + [S] - [X])$$

$$= [ABS] - [AB] - [S] + [X]$$

which is the computational formula for SS_{res}.

MINIMIZING TIME AND LOCATION EFFECTS
BY THE USE OF A RANDOMIZED
BLOCK FACTORIAL DESIGN

A useful application of a type RBF-pq design may not be apparent to the reader. Situations may arise in behavioral research in which all the *pq* treatment combinations can be administered to only one set of subjects at a time. At a later time, or possibly at a different location, another set of subjects receives the same treatment combinations. In this type of experiment, the subjects in a set are *matched* in the sense that they each receive their treatment combinations at the same time or at the same place. Differences among blocks (sets) of subjects represent a time or place variable in addition to individual differences. The analysis of the data by a randomized block factorial experiment permits the isolation of the extraneous variables of time and place. An alternative analysis procedure, which is generally less desirable, is to pool all subjects who receive the same treatment combination and compute a within-cell error term. The data are analyzed by means of a completely randomized factorial design. The disadvantage of this procedure is that extraneous variables may produce systematic differences among the blocks of subjects. Under this condition, the within-cell error term includes both experimental error and the effects of the confounding variable. It is apparent that the same number of subjects is required in either analysis procedure, but the randomized block factorial design permits the isolation of a nuisance variable.

7.17   ADVANTAGES AND DISADVANTAGES OF FACTORIAL EXPERIMENTS

The major advantages of factorial experiments are

1. All subjects are used in evaluating the effects of two or more treatments. The effects of each treatment are evaluated with the same precision as if the entire experiment had been devoted to that treatment alone. Factorial experiments thus permit efficient use of resources.

2. Effects can be evaluated over a wide range of experimental conditions with maximum efficiency.

3. Permits interaction effects to be evaluated.

The major disadvantages of factorial experiments are

1. If many treatments and levels are included in the experiment, the number of subjects required may be prohibitive.

2. The design lacks simplicity in interpretation of experimental results if interactions are present. This is not a criticism of the design but simply an acknowledgement of the fact that the interrelationships among variables in the behavioral sciences are often complex.

3. The use of a factorial design commits an investigator to a relatively large experiment. Small exploratory experiments may indicate much more promising lines of investigation than those originally envisioned. Relatively small experiments permit greater freedom in the pursuit of serendipity.

4. Factorial experiments are generally less efficient in determining optimum levels of treatments or treatment combinations than a sequence of relatively small experiments, each based on the results of the preceding experiment.

7.18 REPRESENTATIVE APPLICATIONS OF FACTORIAL DESIGNS IN THE RESEARCH LITERATURE

The following references illustrate a variety of applications of factorial designs.

Barber, Theodore X., and D. S. Calverley. Effects on recall of hypnotic induction, motivational suggestions, and suggested regression: a methodological and experimental analysis. *Journal of Abnormal Psychology*, 1966, **71**, 169–180. Type CRF-33 design.

Blumenthal, Richard, and Julian Meltzoff. Some determinants of persistence in chronic schizophrenic subjects. *Journal of Abnormal Psychology*, 1965, **70**, 246–250. Type CRF-332 design.

Cicirelli, Victor G. Form of the relationship between creativity, IQ, and academic achievement. *Journal of Educational Psychology*, 1965, **56**, 303–308. Type CRF-38 design.

Edwards, Allen L., and Carol Jean Diers. Social desirability and conflict. *Journal of Social Psychology*, 1962, **58**, 349–356. Type CRF-224 design.

Geer, James H. Effect of fear arousal upon task performance and verbal behavior. *Journal of Abnormal Psychology*, 1966, **71**, 119–123. Type CRF-22 design.

Katz, Irwin I., James M. Robinson, Edgar G. Epps, and Patricia Waly. The influence of race of the experimenter and instructions upon the expression of hostility by Negro boys. *Journal of Social Issues*, 1964, **20**, 54–59. Type CRF-22 design.

Klinger, Eric, Arita Albaum, and Mavis Hetherington. Factors influencing the severity of moral judgments. *Journal of Social Psychology*, 1964, **63**, 319–326. Type CRF-2322 design.

Pishkin, Vladimir, and Aaron Wolfgang. Electromyographic gradients in concept identification with numbers of irrelevant dimensions. *Journal of Clinical Psychology*, 1964, **20**, 61–67. Type CRF-33 design.

Singer, Jerome E. Sympathetic activation, drugs, and fear. *Journal of Comparative and Physiological Psychology*, 1963, **56**, 612–615. Type CRF-32 design.

Ware, J. Roger, and Robert A. Baker. Effects of method of presentation, modes and response category knowledge of results on detection. *Journal of Engineering Psychology*, 1964, **3**, 111–116. Type CRF-222 design.

8 / SPLIT-PLOT DESIGN—

FACTORIAL DESIGN WITH BLOCK-TREATMENT CONFOUNDING

8.1 DESCRIPTION OF DESIGN

Subject heterogeneity is the rule rather than the exception in behavioral research. The randomized block design described earlier enables an experimenter to partially isolate the effect of subject heterogeneity in testing treatment effects. This is accomplished by using matched subjects or repeated measures on the same subject. In a randomized block design, blocks of subjects are composed in such a way that variation among subjects within each block is less than the variation among blocks. A split-plot design with repeated measures or matched subjects represents an extension of this principle to experiments having two or more treatments. This design is appropriate for experiments that meet, in addition to the general assumptions of the analysis of variance model, the following conditions:

1. Two or more treatments, with each treatment having two or more levels, that is, p levels of A, which is designated as a between-block or nonrepeated-measurements treatment, and q levels of B, which is designated as a within-block or repeated-measurements treatment, where p and $q \geq 2$.

2. The number of combinations of treatment levels is greater than the desired number of observations within each block.

3. If repeated measurements on the subjects are obtained, each block contains only one subject. If repeated measurements on the subjects are not obtained, each block contains q subjects.

4. For the repeated-measurements case, p samples of n subjects each from a population of subjects are randomly assigned to levels of the non-repeated treatment (A). The sequence of administration of the repeated treatment levels in combination with one level of the nonrepeated treatment is randomized independently for each block. Exception to this procedure is made when the nature of the repeated treatment precludes randomization of the presentation order.

5. For the nonrepeated-measurements case, p samples of n blocks of q subjects from a population of subjects are randomly assigned to levels of treatment (A). After this, levels of treatment (B) are assigned randomly to the q subjects within each block.

A COMPARISON OF THREE
FACTORIAL EXPERIMENTS

A graphic comparison of three experimental designs—a completely randomized factorial design, a randomized block factorial design, and a split-plot design—is shown in Figure 8.1-1. In this figure the split-plot

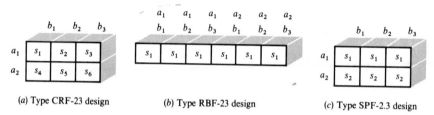

(a) Type CRF-23 design   (b) Type RBF-23 design   (c) Type SPF-2.3 design

Figure 8.1-1 Comparison of three types of designs.

repeated measures design is designated by SPF-2.3. The letters $s_1, s_2 \ldots s_6$ refer to sets of n subjects. In the type CRF-23 design, each set of subjects receives only one of the pq treatment combinations. An examination of part (a) reveals that the design is composed of two completely randomized designs. Subjects assigned to treatment level a_1 comprise one type CR-3 design, while subjects assigned to a_2 comprise the other type CR-3 design. The building block for the designs shown in parts (b) and (c) is a randomized block design. In a type RBF-23 design, a single set of subjects (s_1) receives all pq treatment level combinations. By contrast, in a split-plot design subjects in set s_1 receive only one level of treatment A but all levels of treatment B. The analysis of treatments A and B in a split-plot design, when viewed separately, resembles the analysis for a completely randomized design and a randomized block design, respectively. This analogy is discussed in Section 8.4.

SPECIAL FEATURES OF
SPLIT-PLOT DESIGNS

Split-plot repeated measures designs in which a subject receives all levels of some treatments but only one level of other treatments are sometimes referred to as *mixed designs* (Lindquist, 1953). Winer (1962) uses the designation "multifactor experiments having repeated measures on some elements" for this class of designs.

The origin of the term *mixed design* as a designation for split-plot designs can be readily discerned from an inspection of Figure 8.1-1c. In this figure differences between levels a_1 and a_2 involve differences between s_1 and s_2 as well as the effects of treatment A. However, differences between any two levels of treatment B do not involve differences between

s_1 and s_2 because the same subjects are observed under all levels of B. In a type SPF-2.3 design, the main effects of treatment A are said to be completely confounded with differences between blocks or sets of subjects. The main effects of B and the interaction AB are free from such confounding. A confounding scheme in which a treatment is confounded with blocks does not affect the interpretability of the treatment effects, only the precision of the estimate. The effects of treatment A are described as *between-block* (*subject*) effects, while the effects of treatment B and interaction AB are described as *within-block* (*subject*) effects. Tests on B and AB are generally much more powerful than tests on A.

The general designation for a two-factor repeated-measures split-plot design is SPF-*p.q*. According to this designation all lower-case letters before the dot stand for the number of levels of between-block treatments; letters after the dot stand for levels of within-block treatments.

There are many research problems in the behavioral sciences where split-plot designs are especially appropriate. A general problem inherent in all behavioral research is subject heterogeneity. Differences among subjects are often such as to obscure treatment effects. A repeated measures or matched subjects design offers the advantage of controlling subject heterogeneity. In addition to this advantage, a repeated measures design is particularly useful in assessing certain types of treatment effects. For example, in experiments designed to investigate learning, transfer, fatigue, and so on, the use of repeated measures on the same subjects is often the simplest way to investigate the research problem. Randomization of the order-of-treatment level presentation for these kinds of variables is not always feasible, for the nature of the treatment dictates the order.

A LIMITATION OF THE
USE OF REPEATED MEASURES

A word of caution concerning the use of repeated measurements on the same subject is in order. When matched subjects are assigned to within-block treatment levels, it may be assumed that estimates of treatment effects that have been obtained from the q cells are correlated. The model underlying type SPF-*p.q* designs permits a particular kind of statistical dependency between observations in the q levels of B but requires that the error portion of these scores must be independent of each other and the treatment effects. There is ample reason to believe that in repeated measures experiments the error components of the scores are not independent and that the variance-covariance matrix departs from the required form. That is, the $q \times q$ repeated measures dispersion matrix does not have all diagonal elements equal to σ^2 and all off-diagonal elements equal to $\rho\sigma^2$. Procedures for investigating this issue are presented in Section 8.5. Bargmann (1957) presents a comprehensive discussion of homogeneity assumptions in repeated measures designs. Lana and Lubin

(1963) discuss in detail the problems resulting from unequal correlations among levels of the repeated treatment. Subsequent sections describe suggested procedures for coping with these problems.

The model underlying the F test for a split-plot repeated measures design does not include a term for sequence or carry-over effects. Thus repeated measurements on the same subject should be avoided for treatments in which the administration of one level affects performance on a subsequent level. An exception to this, of course, is when carry-over effects are the primary interest of the experimenter. Gaito (1961) has discussed the problem of *order effect* when repeated measures are obtained on the same subjects and has emphasized the importance of randomizing presentation of treatment levels.

8.2   LAYOUT AND COMPUTATIONAL PROCEDURES FOR TYPE SPF-*p.q* DESIGN

The layout of a type SPF-2.4 design is illustrated in Table 8.2-1. Let us assume that an experimenter is interested in vigilance performance. He has designed an experiment to evaluate the relative effectiveness of two modes of signal presentation during a four-hour monitoring period. Treatment A, which is designated as mode of signal presentation, has two levels, a_1 = auditory signal (tone) and a_2 = visual signal (light). Treatment B has four levels corresponding to successive monitoring periods: $b_1 = 1$ hour, $b_2 = 2$ hours, $b_3 = 3$ hours, and $b_4 = 4$ hours. The research hypotheses leading to this experiment can be evaluated by means of statistical tests of the following null hypotheses:

$$H_0 : \alpha_i = 0 \qquad \text{for all } i$$
$$H_1 : \alpha_i \neq 0 \qquad \text{for some } i$$

$$H_0 : \beta_j = 0 \qquad \text{for all } j$$
$$H_1 : \beta_j \neq 0 \qquad \text{for some } j$$

$$H_0 : \alpha\beta_{ij} = 0 \qquad \text{for all } ij$$
$$H_1 : \alpha\beta_{ij} \neq 0 \qquad \text{for some } ij.$$

The level of significance adopted for all tests is .05.

A total of eight subjects representing two random samples of four subjects each has been obtained from a common population. The two samples of subjects are randomly assigned to the $p = 2$ levels of A and observed under all $q = 4$ levels of B. The dependent variable is designated as response latency to the auditory and visual signals. Response

**TABLE 8.2-1 Layout of Type SPF-2.4
Design and Computational Procedures**

(i) Data:

ABS Summary Table

		b_1	b_2	b_3	b_4	$\sum_1^q AS$	$\dfrac{\left(\sum_1^q AS\right)^2}{q}$
	s_1	3	4	7	7	21	110.25
a_1	s_2	6	5	8	8	27	182.25
	s_3	3	4	7	9	23	132.25
	s_4	3	3	6	8	20	100.00
	s_5	1	2	5	10	18	81.00
a_2	s_6	2	3	6	10	21	110.25
	s_7	2	4	5	9	20	100.00
	s_8	2	3	6	11	22	121.00

AB Summary Table

	b_1	b_2	b_3	b_4	$\sum_1^q A$	$\dfrac{\left(\sum_1^q A\right)^2}{nq}$
$n = 4$						
a_1	15	16	28	32	91	517.5625
a_2	7	12	22	40	81	410.0625

$$\sum_1^p B = 22 \quad 28 \quad 50 \quad 72$$

$$\frac{\left(\sum_1^p B\right)^2}{np} = 60.5 \ \ 98.0 \ \ 312.5 \ \ 648.0$$

(ii) Computational symbols:

$$\sum_1^q \sum_1^N ABS = 3 + 6 + 3 + \cdots + 11 = 172.000$$

$$\sum_1^q \sum_1^N (ABS)^2 = [ABS] = (3)^2 + (6)^2 + (3)^2 + \cdots + (11)^2 = 1160.000$$

$$\frac{\left(\sum_1^q \sum_1^N ABS\right)^2}{qN} = [X] = \frac{(172)^2}{(4)(8)} = 924.500$$

$$\sum_1^N \frac{\left(\sum_1^q AS\right)^2}{q} = [AS] = 110.25 + 182.25 + \cdots + 121.00 = 937.000$$

$$\sum_1^p \frac{\left(\sum_1^q A\right)^2}{nq} \doteq [A] = 517.5625 + 410.0625 = 927.625$$

$$\sum_1^q \frac{\left(\sum_1^p B\right)^2}{np} = [B] = 60.5 + 98.0 + \cdots + 648.0 = 1119.000$$

$$\sum_1^p \sum_1^q \frac{(AB)^2}{n} = [AB] = \frac{(15)^2}{4} + \frac{(16)^2}{4} + \cdots + \frac{(40)^2}{4} = 1141.500$$

(iii) Computational formulas:

$$\text{SS}_{\text{total}} = [ABS] - [X] = 235.500$$
$$\text{SS}_{\text{between subj}} = [AS] - [X] = 12.500$$
$$\text{SS}_A = [A] - [X] = 3.125$$
$$\text{SS}_{\text{subj w.groups}} = [AS] - [A] = 9.375$$

$$\text{SS}_{\text{within subj}} = [ABS] - [AS] = 223.000$$
$$\text{SS}_B = [B] - [X] = 194.500$$
$$\text{SS}_{AB} = [AB] - [A] - [B] + [X] = 19.375$$
$$\text{SS}_{B \times \text{subj w.groups}} = [ABS] - [AB] - [AS] + [A] = 9.125$$

TABLE 8.2-2   Analysis of Variance Table

Source	SS	df
1 Between subjects	12.500	$np - 1 = 7$
2 A (type of signal)	3.125	$p - 1 = 1$
3 Subj w.groups	9.375	$p(n - 1) = 6$
4 Within subjects	223.000	$np(q - 1) = 24$
5 B (periods of time)	194.500	$q - 1 = 3$
6 AB	19.375	$(p - 1)(q - 1) = 3$
7 $B \times$ subj w.groups	9.125	$p(n - 1)(q - 1) = 18$
8 Total	235.500	$npq - 1 = 31$

*$p < .01.$

latency scores are subjected to a logarithmic transformation as described in Section 2.7. The data that are analyzed are means of transformed latency scores computed for each successive hour during the four-hour monitoring session.

The layout of the type SPF-2.4 design, computational tables, and formulas are shown in Table 8.2-1, where the following notation is used:

$$p \text{ levels of } a_i, \text{ where } p = 2$$

$$q \text{ levels of } b_j, \text{ where } q = 4$$

$$n \text{ levels of } s_m, \text{ where } n = 4$$

$$\sum_1^N = \sum_1^p \sum_1^n.$$

The analysis of variance is summarized in Table 8.2-2, which shows the degrees of freedom for each sum of squares as well as the expected values of the mean squares for Model III.

According to the analysis of variance in Table 8.2-2, treatment A is not significant. Treatment B and the interaction of type of signal with periods of time are significant. An inspection of the AB Summary Table in Table 8.2-1 suggests that response latency is shorter for the visual signals than for the auditory signals during the first three hours of monitoring but longer during the fourth hour. Thus the best type of signal may depend on the particular time period of the monitoring task. Procedures for testing the significance of differences between the two types of signals for each of the four monitoring periods are described in Section 8.6. These tests, which are referred to as simple main-effects tests, shed further light on the interpretation of treatments A and B when the interaction is significant. The present example illustrates the importance of selecting an experimental design that provides for a test of interaction effects. Tests of

TABLE 8.2-2 (continued)

MS	F	E(MS) A and B fixed effects, Subjects Random
3.125	$\left[\frac{2}{3}\right] = 2.00$	$\sigma_\varepsilon^2 + q\sigma_\pi^2 + nq\sigma_\alpha^2$
1.563		$\sigma_\varepsilon^2 + q\sigma_\pi^2$
64.833	$\left[\frac{5}{7}\right] = 127.88*$	$\sigma_\varepsilon^2 + \sigma_{\beta\pi}^2 + np\sigma_\beta^2$
6.458	$\left[\frac{6}{7}\right] = 12.74*$	$\sigma_\varepsilon^2 + \sigma_{\beta\pi}^2 + n\sigma_{\alpha\beta}^2$
.507		$\sigma_\varepsilon^2 + \sigma_{\beta\pi}^2$

simple main effects described in Section 8.6 will show that differences between levels of treatment A are obscured by the interaction of A with B.

8.3   CHECK ON ACCURACY OF COMPUTATIONAL FORMULAS

Procedures illustrated in this section provide a partial check on the accuracy of the computational formulas in Table 8.2-1. When added together, sum of squares formulas designated as between-subject components should equal $[AS] - [X]$. The within-subject sum of squares formulas should sum to $([ABS] - [AS])$.
For example,

$$\text{SS}_A \qquad + \text{SS}_{\text{subj w.groups}} = \text{SS}_{\text{between subj}}$$
$$([A] - [X]) + ([AS] - [A]) = [AS] - [X]$$

and

$$\text{SS}_B \qquad + \text{SS}_{AB}$$
$$([B] - [X]) + ([AB] - [A] - [B] + [X])$$
$$+ \text{SS}_{B \times \text{subj w.groups}} \qquad = \text{SS}_{\text{within subj}}$$
$$+ ([ABS] - [AB] - [AS] + [A]) = [ABS] - [AS].$$

It follows that all of the sum of squares formulas for *between-subject* and *within-subject* components add up to $([ABS] - [X])$, which is the formula for total sum of squares. This quick check is useful when computational formulas are derived for multifactor designs. The use of the abbreviated notation system facilitates this check besides illustrating more clearly the pattern underlying the formulas.

8.4   ASSUMPTIONS OF THE
MODEL FOR TYPE SPF-$p.q$ DESIGN

Let X_{ijm} be a measure for a randomly selected subject m in treatment population ab_{ij}. Under the mixed linear model,

$$X_{ijm} = \mu + \alpha_i + \pi_{m(i)} + \beta_j + \alpha\beta_{ij} + \beta\pi_{jm(i)} + \varepsilon_{o(ijm)},$$

where μ = grand mean of treatment populations.

α_i = effect of treatment i, which is a constant for all subjects within treatment population i.

β_j = effect of treatment j, which is a constant for all subjects within treatment population j.

$\pi_{m(i)}$ = constant associated with person m, who is nested under level α_i.

$\alpha\beta_{ij}$ = effect that represents nonadditivity of effects α_i and β_j.

$\beta\pi_{jm(i)}$ = effect that represents nonadditivity of effects β_j and $\pi_{m(i)}$.

$\varepsilon_{o(ijm)}$ = experimental error, which is independent of other ε's and is normally distributed with mean = 0 and variance = σ_ε^2. In this design $\varepsilon_{o(ijm)}$ cannot be estimated separately from $\beta\pi_{jm(i)}$.

The F ratios in Table 8.2-2 are distributed as the F distribution under the conditions that (1) the n subjects in the p levels of A constitute random samples from the same population, (2) A and B represent fixed effects (Models I and II are discussed in Section 8.9), (3) all pqn populations are normal, (4) the variances of each of the pqn populations are equal, and (5) the $q(q - 1)/2$ population covariances for all pairs of levels j and j' are equal, and this equality exists at each level of population A. This assumption is discussed in detail in Section 8.5.

NATURE OF SS$_{\text{subj w.groups}}$ AND SS$_{B \times \text{subj w.groups}}$

The SPF-$p.q$ design has two error terms. One corresponds to the pooled variation between subjects within p groups, while the other source is the pooled interaction of treatment B with subjects in each block. The nature of these terms can be understood by breaking them down. It will be shown that the ratio $MS_A/MS_{\text{subj w.groups}}$ is the same as MS_{BG}/MS_{WG} in a completely randomized design and that $MS_B/MS_{B \times \text{sub w.groups}}$ is the same as MS_B/MS_{res} in a randomized block design.

COMPARISON OF SS$_{\text{subj w.groups}}$ WITH SS$_{\text{within groups}}$

We can compute the sum of squares between subjects in levels a_1 and a_2, respectively, by means of formulas:

(1)
$$SS_{\text{subj w.group } a_1} = \sum_{1}^{n} \frac{\left(\sum_{1}^{q} AS_{1jm}\right)^2}{q} - \frac{\left(\sum_{1}^{q} A_{1j}\right)^2}{nq}.$$

(2)
$$SS_{\text{subj w.group } a_2} = \sum_{1}^{n} \frac{\left(\sum_{1}^{q} AS_{2jm}\right)^2}{q} - \frac{\left(\sum_{1}^{q} A_{2j}\right)^2}{nq}.$$

Referring to Table 8.2-1, the required terms are

$$SS_{a_1} = [110.25 + 182.25 + \cdots + 100.00] - 517.5625 = 7.1875.$$

$$SS_{a_2} = [\ 81.00 + 110.25 + \cdots + 121.00] - 410.0625 = 2.1875.$$

If the data in Table 8.2-1 are recast so as to ignore the B and AB effects, the scores can be summarized as shown in Table 8.4-1. Because the eight

TABLE 8.4-1   *AS* **Summary Table**

	a_1		a_2
$s_1 =$	21	$s_5 =$	18
$s_2 =$	27	$s_6 =$	21
$s_3 =$	23	$s_7 =$	20
$s_4 =$	20	$s_8 =$	22
$\sum_{1}^{n} A =$	91		81
$\sum_{1}^{n} A^2 =$	2099		1649
$\dfrac{\left(\sum_{1}^{n} A\right)^2}{n} =$	2070.25		1640.25

subjects were randomly assigned to the two levels of A, a completely randomized design can be used to analyze the data. In this form, a test of MS_{BG} is equivalent to a test of MS_A. The denominator of an F ratio for a type CR-2 design can be computed by

$$SS_{\text{WG}} = \sum_{1}^{k} \left[\sum_{1}^{n} A^2 - \frac{\left(\sum_{1}^{n} A\right)^2}{n} \right]$$

$$= (2099 - 2070.25) + (1649 - 1640.25) = 28.75 + 8.75.$$

Each of the scores in Table 8.4-1 is the sum of four scores, that is, $21 = 3 + 4 + 7 + 7$. Computing the means of the two

$$\left[\sum_{1}^{n} A^2 - \frac{\left(\sum_{1}^{n} A\right)^2}{n} \right]$$

terms, we obtain $28.75/4 = 7.1875$ and $8.75/4 = 2.1875$. These means are identical with SS_{a_1} and SS_{a_2}, which were computed by formulas (1) and (2). It should be obvious from this example that $SS_{subj\ w.groups}$ is analogous to SS_{WG} and that the ratio $F = MS_A/MS_{subj\ w.groups}$ is analogous to $F = MS_{BG}/MS_{WG}$. Thus $SS_{subj\ w.group\ a_1}$ and $SS_{subj\ w.group\ a_2}$ are simply within-group sum of squares at each level of A.

Table 8.4-2 summarizes the partitioning of the $SS_{subj\ w.groups}$ error term. In order for the F ratio to follow an F distribution, the sources of variation represented by $MS_{subj\ w.group\ a_1}$ and $MS_{subj\ w.group\ a_2}$ must be homogeneous. This is easily tested by means of the F_{max} test (Section 2.6).

TABLE 8.4-2   Partition of Subjects Within-Groups Sum of Squares

Source	SS	df	MS
Subjects within groups	9.3750	$p(n - 1) = 6$	
Subjects within group a_1	7.1875	$n - 1 = 3$	2.396
Subjects within group a_2	2.1875	$n - 1 = 3$	.729

$$F_{max} = \frac{\text{largest } MS_{subj\ w.group\ a_i}}{\text{smallest } MS_{subj\ w.group\ a_i}} = \frac{2.396}{.729} = 3.29$$

$F_{max.05;2,3} = 15.4$

Since $F_{max(obs)} < F_{max.05;2,3}$, we conclude that the population variances for subjects within groups a_1 and a_2 are homogeneous and can be pooled to form the $MS_{subj\ w.groups}$ error term.

COMPARISON OF $SS_{B \times subj\ w.groups}$ WITH $SS_{residual}$

The nature of the $B \times$ subjects within groups error term can also be understood by breaking it down.

(3)

$$SS_{B \times subj\ w.group\ a_1} = \sum_1^q \sum_1^n ABS_{1jm}^2 - \sum_1^q \frac{(AB_{1j})^2}{n} - \sum_1^n \frac{\left(\sum_1^q AS_{1jm}\right)^2}{q} + \frac{\left(\sum_1^q A_{1j}\right)^2}{nq}$$

$$= 585.0000 - 572.2500 - 524.7500 + 517.5625$$

$$= 5.5625.$$

(4)

$$SS_{B \times subj \, w.group \, a_2} = \sum_1^q \sum_1^n ABS_{2jm}^2 - \sum_1^q \frac{(AB_{2j})^2}{n} - \sum_1^n \frac{\left(\sum_1^q AS_{2jm} \right)^2}{q} + \frac{\left(\sum_1^q A_{2j} \right)^2}{nq}$$

$$= 575.0000 - 569.2500 - 412.2500 + 410.0625$$

$$= 3.5625.$$

TABLE 8.4-3

(a) Type RB-4 Design for a_1				(b) Type RB-4 Design for a_2		
Source	SS	df		*Source*	SS	df
Between columns	54.6875	3		Between columns	159.1875	3
Between rows	7.1875	3		Between rows	2.1875	3
Residual	5.5625	9		Residual	3.5625	9
Total	67.4375	15		Total	164.9375	15

If we consider the scores in treatment a_1 as one randomized block experiment and the scores in a_2 as a second randomized block experiment, we can make the analyses in Table 8.4-3a and b.

It is evident that the residual (interaction of subjects $\times$ treatment levels) in the two type RB-4 designs is equal to $SS_{B \times subj \, w.group \, a_i}$ in formulas (3) and (4). Thus the $SS_{B \times subj \, w.groups}$ error term represents the pooled interaction of subjects $\times$ treatment levels error terms from the two randomized block designs.

In order for the F ratios of the within-subject effects to be distributed as the F distribution, the two pooled residual terms must be homogeneous. Partitioning of the $SS_{B \times subj \, w.groups}$ is summarized in Table 8.4-4. The F_{max} ratio for homogeneity $= .618/.396 = 1.56$. The tabled value for F_{max} $_{.05;2,9} = 4.03$. Since $F_{max(obs)} < F_{max \, .05;2,9}$, we conclude that the two variances are homogeneous and can be pooled. If either the $MS_{subj \, w.groups}$ or the $MS_{B \times subj \, w.groups}$ are not composed of homogeneous variances, a transformation that will result in homogeneity may be found. Procedures for selecting a transformation are described in Section 2.7.

TABLE 8.4-4   Partition of $B \times$ Subjects Within Groups Sum of Squares

Source	SS	df	MS
$B \times$ subjects within groups	9.1250	$p(n - 1)(q - 1) = 18$	
$B \times$ subj w.group a_1	5.5625	$(n - 1)(q - 1) = 9$	.618
$B \times$ subj w.group a_2	3.5625	$(n - 1)(q - 1) = 9$	.396

8.5   TEST OF EQUALITY AND SYMMETRY OF COVARIANCE MATRICES FOR TYPE SPF-$p.q$ DESIGN

In Section 5.3 it was pointed out that experiments in which a subject is observed under several levels of a treatment may be analyzed by either univariate or multivariate analysis of variance procedures. If certain assumptions are fulfilled, the former analysis procedure is preferable to a multivariate procedure from the standpoint of computational labor and ease of interpretation. The model underlying a univariate analysis requires that the n experimental units in the p levels of treatment A constitute random samples from the same normal population. We also noted in Section 5.3 that experimental designs involving repeated measures or matched subjects require a highly restrictive set of assumptions concerning population treatment variances (σ_j^2) and covariances ($\rho\sigma_{jj'}^2$). Furthermore, we saw that the usual computational formulas for mean squares obscure the nature of the sources that are pooled and that must be homogeneous. It can be shown, for example, that

$$\mathrm{MS}_{\text{subj w.groups}} = \text{ave } \hat{\sigma}_j^2 + (q-1) \text{ ave } \rho\hat{\sigma}_{jj'}^2$$

and

$$\mathrm{MS}_{B \times \text{subj w.groups}} = \text{ave } \hat{\sigma}_j^2 - \text{ave } \rho\hat{\sigma}_{jj'}^2,$$

where ave $\hat{\sigma}_j^2$ is the average of q unbiased estimates of the population treatment variances and ave $\rho\hat{\sigma}_{jj'}^2$ is the average of $[q(q-1)]/2$ unbiased estimates of the population covariances. These averages can be computed from a table like Table 8.5-3 in which the corresponding values of $\hat{\sigma}_j^2$ and the corresponding values of $\rho\hat{\sigma}_{jj'}^2$ have been pooled over the p levels of treatment A. By examining the above formulas it is evident that $\mathrm{MS}_{B \times \text{subj w.groups}} < \mathrm{MS}_{\text{subj w.groups}}$ if the average correlation between treatment levels is positive. It is assumed that the q population variances are equal and the $[q(q-1)]/2$ population covariances are equal.

A variance-covariance matrix for level a_i of a type SPF-2.4 design has the following form:

(matrix 1)   Level a_i

$$
\begin{array}{c c}
 & \begin{array}{cccc} b_1 & b_2 & b_3 & b_4 \end{array} \\
\begin{array}{c} b_1 \\ b_2 \\ b_3 \\ b_4 \end{array} &
\left[
\begin{array}{cccc}
\sigma_1^2 & \rho\sigma_{12}^2 & \rho\sigma_{13}^2 & \rho\sigma_{14}^2 \\
\rho\sigma_{21}^2 & \sigma_2^2 & \rho\sigma_{23}^2 & \rho\sigma_{24}^2 \\
\rho\sigma_{31}^2 & \rho\sigma_{32}^2 & \sigma_3^2 & \rho\sigma_{34}^2 \\
\rho\sigma_{41}^2 & \rho\sigma_{42}^2 & \rho\sigma_{43}^2 & \sigma_4^2
\end{array}
\right]
\end{array}
$$

This form is duplicated at each level of A. Formulas for computing estimates of the population variances and covariances are, respectively,

(1)
$$\hat{\sigma}_j^2 = \frac{\sum\limits_1^n B_{jm}^2 - \dfrac{\left(\sum\limits_1^n B_{jm}\right)^2}{n}}{n-1}$$

(2)
$$\hat{\rho\sigma}_{jj'}^2 = \frac{\sum\limits_1^n B_{jm}B_{j'm} - \dfrac{\left(\sum\limits_1^n B_{jm}\right)\left(\sum\limits_1^n B_{j'm}\right)}{n}}{n-1}.$$

If the variances are equal and the covariances are zero (equal variances-zero covariances), the matrix for each level of A has the form shown in matrix 2 where $\sigma_1^2 = \sigma_2^2 = \cdots = \sigma_4^2 = \sigma^2$.

(matrix 2)   Level a_i

$$\begin{array}{c} \\ b_1 \\ b_2 \\ b_3 \\ b_4 \end{array} \begin{array}{cccc} b_1 & b_2 & b_3 & b_4 \\ \left[\begin{array}{cccc} \sigma^2 & 0 & 0 & 0 \\ 0 & \sigma^2 & 0 & 0 \\ 0 & 0 & \sigma^2 & 0 \\ 0 & 0 & 0 & \sigma^2 \end{array}\right] \end{array}$$

Covariances of within-block effects (B) in which the same subjects participate under all levels of one or more treatments are rarely equal to zero. Generally a correlation exists between the levels for treatment B. This does not negate the use of univariate analysis procedures *if* the covariances are constant. The condition of equal variances-constant covariances is shown in matrix 3

(matrix 3)

$$\begin{array}{c} \\ b_1 \\ b_2 \\ b_3 \\ b_4 \end{array} \begin{array}{cccc} b_1 & b_2 & b_3 & b_4 \\ \left[\begin{array}{cccc} \sigma^2 & \rho\sigma^2 & \rho\sigma^2 & \rho\sigma^2 \\ \rho\sigma^2 & \sigma^2 & \rho\sigma^2 & \rho\sigma^2 \\ \rho\sigma^2 & \rho\sigma^2 & \sigma^2 & \rho\sigma^2 \\ \rho\sigma^2 & \rho\sigma^2 & \rho\sigma^2 & \sigma^2 \end{array}\right] \end{array}$$

where $\rho\sigma_{jj'}^2$ for all pairs of treatment levels j and j' are equal. For experiments in which the variances are unequal and the covariances are neither equal to zero nor constant, univariate analysis procedures do not provide an exact test of the null hypothesis. Under these conditions multivariate analysis procedures can be used to obtain an exact test of the hypothesis of equality of means. For a detailed discussion of these procedures, see Anderson (1958). It should be emphasized that the *zero* or *constant* covariance requirement applies only to within-block effects (B and AB) and not to between-block effects (A). A test for treatment A is valid as long as the variances for $i = 1, \ldots, p$ populations are homogeneous. This follows because the between-block effects depend only on the $np = N$ block means (Danford, Hughes, and McNee, 1960).

TEST FOR EQUALITY OF VARIANCE-COVARIANCE MATRICES

Tests suggested by Box (1950) can be used to determine if conventional univariate analysis procedures are appropriate for experiments in which subjects participate under more than one treatment level. Specifically, these tests enable an experimenter to determine (1) if the variance-covariance matrices are equal for all levels of A and (2) if the variance-covariance matrix meets the symmetry conditions illustrated in matrices 2 and 3 above.

TABLE 8.5-1   Original Scores

		b_1	b_2	b_3	b_4
a_1	s_1	2.9	4.5	7.4	6.6
	s_2	6.5	5.4	7.7	8.5
	s_3	3.0	1.6	7.4	9.4
	s_4	2.6	4.5	5.5	7.5
a_2	s_5	.6	1.5	4.6	10.0
	s_6	2.0	2.6	6.3	10.0
	s_7	1.5	4.5	4.6	8.6
	s_8	2.9	3.4	6.5	11.4

To illustrate, assume that the data in Table 8.2-1 were rounded to the nearest whole number. The unrounded original scores are shown in Table 8.5-1. The population variance for treatment combination ab_{11} using formula (1) is estimated by

$$\hat{\sigma}_1^2 = \frac{(2.9)^2 + (6.5)^2 + \cdots + (2.6)^2 - (15)^2/4}{4 - 1} = 3.390.$$

The population covariance for treatment combinations ab_{11} and ab_{12} according to formula (2) is estimated by

$$\hat{\rho\sigma}_{12}^2 = \frac{(2.9)(4.5) + (6.5)(5.4) + \cdots + (2.6)(4.5) - (15)(16)/4}{4 - 1} = 1.550.$$

The estimated variances and covariances for these data are shown in Table 8.5-2.

A test for equality of the variance-covariance matrices for p levels of A is given by

TABLE 8.5-2   Variances and Covariances for Data in Table 8.5-1

		b_1	b_2	b_3	b_4			b_1	b_2	b_3	b_4
	b_1	3.390	1.550	1.003	.697		b_1	.923	.570	.870	.653
	b_2	1.550	2.740	−.177	−1.203		b_2	.570	1.607	.027	−.513
a_1	b_3	1.003	−.177	1.020	.367	a_2	b_3	.870	.027	1.087	.887
	b_4	.697	−1.203	.367	1.473		b_4	.653	−.513	.887	1.307

$$\chi_1^2 = (1 - E_1)M_1,$$

where

$$M_1 = (N - p) \ln |A_{\text{pooled}}| - \sum_1^p [(n_i - 1) \ln |A_i|]$$

$$E_1 = \frac{2q^2 + 3q - 1}{6(q + 1)(p - 1)} \left(\sum_1^p \frac{1}{n_i - 1} - \frac{1}{N - p} \right).$$

The statistic χ_1^2 has a sampling distribution that is approximated by a chi-square distribution with

$$\text{df}_1 = \frac{q(q + 1)(p - 1)}{2}.$$

The subscript *one* for χ_1^2, E_1, and M_1 has no meaning apart from identifying the statistics involved in this test. Percentage points for the chi-square distribution appear in Table D.6.

   A variance-covariance matrix for A_{pooled} is obtained by averaging the corresponding entries for matrices A_1 and A_2. For example, b_1 for $A_{\text{pooled}} = (3.390 + .923)/2 = 2.156$. The average values are shown in Table 8.5-3. The numerical values of the determinants for the three variance-covariance matrices are

$$|A_1| = .000365, \quad |A_2| = .000996, \quad |A_{\text{pooled}}| = .535459.$$

Determinants of large matrices can be obtained easily with a digital computer.

TABLE 8.5-3   Pooled Variances and Covariances

		b_1	b_2	b_3	b_4
	b_1	2.156	1.060	.936	.675
	b_2	1.060	2.174	−.075	−.858
$A_{\text{pooled}} =$	b_3	.936	−.075	1.054	.627
	b_4	.675	−.858	.627	1.390

The computation required to compute χ_1^2 is as follows:

$$M_1 = (8 - 2) \ln (.535459) - (4 - 1) \ln (.000365) - (4 - 1) \ln (.000996)$$

$$= (6)(-.6255) - 3(-7.9157) - 3(-6.9118) = 40.7295$$

$$E_1 = \frac{2(16) + 3(4) - 1}{6(4 + 1)(2 - 1)} \left[\frac{1}{4 - 1} + \frac{1}{4 - 1} - \frac{1}{8 - 2} \right] = .7167$$

$$\text{df}_1 = \frac{4(4 + 1)(2 - 1)}{2} = 10$$

$$\chi_1^2 = (1 - .7167)(40.7295) = 11.539$$

$$\chi_{.05,10}^2 = 18.307.$$

The obtained value for χ_1^2 is less than the tabled value for $\chi_{.05,10}^2$. Thus the hypothesis of equality of the p variance-covariance matrices is tenable. When n_i is small or q and/or p are large, a more precise test is given by

$$F = \frac{M_1}{b_1}$$

with degrees of freedom equal to df_1 and

$$\text{df}_2 = (\text{df}_1 + 2)/(E_2 - E_1^2)$$

$$E_2 = \frac{(q - 1)(q + 2)}{6(p - 1)} \left[\sum_1^p \frac{1}{(n_i - 1)^2} - \frac{1}{(N - p)^2} \right]$$

$$b_1 = \frac{\text{df}_1}{(1 - E_1) - (\text{df}_1/\text{df}_2)}.$$

This alternative test is equal to

$$F = \frac{40.7295}{44.3459} = .92$$

with degrees of freedom equal to 10 and 173. The F_{obs} value is not significant. This computational procedure leads to the same decision as the χ_1^2 test computed previously.

TEST FOR SYMMETRY OF VARIANCE-COVARIANCE MATRIX

A test for symmetry of the pooled variance-covariance matrix (that each entry on the main diagonal is equal to σ^2, and each entry off the main diagonal is equal to $\rho\sigma^2$) should be made if the test for equality of the matrices is insignificant. This test is given by

$$\chi_2^2 = (1 - E_3)M_2,$$

where

$$M_2 = -(N - p) \ln \frac{|A_{pooled}|}{|A_{ave}|}$$

$$E_3 = \frac{q(q + 1)^2(2q - 3)}{6(N - p)(q - 1)(q^2 + q - 4)}$$

$$df_3 = \frac{q^2 + q - 4}{2}.$$

Under the hypothesis that the variance-covariance matrix has the required symmetry, χ_2^2 is approximately distributed as a chi-square distribution with degrees of freedom equal to df_3. The A_{ave} matrix has as the main diagonal the average value of the main diagonal of matrix A_{pooled}. The off-diagonal entries of A_{ave} are the average of the off-diagonal entries of A_{pooled}.

$$A_{ave} = \begin{array}{c|cccc} & b_1 & b_2 & b_3 & b_4 \\ \hline b_1 & 1.694 & .394 & .394 & .394 \\ b_2 & .394 & 1.694 & .394 & .394 \\ b_3 & .394 & .394 & 1.694 & .394 \\ b_4 & .394 & .394 & .394 & 1.694 \end{array}$$

The determinant of matrix $A_{ave} = 6.318572$. The computational example for χ_2^2 is shown below.

$$M_2 = -(8 - 2) \ln \frac{.535459}{6.318572} = -(6)(-2.4687) = 14.8122$$

$$E_3 = \frac{4(4 + 1)^2[(2)(4) - 3]}{6(8 - 2)(4 - 1)[(4)^2 + 4 - 4]} = .2894$$

$$df_3 = \frac{(4)^2 + 4 - 4}{2} = 8$$

$$\chi_2^2 = (1 - .2894)(14.8122) = 10.526$$

$$\chi_{.05,8}^2 = 15.507.$$

Because $\chi_2^2 < \chi_{.05,8}^2$, we conclude that the variance-covariance matrix has the required symmetry, and univariate analysis of variance can be used to test the hypothesis of equality of means. When n_i is small and q is relatively large, a more precise test is given by $F = M_2/b_2$, with df_3 and

$$df_4 = \frac{df_3 + 2}{E_4 - E_3^2}.$$

$$E_4 = \frac{(q - 1)q(q + 1)(q + 2)}{6(N - p)^2(q^2 + q - 4)}$$

$$b_2 = \frac{df_3}{(1 - E_4) - (df_3/df_4)}.$$

The value of this alternative test is

$$F = \frac{14.8122}{9.0961} = 1.63$$

with degrees of freedom equal to 8 and 490. The tabled value of F at the .05 level is 1.96. The alternative test leads to the same decision as the χ_2^2 test.

GEISSER-GREENHOUSE CONSERVATIVE F TEST

If the variance-covariance matrices have the equality and symmetry shown in matrix 2 or 3, univariate analysis procedures provide an exact test of the hypothesis of equality of means. An approximate conservative test was described in Section 5.3 for the case in which the variances and covariances are heterogeneous. This test is negatively biased. That is, an experimenter will err in the direction of not rejecting the null hypothesis when it is false. This conservative test is obtained by multiplying the conventional degrees of freedom by θ, which is set equal to $1/(q - 1)$. $1/(q - 1)$ corresponds to the lowest bound that the statistic θ can take (Geisser and Greenhouse, 1958). If the variances are homogeneous and the covariances are homogeneous, $\theta = 1$. As heterogeneity increases, θ decreases until it equals $1/(q - 1)$. A comparison of the conventional and conservative degrees of freedom is shown in Table 8.5-4. Computational procedures

TABLE 8.5-4   Conventional and Conservative F Ratio Degrees of Freedom for Model III

Numerator of F ratio	Conventional df	Conservative df
MS_B	$(q - 1), p(n - 1)(q - 1)$	$1, p(n - 1)$
MS_{AB}	$(p - 1)(q - 1), p(n - 1)(q - 1)$	$(p - 1), p(n - 1)$

for a conservative F test are identical to those of a conventional F test except that different degrees of freedom are used. If F ratios for MS_B and MS_{AB} are significant, with θ assumed to equal its lower bound, there is no need to proceed further because an exact test would also be significant. If, however, the conservative tests are not significant, an experimenter should make conventional F tests in which θ is assumed to equal one. If the latter tests, using conventional degrees of freedom, are also insignificant, the experimenter can decide not to reject the null hypothesis. If, however, the conventional test is significant but the conservative test is insignificant, an exact test such as Hotellings T^2 statistic (see Section 5.3) can be used to test the hypothesis that the treatment effects are equal to zero.

The test procedures described here are appropriate for testing the over-all hypothesis of zero treatment effects. If an experimenter has advanced *a priori* hypotheses with respect to specific comparisons among means for treatment *B*, these can be evaluated even though the symmetry requirement is not met. For these tests, the denominator of, say, the *t* ratio should be based on only those data which are relevant to the comparison. A disadvantage of this procedure lies in the loss of degrees of freedom for experimental error.

8.6   TESTS OF SIMPLE MAIN EFFECTS IN TYPE SPF-*p.q* DESIGN

If the *AB* interaction is significant in a type SPF-2.4 design, there is usually little interest in tests of the main effects. A significant interaction means that one treatment behaves differently under different levels of the other treatment. This is graphically illustrated for the vigilance data in Figure 8.6-1.

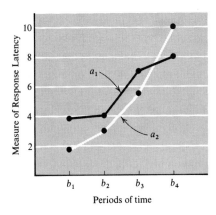 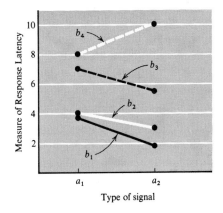

Figure 8.6-1   Illustration of interaction between treatments *A* and *B*.

When the interaction is significant, the experimenter will normally proceed to tests of simple main effects. These tests are designed to answer the following kinds of questions: "Is there a difference between a_1 and a_2 at level b_1 or between a_1 and a_2 at b_2?" "Is there a difference between b_1 and b_2 at a_1 or between b_3 and b_4 at a_2?" Computational procedures for these tests are illustrated in Table 8.6-1 and the results summarized in Table 8.6-2. The conceptual unit for error rate for the simple main-effects tests is the family of comparisons. Procedures for setting the error rate per family at α are described in Section 7.4.

TABLE 8.6-1   Computational Formulas for Simple Main-Effects Sum of Squares

(i)

AB Summary Table

	b_1	b_2	b_3	b_4	$\sum\limits_1^q A$
a_1	15	16	28	32	91
a_2	7	12	22	40	81
$\sum\limits_1^p B =$	22	28	50	72	

(ii)

$$\text{SS}_A \text{ at } b_1 = \sum_1^p \frac{(AB_{i1})^2}{n} - \frac{\left(\sum\limits_1^p B_{i1}\right)^2}{np} = \frac{(15)^2}{4} + \frac{(7)^2}{4} - \frac{(22)^2}{8} = 8.0$$

$$\text{SS}_A \text{ at } b_2 = \sum_1^p \frac{(AB_{i2})^2}{n} - \frac{\left(\sum\limits_1^p B_{i2}\right)^2}{np} = \frac{(16)^2}{4} + \frac{(12)^2}{4} - \frac{(28)^2}{8} = 2.0$$

$$\text{SS}_A \text{ at } b_3 = \sum_1^p \frac{(AB_{i3})^2}{n} - \frac{\left(\sum\limits_1^p B_{i3}\right)^2}{np} = \frac{(28)^2}{4} + \frac{(22)^2}{4} - \frac{(50)^2}{8} = 4.5$$

$$\text{SS}_A \text{ at } b_4 = \sum_1^p \frac{(AB_{i4})^2}{n} - \frac{\left(\sum\limits_1^p B_{i4}\right)^2}{np} = \frac{(32)^2}{4} + \frac{(40)^2}{4} - \frac{(72)^2}{8} = 8.0$$

As a computational check $\sum\limits_1^q \text{SS}_A$ for $b_j = \text{SS}_A + \text{SS}_{AB} = 22.5$.

(iii)

$$\text{SS}_B \text{ at } a_1 = \sum_1^q \frac{(AB_{1j})^2}{n} - \frac{\left(\sum\limits_1^q A_{1j}\right)^2}{nq} = \frac{(15)^2}{4} + \frac{(16)^2}{4} + \cdots + \frac{(32)^2}{4} - \frac{(91)^2}{16} = 54.6875$$

$$\text{SS}_B \text{ at } a_2 = \sum_1^q \frac{(AB_{2j})^2}{n} - \frac{\left(\sum\limits_1^q A_{2j}\right)^2}{nq} = \frac{(7)^2}{4} + \frac{(12)^2}{4} + \cdots + \frac{(40)^2}{4} - \frac{(81)^2}{16} = 159.1875$$

As a computational check $\sum\limits_1^p \text{SS}_B$ for $a_i = \text{SS}_B + \text{SS}_{AB} = 213.875$.

RULE GOVERNING CHOICE OF ERROR TERM FOR SIMPLE EFFECTS

It should be noted that the error term for testing the simple main effects of A is no longer $\text{MS}_{\text{subj w.groups}}$ but $\text{MS}_{\text{w.cell}}$. The error term for testing the simple main effects of B remains $\text{MS}_{B \times \text{subj w.groups}}$. An easy-to-follow rule governs the choice of a proper error term for tests of simple main effects. It was noted in Table 8.6-1 that

$$\sum_{1}^{q} SS_A \text{ for } b_j = SS_A + SS_{AB}$$

and

$$\sum_{1}^{p} SS_B \text{ for } a_i = SS_B + SS_{AB}.$$

The error terms for the A, B, and AB effects are

$$MS_{\text{subj w.groups}} \qquad \text{for } A$$
$$MS_{B \times \text{subj w.groups}} \qquad \text{for } B$$
$$MS_{B \times \text{subj w.groups}} \qquad \text{for } AB.$$

The rule governing the choice of error terms states that if the treatment and interaction which equal the sum of simple main effects have different error terms, as in the case of treatment A, the two error terms should be pooled in testing the simple main effects of A. Because A and AB have different error terms, the pooled error term for testing the simple main effects of A is

$$\text{Pooled error} = \frac{SS_{\text{subj w.groups}} + SS_{B \times \text{subj w.groups}}}{(\text{df for } SS_{\text{subj w.groups}}) + (\text{df for } SS_{B \times \text{subj w.groups}})}$$

$$= \frac{9.375 + 9.125}{6 + 18} = .771.$$

A careful examination of the pooled error term will show that it is $MS_{\text{w.cell}}$ which, for purposes of testing treatments A and B, was partitioned into *between-subject* and *within-subject* components. When the treatment and interaction that equal the sum of simple main effects have the same error terms, as in the case of B, the error term for tests of simple main effects is the regular error term for the treatment.

In a split-plot repeated-measures design, $MS_{\text{w.cell}}$ may be composed of heterogeneous sources of variance. Under these circumstances, an F test for the simple main effects of treatment A will be biased. In general, the bias will be small if the degrees of freedom for $MS_{\text{w.cell}}$ are greater than 30. A general rule cannot be given, for the extent of bias is related to the discrepancy between $MS_{\text{subj w.groups}}$ and $MS_{B \times \text{subj w.groups}}$.

The pooled error term, $MS_{\text{w.cell}}$, which is used in testing simple main effects for treatment A, is based on variation within each of the pq cells. If an experimenter has reason to believe that the pooled variances are heterogeneous, $MS_{\text{w.cell}}$ can be computed from the p cells used to compute the simple main-effects mean squares. The degrees of freedom for this error term are $p(n - 1)$.

INTERPRETATION OF SIMPLE EFFECTS

The analysis in Table 8.6-2 sheds more light on the effects of type of signal (A) and duration of monitoring session (B). On the basis of this

TABLE 8.6-2   Analysis of Variance Table for Simple Effects

	Source	SS	df	MS	F
1	Between subjects				
2	Between A at b_1	8.0000	$p - 1 = 1$	8.000	$\left[\frac{2}{6}\right] =$ 10.38*
3	Between A at b_2	2.0000	$p - 1 = 1$	2.000	$\left[\frac{3}{6}\right] =$ 2.59
4	Between A at b_3	4.5000	$p - 1 = 1$	4.500	$\left[\frac{4}{6}\right] =$ 5.84
5	Between A at b_4	8.0000	$p - 1 = 1$	8.000	$\left[\frac{5}{6}\right] =$ 10.38*
6	Within cell	18.5000	$pq(n - 1) = 24$	.771	
7	Within subjects				
8	Between B at a_1	54.6875	$q - 1 = 3$	18.229	$\left[\frac{8}{11}\right] =$ 35.95**
9	Between B at a_2	159.1875	$q - 1 = 3$	53.062	$\left[\frac{9}{11}\right] =$ 104.66**
10	AB	19.3750	$(p - 1)(q - 1) = 3$	6.458	$\left[\frac{10}{11}\right] =$ 12.74**
11	$B \times$ subj w.groups	9.1250	$p(n - 1)(q - 1) = 18$	.507	
12	Total	235.5000	$npq - 1 = 31$		

*$p < .02$.

**$p < .01$.

analysis and Figure 8.6-1, we conclude that the visual signal (a_2) is superior to the auditory signal (a_1) during the first hour of monitoring but poorer during the fourth hour. Although the experimenter might wish to be able to make an unqualified statement concerning the superiority of the visual signal, such generalizations are rarely possible in the behavioral sciences. Interactions among treatments, which always call for qualified statements, are the rule rather than the exception in research with humans and animals.

8.7   PROCEDURES FOR TESTING DIFFERENCES AMONG MEANS IN TYPE SPF-*p.q* DESIGN

A PRIORI TESTS

If orthogonal comparisons among means have been specified prior to collection of the data, a t statistic may be used to make the comparisons. In comparisons among the p levels of A, the t statistic as described in Section 3.2 is given by

$$t = \frac{C_j(\bar{A}_i) + C_{j'}(\bar{A}_{i'})}{\sqrt{2MS_{\text{subj w.groups}}/nq}}, \qquad df = p(n - 1).$$

Because there are only two levels of treatment A, the a priori t ratio is equivalent to the ratio $F = MS_A/MS_{\text{subj w.groups}}$. The computation of a t ratio is shown for the comparison of $\bar{A}_1$ with $\bar{A}_2$:

$$t = \frac{1(5.69) - 1(5.06)}{\sqrt{2(1.563)/(4)(4)}} = \frac{.63}{.44} = 1.43$$

$t_{.05/2,6} = 2.45.$

Tests among the q levels of B are given by

$$t = \frac{C_j(\bar{B}_j) + C_{j'}(\bar{B}_{j'})}{\sqrt{2MS_{B \times subj \ w.groups}/np}}, \qquad df = p(n - 1)(q - 1).$$

The computation is shown for the comparison of $\bar{B}_1$ with $\bar{B}_3$:

$$t = \frac{1(2.75) - 1(6.25)}{\sqrt{2(.507)/(4)(2)}} = \frac{-3.50}{.36} = -9.72$$

$t_{.05/2,18} = 2.10.$

When the AB interaction is significant, tests of differences among means for main effects are rarely of interest. If *a priori* orthogonal hypotheses concerning simple main effects have been advanced, tests of simple main effects means can be made by the t test. Computational examples for these tests are given below.

Comparison of $\bar{A}_1$ with $\bar{A}_2$ at level b_1

$$t = \frac{C_j(\overline{AB}_{11}) + C_{j'}(\overline{AB}_{21})}{\sqrt{2(MS_{w.cell})/n}} = \frac{1(3.75) - 1(1.75)}{\sqrt{2(.771)/4}} = \frac{2.00}{.62} = 3.23$$

df = see text (corrected significance level for pooled error terms).

Comparison of $\bar{B}_1$ with $\bar{B}_2$ at level a_1

$$t = \frac{C_j(\overline{AB}_{11}) + C_{j'}(\overline{AB}_{12})}{\sqrt{2(MS_{B \times subj \ w.groups})/n}} = \frac{1(3.75) - 1(4.00)}{\sqrt{2(.507)/4}} = \frac{-.25}{.50} = -.50$$

df = $p(n - 1)(q - 1)$

$t_{.05/2,18} = 2.10.$

It should be noted that the denominator for tests among the p levels of $\bar{A}$ at b_j uses the same $MS_{w.cell}$ that was employed in making simple main-effects tests for treatment A.

CORRECTED SIGNIFICANCE LEVEL
FOR POOLED ERROR TERMS

The $MS_{w.cell}$ is composed of variation based on pq cells. In a split-plot design, the corresponding population error variances are probably not homogeneous. Cochran and Cox (1957, 100 and 298) point out that the t ratio, under these conditions, does not follow Student's t distribution except in special cases. They propose a conservative test to be used in situations where error terms estimating different sources of variability are pooled. The critical value for t as described in Section 3.5 is equal to

$$t'_{\alpha/2} = \frac{t_{(a)}\text{MS}_{\text{subj w.groups}} + t_{(b)}\text{MS}_{B \times \text{subj w.groups}}(q - 1)}{\text{MS}_{\text{subj w.groups}} + \text{MS}_{B \times \text{subj w.groups}}(q - 1)}$$

$$= \frac{2.45(1.563) + 2.10(.507)(4 - 1)}{1.563 + .507(4 - 1)} = 2.28.$$

The value of t that is significant, assuming heterogeneous error variances, is given by $t'_{\alpha/2}$. The values of $t_{(a)}$ and $t_{(b)}$ are the tabled t values at α level of significance for the df associated with $\text{MS}_{\text{subj w.groups}}$ and $\text{MS}_{B \times \text{subj w.groups}}$ error terms, respectively. The value of $t'_{\alpha/2}$ will always be between those for $t_{(a)}$ and $t_{(b)}$ except when the degrees of freedom for the two error terms are the same. When $\text{df}_{(a)} = \text{df}_{(b)}$, the value of $t'_{\alpha/2}$ is the ordinary t value. Taylor (1950) discusses standard error formulas and approximate degrees of freedom for *a priori* comparisons.

A POSTERIORI TESTS

A posteriori comparisons among means may be made either by Tukey's ratio or, when the comparison involves more than two means, by Scheffé's ratio. Formulas and computational examples for the two tests are presented in the following paragraphs. The rationale and procedures underlying *a posteriori* tests are described in Section 3.4.

The form for comparisons among two means by Tukey's test is shown below.

Comparison of $\bar{A}_1$ with $\bar{A}_2$

$$q = \frac{C_j(\bar{A}_1) + C_{j'}(\bar{A}_2)}{\sqrt{\text{MS}_{\text{subj w.groups}}/nq}} = \frac{1(5.69) - 1(5.06)}{\sqrt{1.563/(4)(4)}} = \frac{.63}{.31} = 2.03$$

$$\text{df} = p, p(n - 1)$$

$$q_{.05;2,6} = 3.46.$$

Comparison of $\bar{B}_1$ with $\bar{B}_3$

$$q = \frac{C_j(\bar{B}_1) + C_{j'}(\bar{B}_3)}{\sqrt{\text{MS}_{B \times \text{subj w.groups}}/np}} = \frac{1(2.75) - 1(6.25)}{\sqrt{.507/(4)(2)}} = \frac{-3.50}{.25} = -14.00$$

$$\text{df} = q, p(n - 1)(q - 1)$$

$$q_{.05;4,18} = 4.00.$$

Comparison of $\bar{A}_1$ with $\bar{A}_2$ at level b_1

$$q = \frac{C_j(\overline{AB}_{11}) + C_{j'}(\overline{AB}_{21})}{\sqrt{\text{MS}_{\text{w.cell}}/n}} = \frac{1(3.75) - 1(1.75)}{\sqrt{.771/4}} = \frac{2.00}{.44} = 4.54$$

$$q'_{.05} = 3.22 \text{ (see } q' \text{ approximation below)}.$$

An approximation of the critical value of q' when two different estimates of experimental error are pooled is given by

$$q'_\alpha = \frac{q_{(a)}\text{MS}_{\text{subj w.groups}} + q_{(b)}\text{MS}_{B \times \text{subj w.groups}}(q - 1)}{\text{MS}_{\text{subj w.groups}} + \text{MS}_{B \times \text{subj w.groups}}(q - 1)}$$

where $q_{(a)}$ and $q_{(b)}$ refer to the critical values of q for the degrees of freedom associated with $\text{MS}_{\text{subj w.groups}}$ and $\text{MS}_{B \times \text{subj w.groups}}$, respectively.

$$q'_{.05} = \frac{3.461(1.563) + 2.97(.507)(4 - 1)}{1.563 + .507(4 - 1)} = 3.22.$$

The form for comparisons among two or more means by Scheffé's ratio is shown below. The value of F that is significant is given by $(k - 1)$ $F_{\alpha;v_1,v_2}$, where k is the number of means from which comparisons can be formed.

Comparison of $\bar{A}_1$ with $\bar{A}_2$

$$F = \frac{[C_j(\bar{A}_1) + C_{j'}(\bar{A}_2)]^2}{\text{MS}_{\text{subj w.groups}}\left[\dfrac{(C_j)^2}{nq} + \dfrac{(C_{j'})^2}{nq}\right]} = \frac{[1(7.58) - 1(6.75)]^2}{1.563\left[\dfrac{(1)^2}{(4)(4)} + \dfrac{(-1)^2}{(4)(4)}\right]} = \frac{(.83)^2}{.1954}$$

$$= 3.53$$

$(k - 1)F_{.05;1,6} = (2 - 1)(5.99) = 5.99.$

Comparison of $\bar{B}_1$ with $\bar{B}_2$ and $\bar{B}_3$

$$F = \frac{[C_j(\bar{B}_1) + C_{j'}(\bar{B}_2) + C_{j''}(\bar{B}_3)]^2}{\text{MS}_{B \times \text{subj w.groups}}\left[\dfrac{(C_j)^2}{np} + \dfrac{(C_{j'})^2}{np} + \dfrac{(C_{j''})^2}{np}\right]}$$

$$= \frac{[1(2.75) - \frac{1}{2}(3.50) - \frac{1}{2}(6.25)]^2}{.507\left[\dfrac{(1)^2}{4(2)} + \dfrac{(-\frac{1}{2})^2}{4(2)} + \dfrac{(-\frac{1}{2})^2}{4(2)}\right]}$$

$$= \frac{(-2.125)^2}{.9506} = 47.50$$

$(k - 1)F_{.05;3,18} = (4 - 1)(3.16) = 9.48.$

Comparison of $\bar{B}_1$ with $\bar{B}_2$ and $\bar{B}_3$ at level a_1

$$F = \frac{[C_j(\overline{AB}_{11}) + C_{j'}(\overline{AB}_{12}) + C_{j''}(\overline{AB}_{13})]^2}{\text{MS}_{B \times \text{subj w.groups}}\left[\dfrac{(C_j)^2}{n} + \dfrac{(C_{j'})^2}{n} + \dfrac{(C_{j''})^2}{n}\right]}$$

$$= \frac{[1(3.75) - \frac{1}{2}(4.00) - \frac{1}{2}(7.00)]^2}{.507\left[\dfrac{(1)^2}{4} + \dfrac{(-\frac{1}{2})^2}{4} + \dfrac{(-\frac{1}{2})^2}{4}\right]}$$

$$= \frac{(-1.75)^2}{.1901} = 16.11$$

$$(k-1)F_{.05;3,18} = (4-1)(3.16) = 9.48.$$

8.8   TESTS FOR TRENDS
IN TYPE SPF-$p.q$ DESIGN

General procedures for trend analysis are described in Sections 4.7 and 7.7. These procedures generalize with slight modification to split-plot repeated measures designs, and the reader should refer to the earlier discussions.

The vigilance data in Table 8.2-1 are suitable for trend analysis because treatment B represents a quantitative variable. An answer to the question, "Is there a trend in the data for treatment B?" is provided by the test

$$F = \frac{MS_B}{MS_{B \times \text{subj w.groups}}}.$$

The MS_B corresponding to periods of time is significant according to the analysis in Table 8.2-2. The significance of the linear component of the B trend can be tested by

$$F = \frac{MS_{\text{lin } b}}{MS_{B \times \text{subj w.groups}}}.$$

A test for departure from linearity is given by

$$F = \frac{MS_{\text{dep from lin } b}}{MS_{B \times \text{subj w.groups}}},$$

where

$$MS_{\text{dep from lin } b} = \frac{SS_B - SS_{\text{lin } b}}{q - 2}.$$

Procedures for computing $MS_{\text{lin } b}$, $MS_{\text{quad } b}$, $MS_{\text{cubic } b}$, and $MS_{\text{dep from lin } b}$ are described in Section 7.7.

SIGNIFICANCE OF DIFFERENCES
AMONG LINEAR TREND COMPONENTS

In experiments involving more than one treatment, the investigator is often interested in determining whether the trend for one treatment is the same at all levels of a second treatment. This question is answered by a test of the AB interaction

$$F = \frac{MS_{AB}}{MS_{B \times \text{subj w.groups}}}.$$

If the interaction is significant, the experimenter may want to determine whether the interaction is due to differences in the linear trend, the quadratic trend, the cubic trend, or several of the trends. The interaction of *type of signal* with *periods of time* is illustrated in Figure 8.6-1. The interaction of A and B is significant for these data. The question can be raised, "Is there a difference in the B treatment linear trend for levels a_1 and a_2?" If treatment A represented a quantitative variable, the same question could be raised with respect to the A treatment trend components for each level of treatment B.

Computational procedures for testing the significance of differences in the B linear trend for a_1 and a_2 are shown in Table 8.8-1. The numerical values in part (i) are obtained from Table 8.2-1.

It is apparent that part of the AB interaction is due to differences in the linear trend. The sum of squares for the interaction is equal to 19.375. Thus the $SS_{AB \text{ diff in lin trend}}$ accounts for most of the AB interaction; for example, $13.225/19.375 = 68.3$ percent. This means that differences in quadratic and cubic trends account for only 31.7 percent of the AB interaction.

TABLE 8.8-1   Procedures for Testing Differences in Linear Trend

(i) Linear coefficients (c_1)

		$c_1 =$	-3	-1	$+1$	$+3$	$\sum_1^q c_1^2 = 20$		

		b_1	b_2	b_3	b_4	$B_1' = \sum_1^q (c_1)(ABS)$	$B_1'^2$	$AB_1' = \sum_1^n \sum_1^q (c_1)(ABS)$
	s_1	3	4	7	7	15	225	
	s_2	6	5	8	8	9	81	63
a_1	s_3	3	4	7	9	21	441	
	s_4	3	3	6	8	18	324	
	s_5	1	2	5	10	30	900	
	s_6	2	3	6	10	27	729	109
a_2	s_7	2	4	5	9	22	484	
	s_8	2	3	6	11	30	900	

$$\sum_1^p \sum_1^n B_1' = 172 \qquad \sum_1^p \sum_1^n B_1'^2 = 4084 \qquad \sum_1^p (AB_1')^2 = 15850$$

TABLE 8.8-1 (continued)

(ii)

$$SS_{\text{lin }b} = \frac{\left(\sum_1^p \sum_1^n B'_1\right)^2}{np\sum_1^q c_1^2} = \frac{(172)^2}{(4)(2)(20)} = 184.900$$

$$df = 1$$

$$SS_{AB \text{ diff in lin trend}} = \frac{\sum_1^p (AB'_1)^2}{n\sum_1^q c_1^2} - \frac{\left(\sum_1^p \sum_1^n B'_1\right)^2}{np\sum_1^q c_1^2} = \frac{15850}{(4)(20)} - \frac{(172)^2}{(4)(2)(20)} = 13.225$$

$$df = p - 1 = 1$$

$$SS_{B \times \text{subj w.groups (lin)}} = \frac{\sum_1^p \sum_1^n B'^2_1}{\sum_1^q c_1^2} - \frac{\sum_1^p (AB'_1)^2}{n\sum_1^q c_1^2} = \frac{4084}{(20)} - \frac{15850}{4(20)} = 6.075$$

$$df = p(n - 1) = 6$$

$$F = \frac{SS_{AB \text{ diff in lin trend}}/(p - 1)}{SS_{B \times \text{subj w.groups (lin)}}/p(n - 1)} = \frac{13.225/1}{6.075/6} = 13.07$$

$$F_{.05;1,6} = 5.99$$

SIGNIFICANCE OF DIFFERENCES AMONG QUADRATIC TREND AND CUBIC TREND COMPONENTS

Computational procedures for testing the significance of differences in quadratic and cubic trends appear in Tables 8.8-2 and 8.8-3, respectively. A summary of the analysis of differences in trends is shown in Table 8.8-4. The conceptual unit for error rate for the trend tests described is the individual trend comparison. If an experimenter wants to set the error rate per family of trend comparisons at .05, the tabled value of $F_{.017;1,6}$ can be used for each test. This procedure divides the critical region evenly among the three comparisons within each family. It should be noted that the three error terms, $B \times$ subj w.groups (lin, quad, and cubic), need not be homogeneous, for they estimate different sources of variation. A general check on the computation can be made by determining if the partitioned sum of squares of an effect adds up to the unpartitioned effect. For example, $SS_{AB} = SS_{AB \text{ diff in lin trend}} + SS_{AB \text{ diff in quad trend}} + SS_{AB \text{ diff in cubic trend}}$.

TABLE 8.8-2   Procedures for Testing Differences
in Quadratic Trend

(i) Quadratic coefficients (c_2)

$$c_2 = 1 \quad -1 \quad -1 \quad +1 \qquad \sum_1^q c_2^2 = 4$$

		b_1	b_2	b_3	b_4	$B_2' = \sum_1^q (c_2)(ABS)$	$B_2'^2$	$AB_2' = \sum_1^n \sum_1^q (c_2)(ABS)$
	s_1	3	4	7	7	-1	1	
	s_2	6	5	8	8	1	1	3
a_1	s_3	3	4	7	9	1	1	
	s_4	3	3	6	8	2	4	
	s_5	1	2	5	10	4	16	
	s_6	2	3	6	10	3	9	13
a_2	s_7	2	4	5	9	2	4	
	s_8	2	3	6	11	4	16	

$$\sum_1^p \sum_1^n B_2' = 16 \qquad \sum_1^p \sum_1^n B_2'^2 = 52 \qquad \sum_1^p (AB_2')^2 = 178$$

(ii)

$$SS_{\text{quad } b} = \frac{\left(\sum_1^p \sum_1^n B_2'\right)^2}{np \sum_1^q c_2^2} = \frac{(16)^2}{(4)(2)(4)} = 8.000$$
$$df = 1$$

$$SS_{AB \text{ diff in quad trend}} = \frac{\sum_1^p (AB_2')^2}{n \sum_1^q c_2^2} - \frac{\left(\sum_1^p \sum_1^n B_2'\right)^2}{np \sum_1^q c_2^2} = \frac{178}{4(4)} - \frac{(16)^2}{(4)(2)(4)} = 3.125$$
$$df = p - 1 = 1$$

$$SS_{B \times \text{subj w.groups (quad)}} = \frac{\sum_1^p \sum_1^n B_2'^2}{\sum_1^q c_2^2} - \frac{\sum_1^p (AB_2')^2}{n \sum_1^q c_2^2} = \frac{52}{(4)} - \frac{178}{4(4)} = 1.875$$
$$df = p(n - 1) = 6$$

$$F = \frac{SS_{AB \text{ diff in quad trend}}/(p - 1)}{SS_{B \times \text{subj w.groups (quad)}}/p(n - 1)} = \frac{3.125/1}{1.875/6} = 10.02$$

$$F_{.05;1,6} = 5.99$$

TABLE 8.8-3   Procedures for Testing Differences in Cubic Trend

(i) Cubic coefficients (c_3)

$$c_3 = -1 \quad 3 \quad -3 \quad 1 \qquad \sum_1^q c_3^2 = 20$$

		b_1	b_2	b_3	b_4	$B'_3 = \sum_1^q (c_3)(ABS)$	B'^2_3	$AB'_3 = \sum_1^n \sum_1^q (c_3)(ABS)$
	s_1	3	4	7	7	-5	25	
a_1	s_2	6	5	8	8	-7	49	-19
	s_3	3	4	7	9	-3	9	
	s_4	3	3	6	8	-4	16	
	s_5	1	2	5	10	0	0	
a_2	s_6	2	3	6	10	-1	1	3
	s_7	2	4	5	9	4	16	
	s_8	2	3	6	11	0	0	

$$\sum_1^p \sum_1^n B'_3 = -16 \qquad \sum_1^p \sum_1^n B'^2_3 = 116 \qquad \sum_1^p (AB'_3)^2 = 370$$

(ii)

$$SS_{\text{cubic } b} = \frac{\left(\sum_1^p \sum_1^n B'_3\right)^2}{np\sum_1^q c_3^2} = \frac{(-16)^2}{(4)(2)(20)} = 1.600$$

$$\text{df} = 1$$

$$SS_{AB \text{ diff in cubic trend}} = \frac{\sum_1^p (AB'_3)^2}{n\sum_1^q c_3^2} - \frac{\left(\sum_1^p \sum_1^n B'_3\right)^2}{np\sum_1^q c_3^2} = \frac{370}{4(20)} - \frac{(-16)^2}{(4)(2)(20)} = 3.025$$

$$\text{df} = p - 1 = 1$$

$$SS_{B \times \text{subj w.groups (cubic)}} = \frac{\sum_1^p \sum_1^n B'^2_3}{\sum_1^q c_3^2} - \frac{\sum_1^p (AB'_3)^2}{n\sum_1^q c_3^2} = \frac{116}{20} - \frac{370}{4(20)} = 1.175$$

$$\text{df} = p(n - 1) = 6$$

$$F = \frac{SS_{AB \text{ diff in cubic trend}}/(p - 1)}{SS_{B \times \text{subj w.groups (cubic)}}/p(n - 1)} = \frac{3.025/1}{1.175/6} = 15.43$$

$$F_{.05;1,6} = 5.99$$

TABLE 8.8-4   Summary of Trend Analysis

	Source	SS	df	MS	F
1	Between subjects	12.500	$np - 1 = 7$		
2	A	3.125	$p - 1 = 1$	3.125	$[\frac{2}{3}] = 2.00$
3	Subjects within groups	9.375	$p(n - 1) = 6$	1.563	
4	Within subjects	223.000	$np(q - 1) = 24$		
5	B	194.500	$q - 1 = 3$	64.833	$[\frac{5}{13}] = 127.88**$
6	Linear trend	184.900	1	184.900	$[\frac{6}{14}] = 182.71**$
7	Quadratic trend	8.000	1	8.000	$[\frac{7}{15}] = 25.64**$
8	Cubic trend	1.600	1	1.600	$[\frac{8}{16}] = 8.16*$
9	AB	19.375	$(p - 1)(q - 1) = 3$	6.458	$[\frac{9}{13}] = 12.74**$
10	Diff in lin trend	13.225	$p - 1 = 1$	13.225	$[\frac{10}{14}] = 13.07*$
11	Diff in quad trend	3.125	$p - 1 = 1$	3.125	$[\frac{11}{15}] = 10.02*$
12	Diff in cubic trend	3.025	$p - 1 = 1$	3.025	$[\frac{12}{16}] = 15.43**$
13	$B \times$ subjects within groups	9.125	$p(n - 1)(q - 1) = 18$	.507	
14	$B \times$ subj w.groups (lin)	6.075	$p(n - 1) = 6$	1.012	
15	$B \times$ subj w.groups (quad)	1.875	$p(n - 1) = 6$	.312	
16	$B \times$ subj w.groups (cubic)	1.175	$p(n - 1) = 6$	.196	
17	Total	235.500	$npq - 1 = 31$		

$*p < .05.$

$**p < .01.$

8.9   GENERAL PROCEDURE FOR DETERMINING EXPECTED VALUES OF MEAN SQUARES IN TYPE SPF-$p.q$ DESIGN

The expected values of mean squares for Models I, II, and III can easily be obtained by following the procedures described in Section 7.10. The expected values in Table 8.9-1 were obtained by the Bennett-Franklin algorithm procedure (Bennett and Franklin, 1954, 413). The method described by Cornfield and Tukey (1956) leads to the same results. The terms $1 - (p/P)$, $1 - (q/Q)$, and $1 - (n/N)$ in the table become zero if the corresponding terms A, B, or subjects represent fixed effects and one if the corresponding terms are random.

If, for example, subjects are selected by random sampling from a population and treatments A and B represent fixed and random effects, respectively, the E(MS) for A is

TABLE 8.9-1   Table for Determining E(MS) in Type SPF-$p.q$ Design

Effect	E(MS)
A	$\sigma_\varepsilon^2 + \left(1 - \dfrac{n}{N}\right)\left(1 - \dfrac{q}{Q}\right)\sigma_{\beta\pi}^2 + n\left(1 - \dfrac{q}{Q}\right)\sigma_{\alpha\beta}^2 + q\left(1 - \dfrac{n}{N}\right)\sigma_\pi^2 + nq\sigma_\alpha^2$
Subj w.groups	$\sigma_\varepsilon^2 + \left(1 - \dfrac{q}{Q}\right)\sigma_{\beta\pi}^2 + q\,\sigma_\pi^2$
B	$\sigma_\varepsilon^2 + \left(1 - \dfrac{n}{N}\right)\sigma_{\beta\pi}^2 + n\left(1 - \dfrac{p}{P}\right)\sigma_{\alpha\beta}^2 + np\sigma_\beta^2$
AB	$\sigma_\varepsilon^2 + \left(1 - \dfrac{n}{N}\right)\sigma_{\beta\pi}^2 + n\sigma_{\alpha\beta}^2$
B × subj w.groups	$\sigma_\varepsilon^2 + \sigma_{\beta\pi}^2$

$$E(MS_A) = \sigma_\varepsilon^2 + \sigma_{\beta\pi}^2 + n\sigma_{\alpha\beta}^2 + q\sigma_\pi^2 + nq\sigma_\alpha^2.$$

Under these conditions, the error term $MS_{\text{subj w.groups}}$ does not include the required expected values for testing MS_A. An error term for MS_A can be found using the quasi F' ratio procedure described in Section 7.11. The F' ratio for this test is given by

$$F' = \frac{MS_A}{MS_{\text{subj w.groups}} + MS_{AB} - MS_{B \times \text{subj w.groups}}}, \qquad df = 1, 4.$$

The degrees of freedom for the denominator is given by

$$df = \frac{(MS_{\text{subj w.groups}} + MS_{AB} - MS_{B \times \text{subj w.groups}})^2}{\dfrac{(MS_{\text{subj w.groups}})^2}{df_{\text{subj w.groups}}} + \dfrac{(MS_{AB})^2}{df_{AB}} + \dfrac{(MS_{B \times \text{subj w.groups}})^2}{df_{B \times \text{subj w.groups}}}}$$

$$df = \frac{(1.563 + 6.458 - .507)^2}{\dfrac{(1.563)^2}{6} + \dfrac{(6.458)^2}{3} + \dfrac{(.507)^2}{18}} \simeq 4.0.$$

8.10   THE PROBLEM OF MISSING SCORES AND UNEQUAL SIZE SUBGROUPS

Numerous reasons exist in research for not having an equal number of blocks in the p levels of treatment A. It is important to distinguish between two general classes of reasons for this. In the first case, the experimenter may have intended to have an equal number of blocks at each level, but subjects comprising blocks were *lost* for reasons unrelated to the conduct of the experiment. Under these conditions, the analysis should be carried out using an unweighted-means solution. In the second case, the experimenter may have deliberately employed an unequal number of blocks, as in stratified sampling, or blocks may have been *lost* as a result of the particular treatments employed. Under either of these last conditions, a least-squares solution should be used.

UNWEIGHTED-MEANS SOLUTION

The unweighted-means solution will be shown first. Assume that in the vigilance experiment described in Section 8.2 five subjects were assigned to each level of treatment A. Data for two subjects assigned to treatment level a_1 (auditory signal) were lost as a result of a faulty relay in a reaction time print-out device. It is reasonable to assume that the loss of two subjects due to the relay malfunction is not a result of the conduct of the experiment or of the particular treatments employed. Table 8.10-1 shows the appropriate computational procedures for this situation. Table 8.10-2 summarizes the results of the unweighted-means analysis. Note in Table 8.10-2 that the sum of squares will not add up to the total sum of squares because equal weight is given to each AB cell in the computation procedure.

A modification of the formulas for the t ratio and Tukey's ratio is required when an unweighted-means analysis is employed. The modifications take the following form:

$$t = \frac{C_j(\bar{A}_i) + C_{j'}(\bar{A}_{i'})}{\sqrt{\mathrm{MS}_{\text{subj w.groups}}\left(\dfrac{1}{n_{ij}q} + \dfrac{1}{n_{ij'}q}\right)}} \qquad q = \frac{C_j(\bar{A}_i) + C_{j'}(\bar{A}_{i'})}{\sqrt{\dfrac{\mathrm{MS}_{\text{subj w.groups}}}{\tilde{n}q}}}$$

$$n_{ij} = 3, \; n_{ij'} = 5 \qquad\qquad \tilde{n} = 3.75$$

$$t = \frac{C_j(\bar{B}_j) + C_{j'}(\bar{B}_{j'})}{\sqrt{\mathrm{MS}_{B \times \text{subj w.groups}}\left(\dfrac{1}{n_j} + \dfrac{1}{n_{j'}}\right)}} \qquad q = \frac{C_j(\bar{B}_j) + C_{j'}(\bar{B}_{j'})}{\sqrt{\dfrac{\mathrm{MS}_{B \times \text{subj w.groups}}}{\tilde{n}p}}}$$

$$n_j = n_{j'} = 8.$$

Modification for Scheffé's ratio follows that for the t ratio. SS's for simple main effects take the following form:

$$\mathrm{SS}_A \text{ for } b_1 = \tilde{n}\left[\sum_1^p (\overline{AB}_{i1})^2 - \frac{\left(\sum_1^p \bar{B}_{i1}\right)^2}{p}\right]$$

$$\mathrm{SS}_B \text{ for } a_1 = \tilde{n}\left[\sum_1^q (\overline{AB}_{1j})^2 - \frac{\left(\sum_1^q \bar{A}_{1j}\right)^2}{q}\right].$$

TABLE 8.10-1   Computational Procedures for Unweighted-Means Solution for Type SPF-2.4 Design

(i) Data:

ABS Summary Table

		b_1	b_2	b_3	b_4	$\sum\limits_{1}^{q} AS$	$\dfrac{\left(\sum\limits_{1}^{q} AS\right)^2}{q}$
a_1	s_1	3	4	7	7	21	110.25
	s_2	6	5	8	8	27	182.25
	s_3	3	4	7	9	23	132.25
a_2	s_4	3	3	6	8	20	100.00
	s_5	1	2	5	10	18	81.00
	s_6	2	3	6	10	21	110.25
	s_7	2	4	5	9	20	100.00
	s_8	2	3	6	11	22	121.00

AB Summary Table

	b_1	b_2	b_3	b_4	$\sum\limits_{1}^{q} A$	$\dfrac{\left(\sum\limits_{1}^{q} A\right)^2}{n_{ij}q}$
a_1	$n_{1j} = 3$					
	12	13	22	24	71	420.083
a_2	$n_{2j} = 5$					
	10	15	28	48	101	510.050

$$\sum\limits_{1}^{p} B = 22 \quad 28 \quad 50 \quad 72$$

$$\frac{\left(\sum\limits_{1}^{p} B\right)^2}{n_j} = 60.5 \quad 98.0 \quad 312.5 \quad 648.0$$

$\overline{AB}$ Summary Table

	b_1	b_2	b_3	b_4	$\sum\limits_{1}^{q} \bar{A}$	$\dfrac{\left(\sum\limits_{1}^{q} \bar{A}\right)^2}{q}$
a_1	4.000	4.333	7.333	8.000	23.666	140.020
a_2	2.000	3.000	5.600	9.600	20.200	102.010

$$\sum\limits_{1}^{p} \bar{B} = 6.000 \quad 7.333 \quad 12.933 \quad 17.600$$

$$\frac{\left(\sum\limits_{1}^{p} \bar{B}\right)^2}{p} = 18.000 \quad 26.886 \quad 83.631 \quad 154.880$$

(ii) Computational symbols:

$$\sum\limits_{1}^{q}\sum\limits_{1}^{N} ABS = 3 + 6 + 3 + \cdots + 11 = 172.000$$

$$\sum\limits_{1}^{q}\sum\limits_{1}^{N} (ABS)^2 = [ABS] = (3)^2 + (6)^2 + (3)^2 + \cdots + (11)^2 = 1160.000$$

$$*\frac{\left(\sum\limits_{1}^{q}\sum\limits_{1}^{N} ABS\right)^2}{qN} = [X] = \frac{(172)^2}{(4)(8)} = 924.500$$

$$\sum\limits_{1}^{N} \frac{\left(\sum\limits_{1}^{q} AS\right)^2}{q} = [AS] = 110.25 + 182.25 + \cdots + 121.00 = 937.000$$

*These terms are required for least-squares solution but not for unweighted-means solution.

TABLE 8.10-1 (continued)

$$\sum_{1}^{p} \frac{\left(\sum_{1}^{q} A\right)^2}{n_{ij}q} = [A] = 420.083 + 510.050 = 930.133$$

$$*\sum_{1}^{q} \frac{\left(\sum_{1}^{p} B\right)^2}{n_j} = [B] = 60.5 + 98.0 + \cdots + 648.0 = 1119.000$$

$$\sum_{1}^{p}\sum_{1}^{q} \frac{(AB)^2}{n_{ij}} = [AB] = \frac{(12)^2}{3} + \frac{(13)^2}{3} + \cdots + \frac{(48)^2}{5} = 1140.267$$

$$\tilde{n} = \frac{p}{(1/n_{ij} + 1/n_{ij} + \cdots + 1/n_{ij})} = \frac{2}{\frac{1}{3} + \frac{1}{5}} = 3.750$$

$$\sum_{1}^{p}\sum_{1}^{q}(\overline{AB})^2 = [\overline{AB}] = (4.000)^2 + (4.333)^2 + \cdots + (9.600)^2 = 289.068$$

$$\frac{\left(\sum_{1}^{p}\sum_{1}^{q}\overline{AB}\right)^2}{pq} = [\overline{X}] = \frac{(43.866)^2}{2(4)} = 240.528$$

$$\sum_{1}^{p} \frac{\left(\sum_{1}^{q}\overline{A}\right)^2}{q} = [\overline{A}] = 140.020 + 102.010 = 242.030$$

$$\sum_{1}^{q} \frac{\left(\sum_{1}^{p}\overline{B}\right)^2}{p} = [\overline{B}] = 18.000 + 26.886 + \cdots + 154.880 = 283.397$$

(iii) Computational formulas:

$$\mathrm{SS}_A = \tilde{n}([\overline{A}] - [\overline{X}]) = 5.632$$

$$\mathrm{SS}_{AB} = \tilde{n}([\overline{AB}] - [\overline{A}] - [\overline{B}] + [\overline{X}])$$
$$= 15.634$$

$$\mathrm{SS}_{\text{subj w.groups}} = [AS] - [A] = 6.867$$

$$\mathrm{SS}_{B \times \text{subj w.groups}} = [ABS] - [AB] - [AS]$$

$$\mathrm{SS}_B = \tilde{n}([\overline{B}] - [\overline{X}]) = 160.759$$
$$+ [A] = 12.866$$

TABLE 8.10-2   Analysis of Variance Table for Unweighted-Means Solution

	Source	SS	df	MS	F
1	A	5.632	$p - 1 = 1$	5.632	$\left[\frac{1}{2}\right] = 4.92$
2	Subj w.groups	6.867	$N - p = 6$	1.144	
3	B	160.759	$q - 1 = 3$	53.586	$\left[\frac{3}{5}\right] = 74.95*$
4	AB	15.634	$(p - 1)(q - 1) = 3$	5.211	$\left[\frac{4}{5}\right] = 7.29*$
5	$B \times$ subj w.groups	12.866	$(N - p)(q - 1) = 18$	.715	

$*p < .01.$

LEAST-SQUARES SOLUTION

A least-squares solution weights each cell in the *AB* Summary Table in proportion to the number of original scores in the cell. This solution is appropriate for many research situations. For example, in the vigilance experiment, subjects assigned to the auditory display condition a_1 might find this mode of signal presentation unpleasant. As a result, two of the subjects might refuse to complete the experiment. In this example, unequal cell frequencies result from the nature of the experimental treatments. A least-squares analysis, rather than an unweighted-means analysis, should be used. Computational formulas based on the data in Table 8.10-1 are given in Table 8.10-3.

TABLE 8.10-3   Computational Procedures for Least-Squares Solution for Type SPF-2.4 Design

$$SS_{total} = [ABS] - [X] = 235.500$$
$$SS_{between\ subj} = [AS] - [X] = 12.500$$
$$SS_A = [A] - [X] = 5.633$$
$$SS_{subj\ w.groups} = [AS] - [A] = 6.867$$
$$SS_{within\ subj} = [ABS] - [AS] = 223.000$$
$$SS_B = [B] - [X] = 194.500$$
$$SS_{AB} = [AB] - [A] - [B] + [X] = 15.634$$
$$SS_{B \times subj\ w.groups} = [ABS] - [AB] - [AS] + [A] = 12.866$$

The analysis is summarized in Table 8.10-4. In a least-squares analysis, the partitioned sum of squares add up to the total sum of squares.

Tests of simple main effects and comparisons among means have the same general form as tests based on equal cell frequencies. These procedures are illustrated in Sections 8.6 and 8.7. They generalize to the least-squares solution but require the substitution of the appropriate value for n.

TABLE 8.10-4   Analysis of Variance Table for Least-Squares Solution

	Source	SS	df	MS	F
1	Between subjects	12.500	$N - 1 = 7$		
2	A	5.633	$p - 1 = 1$	5.633	$[\frac{2}{3}] = 4.92$
3	Subj w.groups	6.867	$N - p = 6$	1.144	
4	Within subjects	223.000	$N(q - 1) = 24$		
5	B	194.500	$q - 1 = 3$	64.833	$[\frac{5}{7}] = 90.68*$
6	AB	15.634	$(p - 1)(q - 1) = 3$	5.211	$[\frac{6}{7}] = 7.29*$
7	$B \times$ subj w.groups	12.866	$(N - p)(q - 1) = 18$	.715	
8	Total	235.500	$Nq - 1 = 31$		

*$p < .01$.

The two solutions for unequal n's illustrated in this section each require that the number of observations within each block be equal.

THE PROBLEM OF ONE MISSING SCORE

The preceding solutions are appropriate when an entire block is missing. The following procedure is applicable when only one score in a block is missing. It is analogous to the method in Section 5.6 for estimating missing values in a randomized block design. A missing score is estimated by

$$ABS_{ijm} = \frac{n(\Sigma S_m) + q(\Sigma AB_{ij}) - \Sigma A_i}{(n-1)(q-1)},$$

where n = number of blocks in level A_i.

q = number of levels of B.

ΣS_m = sum of remaining scores in block containing missing score.

ΣAB_{ij} = sum of remaining scores in treatment combination AB_{ij} containing missing score.

ΣA_i = sum of remaining scores in treatment A_i containing missing score.

For example, assume that score ABS_{122} in Table 8.2-1 is missing. This score is estimated by

$$ABS_{122} = \frac{4(22) + 4(11) - 86}{(4-1)(4-1)} = 5.1,$$

where $\Sigma S_2 = 27 - 5 = 22$.

$\Sigma AB_{12} = 16 - 5 = 11$.

$\Sigma A_1 = 91 - 5 = 86$.

The estimated score is reasonably close to the original score in that cell, which is 5.

After inserting the estimate of the missing score into the data matrix, the analysis of variance is carried out in the normal way. The degrees of freedom for $MS_{B \times subj\ w.groups}$ should be reduced by one; for example, $df = p(n-1)(q-1) - 1$. An unbiased estimate of $MS_{B \times subj\ w.groups}$ is obtained by this procedure, but all other mean squares are slightly overestimated. According to Anderson (1946), the biases are small. He gives methods for obtaining unbiased estimates, but it is doubtful if the added labor is justified. If another missing score occurs in the same A_i treatment, the iterative procedure described in Chapter 5 may be used. If the second missing score occurs in a different level of treatment A, the procedure of estimating the score described above is repeated. A more complete discussion of procedures for estimating missing scores may be found in Anderson (1946) and Khargonkar (1948).

Standard error formulas due to Anderson (1946) for making comparisons among means by the t test, when only one score has been estimated, are shown below.

Comparisons among $\bar{A}_i$ means can be made using the following t denominator:

$$\sqrt{\frac{2[\text{MS}_{\text{subj w.groups}} + \frac{1}{2}(n - 1)(q - 1)(\text{MS}_{B \times \text{subj w.groups}})]}{nq}}.$$

Comparisons among $\bar{B}_j$ means employ the following t denominator:

$$\sqrt{\frac{2\text{MS}_{B \times \text{subj w.groups}}[1 + \frac{1}{2}(n - 1)(q - 1)(q/p)]}{np}}.$$

Comparisons among $\overline{AB}_{ij}$ means at level a_i use the following denominator:

$$\sqrt{\frac{2\text{MS}_{B \times \text{subj w.groups}}[1 + \frac{1}{2}(n - 1)(q - 1)(q/p)]}{n}}.$$

Comparisons among $\overline{AB}_{ij}$ means at level b_j use the following denominator:

$$\sqrt{\frac{2\text{MS}_{\text{subj w.groups}}/nq + 2\text{MS}_{B \times \text{subj w.groups}}[(q - 1) + \frac{1}{2}(n - 1)(q - 1)(q^2)]}{nq}}.$$

The foregoing formulas are used in comparing means based on one estimated missing score. Procedures for determining the critical value for the t test for pooled error terms appear in Section 8.7. If a comparison among means does not involve a missing score, formulas given in Section 8.7 are appropriate.

If several missing scores occur in designs having three or more treatments, the reader should consult Hazel (1946), Henderson (1953), and Krishna Iyer (1940).

8.11   RELATIVE EFFICIENCY
OF SPLIT-PLOT DESIGN

An experimenter wishing to use a multitreatment factorial design with subjects assigned to blocks may consider two of the designs described thus far—a randomized block factorial design and a split-plot design. However, he should examine several factors in choosing between these two designs. If it is not possible to administer all treatment level combinations within each block, there is no choice. A split-plot design is required. On the other hand, if there is a choice concerning the assignment of treatment combinations in each block, the relative efficiency of the A,

B, and AB comparisons should be considered. In a split-plot design, the B and AB effects are usually estimated more accurately than the A effects. This results from the fact that variation within a block is usually smaller than variation among blocks. The average standard error of a difference is equal for both the randomized block factorial design and the split-plot design. Thus the increased accuracy of the B and AB effects estimates is obtained by sacrificing accuracy on the A effects. If the experimenter is as interested in the A effects as he is in the B and AB effects, the randomized block factorial design should be used. It should also be noted that the F ratio denominator degrees of freedom for A, B, and AB in the randomized block factorial design are larger than the corresponding degrees of freedom in a split-plot design.

A numerical index of relative efficiency of the two designs, disregarding differences in degrees of freedom, is given by the following formulas (Federer, 1955, 274). The data used in this example are from Table 8.2-2.

A efficiency

$$= \frac{[(p-1)\text{MS}_{\text{subj w.groups}} + p(n-1)\text{MS}_{B \times \text{subj w.groups}}]/(pq-1)}{\text{MS}_{\text{subj w.groups}}}$$

$$= \frac{[(2-1)1.563 + 2(4-1).507]/[(2)(4)-1]}{1.563} = \frac{.658}{1.563} \times 100$$

$$= 42.1 \text{ percent.}$$

B and AB efficiency

$$= \frac{[(p-1)\text{MS}_{\text{subj w.groups}} + p(n-1)\text{MS}_{B \times \text{subj w.groups}}]/(pq-1)}{\text{MS}_{B \times \text{subj w.groups}}}$$

$$= \frac{[(2-1)1.563 + 2(4-1).507]/[(2)(4)-1]}{.507} = \frac{.658}{.507} \times 100$$

$$= 129.8 \text{ percent.}$$

Hence, in this example, a test of the A treatment is less than half as efficient in the split-plot design as it is in the randomized block factorial design. On the other hand, the B and AB tests are more efficient in the split-plot design. The relative efficiency of tests is a basic consideration in the design of experiments.

8.12   INTRODUCTION TO TYPE SPF-*pr.q* DESIGN

The split-plot design described so far in this chapter has had two treatments. The general analysis procedure for a two-treatment split-plot design can be extended to designs having three or more treatments.

Numerical examples for the more frequently used split-plot designs are given in subsequent sections of this chapter, and general rules for expanding the design to any combination of between-block and within-block treatments are provided.

DESCRIPTION OF TYPE SPF-*pr.q* DESIGN

The design described here and diagramed in Figure 8.12-1 is a type SPF-22.4 design. The design has two between-block treatments (*A*) and

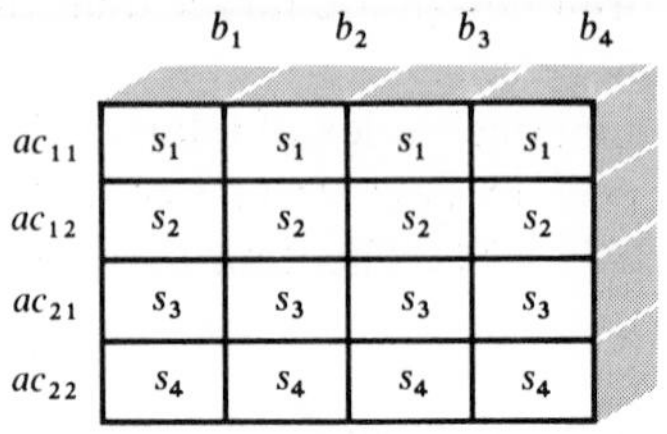

Figure 8.12-1   Type SPF-22.4 design.

(*C*) and one within-block treatment (*B*). It is assumed that *npr* samples of subjects from a common population have been randomly assigned to the *AC* treatments, with *n* blocks within each *pr* level. If the number of blocks in each *pr* treatment level is not equal, an unweighted-means analysis or least-squares analysis must be used. Conditions under which these procedures are appropriate are described in Section 8.10. The structural model underlying the design is

$$X_{ijkm} = \mu + \alpha_i + \gamma_k + \alpha\gamma_{ik} + \pi_{m(ik)} + \beta_j + \alpha\beta_{ij}$$
$$+ \beta\gamma_{jk} + \alpha\beta\gamma_{ijk} + \beta\pi_{jm(ik)} + \varepsilon_{o(ijkm)}.$$

COMPUTATIONAL PROCEDURES FOR TYPE SPF-22.4 DESIGN

The layout and computational procedures for a type SPF-22.4 design are illustrated in Table 8.12-1. This analysis procedure generalizes to any number of levels of the three treatments as long as the number of levels is two or more. The following notation is used in Table 8.12-1:

p levels of a_i, where $p = 2$

q levels of b_j, where $q = 4$

r levels of c_k, where $r = 2$

n levels of s_m, where $n = 2$

$$\sum_1^N = \sum_1^p \sum_1^r \sum_1^n.$$

TABLE 8.12-1 Computational Procedures for Type SPF-22.4 Design

(i) Data:

ABCS Summary Table

		b_1	b_2	b_3	b_4	$\sum_{1}^{q} ACS$	$\dfrac{\left(\sum_{1}^{q} ACS\right)^2}{q}$
a_1	c_1 s_1	3	4	7	7	21	110.25
	c_1 s_2	6	5	8	8	27	182.25
	c_2 s_3	3	4	7	9	23	132.25
	c_2 s_4	3	3	6	8	20	100.00
a_2	c_1 s_5	1	2	5	10	18	81.00
	c_1 s_6	2	3	6	10	21	110.25
	c_2 s_7	2	4	5	9	20	100.00
	c_2 s_8	2	3	6	11	22	121.00

ABC Summary Table

		b_1	b_2	b_3	b_4
		$n = 2$			
a_1	c_1	9	9	15	15
	c_2	6	7	13	17
a_2	c_1	3	5	11	20
	c_2	4	7	11	20

AC Summary Table

	c_1	c_2
	$nq = 8$	
a_1	48	43
a_2	39	42
$\sum_{1}^{p} C =$	87	85
$\dfrac{\left(\sum_{1}^{p} C\right)^2}{npq} =$	473.0625	451.5625

AB Summary Table

	b_1	b_2	b_3	b_4	$\sum_{1}^{q} A$	$\dfrac{\left(\sum_{1}^{q} A\right)^2}{nqr}$
	$nr = 4$					
a_1	15	16	28	32	91	517.5625
a_2	7	12	22	40	81	410.0625

$$\sum_{1}^{p} B = 22 \quad 28 \quad 50 \quad 72$$

$$\frac{\left(\sum_{1}^{p} B\right)^2}{npr} = 60.5 \quad 98.0 \quad 312.5 \quad 648.0$$

BC Summary Table

	b_1	b_2	b_3	b_4
	$np = 4$			
c_1	12	14	26	35
c_2	10	14	24	37

(ii) Computational symbols:

$$\sum_{1}^{q}\sum_{1}^{N} ABCS = 3 + 6 + 3 + \cdots + 11 = 172.000$$

$$\sum_{1}^{q}\sum_{1}^{N} (ABCS)^2 = [ABCS] = (3)^2 + (6)^2 + (3)^2 + \cdots + (11)^2 = 1160.000$$

TABLE 8.12-1 (continued)

$$\frac{\left(\sum_{1}^{q}\sum_{1}^{N}ABCS\right)^2}{qN} = [X] = \frac{(172)^2}{(4)(8)} = 924.500$$

$$\sum_{1}^{N}\frac{\left(\sum_{1}^{q}ACS\right)^2}{q} = [ACS] = 110.25 + 182.25 + \cdots + 121.00 = 937.000$$

$$\sum_{1}^{p}\frac{\left(\sum_{1}^{q}A\right)^2}{nqr} = [A] = 517.5625 + 410.0625 = 927.625$$

$$\sum_{1}^{r}\frac{\left(\sum_{1}^{r}C\right)^2}{npq} = [C] = 473.0625 + 451.5625 = 924.625$$

$$\sum_{1}^{p}\sum_{1}^{r}\frac{(AC)^2}{nq} = [AC] = \frac{(48)^2}{8} + \frac{(43)^2}{8} + \cdots + \frac{(42)^2}{8} = 929.750$$

$$\sum_{1}^{q}\frac{\left(\sum_{1}^{p}B\right)^2}{npr} = [B] = 60.5 + 98.0 + \cdots + 648.0 = 1119.000$$

$$\sum_{1}^{p}\sum_{1}^{q}\frac{(AB)^2}{nr} = [AB] = \frac{(15)^2}{4} + \frac{(16)^2}{4} + \cdots + \frac{(40)^2}{4} = 1141.500$$

$$\sum_{1}^{q}\sum_{1}^{r}\frac{(BC)^2}{np} = [BC] = \frac{(12)^2}{4} + \frac{(14)^2}{4} + \cdots + \frac{(37)^2}{4} = 1120.500$$

$$\sum_{1}^{p}\sum_{1}^{q}\sum_{1}^{r}\frac{(ABC)^2}{n} = [ABC] = \frac{(9)^2}{2} + \frac{(9)^2}{2} + \cdots + \frac{(20)^2}{2} = 1148.000$$

(iii) Computational formulas:

$$SS_{total} = [ABCS] - [X] = 235.500$$
$$SS_{between\ subj} = [ACS] - [X] = 12.500$$
$$SS_A = [A] - [X] = 3.125$$
$$SS_C = [C] - [X] = .125$$
$$SS_{AC} = [AC] - [A] - [C] + [X] = 2.000$$
$$SS_{subj\ w.groups} = [ACS] - [AC] = 7.250$$
$$SS_{within\ subj} = [ABCS] - [ACS] = 223.000$$
$$SS_B = [B] - [X] = 194.500$$
$$SS_{AB} = [AB] - [A] - [B] + [X] = 19.375$$
$$SS_{BC} = [BC] - [B] - [C] + [X] = 1.375$$
$$SS_{ABC} = [ABC] - [AB] - [AC] - [BC] + [A] + [B] + [C] - [X] = 3.000$$
$$SS_{B \times subj\ w.groups} = [ABCS] - [ABC] - [ACS] + [AC] = 4.750$$

The results of the analysis are summarized in Table 8.12-2. It is apparent that treatment B and the AB interaction are significant. The next step in the analysis is to test the simple main effects of A and B. This can be followed by comparisons among $\overline{AB}_{ij}$ means if such comparisons are of interest to the experimenter.

TABLE 8.12-2   Analysis of Variance Table

	Source	SS	df	MS	F (A, B, and C Fixed Effects, Subjects Random)
1	Between subjects	12.500	$npr - 1 = 7$		
2	A	3.125	$p - 1 = 1$	3.125	$\left[\frac{2}{5}\right] =$ 1.72
3	C	.125	$r - 1 = 1$	.125	$\left[\frac{3}{5}\right] =$ .07
4	AC	2.000	$(p - 1)(r - 1) = 1$	2.000	$\left[\frac{4}{5}\right] =$ 1.10
5	Subj w.groups	7.250	$pr(n - 1) = 4$	1.812	
6	Within subjects	223.000	$npr(q - 1) = 24$		
7	B	194.500	$q - 1 = 3$	64.833	$\left[\frac{7}{11}\right] = 163.72*$
8	AB	19.375	$(p - 1)(q - 1) = 3$	6.458	$\left[\frac{8}{11}\right] = 16.31*$
9	BC	1.375	$(q - 1)(r - 1) = 3$	.458	$\left[\frac{9}{11}\right] =$ 1.16
10	ABC	3.000	$(p - 1)(q - 1)(r - 1) = 3$	1.000	$\left[\frac{10}{11}\right] =$ 2.53
11	B × subj w.groups	4.750	$pr(n - 1)(q - 1) = 12$	.396	
12	Total	235.500	$npqr - 1 = 31$		

*$p < .01$.

TESTS FOR HOMOGENEITY OF ERROR TERMS

Before turning to procedures for analyzing simple main effects, we shall describe tests of homogeneity of the two error terms. Table 8.12-3 parts (i) and (ii) show the sources of variation that are pooled in computing $MS_{subj\ w.groups}$ and $MS_{B \times subj\ w.groups}$, respectively. In order for an F ratio to follow the F distribution, error sources of variation that are pooled must be homogeneous. Homogeneity of each of the terms, $MS_{subj\ w.groups}$ and $MS_{B \times subj\ w.groups}$, can be tested by means of the F_{max} test (Section 2.6). Partitioning of the two error terms and F_{max} ratios are shown in Table 8.12-3. The F_{max} test indicates that the assumption of homogeneity of the partitioned parts of the within-cell variation is tenable.

When repeated measures are used, as opposed to matched subjects, the assumptions of equality of within-cell population variances and equality of correlations between repeated measurements is questionable. Associated with a type SPF-22.4 design are $q \times q$ variance-covariance matrices at levels ac_{11}, ac_{12}, ac_{21}, and ac_{22}. Procedures for determining if the variance-covariance matrices have the required equality and if the pooled $q \times q$ dispersion matrix has the required symmetry (all σ^2 equal and all $\rho\sigma^2$ equal) are described in Section 8.5. If there is reason to doubt the appropriateness of the required assumptions, conservative tests should be used. A conservative test consists of computing the F ratios in the

TABLE 8.12-3   Partitioning of Error Terms for Tests of Homogeneity

(i)

$$SS_{\text{subj w.group } ac_{11}} = \sum_1^n \frac{\left(\sum_1^q ACS_{1j1m}\right)^2}{q} - \frac{(AC_{11})^2}{nq} = 110.25 + 182.25 - \frac{(48)^2}{8} = 4.500$$

$$SS_{\text{subj w.group } ac_{12}} = \sum_1^n \frac{\left(\sum_1^q ACS_{1j2m}\right)^2}{q} - \frac{(AC_{12})^2}{nq} = 132.25 + 100.00 - \frac{(43)^2}{8} = 1.125$$

$$SS_{\text{subj w.group } ac_{21}} = \sum_1^n \frac{\left(\sum_1^q ACS_{2j1m}\right)^2}{q} - \frac{(AC_{21})^2}{nq} = 81.00 + 110.25 - \frac{(39)^2}{8} = 1.125$$

$$SS_{\text{subj w.group } ac_{22}} = \sum_1^n \frac{\left(\sum_1^q ACS_{2j2m}\right)^2}{q} - \frac{(AC_{22})^2}{nq} = 100.00 + 121.00 - \frac{(42)^2}{8} = .500$$

Computational check $\sum_1^p \sum_1^r SS_{\text{subj w.group } ac_{ik}} = SS_{\text{subj w.groups}} = 7.250.$

$$F_{\max} = \frac{4.5/1}{0.5/1} = 9.00$$

$$F_{\max .05; pr, n-1} > 142$$

(ii)

$$SS_{B \times \text{subj w.group } ac_{11}} = \sum_1^q \sum_1^n ABCS_{1j1m}^2 - \sum_1^q \frac{(ABC_{1j1})^2}{n} - \sum_1^n \frac{\left(\sum_1^q ACS_{1j1m}\right)^2}{q} + \frac{(AC_{11})^2}{nq}$$

$$= [(3)^2 + \cdots + (8)^2] - \left[\frac{(9)^2}{2} + \cdots + \frac{(15)^2}{2}\right]$$

$$- \left[\frac{(21)^2}{4} + \frac{(27)^2}{4}\right] + \frac{(48)^2}{8} = 1.500$$

$$SS_{B \times \text{subj w.group } ac_{12}} = \sum_1^q \sum_1^n ABCS_{1j2m}^2 - \sum_1^q \frac{(ABC_{1j2})^2}{n} - \sum_1^n \frac{\left(\sum_1^q ACS_{1j2m}\right)^2}{q} + \frac{(AC_{12})^2}{nq} = .375$$

$$SS_{B \times \text{subj w.group } ac_{21}} = \sum_1^q \sum_1^n ABCS_{2j1m}^2 - \sum_1^q \frac{(ABC_{2j1})^2}{n} - \sum_1^n \frac{\left(\sum_1^q ACS_{2j1m}\right)^2}{q} + \frac{(AC_{21})^2}{nq} = .375$$

$$SS_{B \times \text{subj w.group } ac_{22}} = \sum_1^q \sum_1^n ABCS_{2j2m}^2 - \sum_1^q \frac{(ABC_{2j2})^2}{n} - \sum_1^n \frac{\left(\sum_1^q ACS_{2j2m}\right)^2}{q} + \frac{(AC_{22})^2}{nq} = 2.500$$

Computational check $\sum_1^p \sum_1^r SS_{B \times \text{subj w.group } ac_{ik}} = SS_{B \times \text{subj w.groups}} = 4.750.$

$$F_{\max} = \frac{2.500/3}{0.375/3} = 6.66$$

$$F_{\max .05; pr, (n-1)(q-1)} = 39.2$$

normal way but entering the F table with modified degrees of freedom as shown in Table 8.12-4. The general rule used in constructing Table 8.12-4 is to divide all degrees of freedom involving the repeated treatment (B) by ($q - 1$).

TABLE 8.12-4   Conservative F Ratio Degrees of Freedom (Model III)

Numerator of F ratio	df
MS_B	$1, pr(n - 1)$
MS_{AB}	$p - 1, pr(n - 1)$
MS_{BC}	$r - 1, pr(n - 1)$
MS_{ABC}	$(p - 1)(r - 1), pr(n - 1)$

TESTS OF SIMPLE EFFECTS

When interactions are significant, additional insight into the effects of the treatments can often be achieved by analyzing simple main effects. Procedures for making these tests are illustrated in Table 8.12-5. Tests of simple main effects should only be made when the interaction involving the main effects is significant. For the data analyzed in Table 8.12-2, only the simple effects of A at b_j and B at a_i should be computed. The appropriate error term for each test is given below the formulas in Table 8.12-5. For example, the error term for MS_A at b_1 is the pooled sum of squares for subj w.groups and $B \times$ subj w.groups. The rule governing the choice of error terms is given in Section 8.6. It can be shown that

$$\frac{MS_{\text{subj w.groups}} + MS_{B \times \text{subj w.groups}}(q - 1)}{q} = \frac{SS_{\text{subj w.groups}} + SS_{B \times \text{subj w.groups}}}{pr(n - 1) + pr(n - 1)(q - 1)}.$$

Computational checks can be made by summing the sum of squares for simple effects. This sum should equal the main effects plus its interaction. For example,

$$\sum_1^q SS_A \text{ for } b_j = SS_A + SS_{AB}$$

$$\sum_1^p SS_B \text{ for } a_i = SS_B + SS_{AB}$$

$$\sum_1^r SS_A \text{ for } c_k = SS_A + SS_{AC}$$

$$\sum_1^q \sum_1^r SS_A \text{ for } bc_{jk} = SS_A + SS_{AB} + SS_{AC} + SS_{ABC}$$

TABLE 8.12-5   Formulas for Testing Simple Effects

(i) AB interaction significant:

$$SS_A \text{ at } b_1 = \sum_1^p \frac{(AB_{i1})^2}{nr} - \frac{\left(\sum_1^p B_{i1}\right)^2}{npr} = \frac{(15)^2}{4} + \frac{(7)^2}{4} - \frac{(22)^2}{8} = 8.0000$$

$$SS_A \text{ at } b_4 = \sum_1^p \frac{(AB_{i4})^2}{nr} - \frac{\left(\sum_1^p B_{i4}\right)^2}{npr} = \frac{(32)^2}{4} + \frac{(40)^2}{4} - \frac{(72)^2}{8} = 8.0000$$

$$\text{Error term} = \frac{MS_{\text{subj w.groups}} + MS_{B \times \text{subj w.groups}}(q-1)}{q} = .7500*$$

$$SS_B \text{ at } a_1 = \sum_1^q \frac{(AB_{1j})^2}{nr} - \frac{\left(\sum_1^q A_{1j}\right)^2}{nqr} = \frac{(15)^2}{4} + \cdots + \frac{(32)^2}{4} - \frac{(91)^2}{8} = 54.6875$$

$$SS_B \text{ at } a_2 = \sum_1^q \frac{(AB_{2j})^2}{nr} - \frac{\left(\sum_1^q A_{2j}\right)^2}{nqr} = \frac{(7)^2}{4} + \cdots + \frac{(40)^2}{4} - \frac{(81)^2}{8} = 159.1875$$

$$\text{Error term} = MS_{B \times \text{subj w.groups}} = .3958*$$

(ii) AC interaction significant:

$$SS_A \text{ at } c_1 = \sum_1^p \frac{(AC_{i1})^2}{nq} - \frac{\left(\sum_1^p C_{i1}\right)^2}{npq} = \frac{(48)^2}{8} + \frac{(39)^2}{8} - \frac{(87)^2}{16} = 5.0625$$

$$SS_A \text{ at } c_2 = \sum_1^p \frac{(AC_{i2})^2}{nq} - \frac{\left(\sum_1^p C_{i2}\right)^2}{npq} = \frac{(43)^2}{8} + \frac{(42)^2}{8} - \frac{(85)^2}{16} = .0625$$

$$SS_C \text{ at } a_1 = \sum_1^r \frac{(AC_{1k})^2}{nq} - \frac{\left(\sum_1^r A_{1k}\right)^2}{nqr} = \frac{(48)^2}{8} + \frac{(43)^2}{8} - \frac{(91)^2}{16} = 1.5625$$

$$SS_C \text{ at } a_2 = \sum_1^r \frac{(AC_{2k})^2}{nq} - \frac{\left(\sum_1^r A_{2k}\right)^2}{nqr} = \frac{(39)^2}{8} + \frac{(42)^2}{8} - \frac{(81)^2}{16} = .5625$$

$$\text{Error term} = MS_{\text{subj w.groups}} = 1.8125$$

(iii) BC interaction significant:

$$SS_B \text{ at } c_1 = \sum_1^q \frac{(BC_{j1})^2}{np} - \frac{\left(\sum_1^q C_{j1}\right)^2}{npq} = \frac{(12)^2}{4} + \cdots + \frac{(35)^2}{4} - \frac{(87)^2}{8} = 87.1875$$

$$SS_B \text{ at } c_2 = \sum_1^q \frac{(BC_{j2})^2}{np} - \frac{\left(\sum_1^q C_{j2}\right)^2}{npq} = \frac{(10)^2}{4} + \cdots + \frac{(37)^2}{4} - \frac{(85)^2}{8} = 108.6875$$

$$\text{Error term} = MS_{B \times \text{subj w.groups}} = .3958$$

*Error terms are appropriate if A, B, and C represent fixed effects and subjects represent random effects.

TABLE 8.12-5 (continued)

$$\text{SS}_C \text{ at } b_1 = \sum_1^r \frac{(BC_{1k})^2}{np} - \frac{\left(\sum_1^r B_{1k}\right)^2}{npr} = \frac{(12)^2}{4} + \frac{(10)^2}{4} - \frac{(22)^2}{8} = \qquad .5000$$

$$\text{SS}_C \text{ at } b_4 = \sum_1^r \frac{(BC_{4k})^2}{np} - \frac{\left(\sum_1^r B_{4k}\right)^2}{npr} = \frac{(35)^2}{4} + \frac{(37)^2}{4} - \frac{(72)^2}{8} = \qquad .5000$$

$$\text{Error term} = \frac{\text{MS}_{\text{subj w.groups}} + \text{MS}_{B \times \text{subj w.groups}}(q - 1)}{q} = .7500$$

(iv) *ABC* interaction significant:

$$\text{SS}_A \text{ at } bc_{11} = \sum_1^p \frac{(ABC_{i11})^2}{n} - \frac{(BC_{11})^2}{np} = \frac{(9)^2}{2} + \frac{(3)^2}{2} - \frac{(12)^2}{4} = 9.0000$$

$$\text{Error term} = \frac{\text{MS}_{\text{subj w.groups}} + \text{MS}_{B \times \text{subj w.groups}}(q - 1)}{q} = .7500$$

$$\text{SS}_B \text{ at } ac_{11} = \sum_1^q \frac{(ABC_{1j1})^2}{n} - \frac{(AC_{11})^2}{nq} = \frac{(9)^2}{2} + \cdots + \frac{(15)^2}{2} - \frac{(48)^2}{8} = 18.0000$$

$$\text{Error term} = \text{MS}_{B \times \text{subj w.groups}} = .3958$$

$$\text{SS}_C \text{ at } ab_{11} = \sum_1^r \frac{(ABC_{11k})^2}{n} - \frac{(AB_{11})^2}{nr} = \frac{(9)^2}{2} + \frac{(6)^2}{2} - \frac{(15)^2}{4} = 2.2500$$

$$\text{Error term} = \frac{\text{MS}_{\text{subj w.groups}} + \text{MS}_{B \times \text{subj w.groups}}(q - 1)}{q} = .7500$$

$$\text{SS}_{AB} \text{ at } c_1 = \left[\sum_1^p \sum_1^q \frac{(ABC_{ij1})^2}{n} - \frac{\left(\sum_1^p C_{i1}\right)^2}{npq} \right] - \text{SS}_A \text{ at } c_1 - \text{SS}_B \text{ at } c_1$$

$$= \left[\frac{(9)^2}{2} + \frac{(9)^2}{2} + \cdots + \frac{(20)^2}{2} - \frac{(87)^2}{16} \right] - 5.0625 - 87.1875 = 18.1875$$

$$\text{Error term} = \text{MS}_{B \times \text{subj w.groups}} = .3958$$

$$\text{SS}_{AC} \text{ at } b_1 = \left[\sum_1^p \sum_1^r \frac{(ABC_{i1k})^2}{n} - \frac{\left(\sum_1^p B_{i1}\right)^2}{npr} \right] - \text{SS}_A \text{ at } b_1 - \text{SS}_C \text{ at } b_1$$

$$= \left[\frac{(9)^2}{2} + \frac{(6)^2}{2} + \frac{(3)^2}{2} + \frac{(4)^2}{2} - \frac{(22)^2}{8} \right] - 8.000 - .5000 = 2.0000$$

$$\text{Error term} = \frac{\text{MS}_{\text{subj w.groups}} + \text{MS}_{B \times \text{subj w.groups}}(q - 1)}{q} = .7500$$

$$\text{SS}_{BC} \text{ at } a_1 = \left[\sum_1^q \sum_1^r \frac{(ABC_{1jk})^2}{n} - \frac{\left(\sum_1^q A_{1j}\right)^2}{nqr} \right] - \text{SS}_B \text{ at } a_1 - \text{SS}_C \text{ at } a_1$$

$$= \left[\frac{(9)^2}{2} + \frac{(9)^2}{2} + \cdots + \frac{(17)^2}{2} - \frac{(91)^2}{16} \right] - 54.6875 - 1.5625 = 3.6875$$

$$\text{Error term} = \text{MS}_{B \times \text{subj w.groups}} = .3958$$

$$\sum_{1}^{p}\sum_{1}^{r} SS_B \text{ for } ac_{ik} = SS_B + SS_{AB} + SS_{BC} + SS_{ABC}.$$

When there are three treatments, it may be of interest to analyze the simple interactions. Formulas for computing SS_{AB} at c_k, SS_{AC} at b_j, and SS_{BC} at a_i appear in Table 8.12-5.

COMPARISONS AMONG MEANS

Comparisons among means follow the procedures described in Sections 3.2, 3.4, and 8.7. The error terms that should be substituted in the formulas in Section 8.7 are given in Table 8.12-6. For example, the t ratio and Tukey's ratio for the comparison $\hat{\psi} = \overline{AB}_{11} - \overline{AB}_{21}$ are

$$t = \frac{C_j(\overline{AB}_{11}) + C_{j'}(\overline{AB}_{21})}{\sqrt{\dfrac{2[MS_{\text{subj w.groups}} + MS_{B \times \text{subj w.groups}}(q - 1)]}{nqr}}}$$

and

$$q = \frac{C_j(\overline{AB}_{11}) + C_{j'}(\overline{AB}_{21})}{\sqrt{\dfrac{MS_{\text{subj w.groups}} + MS_{B \times \text{subj w.groups}}(q - 1)}{nqr}}}.$$

When the denominator of a ratio is composed of two pooled error terms, the critical values of t and q are approximated by $t'_{\alpha/2}$ and q'_{α}, as described in Section 8.7.

TABLE 8.12-6 Error terms for Comparisons Among Means

Comparison	Error Term (A, B, and C Fixed Effects, Subjects Random)
$\overline{A}_1 - \overline{A}_2$	$\dfrac{MS_{\text{subj w.groups}}}{nqr}$
$\overline{B}_1 - \overline{B}_2$	$\dfrac{MS_{B \times \text{subj w.groups}}}{npr}$
$\overline{C}_1 - \overline{C}_2$	$\dfrac{MS_{\text{subj w.groups}}}{npq}$
$\overline{AB}_{1j} - \overline{AB}_{2j}$	$\dfrac{MS_{\text{subj w.groups}} + MS_{B \times \text{subj w.groups}}(q - 1)}{nqr}$
$\overline{AB}_{i1} - \overline{AB}_{i2}$	$\dfrac{MS_{B \times \text{subj w.groups}}}{nr}$
$\overline{AC}_{1k} - \overline{AC}_{2k}$	$\dfrac{MS_{\text{subj w.groups}}}{nq}$
$\overline{AC}_{i1} - \overline{AC}_{i2}$	$\dfrac{MS_{\text{subj w.groups}}}{nq}$
$\overline{BC}_{1k} - \overline{BC}_{2k}$	$\dfrac{MS_{B \times \text{subj w.groups}}}{np}$

TABLE 8.12-6 (continued)

$\overline{BC}_{j1} - \overline{BC}_{j2}$	$\dfrac{\text{MS}_{\text{subj w.groups}} + \text{MS}_{B \times \text{subj w.groups}}(q-1)}{npq}$
$\overline{ABC}_{1jk} - \overline{ABC}_{2jk}$	$\dfrac{\text{MS}_{\text{subj w.groups}} + \text{MS}_{B \times \text{subj w.groups}}(q-1)}{nq}$
$\overline{ABC}_{i1k} - \overline{ABC}_{i2k}$	$\dfrac{\text{MS}_{B \times \text{subj w.groups}}}{n}$
$\overline{ABC}_{ij1} - \overline{ABC}_{ij2}$	$\dfrac{\text{MS}_{\text{subj w.groups}} + \text{MS}_{B \times \text{subj w.groups}}(q-1)}{nq}$

TABLE 8.12-7   Procedure for Determining E(MS) in Type SPF-*pr.q* Design

Source	E(MS)
A	$\sigma_\varepsilon^2 + \left(1 - \dfrac{n}{N}\right)\left(1 - \dfrac{q}{Q}\right)\sigma_{\beta\pi}^2 + n\left(1 - \dfrac{q}{Q}\right)\left(1 - \dfrac{r}{R}\right)\sigma_{\alpha\beta\gamma}^2$ $+ nr\left(1 - \dfrac{q}{Q}\right)\sigma_{\alpha\beta}^2 + q\left(1 - \dfrac{n}{N}\right)\sigma_\pi^2$ $+ nq\left(1 - \dfrac{r}{R}\right)\sigma_{\alpha\gamma}^2 + nqr\sigma_\alpha^2$
C	$\sigma_\varepsilon^2 + \left(1 - \dfrac{n}{N}\right)\left(1 - \dfrac{q}{Q}\right)\sigma_{\beta\pi}^2 + n\left(1 - \dfrac{p}{P}\right)\left(1 - \dfrac{q}{Q}\right)\sigma_{\alpha\beta\gamma}^2$ $+ np\left(1 - \dfrac{q}{Q}\right)\sigma_{\beta\gamma}^2 + q\left(1 - \dfrac{n}{N}\right)\sigma_\pi^2$ $+ nq\left(1 - \dfrac{p}{P}\right)\sigma_{\alpha\gamma}^2 + npq\sigma_\gamma^2$
AC	$\sigma_\varepsilon^2 + \left(1 - \dfrac{n}{N}\right)\left(1 - \dfrac{q}{Q}\right)\sigma_{\beta\pi}^2 + n\left(1 - \dfrac{q}{Q}\right)\sigma_{\alpha\beta\gamma}^2$ $+ q\left(1 - \dfrac{n}{N}\right)\sigma_\pi^2 + nq\sigma_{\alpha\gamma}^2$
Subj w.groups	$\sigma_\varepsilon^2 + \left(1 - \dfrac{q}{Q}\right)\sigma_{\beta\pi}^2 + q\sigma_\pi^2$
B	$\sigma_\varepsilon^2 + \left(1 - \dfrac{n}{N}\right)\sigma_{\beta\pi}^2 + n\left(1 - \dfrac{p}{P}\right)\left(1 - \dfrac{r}{R}\right)\sigma_{\alpha\beta\gamma}^2$ $+ np\left(1 - \dfrac{r}{R}\right)\sigma_{\beta\gamma}^2 + nr\left(1 - \dfrac{p}{P}\right)\sigma_{\alpha\beta}^2 + npr\sigma_\beta^2$
AB	$\sigma_\varepsilon^2 + \left(1 - \dfrac{n}{N}\right)\sigma_{\beta\pi}^2 + n\left(1 - \dfrac{r}{R}\right)\sigma_{\alpha\beta\gamma}^2 + nr\sigma_{\alpha\beta}^2$
BC	$\sigma_\varepsilon^2 + \left(1 - \dfrac{n}{N}\right)\sigma_{\beta\pi}^2 + n\left(1 - \dfrac{p}{P}\right)\sigma_{\alpha\beta\gamma}^2 + np\sigma_{\beta\gamma}^2$
ABC	$\sigma_\varepsilon^2 + \left(1 - \dfrac{n}{N}\right)\sigma_{\beta\pi}^2 + n\sigma_{\alpha\beta\gamma}^2$
$B \times$ subj w.groups	$\sigma_\varepsilon^2 + \sigma_{\beta\pi}^2$

EXPECTED VALUES OF MEAN SQUARES

The expected values of mean squares for Models I, II, and III can be obtained from Table 8.12-7. The terms $1 - (p/P)$, $1 - (q/Q)$, $1 - (r/R)$, and $1 - (n/N)$ become zero if the corresponding effects are fixed effects and one if the effects are random.

8.13 COMPUTATIONAL PROCEDURES FOR TYPE SPF-*pru.q* DESIGN

The inclusion of a fourth treatment in a type SPF-*pru.q* design presents no new computational problems. A block diagram of a type SPF-222.4 design, shown in Figure 8.13-1, has three between-block treatments (A,C,D) and one within-block treatment (B). The structural model for this design is

$$X_{ijklm} = \mu + \alpha_i + \gamma_k + \delta_l + \alpha\gamma_{ik} + \alpha\delta_{il} + \gamma\delta_{kl} + \alpha\gamma\delta_{ikl} + \pi_{m(ikl)}$$

$$+ \beta_j + \alpha\beta_{ij} + \beta\gamma_{jk} + \beta\delta_{jl} + \alpha\beta\gamma_{ijk} + \alpha\beta\delta_{ijl} + \beta\gamma\delta_{jkl} + \alpha\beta\gamma\delta_{ijkl}$$

$$+ \beta\pi_{jm(ikl)} + \varepsilon_{o(ijklm)}.$$

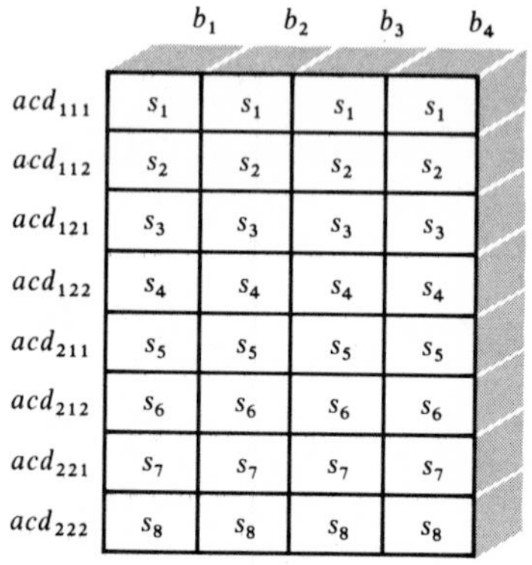

	b_1	b_2	b_3	b_4
acd_{111}	s_1	s_1	s_1	s_1
acd_{112}	s_2	s_2	s_2	s_2
acd_{121}	s_3	s_3	s_3	s_3
acd_{122}	s_4	s_4	s_4	s_4
acd_{211}	s_5	s_5	s_5	s_5
acd_{212}	s_6	s_6	s_6	s_6
acd_{221}	s_7	s_7	s_7	s_7
acd_{222}	s_8	s_8	s_8	s_8

Figure 8.13-1 Block diagram of type SPF-222.4 design.

An outline of computational procedures appears in Table 8.13-1, where the following notation is used:

$$p \text{ levels of } a_i$$

$$q \text{ levels of } b_j$$

$$r \text{ levels of } c_k$$

$$u \text{ levels of } d_l$$

$$n \text{ levels of } s_m$$

$$\sum_{1}^{N} = \sum_{1}^{p}\sum_{1}^{r}\sum_{1}^{u}\sum_{1}^{n}.$$

TABLE 8.13-1   Outline of Computational Procedures for Type SPF-*pru.q* Design

(i) Summary tables required:

AB Table	*BD* Table	*ACD* Table
AC Table	*CD* Table	*BCD* Table
AD Table	*ABC* Table	*ABCD* Table
BC Table	*ABD* Table	*ABCDS* Table

(ii) Computational symbols:

AC Table $\quad [A] = \sum_{1}^{p} \dfrac{\left(\sum_{1}^{r} A\right)^2}{nqru}$

AB Table $\quad [B] = \sum_{1}^{q} \dfrac{\left(\sum_{1}^{p} B\right)^2}{npru}$

AC Table $\quad [C] = \sum_{1}^{r} \dfrac{\left(\sum_{1}^{p} C\right)^2}{npqu}$

AD Table $\quad [D] = \sum_{1}^{u} \dfrac{\left(\sum_{1}^{p} D\right)^2}{npqr}$

AB Table $\quad [AB] = \sum_{1}^{p}\sum_{1}^{q} \dfrac{(AB)^2}{nru}$

AC Table $\quad [AC] = \sum_{1}^{p}\sum_{1}^{r} \dfrac{(AC)^2}{nqu}$

AD Table $\quad [AD] = \sum_{1}^{p}\sum_{1}^{u} \dfrac{(AD)^2}{nqr}$

BC Table $\quad [BC] = \sum_{1}^{q}\sum_{1}^{r} \dfrac{(BC)^2}{npu}$

BD Table $\quad [BD] = \sum_{1}^{q}\sum_{1}^{u} \dfrac{(BD)^2}{npr}$

CD Table $\quad [CD] = \sum_{1}^{r}\sum_{1}^{u} \dfrac{(CD)^2}{npq}$

ABC Table $\quad [ABC] = \sum_{1}^{p}\sum_{1}^{q}\sum_{1}^{r} \dfrac{(ABC)^2}{nu}$

ABD Table $\quad [ABD] = \sum_{1}^{p}\sum_{1}^{q}\sum_{1}^{u} \dfrac{(ABD)^2}{nr}$

ACD Table $\quad [ACD] = \sum_{1}^{p}\sum_{1}^{r}\sum_{1}^{u} \dfrac{(ACD)^2}{nq}$

BCD Table $\quad [BCD] = \sum_{1}^{q}\sum_{1}^{r}\sum_{1}^{u} \dfrac{(BCD)^2}{np}$

ABCD Table $\quad [ABCD] = \sum_{1}^{p}\sum_{1}^{q}\sum_{1}^{r}\sum_{1}^{u} \dfrac{(ABCD)^2}{n}$

ABCDS Table $\quad [ACDS] = \sum_{1}^{p}\sum_{1}^{r}\sum_{1}^{u}\sum_{1}^{n} \dfrac{\left(\sum_{1}^{q} ACDS\right)^2}{q}$

ABCDS Table $\quad [ABCDS] = \sum_{1}^{p}\sum_{1}^{q}\sum_{1}^{r}\sum_{1}^{u}\sum_{1}^{n}(ABCDS)^2$

ABCDS Table $[X] = \dfrac{\left(\sum_{1}^{p}\sum_{1}^{q}\sum_{1}^{r}\sum_{1}^{u}\sum_{1}^{n} ABCDS\right)^2}{npqru}$

TABLE 8.13-1 (continued)

(iii) Computational formulas:

$$SS_{total} = [ABCDS] - [X]$$

$$SS_{between\ subj} = [ACDS] - [X]$$

$$SS_A = [A] - [X]$$

$$SS_C = [C] - [X]$$

$$SS_D = [D] - [X]$$

$$SS_{AC} = [AC] - [A] - [C] + [X]$$

$$SS_{AD} = [AD] - [A] - [D] + [X]$$

$$SS_{CD} = [CD] - [C] - [D] + [X]$$

$$SS_{ACD} = [ACD] - [AC] - [AD] - [CD] + [A] + [C] + [D] - [X]$$

$$SS_{subj\ w.groups} = [ACDS] - [ACD]$$

$$SS_{within\ subj} = [ABCDS] - [ACDS]$$

$$SS_B = [B] - [X]$$

$$SS_{AB} = [AB] - [A] - [B] + [X]$$

$$SS_{BC} = [BC] - [B] - [C] + [X]$$

$$SS_{BD} = [BD] - [B] - [D] + [X]$$

$$SS_{ABC} = [ABC] - [AB] - [AC] - [BC] + [A] + [B] + [C] - [X]$$

$$SS_{ABD} = [ABD] - [AB] - [AD] - [BD] + [A] + [B] + [D] - [X]$$

$$SS_{BCD} = [BCD] - [BC] - [BD] - [CD] + [B] + [C] + [D] - [X]$$

$$SS_{ABCD} = [ABCD] - [ABC] - [ABD] - [ACD] - [BCD] + [AB] + [AC]$$
$$+ [AD] + [BC] + [BD] + [CD] - [A] - [B] - [C] - [D] + [X]$$

$$SS_{B \times subj\ w.groups} = [ABCDS] - [ABCD] - [ACDS] + [ACD]$$

PATTERN UNDERLYING
COMPUTATIONAL FORMULAS

The pattern underlying the computational formulas should be evident to the reader. The general pattern is described in Section 7.13. Procedures for checking the accuracy of the formulas are presented in Section 8.3. A three-factor interaction involving treatments A, B, and C has the following form:

$$SS_{ABC} = [ABC] - [AB] - [AC] - [BC] + [A] + [B] + [C] - [X].$$

The ABC term is followed by all two-factor terms involving the letters A, B, and C. A minus sign is given to these two-factor terms, that is, $-[AB]$, $-[AC]$, and $-[BC]$. The two-factor terms are followed by the main-effects terms $[A]$, $[B]$, and $[C]$, each of which is given a plus sign. The final term is always $[X]$. Note that the sign changes for each group of terms. Perhaps less obvious to the reader is the pattern which underlies the computational formulas for $SS_{\text{subj w.groups}}$ and $SS_{B \times \text{subj w.groups}}$. These two formulas are shown for designs having one, two, three, and four between-block treatments. The pattern is then apparent.

	$SS_{\text{subj w.groups}}$	$SS_{B \times \text{subj w.groups}}$
type SPF-*p.q* design	$[AS] - [A]$	$[ABS] - [AB] - [AS] + [A]$
type SPF-*pr.q* design	$[ACS] - [AC]$	$[ABCS] - [ABC] - [ACS] + [AC]$
type SPF-*pru.q* design	$[ACDS] - [ACD]$	$[ABCDS] - [ABCD] - [ACDS] + [ACD]$

Obviously, for a five-treatment design, the formulas would have the form

$$SS_{\text{subj w.groups}} = [ACDES] - [ACDE]$$

and

$$SS_{B \times \text{subj w.groups}} = [ABCDES] - [ABCDE] - [ACDES] + [ACDE].$$

MODIFICATION OF COMPUTATIONAL FORMULAS FOR UNWEIGHTED-MEANS ANALYSIS

The formulas in Table 8.13-1 can be easily modified for an un-weighted-means analysis. This type of analysis is required if the number of subjects in the levels of A or C or D is not equal. Formulas for $SS_{\text{subj w.groups}}$ and $SS_{B \times \text{subj w.groups}}$ are not changed. All main effects and interaction formulas are computed from summary tables that have means instead of sums of scores in the cells. For example,

$$SS_A = \tilde{n}([\overline{A}] - [\overline{X}])$$
$$SS_{AC} = \tilde{n}([\overline{AC}] - [\overline{A}] - [\overline{C}] + [\overline{X}]).$$

An example of an unweighted-means analysis for a type SPF-*p.q* design is given in Section 8.10.

ANALYSIS OF VARIANCE TABLE FOR TYPE SPF-*pru.q* DESIGN

Table 8.13-2 presents an analysis of variance table for the type SPF-222.4 design; the degrees of freedom for a regular analysis and an unweighted-means analysis are included.

TABLE 8.13-2   Analysis of Variance Table for
Type SPF-*pru.q* Design

Source	Regular df	Unweighted-means df	F (A, B, C, and D Fixed Effects, Subjects Random)
1 Between subjects	$npru - 1$	$N - 1$	
2 A	$p - 1$	$p - 1$	$[\frac{2}{9}]$
3 C	$r - 1$	$r - 1$	$[\frac{3}{9}]$
4 D	$u - 1$	$u - 1$	$[\frac{4}{9}]$
5 AC	$(p - 1)(r - 1)$	$(p - 1)(r - 1)$	$[\frac{5}{9}]$
6 AD	$(p - 1)(u - 1)$	$(p - 1)(u - 1)$	$[\frac{6}{9}]$
7 CD	$(r - 1)(u - 1)$	$(r - 1)(u - 1)$	$[\frac{7}{9}]$
8 ACD	$(p - 1)(r - 1)(u - 1)$	$(p - 1)(r - 1)(u - 1)$	$[\frac{8}{9}]$
9 Subj w.groups	$pru(n - 1)$	$N - pru$	
10 Within subjects	$npru(q - 1)$	$N(q - 1)$	
11 B	$q - 1$	$q - 1$	$[\frac{11}{19}]$
12 AB	$(p - 1)(q - 1)$	$(p - 1)(q - 1)$	$[\frac{12}{19}]$
13 BC	$(q - 1)(r - 1)$	$(q - 1)(r - 1)$	$[\frac{13}{19}]$
14 BD	$(q - 1)(u - 1)$	$(q - 1)(u - 1)$	$[\frac{14}{19}]$
15 ABC	$(p - 1)(q - 1)(r - 1)$	$(p - 1)(q - 1)(r - 1)$	$[\frac{15}{19}]$
16 ABD	$(p - 1)(q - 1)(u - 1)$	$(p - 1)(q - 1)(u - 1)$	$[\frac{16}{19}]$
17 BCD	$(q - 1)(r - 1)(u - 1)$	$(q - 1)(r - 1)(u - 1)$	$[\frac{17}{19}]$
18 $ABCD$	$(p - 1)(q - 1)(r - 1)(u - 1)$	$(p - 1)(q - 1)(r - 1)(u - 1)$	$[\frac{18}{19}]$
19 $B \times$ subj w.groups	$pru(n - 1)(q - 1)$	$(N - pru)(q - 1)$	
20 Total	$npqru - 1$	$Nq - 1$	

8.14   COMPUTATIONAL PROCEDURES FOR TYPE SPF-*p.qr* DESIGN

A split-plot design can be used in research situations requiring repeated measures on two or more treatments. One variation of this design, called a type SPF-*p.qr* design, is described here. This design has one between-block treatment (A) and two within-block treatments (B, C). The design requires np samples of subjects who are randomly assigned to treatment A, with n subjects (blocks) in each level. The sequence of administration of the BC treatment combinations within an np block is randomized independently for each subject. An alternative to using repeated measures on each subject is to randomly assign the *BC* treatment combinations to *qr* matched subjects within each block. This latter design requires a total of *npqr* subjects.

These three-treatment designs are similar to split-split-plot designs used in agricultural research. The essential difference is that, in a split-split-plot design, levels of treatment *A* are assigned to plots (plots correspond to blocks of subjects in behavioral research). These plots are then subdivided for the levels of treatment *B* and subdivided again for the levels of treatment *C*. The levels of treatment *B* are randomly assigned to split-plots and levels of *C* are randomly assigned to split-split-plots. This randomization procedure can be contrasted with that used for a type SPF-*p.qr* design, where the *BC* treatment combinations are randomly assigned within each block. The two randomization procedures lead to different error terms for testing treatment *C* and all interactions involving *C*.

Figure 8.14-1 shows a block diagram of a type SPF-2.22 design. The structural model for this design is

$$X_{ijkm} = \mu + \alpha_i + \pi_{m(i)} + \beta_j + \gamma_k + \alpha\beta_{ij} + \alpha\gamma_{ik} + \beta\gamma_{jk} + \alpha\beta\gamma_{ijk}$$

$$+ \beta\pi_{jm(i)} + \gamma\pi_{km(i)} + \beta\gamma\pi_{jkm(i)} + \varepsilon_{o(ijkm)}.$$

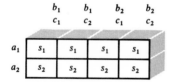

Figure 8.14-1   Block diagram of type SPF-2.22 design.

Because the analysis of this design poses computational problems not previously discussed, a numerical example is given in Table 8.14-1, where the following notation is used:

$$p \text{ levels of } a_i = 2$$

$$q \text{ levels of } b_j \doteq 2$$

$$r \text{ levels of } c_k = 2$$

$$n \text{ levels of } s_m = 4$$

$$\sum_1^N = \sum_1^p \sum_1^n.$$

The analysis is summarized in Table 8.14-2.

TABLE 8.14-1   Computational Procedures for Type SPF-2.22 Design

(i) Data:

ABCS Summary Table

		b_1	b_1	b_2	b_2	$\sum_1^q \sum_1^r AS$	$\dfrac{\left(\sum_1^q \sum_1^r AS\right)^2}{qr}$
		c_1	c_2	c_1	c_2		
a_1	s_1	3	4	7	7	21	110.25
	s_2	6	5	8	8	27	182.25
	s_3	3	4	7	9	23	132.25
	s_4	3	3	6	8	20	100.00
a_2	s_5	1	2	5	10	18	81.00
	s_6	2	3	6	10	21	110.25
	s_7	2	4	5	9	20	100.00
	s_8	2	3	6	11	22	121.00

ABC Summary Table

	b_1 c_1	b_1 c_2	b_2 c_1	b_2 c_2
	$n = 4$			
a_1	15	16	28	32
a_2	7	12	22	40

AB Summary Table

	b_1	b_2	$\sum_1^q A$	$\dfrac{\left(\sum_1^q A\right)^2}{nqr}$
	$nr = 8$			
a_1	31	60	91	517.5625
a_2	19	62	81	410.0625

$$\sum_1^p B = \quad 50 \quad 122$$

$$\dfrac{\left(\sum_1^p B\right)^2}{npr} = 156.25 \ 930.25$$

AC Summary Table

	c_1	c_2
	$nq = 8$	
a_1	43	48
a_2	29	52

$$\sum_1^p C = \quad 72 \quad 100$$

$$\dfrac{\left(\sum_1^p C\right)^2}{npq} = 324 \quad 625$$

BC Summary Table

	c_1	c_2
	$np = 8$	
b_1	22	28
b_2	50	72

ABS Summary Table

		b_1	b_2
		$r = 2$	
a_1	s_1	7	14
	s_2	11	16
	s_3	7	16
	s_4	6	14
a_2	s_5	3	15
	s_6	5	16
	s_7	6	14
	s_8	5	17

ACS Summary Table

		c_1	c_2
		$q = 2$	
a_1	s_1	10	11
	s_2	14	13
	s_3	10	13
	s_4	9	11
a_2	s_5	6	12
	s_6	8	13
	s_7	7	13
	s_8	8	14

TABLE 8.14-1 (continued)

(ii) Computational symbols:

$$\sum_1^q \sum_1^r \sum_1^N ABCS = 3 + 6 + 3 + \cdots + 11 = 172.000$$

$$\sum_1^q \sum_1^r \sum_1^N (ABCS)^2 = [ABCS] = (3)^2 + (6)^2 + \cdots + (11)^2 = 1160.000$$

$$\frac{\left(\sum_1^q \sum_1^r \sum_1^N ABCS\right)^2}{qrN} = [X] = \frac{(172)^2}{(2)(2)(8)} = 924.500$$

$$\sum_1^N \frac{\left(\sum_1^q \sum_1^r AS\right)^2}{qr} = [AS] = 110.25 + 182.25 + \cdots + 121.00 = 937.000$$

$$\sum_1^p \frac{\left(\sum_1^q A\right)^2}{nqr} = [A] = 517.5625 + 410.0625 = 927.625$$

$$\sum_1^q \frac{\left(\sum_1^p B\right)^2}{npr} = [B] = 156.25 + 930.25 = 1086.500$$

$$\sum_1^p \sum_1^q \frac{(AB)^2}{nr} = [AB] = \frac{(31)^2}{8} + \frac{(60)^2}{8} + \cdots + \frac{(62)^2}{8} = 1095.750$$

$$\sum_1^p \sum_1^q \sum_1^n \frac{(ABS)^2}{r} = [ABS] = \frac{(7)^2}{2} + \frac{(14)^2}{2} + \cdots + \frac{(17)^2}{2} = 1110.000$$

$$\sum_1^r \frac{\left(\sum_1^p C\right)^2}{npq} = [C] = 324 + 625 = 949.000$$

$$\sum_1^p \sum_1^r \frac{(AC)^2}{nq} = [AC] = \frac{(43)^2}{8} + \frac{(48)^2}{8} + \cdots + \frac{(52)^2}{8} = 962.250$$

$$\sum_1^p \sum_1^r \sum_1^n \frac{(ACS)^2}{q} = [ACS] = \frac{(10)^2}{2} + \frac{(11)^2}{2} + \cdots + \frac{(14)^2}{2} = 974.000$$

$$\sum_1^q \sum_1^r \frac{(BC)^2}{np} = [BC] = \frac{(22)^2}{8} + \frac{(28)^2}{8} + \cdots + \frac{(72)^2}{8} = 1119.000$$

$$\sum_1^p \sum_1^q \sum_1^r \frac{(ABC)^2}{n} = [ABC] = \frac{(15)^2}{4} + \frac{(16)^2}{4} + \cdots + \frac{(40)^2}{4} = 1141.500$$

(iii) Computational formulas:

$$SS_{total} = [ABCS] - [X] = 235.500$$
$$SS_{between\ subj} = [AS] - [X] = 12.500$$
$$SS_A = [A] - [X] = 3.125$$
$$SS_{subj\ w.groups} = [AS] - [A] = 9.375$$
$$SS_{within\ subj} = [ABCS] - [AS] = 223.000$$
$$SS_B = [B] - [X] = 162.000$$
$$SS_{AB} = [AB] - [A] - [B] + [X] = 6.125$$
$$SS_{B \times subj\ w.groups} = [ABS] - [AB] - [AS] + [A] = 4.875$$

TABLE 8.14-1 (continued)

$$SS_C = [C] - [X] = 24.500$$
$$SS_{AC} = [AC] - [A] - [C] + [X] = 10.125$$
$$SS_{C \times \text{subj w.groups}} = [ACS] - [AC] - [AS] + [A] = 2.375$$
$$SS_{BC} = [BC] - [B] - [C] + [X] = 8.000$$
$$SS_{ABC} = [ABC] - [AB] - [AC] - [BC] + [A] + [B] + [C] - [X] = 3.125$$
$$SS_{BC \times \text{subj w.groups}} = [ABCS] - [ABC] - [ABS] - [ACS] + [AB] + [AC] + [AS]$$
$$- [A] = 1.875$$

TABLE 8.14-2   Analysis of Variance Table

	Source	SS	df
1	Between subjects	12.500	$np - 1 = 7$
2	A	3.125	$p - 1 = 1$
3	Subj w.groups	9.375	$p(n - 1) = 6$
4	Within subjects	223.000	$np(qr - 1) = 24$
5	B	162.000	$q - 1 = 1$
6	AB	6.125	$(p - 1)(q - 1) = 1$
7	$B \times$ subj w.groups	4.875	$p(n - 1)(q - 1) = 6$
8	C	24.500	$r - 1 = 1$
9	AC	10.125	$(p - 1)(r - 1) = 1$
10	$C \times$ subj w.groups	2.375	$p(n - 1)(r - 1) = 6$
11	BC	8.000	$(q - 1)(r - 1) = 1$
12	ABC	3.125	$(p - 1)(q - 1)(r - 1) = 1$
13	$BC \times$ subj w.groups	1.875	$p(n - 1)(q - 1)(r - 1) = 6$
14	Total	235.500	$npqr - 1 = 31$

*$p < .05$.

**$p < .01$.

TESTS FOR HOMOGENEITY OF ERROR TERMS

Four sets of error terms in a type SPF-2.22 design can be tested for homogeneity. The variances estimated by $MS_{\text{subj w.group } a_i}$ at p levels of A should be homogeneous. Similarly, the variances estimated by $MS_{B \times \text{subj w.group } a_i}$ at p levels of A should be homogeneous, and the same is true for $MS_{C \times \text{subj w.group } a_i}$ and $MS_{BC \times \text{subj w.group } a_i}$. Computational procedures for computing the required mean squares at level a_1 appear in Table 8.14-3. The formulas at level a_2 follow the same pattern as those at level a_1. An $F_{\max}$ ratio for these partitioned error terms has the form

$$F_{\max} = \left[\frac{\text{largest MS}}{\text{smallest MS}}\right]\text{with } v_1 \text{ and } v_2 \text{ degrees of freedom.}$$

Six variance-covariance matrices are associated with a type SPF-2.22 design—$q \times q$ at a_1, $q \times q$ at a_2, $r \times r$ at a_1, $r \times r$ at a_2, $qr \times qr$ at a_1, and $qr \times qr$ at a_2. In order for each of the within-subjects F ratios to be distributed as the F distribution, all variances for a particular population dispersion matrix should be equal to σ^2 and all covariances equal to $\rho\sigma^2$ Section 8.5 described procedures for determining the tenability of the hypotheses that, for example, (1) the $q \times q$ population matrix at level a_1 is equal to the $q \times q$ matrix at a_2 and (2) the pooled dispersion matrix

MS	F	E(MS) A, B, and C Fixed Effects, Subjects Random
3.125	$[\frac{2}{3}] =$ 2.00	$\sigma_\varepsilon^2 + qr\sigma_\pi^2 + nqr\sigma_\alpha^2$
1.562		$\sigma_\varepsilon^2 + qr\sigma_\pi^2$
162.000	$[\frac{5}{7}] =$ 199.51**	$\sigma_\varepsilon^2 + r\sigma_{\beta\pi}^2 + npr\sigma_\beta^2$
6.125	$[\frac{6}{7}] =$ 7.54*	$\sigma_\varepsilon^2 + r\sigma_{\beta\pi}^2 + nr\sigma_{\alpha\beta}^2$
.812		$\sigma_\varepsilon^2 + r\sigma_{\beta\pi}^2$
24.500	$[\frac{8}{10}] =$ 61.87**	$\sigma_\varepsilon^2 + q\sigma_{\gamma\pi}^2 + npq\sigma_\gamma^2$
10.125	$[\frac{9}{10}] =$ 25.57**	$\sigma_\varepsilon^2 + q\sigma_{\gamma\pi}^2 + nq\sigma_{\alpha\gamma}^2$
.396		$\sigma_\varepsilon^2 + q\sigma_{\gamma\pi}^2$
8.000	$[\frac{11}{13}] =$ 25.64**	$\sigma_\varepsilon^2 + \sigma_{\beta\gamma\pi}^2 + np\sigma_{\beta\gamma}^2$
3.125	$[\frac{12}{13}] =$ 10.02*	$\sigma_\varepsilon^2 + \sigma_{\beta\gamma\pi}^2 + n\sigma_{\alpha\beta\gamma}^2$
.312		$\sigma_\varepsilon^2 + \sigma_{\beta\gamma\pi}^2$

for the two levels of A has the symmetry described above. Identical tests can be performed for the $r \times r$ dispersion matrices and $qr \times qr$ dispersion matrices. If the assumptions of equality and symmetry of the variance-covariance matrices are not tenable, conservative F tests as presented in Table 8.14-4 can be computed. It will be recalled from Section 8.5 that a conservative F test is computed in the usual way but that the F table is entered with modified degrees of freedom.

TESTS OF SIMPLE EFFECTS

It is apparent from Table 8.14-2 that treatments B and C, as well as the AB, AC, BC, and ABC interactions, are significant. Because the triple

TABLE 8.14-3   Partitioning of Error Terms for Tests of Homogeneity

$$SS_{\text{subj w.group } a_1} = \sum_1^n \frac{\left(\sum_1^q \sum_1^r AS_{1jkm}\right)^2}{qr} - \frac{\left(\sum_1^q A_{1j}\right)^2}{nqr}$$

$$df = n - 1$$

$$SS_{B \times \text{subj w.group } a_1} = \sum_1^q \sum_1^n \frac{(ABS_{1jm})^2}{r} - \sum_1^q \frac{(AB_{1j})^2}{nr} - \sum_1^n \frac{\left(\sum_1^q \sum_1^r AS_{1jkm}\right)^2}{qr} + \frac{\left(\sum_1^q A_{1j}\right)^2}{nqr}$$

$$df = (n - 1)(q - 1)$$

$$SS_{C \times \text{subj w.group } a_1} = \sum_1^r \sum_1^n \frac{(ACS_{1km})^2}{q} - \sum_1^r \frac{(AC_{1k})^2}{nq} - \sum_1^n \frac{\left(\sum_1^q \sum_1^r AS_{1jkm}\right)^2}{qr} + \frac{\left(\sum_1^q A_{1j}\right)^2}{nqr}$$

$$df = (n - 1)(r - 1)$$

$$SS_{BC \times \text{subj w.group } a_1} = \sum_1^q \sum_1^r \sum_1^n ABCS_{1jkm}^2 - \sum_1^q \sum_1^r \frac{(ABC_{1jk})^2}{n} - \sum_1^q \sum_1^n \frac{(ABS_{1jm})^2}{r} - \sum_1^r \sum_1^n \frac{(ACS_{1km})^2}{q}$$

$$+ \sum_1^q \frac{(AB_{1j})^2}{nr} + \sum_1^r \frac{(AC_{1k})^2}{nq} + \sum_1^n \frac{\left(\sum_1^q \sum_1^r AS_{1jkm}\right)^2}{qr} - \frac{\left(\sum_1^q A_{1j}\right)^2}{nqr}$$

$$df = (n - 1)(q - 1)(r - 1)$$

TABLE 8.14-4   Conservative F Ratio Degrees of Freedom

Numerator of F ratio	df
MS_B	$1, p(n - 1)$
MS_{AB}	$(p - 1), p(n - 1)$
MS_C	$1, p(n - 1)$
MS_{AC}	$p - 1, p(n - 1)$
MS_{BC}	$1, p(n - 1)$
MS_{ABC}	$p - 1, p(n - 1)$

interaction is significant, the experimenter might want to test the significance of simple-simple main effects and simple interaction effects. These tests are outlined in Table 8.14-5. The formulas are given for the first level of each treatment only. The formulas at other levels of the treatments follow the pattern given for the first level. The error terms appearing in Table 8.14-5 for each test are appropriate for a mixed model.

The rationale underlying the selection of a denominator for F ratios is presented in Section 8.6. The reader should be certain that he understands the principles on which the determination of the correct error terms is based. The terms given in the table are only correct for the mixed model in which A, B, and C are fixed effects and subjects are random effects. No difficulty should be encountered in determining the error term for other models if one remembers that

TABLE 8.14-5   Formulas for Testing Simple Effects

(i) *AB* interaction significant: *Error Term (A, B, and C Fixed Effects, Subjects Random)*

$$SS_A \text{ at } b_1 = \sum_1^p \frac{(AB_{i1})^2}{nr} - \frac{\left(\sum_1^p B_{i1}\right)^2}{npr}$$

$$\frac{MS_{\text{subj w.groups}} + MS_{B \times \text{subj w.groups}}(q-1)}{q}$$

$$SS_B \text{ at } a_1 = \sum_1^q \frac{(AB_{1j})^2}{nr} - \frac{\left(\sum_1^q A_{1j}\right)^2}{nqr}$$

$$MS_{B \times \text{subj w.groups}}$$

(ii) *AC* interaction significant:

$$SS_A \text{ at } c_1 = \sum_1^p \frac{(AC_{i1})^2}{nq} - \frac{\left(\sum_1^p C_{i1}\right)^2}{npq}$$

$$\frac{MS_{\text{subj w.groups}} + MS_{C \times \text{subj w.groups}}(r-1)}{r}$$

$$SS_C \text{ at } a_1 = \sum_1^r \frac{(AC_{1k})^2}{nq} - \frac{\left(\sum_1^r A_{1k}\right)^2}{nqr}$$

$$MS_{C \times \text{subj w.groups}}$$

(iii) *BC* interaction significant:

$$SS_B \text{ at } c_1 = \sum_1^q \frac{(BC_{j1})^2}{np} - \frac{\left(\sum_1^q C_{j1}\right)^2}{npq}$$

$$\frac{MS_{B \times \text{subj w.groups}} + MS_{BC \times \text{subj w.groups}}(r-1)}{r}$$

$$SS_C \text{ at } b_1 = \sum_1^r \frac{(BC_{1k})^2}{np} - \frac{\left(\sum_1^r B_{1k}\right)^2}{npr}$$

$$\frac{MS_{C \times \text{subj w.groups}} + MS_{BC \times \text{subj w.groups}}(q-1)}{q}$$

(iv) *ABC* interaction significant:

$$SS_A \text{ at } bc_{11} = \sum_1^p \frac{(ABC_{i11})^2}{n} - \frac{(BC_{11})^2}{np}$$

$$MS_{\text{w.cell}}$$

$$SS_B \text{ at } ac_{11} = \sum_1^q \frac{(ABC_{1j1})^2}{n} - \frac{(AC_{11})^2}{nq}$$

$$\frac{MS_{B \times \text{subj w.groups}} + MS_{BC \times \text{subj w.groups}}(r-1)}{r}$$

$$SS_C \text{ at } ab_{11} = \sum_1^r \frac{(ABC_{11k})^2}{n} - \frac{(AB_{11})^2}{nr}$$

$$\frac{MS_{C \times \text{subj w.groups}} + MS_{BC \times \text{subj w.groups}}(q-1)}{q}$$

$$SS_{AB} \text{ at } c_1 = \left[\sum_1^p\sum_1^q \frac{(ABC_{ij1})^2}{n} - \frac{\left(\sum_1^p C_{i1}\right)^2}{npq}\right]$$
$$- SS_A \text{ at } c_1 - SS_B \text{ at } c_1$$

$$\frac{MS_{B \times \text{subj w.groups}} + MS_{BC \times \text{subj w.groups}}(r-1)}{r}$$

$$SS_{AC} \text{ at } b_1 = \left[\sum_1^p\sum_1^r \frac{(ABC_{i1k})^2}{n} - \frac{\left(\sum_1^p B_{i1}\right)^2}{npr}\right]$$
$$- SS_A \text{ at } b_1 - SS_C \text{ at } b_1$$

$$\frac{MS_{C \times \text{subj w.groups}} + MS_{BC \times \text{subj w.groups}}(q-1)}{q}$$

$$SS_{BC} \text{ at } a_1 = \left[\sum_1^q\sum_1^r \frac{(ABC_{1jk})^2}{n} - \frac{\left(\sum_1^q A_{1j}\right)^2}{nqr}\right]$$
$$- SS_B \text{ at } a_1 - SS_C \text{ at } a_1$$

$$MS_{BC \times \text{subj w.groups}}$$

$$\sum_1^q \text{SS}_A \text{ for } b_j = \text{SS}_A + \text{SS}_{AB}$$

$$\sum_1^q \sum_1^r \text{SS}_A \text{ for } bc_{jk} = \text{SS}_A + \text{SS}_{AB} + \text{SS}_{AC} + \text{SS}_{ABC}$$

$$\sum_1^r \text{SS}_{AB} \text{ for } c_k = \text{SS}_{AB} + \text{SS}_{ABC}.$$

One can see that whenever the main effects have different error terms, these error terms are pooled in testing the simple main effects. The error terms in Table 8.14-5 are given as weighted pooled mean squares divided by their pooled degrees of freedom. For example, the error term for testing SS_A at b_1 can be computed by either of the following formulas:

$$\frac{\text{MS}_{\text{subj w.groups}} + \text{MS}_{B \times \text{subj w.groups}}(q - 1)}{q} = \frac{1.562 + .812(1)}{2} = 1.187$$

$$\frac{\text{SS}_{\text{subj w.groups}} + \text{SS}_{B \times \text{subj w.groups}}}{p(n - 1) + p(n - 1)(q - 1)} = \frac{9.375 + 4.875}{2(3) + 2(3)(1)} = 1.188.$$

The two answers agree within rounding error.

COMPARISONS AMONG MEANS

Tests of differences among means follow the procedures described in Section 8.7. For example, the error term for Tukey's ratio for the comparison $\hat{\psi} = \bar{A}_1 - \bar{A}_2$ is

$$\sqrt{\frac{\text{MS}_{\text{subj w.groups}}}{nqr}}.$$

The divisor, nqr, is the sample size for $\bar{A}_i$. The comparison $\hat{\psi} = \overline{AB}_{11} - \overline{AB}_{21}$ has as its error term

$$\sqrt{\frac{\text{MS}_{\text{subj w.groups}} + \text{MS}_{B \times \text{subj w.groups}}(q - 1)}{nr(q)}}.$$

The term $[\text{MS}_{\text{subj w.groups}} + \text{MS}_{B \times \text{subj w.groups}}(q - 1)]/q$ is the F ratio denominator for testing MS_A at b_j. The term $nr = 8$ is the number of scores in each cell of the AB Summary Table.

EXPECTED VALUES OF MEAN SQUARES

The expected values of mean squares for Models I, II, and III can be determined from Table 8.14-6. The terms $1 - p/P$, $1 - q/Q$, $1 - r/R$, and $1 - n/N$ become zero if the corresponding effects are fixed and one if the effects are random.

TABLE 8.14-6　Table for Determining E(MS) for Type SPF-*p.qr* Design

Source	E(MS)
A	$\sigma_\varepsilon^2 + \left(1 - \dfrac{n}{N}\right)\left(1 - \dfrac{q}{Q}\right)\left(1 - \dfrac{r}{R}\right)\sigma_{\beta\gamma\pi}^2 + n\left(1 - \dfrac{q}{Q}\right)\left(1 - \dfrac{r}{R}\right)\sigma_{\alpha\beta\gamma}^2$ $+ q\left(1 - \dfrac{n}{N}\right)\left(1 - \dfrac{r}{R}\right)\sigma_{\gamma\pi}^2 + nq\left(1 - \dfrac{r}{R}\right)\sigma_{\alpha\gamma}^2$ $+ r\left(1 - \dfrac{n}{N}\right)\left(1 - \dfrac{q}{Q}\right)\sigma_{\beta\pi}^2 + nr\left(1 - \dfrac{q}{Q}\right)\sigma_{\alpha\beta}^2$ $+ qr\left(1 - \dfrac{n}{N}\right)\sigma_\pi^2 + nqr\sigma_\alpha^2$
Subj w.groups	$\sigma_\varepsilon^2 + \left(1 - \dfrac{q}{Q}\right)\left(1 - \dfrac{r}{R}\right)\sigma_{\beta\gamma\pi}^2 + q\left(1 - \dfrac{r}{R}\right)\sigma_{\gamma\pi}^2$ $+ r\left(1 - \dfrac{q}{Q}\right)\sigma_{\beta\pi}^2 + qr\sigma_\pi^2$
B	$\sigma_\varepsilon^2 + \left(1 - \dfrac{n}{N}\right)\left(1 - \dfrac{r}{R}\right)\sigma_{\beta\gamma\pi}^2 + n\left(1 - \dfrac{p}{P}\right)\left(1 - \dfrac{r}{R}\right)\sigma_{\alpha\beta\gamma}^2$ $+ np\left(1 - \dfrac{r}{R}\right)\sigma_{\beta\gamma}^2 + r\left(1 - \dfrac{n}{N}\right)\sigma_{\beta\pi}^2 + nr\left(1 - \dfrac{p}{P}\right)\sigma_{\alpha\beta}^2 + npr\sigma_\beta^2$
AB	$\sigma_\varepsilon^2 + \left(1 - \dfrac{n}{N}\right)\left(1 - \dfrac{r}{R}\right)\sigma_{\beta\gamma\pi}^2 + n\left(1 - \dfrac{r}{R}\right)\sigma_{\alpha\beta\gamma}^2 + r\left(1 - \dfrac{n}{N}\right)\sigma_{\beta\pi}^2$ $+ nr\sigma_{\alpha\beta}^2$
$B \times$ subj w.groups	$\sigma_\varepsilon^2 + \left(1 - \dfrac{r}{R}\right)\sigma_{\beta\gamma\pi}^2 + r\sigma_{\beta\pi}^2$
C	$\sigma_\varepsilon^2 + \left(1 - \dfrac{n}{N}\right)\left(1 - \dfrac{q}{Q}\right)\sigma_{\beta\gamma\pi}^2 + n\left(1 - \dfrac{p}{P}\right)\left(1 - \dfrac{q}{Q}\right)\sigma_{\alpha\beta\gamma}^2$ $+ np\left(1 - \dfrac{q}{Q}\right)\sigma_{\beta\gamma}^2 + q\left(1 - \dfrac{n}{N}\right)\sigma_{\gamma\pi}^2 + nq\left(1 - \dfrac{p}{P}\right)\sigma_{\alpha\gamma}^2 + npq\sigma_\gamma^2$
AC	$\sigma_\varepsilon^2 + \left(1 - \dfrac{n}{N}\right)\left(1 - \dfrac{q}{Q}\right)\sigma_{\beta\gamma\pi}^2 + n\left(1 - \dfrac{q}{Q}\right)\sigma_{\alpha\beta\gamma}^2 + q\left(1 - \dfrac{n}{N}\right)\sigma_{\gamma\pi}^2$ $+ nq\sigma_{\alpha\gamma}^2$
$C \times$ subj w.groups	$\sigma_\varepsilon^2 + \left(1 - \dfrac{q}{Q}\right)\sigma_{\beta\gamma\pi}^2 + q\sigma_{\gamma\pi}^2$
BC	$\sigma_\varepsilon^2 + \left(1 - \dfrac{n}{N}\right)\sigma_{\beta\gamma\pi}^2 + n\left(1 - \dfrac{p}{P}\right)\sigma_{\alpha\beta\gamma}^2 + np\sigma_{\beta\gamma}^2$
ABC	$\sigma_\varepsilon^2 + \left(1 - \dfrac{n}{N}\right)\sigma_{\beta\gamma\pi}^2 + n\sigma_{\alpha\beta\gamma}^2$
$BC \times$ subj w.groups	$\sigma_\varepsilon^2 + \sigma_{\beta\gamma\pi}^2$

8.15   COMPUTATIONAL PROCEDURES
FOR TYPE SPF-*p.qru* DESIGN

Figure 8.15-1 shows a block diagram of a type SPF-2.222 design. The structural model for the design is

$$X_{ijklm} = \mu + \alpha_i + \pi_{m(i)} + \beta_j + \alpha\beta_{ij} + \beta\pi_{jm(i)} + \gamma_k + \alpha\gamma_{ik} + \gamma\pi_{km(i)}$$
$$+ \delta_l + \alpha\delta_{il} + \delta\pi_{lm(i)} + \beta\gamma_{jk} + \alpha\beta\gamma_{ijk} + \beta\gamma\pi_{jkm(i)} + \beta\delta_{jl} + \alpha\beta\delta_{ijl}$$
$$+ \beta\delta\pi_{jlm(i)} + \gamma\delta_{kl} + \alpha\gamma\delta_{ikl} + \gamma\delta\pi_{klm(i)} + \beta\gamma\delta_{jkl} + \alpha\beta\gamma\delta_{ijkl}$$
$$+ \beta\gamma\delta\pi_{jklm(i)} + \varepsilon_{o(ijklm)}.$$

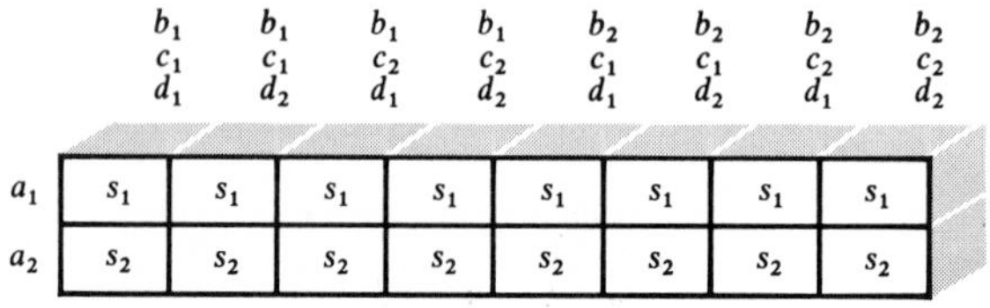

Figure 8.15-1   Block diagram of type SPF-2.222 design.

An outline of the computational procedures appears in Table 8.15-1, where the following notation is used:

$$p \text{ levels of } a_i$$
$$q \text{ levels of } b_j$$
$$r \text{ levels of } c_k$$
$$u \text{ levels of } d_l$$
$$n \text{ levels of } s_m$$
$$\sum_1^N = \sum_1^p \sum_1^n.$$

TABLE 8.15-1   Outline of Computational Procedures for Type SPF-*p.qru* Design

(i) Summary tables required:			
	AB Table	*ABC* Table	*ADS* Table
	AC Table	*ABD* Table	*ABCD* Table
	AD Table	*ACD* Table	*ABCS* Table
	BC Table	*BCD* Table	*ABDS* Table
	BD Table	*ABS* Table	*ACDS* Table
	CD Table	*ACS* Table	*ABCDS* Table

TABLE 8.15-1 (continued)

(ii) Computational symbols:

$$AB \text{ Table } [A] = \sum_1^p \frac{\left(\sum_1^q A\right)^2}{nqru} \qquad\qquad ABD \text{ Table } [ABD] = \sum_1^p \sum_1^q \sum_1^u \frac{(ABD)^2}{nr}$$

$$AB \text{ Table } [B] = \sum_1^q \frac{\left(\sum_1^p B\right)^2}{npru} \qquad\qquad ACD \text{ Table } [ACD] = \sum_1^p \sum_1^r \sum_1^u \frac{(ACD)^2}{nq}$$

$$AC \text{ Table } [C] = \sum_1^r \frac{\left(\sum_1^p C\right)^2}{npqu} \qquad\qquad BCD \text{ Table } [BCD] = \sum_1^q \sum_1^r \sum_1^u \frac{(BCD)^2}{np}$$

$$AD \text{ Table } [D] = \sum_1^u \frac{\left(\sum_1^p D\right)^2}{npqr} \qquad\qquad ABS \text{ Table } [ABS] = \sum_1^p \sum_1^q \sum_1^n \frac{(ABS)^2}{ru}$$

$$AB \text{ Table } [AB] = \sum_1^p \sum_1^q \frac{(AB)^2}{nru} \qquad\qquad ACS \text{ Table } [ACS] = \sum_1^p \sum_1^r \sum_1^n \frac{(ACS)^2}{qu}$$

$$AC \text{ Table } [AC] = \sum_1^p \sum_1^r \frac{(AC)^2}{nqu} \qquad\qquad ADS \text{ Table } [ADS] = \sum_1^p \sum_1^u \sum_1^n \frac{(ADS)^2}{qr}$$

$$AD \text{ Table } [AD] = \sum_1^p \sum_1^u \frac{(AD)^2}{nqr} \qquad\qquad ABCD \text{ Table } [ABCD] = \sum_1^p \sum_1^q \sum_1^r \sum_1^u \frac{(ABCD)^2}{n}$$

$$BC \text{ Table } [BC] = \sum_1^q \sum_1^r \frac{(BC)^2}{npu} \qquad\qquad ABCS \text{ Table } [ABCS] = \sum_1^p \sum_1^q \sum_1^r \sum_1^n \frac{(ABCS)^2}{u}$$

$$BD \text{ Table } [BD] = \sum_1^q \sum_1^u \frac{(BD)^2}{npr} \qquad\qquad ABDS \text{ Table } [ABDS] = \sum_1^p \sum_1^q \sum_1^u \sum_1^n \frac{(ABDS)^2}{r}$$

$$CD \text{ Table } [CD] = \sum_1^r \sum_1^u \frac{(CD)^2}{npq} \qquad\qquad ACDS \text{ Table } [ACDS] = \sum_1^p \sum_1^r \sum_1^u \sum_1^n \frac{(ACDS)^2}{q}$$

$$ABCDS \text{ Table } [AS] = \sum_1^p \sum_1^n \frac{\left(\sum_1^q \sum_1^r \sum_1^u AS\right)^2}{qru} \qquad ABCDS \text{ Table } [ABCDS] = \sum_1^p \sum_1^q \sum_1^r \sum_1^u \sum_1^n (ABCDS)^2$$

$$ABC \text{ Table } [ABC] = \sum_1^p \sum_1^q \sum_1^r \frac{(ABC)^2}{nu} \qquad ABCDS \text{ Table } [X] = \frac{\left(\sum_1^p \sum_1^q \sum_1^r \sum_1^u \sum_1^n ABCDS\right)^2}{pqrun}$$

(iii) Computational formulas:

		df	*F ratio (A, B, C, and D Fixed Effects, Subjects Random)*
1	$SS_{\text{between subj}} = [AS] - [X]$	$np - 1$	
2	$SS_A = [A] - [X]$	$p - 1$	$\left[\frac{2}{3}\right]$
3	$SS_{\text{subj w.groups}} = [AS] - [A]$	$p(n - 1)$	
4	$SS_{\text{within subj}} = [ABCDS] - [AS]$	$np(qru - 1)$	
5	$SS_B = [B] - [X]$	$q - 1$	$\left[\frac{5}{19}\right]$
6	$SS_C = [C] - [X]$	$r - 1$	$\left[\frac{6}{20}\right]$
7	$SS_D = [D] - [X]$	$u - 1$	$\left[\frac{7}{21}\right]$
8	$SS_{AB} = [AB] - [A] - [B] + [X]$	$(p - 1)(q - 1)$	$\left[\frac{8}{19}\right]$

TABLE 8.15-1 (continued)

9      $SS_{AC} = [AC] - [A] - [C] + [X]$ $(p-1)(r-1)$ $\left[\frac{9}{20}\right]$

10      $SS_{AD} = [AD] - [A] - [D] + [X]$ $(p-1)(u-1)$ $\left[\frac{10}{21}\right]$

11      $SS_{BC} = [BC] - [B] - [C] + [X]$ $(q-1)(r-1)$ $\left[\frac{11}{22}\right]$

12      $SS_{BD} = [BD] - [B] - [D] + [X]$ $(q-1)(u-1)$ $\left[\frac{12}{23}\right]$

13      $SS_{CD} = [CD] - [C] - [D] + [X]$ $(r-1)(u-1)$ $\left[\frac{13}{24}\right]$

14      $SS_{ABC} = [ABC] - [AB] - [AC]$
$$- [BC] + [A] + [B]$$
$$+ [C] - [X] \qquad (p-1)(q-1)(r-1) \qquad \left[\frac{14}{22}\right]$$

15      $SS_{ABD} = [ABD] - [AB] - [AD]$
$$- [BD] + [A] + [B]$$
$$+ [D] - [X] \qquad (p-1)(q-1)(u-1) \qquad \left[\frac{15}{23}\right]$$

16      $SS_{ACD} = [ACD] - [AC] - [AD]$
$$- [CD] + [A] + [C]$$
$$+ [D] - [X] \qquad (p-1)(r-1)(u-1) \qquad \left[\frac{16}{24}\right]$$

17      $SS_{BCD} = [BCD] - [BC] - [BD]$
$$- [CD] + [B] + [C]$$
$$+ [D] - [X] \qquad (q-1)(r-1)(u-1) \qquad \left[\frac{17}{25}\right]$$

18      $SS_{ABCD} = [ABCD] - [ABC] - [ABD]$
$$- [ACD] - [BCD] + [AB]$$
$$+ [AC] + [AD] + [BC]$$
$$+ [BD] + [CD] - [A]$$
$$- [B] - [C] - [D] + [X] \quad (p-1)(q-1)(r-1)(u-1) \qquad \left[\frac{18}{25}\right]$$

19      $SS_{B \times \text{subj w.groups}} = [ABS] - [AB] - [AS]$
$$+ [A] \qquad p(n-1)(q-1)$$

20      $SS_{C \times \text{subj w.groups}} = [ACS] - [AC] - [AS]$
$$+ [A] \qquad p(n-1)(r-1)$$

21      $SS_{D \times \text{subj w.groups}} = [ADS] - [AD] - [AS]$
$$+ [A] \qquad p(n-1)(u-1)$$

22      $SS_{BC \times \text{subj w.groups}} = [ABCS] - [ABC] - [ABS]$
$$- [ACS] + [AB] + [AC]$$
$$+ [AS] - [A] \qquad p(n-1)(q-1)(r-1)$$

23      $SS_{BD \times \text{subj w.groups}} = [ABDS] - [ABD] - [ABS]$
$$- [ADS] + [AB] + [AD]$$
$$+ [AS] - [A] \qquad p(n-1)(q-1)(u-1)$$

24      $SS_{CD \times \text{subj w.groups}} = [ACDS] - [ACD] - [ACS]$
$$- [ADS] + [AC] + [AD]$$
$$+ [AS] - [A] \qquad p(n-1)(r-1)(u-1)$$

25      $SS_{BCD \times \text{subj w.groups}} = [ABCDS] - [ABCD]$
$$- [ABCS] - [ABDS]$$
$$- [ACDS] + [ABC]$$

TABLE 8.15-1 (continued)

$$+ [ABD] + [ACD]$$
$$+ [ABS] + [ACS]$$
$$+ [ADS] - [AB] - [AC]$$
$$- [AD] - [AS] + [A] \qquad p(n-1)(q-1)(r-1)(u-1)$$

26　　　$SS_{total} = [ABCDS] - [X]$ 　　　　　　　$npqru - 1$

8.16　COMPUTATIONAL PROCEDURES FOR TYPE SPF-*pr.qu* DESIGN

A type SPF-*pr.qu* design represents an extension of analysis procedures described for type *pr.q* and *p.qr* designs. A block diagram of this design appears in Figure 8.16-1. The structural model for the design is

$$X_{ijklm} = \mu + \alpha_i + \gamma_k + \alpha\gamma_{ik} + \pi_{m(ik)} + \beta_j + \alpha\beta_{ij} + \beta\gamma_{jk} + \alpha\beta\gamma_{ijk} + \beta\pi_{jm(ik)}$$
$$+ \delta_l + \alpha\delta_{il} + \gamma\delta_{kl} + \alpha\gamma\delta_{ikl} + \delta\pi_{lm(ik)} + \beta\delta_{jl} + \alpha\beta\delta_{ijl} + \beta\gamma\delta_{jkl}$$
$$+ \alpha\beta\gamma\delta_{ijkl} + \beta\delta\pi_{jlm(ik)} + \varepsilon_{o(ijklm)}.$$

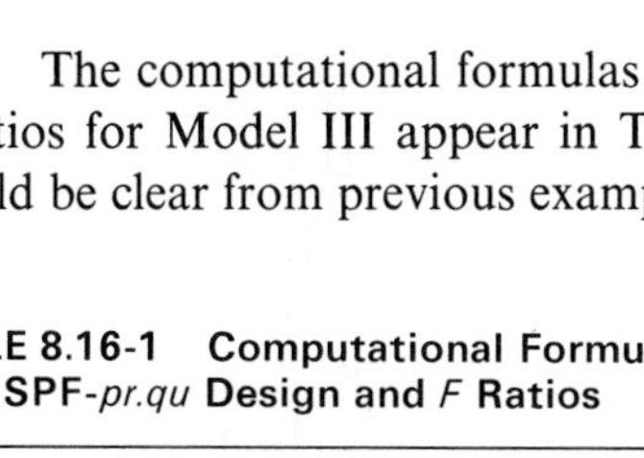

Figure 8.16-1　Block diagram of type SPF-22.22 design.

The computational formulas for the design, degrees of freedom, and F ratios for Model III appear in Table 8.16-1. The meaning of the terms should be clear from previous examples.

TABLE 8.16-1　Computational Formulas for Type SPF-*pr.qu* Design and F Ratios

	Computational Formulas	df	F ratio (A, B, C, and D Fixed Effects, Subjects Random)
1	$SS_{between\ subj} = [ACS] - [X]$	$npr - 1$	
2	$SS_A = [A] - [X]$	$p - 1$	$\left[\frac{2}{5}\right]$
3	$SS_C = [C] - [X]$	$r - 1$	$\left[\frac{3}{5}\right]$

TABLE 8.16-1 (continued)

4	$SS_{AC} = [AC] - [A] - [C] + [X]$	$(p-1)(r-1)$	$\left[\frac{4}{5}\right]$
5	$SS_{\text{subj w.groups}} = [ACS] - [AC]$	$pr(n-1)$	
6	$SS_{\text{within subj}} = [ABCDS] - [ACS]$	$npr(qu-1)$	
7	$SS_B = [B] - [X]$	$q-1$	$\left[\frac{7}{11}\right]$
8	$SS_{AB} = [AB] - [A] - [B] + [X]$	$(p-1)(q-1)$	$\left[\frac{8}{11}\right]$
9	$SS_{BC} = [BC] - [B] - [C] + [X]$	$(q-1)(r-1)$	$\left[\frac{9}{11}\right]$
10	$SS_{ABC} = [ABC] - [AB] - [AC]$ $- [BC] + [A] + [B]$ $+ [C] - [X]$	$(p-1)(q-1)(r-1)$	$\left[\frac{10}{11}\right]$
11	$SS_{B \times \text{subj w.groups}} = [ABCS] - [ABC] - [ACS]$ $+ [AC]$	$pr(n-1)(q-1)$	
12	$SS_D = [D] - [X]$	$u-1$	$\left[\frac{12}{16}\right]$
13	$SS_{AD} = [AD] - [A] - [D] + [X]$	$(p-1)(u-1)$	$\left[\frac{13}{16}\right]$
14	$SS_{CD} = [CD] - [C] - [D] + [X]$	$(r-1)(u-1)$	$\left[\frac{14}{16}\right]$
15	$SS_{ACD} = [ACD] - [AC] - [AD]$ $- [CD] + [A] + [C]$ $+ [D] - [X]$	$(p-1)(r-1)(u-1)$	$\left[\frac{15}{16}\right]$
16	$SS_{D \times \text{subj w.groups}} = [ACDS] - [ACD] - [ACS]$ $+ [AC]$	$pr(n-1)(u-1)$	
17	$SS_{BD} = [BD] - [B] - [D] + [X]$	$(q-1)(u-1)$	$\left[\frac{17}{21}\right]$
18	$SS_{ABD} = [ABD] - [AB] - [AD]$ $- [BD] + [A] + [B]$ $+ [D] - [X]$	$(p-1)(q-1)(u-1)$	$\left[\frac{18}{21}\right]$
19	$SS_{BCD} = [BCD] - [BC] - [BD]$ $- [CD] + [B] + [C]$ $+ [D] - [X]$	$(q-1)(r-1)(u-1)$	$\left[\frac{19}{21}\right]$
20	$SS_{ABCD} = [ABCD] - [ABC] - [ABD]$ $- [ACD] - [BCD] + [AB]$ $+ [AC] + [AD] + [BC]$ $+ [BD] + [CD] - [A] - [B]$ $- [C] - [D] + [X]$	$(p-1)(q-1)(r-1)(u-1)$	$\left[\frac{20}{21}\right]$
21	$SS_{BD \times \text{subj w.groups}} = [ABCDS] - [ABCD]$ $- [ABCS] - [ACDS]$ $+ [ABC] + [ACD] + [ACS]$ $- [AC]$	$pr(n-1)(q-1)(u-1)$	
22	$SS_{\text{total}} = [ABCDS] - [X]$	$npqru-1$	

8.17 COMPUTATIONAL PROCEDURES FOR TYPE SPF-*pr.quv* DESIGN

It is hoped that by examining the designs described, the reader has gained an insight into the pattern underlying the analysis of all split-plot designs. This general pattern can be illustrated for a type SPF-*pr.quv* design, a block diagram of which appears in Figure 8.17-1. The structural model for this design is

$$X_{ijklmo} = \mu + \alpha_i + \gamma_k + \alpha\gamma_{ik} + \pi_{m(ik)} + \beta_j + \alpha\beta_{ij} + \beta\gamma_{jk} + \alpha\beta\gamma_{ijk}$$

$$+ \beta\pi_{jm(ik)} + \delta_l + \alpha\delta_{il} + \gamma\delta_{kl} + \alpha\gamma\delta_{ikl} + \delta\pi_{lm(ik)} + \eta_o + \alpha\eta_{io} + \gamma\eta_{ko}$$

$$+ \alpha\gamma\eta_{iko} + \eta\pi_{om(ik)} + \beta\delta_{jl} + \alpha\beta\delta_{ijl} + \beta\gamma\delta_{jkl} + \alpha\beta\gamma\delta_{ijkl} + \beta\delta\pi_{jlm(ik)}$$

$$+ \beta\eta_{jo} + \alpha\beta\eta_{ijo} + \beta\gamma\eta_{jko} + \alpha\beta\gamma\eta_{ijko} + \beta\eta\pi_{jom(ik)} + \delta\eta_{lo} + \alpha\delta\eta_{ilo}$$

$$+ \gamma\delta\eta_{klo} + \alpha\gamma\delta\eta_{iklo} + \delta\eta\pi_{lom(ik)} + \beta\delta\eta_{jlo} + \alpha\beta\delta\eta_{ijlo}$$

$$+ \beta\gamma\delta\eta_{jklo} + \alpha\beta\gamma\delta\eta_{ijklo} + \beta\delta\eta\pi_{jlom(ik)} + \varepsilon_{h(ijklmo)}.$$

	b_1 d_1 e_1	b_1 d_1 e_2	b_1 d_2 e_1	b_1 d_2 e_2	b_2 d_1 e_1	b_2 d_1 e_2	b_2 d_2 e_1	b_2 d_2 e_2
ac_{11}	s_1	s_1	s_1	s_1	s_1	s_1	s_1	s_1
ac_{12}	s_2	s_2	s_2	s_2	s_2	s_2	s_2	s_2
ac_{21}	s_3	s_3	s_3	s_3	s_3	s_3	s_3	s_3
ac_{22}	s_4	s_4	s_4	s_4	s_4	s_4	s_4	s_4

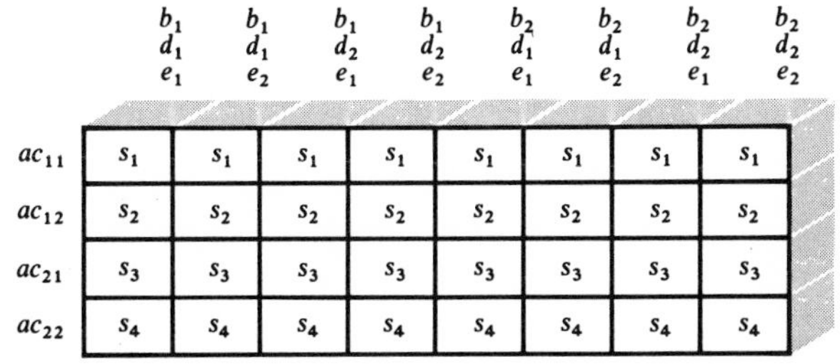

Figure 8.17-1   Block diagram of type SPF-22.222 design.

An outline of the computational procedures is shown in Table 8.17-1. The following notation is used:

$$p \text{ levels of } a_i$$
$$q \text{ levels of } b_j$$
$$r \text{ levels of } c_k$$
$$u \text{ levels of } d_l$$
$$v \text{ levels of } e_o$$
$$n \text{ levels of } s_m$$
$$\sum_1^N = \sum_1^p \sum_1^r \sum_1^n.$$

TABLE 8.17-1   Computational Formulas for Type SPF-$pr.quv$ Design and F Ratios

	Computational Formulas	df	F Ratio (A, B, C, D, and E Fixed Effects, Subjects Random)
1	$SS_{\text{between subj}} = [ACS] - [X]$	$npr - 1$	
2	$SS_A = [A] - [X]$	$p - 1$	$[\frac{2}{5}]$
3	$SS_C = [C] - [X]$	$r - 1$	$[\frac{3}{5}]$
4	$SS_{AC} = [AC] - [A] - [C] + [X]$	$(p-1)(r-1)$	$[\frac{4}{5}]$
5	$SS_{\text{subj w.groups}} = [ACS] - [AC]$	$pr(n-1)$	
6	$SS_{\text{within subj}} = [ABCDES] - [ACS]$	$npr(quv - 1)$	
7	$SS_B = [B] - [X]$	$q - 1$	$[\frac{7}{11}]$
8	$SS_{AB} = [AB] - [A] - [B] + [X]$	$(p-1)(q-1)$	$[\frac{8}{11}]$
9	$SS_{BC} = [BC] - [B] - [C] + [X]$	$(q-1)(r-1)$	$[\frac{9}{11}]$
10	$SS_{ABC} = [ABC] - [AB] - [AC] - [BC] + [A] + [B] + [C] - [X]$	$(p-1)(q-1)(r-1)$	$[\frac{10}{11}]$
11	$SS_{B \times \text{subj w.groups}} = [ABCS] - [ABC] - [ACS] + [AC]$	$pr(n-1)(q-1)$	
12	$SS_D = [D] - [X]$	$u - 1$	$[\frac{12}{16}]$
13	$SS_{AD} = [AD] - [A] - [D] + [X]$	$(p-1)(u-1)$	$[\frac{13}{16}]$
14	$SS_{CD} = [CD] - [C] - [D] + [X]$	$(r-1)(u-1)$	$[\frac{14}{16}]$
15	$SS_{ACD} = [ACD] - [AC] - [AD] - [CD] + [A] + [C] + [D] - [X]$	$(p-1)(r-1)(u-1)$	$[\frac{15}{16}]$
16	$SS_{D \times \text{subj w.groups}} = [ACDS] - [ACD] - [ACS] + [AC]$	$pr(n-1)(u-1)$	
17	$SS_E = [E] - [X]$	$v - 1$	$[\frac{17}{21}]$
18	$SS_{AE} = [AE] - [A] - [E] + [X]$	$(p-1)(v-1)$	$[\frac{18}{21}]$
19	$SS_{CE} = [CE] - [C] - [E] + [X]$	$(r-1)(v-1)$	$[\frac{19}{21}]$
20	$SS_{ACE} = [ACE] - [AC] - [AE] - [CE] + [A] + [C] + [E] - [X]$	$(p-1)(r-1)(v-1)$	$[\frac{20}{21}]$

TABLE 8.17-1 (continued)

	SS	df	
21	$SS_{E \times \text{subj w.groups}} = [ACES] - [ACE] - [ACS] + [AC]$	$pr(n-1)(v-1)$	
22	$SS_{BD} = [BD] - [B] - [D] + [X]$	$(q-1)(u-1)$	$\left[\frac{22}{26}\right]$
23	$SS_{ABD} = [ABD] - [AD] - [BD] + [A] + [B] + [D] - [X]$	$(p-1)(q-1)(u-1)$	$\left[\frac{23}{26}\right]$
24	$SS_{BCD} = [BCD] - [BC] - [BD] - [CD] + [B] + [C] + [D] - [X]$	$(q-1)(r-1)(u-1)$	$\left[\frac{24}{26}\right]$
25	$SS_{ABCD} = [ABCD] - [ABC] - [ABD] - [ACD] - [BCD] + [AB]$ $+ [AC] + [AD] + [BC] + [BD] + [CD] - [A] - [B]$ $- [C] - [D] + [X]$	$(p-1)(q-1)(r-1)(u-1)$	$\left[\frac{25}{26}\right]$
26	$SS_{BD \times \text{subj w.groups}} = [ABCDS] - [ABCD] - [ABCS] - [ACDS] + [ABC]$ $+ [ACD] + [ACS] - [AC]$	$pr(q-1)(u-1)$	
27	$SS_{BE} = [BE] - [B] - [E] + [X]$	$(q-1)(v-1)$	$\left[\frac{27}{31}\right]$
28	$SS_{ABE} = [ABE] - [AB] - [AE] - [BE] + [A] + [B] + [E] - [X]$	$(p-1)(q-1)(v-1)$	$\left[\frac{28}{31}\right]$
29	$SS_{BCE} = [BCE] - [BC] - [BE] - [CE] + [B] + [C] + [E] - [X]$	$(q-1)(r-1)(v-1)$	$\left[\frac{29}{31}\right]$
30	$SS_{ABCE} = [ABCE] - [ABC] - [ABE] - [ACE] - [BCE] + [AB]$ $+ [AC] + [AE] + [BC] + [BE] + [CE] - [A] - [B]$ $- [C] - [E] + [X]$	$(p-1)(q-1)(r-1)(v-1)$	
31	$SS_{BE \times \text{subj w.groups}} = [ABCES] - [ABCE] - [ABCS] - [ACES] + [ABC]$ $+ [ACE] + [ACS] - [AC]$	$pr(q-1)(v-1)$	$\left[\frac{30}{31}\right]$
32	$SS_{DE} = [DE] - [D] - [E] + [X]$	$(u-1)(v-1)$	$\left[\frac{32}{36}\right]$
33	$SS_{ADE} = [ADE] - [AD] - [AE] - [DE] + [A] + [D] + [E] - [X]$	$(p-1)(u-1)(v-1)$	$\left[\frac{33}{36}\right]$
34	$SS_{CDE} = [CDE] - [CD] - [CE] - [DE] + [C] + [D] + [E] - [X]$	$(r-1)(u-1)(v-1)$	$\left[\frac{34}{36}\right]$

TABLE 8.17-1 (continued)

	Computational Formulas	df	F Ratio (A, B, C, D, and E Fixed Effects, Subjects Random)
35	$SS_{ACDE} = [ACDE] - [ACD] - [ACE] - [ADE] - [CDE] + [AC] + [AD] + [AE] + [CD] + [CE] + [DE] - [A] - [C] - [D] - [E] + [X]$	$(p-1)(r-1)(u-1)(v-1)$	$\left[\frac{35}{36}\right]$
36	$SS_{DE \times \text{subj w-groups}} = [ACDES] - [ACDE] - [ACDS] - [ACES] + [ACD] + [ACE] + [ACS] - [AC]$	$pr(u-1)(v-1)(n-1)$	
37	$SS_{BDE} = [BDE] - [BD] - [BE] - [DE] + [B] + [D] + [E] - [X]$	$(q-1)(u-1)(v-1)$	$\left[\frac{37}{41}\right]$
38	$SS_{ABDE} = [ABDE] - [ABD] - [ABE] - [ADE] - [BDE] + [AB] + [AD] + [AE] + [BD] + [BE] + [DE] - [A] - [B] - [D] - [E] + [X]$	$(p-1)(q-1)(u-1)(v-1)$	$\left[\frac{38}{41}\right]$
39	$SS_{BCDE} = [BCDE] - [BCD] - [BCE] - [BDE] - [CDE] + [BC] + [BD] + [BE] + [CD] + [CE] + [DE] - [B] - [C] - [D] - [E] + [X]$	$(q-1)(r-1)(u-1)(v-1)$	$\left[\frac{39}{41}\right]$
40	$SS_{ABCDE} = [ABCDE] - [ABCD] - [ABCE] - [ABDE] - [ACDE] - [BCDE] + [ABC] + [ABD] + [ABE] + [ACD] + [ACE] + [BCD] + [BCE] + [BDE] + [CDE] - [AB] - [AC] - [AD] - [AE] - [BC] - [BD] - [BE] - [CD] - [CE] - [DE] + [A] + [B] + [C] + [D] + [E] - [X]$	$(p-1)(q-1)(r-1)(u-1)(v-1)$	$\left[\frac{40}{41}\right]$
41	$SS_{BDE \times \text{subj w-groups}} = [ABCDES] - [ABCDE] - [ABCDS] - [ABCES] - [ACDES] + [ABCD] + [ABCE] + [ACDE] + [ABCS] + [ACDS] + [ACES] - [ABC] - [ACD] - [ACE] - [ACS] + [AC]$	$pr(n-1)(q-1)(u-1)(v-1)$	
42	$SS_{\text{total}} = [ABCDES] - [X]$	$npqruw - 1$	

8.18   EVALUATION OF SEQUENCE EFFECTS

Unless the nature of treatments for which repeated observations are obtained dictates otherwise, the experimenter should randomize the order of administration of levels independently for each subject, as recommended in Section 8.1. An alternative procedure involves controlling sequence effects by building an order factor into the design. If the administration of one treatment level affects a subject's performance on subsequent levels, the experiment is said to contain *carry-over* effects. That portion of carry-over effects which depends on particular treatment levels being administered first, second, etc. is referred to as *sequence* effects. The inclusion of an order factor in a design permits an experimenter to evaluate sequence effects. If the order variable is significant, it indicates that the dependent variable is influenced by the particular sequence in which the treatment levels are administered. A type SPF-2.3 design has 3! or 6 possible sequences in which treatment B can be administered. If we let levels of treatment C denote the six sequences, the design can be analyzed as a type SPF-26.3 design. The experiment would require a minimum of 24 subjects, with 2 subjects assigned to each AC treatment combination. When the number of levels of a repeated treatment is greater than three, the experimenter can randomly sample from the $q!$ possible sequences. Using a sequence factor is impractical if an experiment involves many levels of repeated treatments, unless a sample of the sequences is used.

8.19   ADVANTAGES AND DISADVANTAGES OF SPLIT-PLOT DESIGN

A split-plot design is appropriate for many research problems. The most likely alternative design, when repeated measures or matched subjects are employed, is a randomized block factorial experiment. The major advantages and disadvantages of a split-plot design relative to a randomized block factorial design are as follows:

1. A type SPF-$p.q$ design can be used in experiments where it is not possible to administer all treatment combinations within each block.

2. In a type SPF-$p.q$ design, estimates of B and AB (within-block) effects are usually more accurate than estimates of A (between-block) effects. Because the average experimental error over all treatments is the same for both designs, the increased precision on B and AB is obtained by sacrificing precision on A. In addition, the number of degrees of freedom for experimental error is larger for B and AB than for A but less than the degrees of freedom for error in a type RBF-pq design.

3. If the experimenter's primary interest is in *within-block effects* (B and AB), a type SPF-$p.q$ design is usually more powerful than a type RBF-pq design. On the other hand, if equal precision for all treatment effects is desired, the average power of a type RBF-pq design is greater.

4. The analysis and randomization procedures for a split-plot design are more complex than for a randomized block factorial design.

5. When missing data occur, the increase in complexity of the analysis is greater for the split-plot design than for the randomized block factorial design.

8.20 REPRESENTATIVE APPLICATIONS OF SPLIT-PLOT DESIGNS IN THE RESEARCH LITERATURE

The following references illustrate a variety of applications of split-plot designs.

Arima, James K. Human probability learning with forced training trials and certain and uncertain outcome choice trials. *Journal of Experimental Psychology*, 1965, **70**, 43–50. Type SPF-22.6 design.

Capaldi, E. J., and Hugh Poynor. Aftereffects and delay of reinforcement. *Journal of Experimental Psychology*, 1966, **71**, 80–88. Type SPF-22.4 design.

Elias, Merrill F. The relation of drive to finger-withdrawal conditioning. *Journal of Experimental Psychology*, 1965, **70**, 109–116. Type SPF-223.5, SPF-2.5 and SPF-32.5 designs.

Goss, Albert E., and Nancy J. Cobb. Formation, maintenance, generalization, and retention of response hierarchies. *Journal of Experimental Psychology*, 1966, **71**, 218–231. Type SPF-522.4 design.

Hetherington, E. Mavis, and Mary Carlson. Effects of candidate support and election results upon attitudes to the presidency. *Journal of Social Psychology*, 1964, **64**, 333–338. Type SPF-2.3 design.

Ison, James R., and David Birch. *T*-maze reversal following differential endbox placement. *Journal of Experimental Psychology*, 1961, **62**, 200–202. Type SPF-2.2 design.

Lerea, Louis, and Blaire Ward. The social schema of normal and speech-defective children. *Journal of Social Psychology*, 1966, **69**, 87–94. Type SPF-22.5 design.

Murstein, Bernard I. Projection of hostility on the TAT as a function of stimulus, background, and personality variables. *Journal of Consulting Psychology*, 1965, **29**, 43–48. Type SPF-2222.3 design.

Wickens, Delos D., Charles K. Allen, and Frances A. Hill. Effect of instructions and UCS strength on extinction of the conditioned GSR. *Journal of Experimental Psychology*, 1963, **66**, 235–240. Type SPF-22.5 design.

Williams, Dean E., Michelle Wark, and Fred D. Minifie. Ratings of stuttering by audio, visual, and audiovisual cues. *Journal of Speech and Hearing Research*, 1963, **6**, 91–100. Type SPF-3., 24, design.

9 / CONFOUNDED FACTORIAL DESIGNS—

FACTORIAL DESIGNS WITH BLOCK-INTERACTION CONFOUNDING

9.1 INTRODUCTION TO CONFOUNDING IN FACTORIAL EXPERIMENTS

The advantages of experimental designs in which all treatment combinations are assigned to blocks of relatively homogeneous subjects were described in Chapters 5 and 7. Within-block homogeneity can be achieved by using litter mates, matched subjects or, if the nature of the treatments permits, repeated measures on the same subjects. The major difficulty an experimenter encounters with block designs is obtaining a sufficient number of homogeneous subjects to form the blocks. Even a type RBF-33 design, a relatively small design, requires nine ($3 \times 3 = 9$) subjects per block. This problem becomes more acute for larger experiments. The use of repeated observations on the same subjects is no solution, for there is a practical limit to the number of treatment combinations that can be assigned to a subject. In many experimental situations, the nature of the treatments precludes obtaining more than one measure per subject.

The split-plot design described in Chapter 8 provides a partial solution to the problem of unwieldly block size by assigning only a portion of the treatment combinations to each block. For a type SPF-$p.qr$ design, all qr treatment combinations are within-block effects, but the p levels of treatment A are between-block effects. By using this design, an experimenter can reduce the number of treatment combinations within each block to qr as compared with a complete block design that would have pqr combinations within each block. The effects attributable to treatment A and blocks cannot be separated in a split-plot design. They are described as being completely confounded. All split-plot designs have confounding of one or more *treatments* with block effects. The designs described in this chapter involve confounding of one or more *interactions* with block effects. In addition to reducing the number of treatment combinations within each block, this type of confounding has an important advantage over the confounding scheme of a split-plot design. If one of the interactions is known to be negligible, it can be *sacrificed* in order to estimate all main effects and important interactions with equal precision. Thus an experimenter can achieve a reduction in block size without sacrificing power in evaluating one or more main effects.

Factorial experiments in which block effects are confounded with one or more interactions can be constructed by using either a randomized block or a Latin-square building block design. The letters RBCF or LSCF are used to designate factorial experiments in which an interaction is *completely* confounded with between-block variation. If an interaction is *partially* confounded with between-block variation, the design is designated by the letters RBPF. This latter design provides partial information with respect to the confounded interactions. A comparison among three 3×3 factorial designs is shown in Figure 9.1-1. For purposes of comparison, assume that in each design shown in Figure 9.1-1 repeated

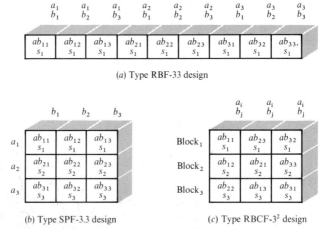

(a) Type RBF-33 design

(b) Type SPF-3.3 design   (c) Type RBCF-3^2 design

Figure 9.1-1 Comparison of three types of designs.

measures are obtained on the subjects (s_m). In the type RBF-33 design, each subject in the set designated s_1 receives all nine treatment combinations. In the type SPF-3.3 design, subjects in s_1 receive one level of treatment A but all three levels of treatment B. In contrast, in a type RBCF-3^2 design, subjects in set s_1 receive three different levels of treatment A and three different levels of treatment B.

The designation RBCF-p^k indicates that the design is restricted to the case in which k treatments each have p levels. The treatment combinations in a type RBCF-3^2 design are laid out so that a particular treatment level occurs only once in each block (row). Later it will be shown that the arrangement in part (c) confounds a component of the AB interaction within between-block variation but does not confound either treatment. It is assumed in type RBCF, RBPF, and LSCF designs that treatments represent fixed effects and blocks represent a random sample from a common population of blocks. A block may correspond to a single subject or to a set of matched subjects.

Type RBCF, RBPF, and LSCF designs are appropriate for experiments that meet, in addition to the general assumptions of the analysis of variance model, the following conditions:

1. Two or more treatments with each treatment having p levels, where $p \geq 2$. Exceptions to the general requirement that all treatments must have p levels are discussed in Sections 9.10 and 9.11.

2. Treatment combinations are assigned to blocks so that only a fraction of all possible combinations are represented within any one block. Variation between blocks is confounded with one or more interactions. Thus an experimenter must be willing to sacrifice information on an interaction in order to achieve small block size. The interaction that is confounded should be one thought to be insignificant.

3. It must be permissible to administer the levels of each treatment in every possible sequence. This requirement precludes the use of treatments whose levels consist of successive periods of time.

4. If repeated observations are obtained on subjects, w samples of z subjects from a population of subjects are randomly assigned to the blocks. The sequence of administration of the treatment combinations is randomized independently for each subject.

5. If matched subjects are used, wz samples containing v subjects are randomly assigned to the blocks. Within each block, subjects are randomly assigned to the treatment combinations.

The construction of randomized block confounded factorial designs is described in the first part of this chapter. Confounding by means of a Latin square is covered in Section 9.11.

9.2   USE OF MODULAR ARITHMETIC IN CONSTRUCTING CONFOUNDED DESIGNS

The construction of type RBCF and RBPF designs requires the use of some scheme for assigning treatment combinations to blocks so that variation between blocks is confounded with one or more interactions. Several schemes have been devised for this purpose (Yates, 1937; Kempthorne, 1952). One scheme, which is general in nature, involves the use of modular arithmetic, the basic operations of which are relatively simple. An integer I modulus an integer m equals the remainder x that is obtained when I is divided by m. That is, $I(\text{mod } m) = x$. For example, the integer 17 to the modulus 3 equals 2, because the remainder after division of 17 by 3 is 2. This may be written

$$17(\text{mod } 3) = 2$$

and is read 17 modulo 3 equals 2. Seventeen is said to be *congruent* to 2, modulus 3. It can be shown that all integers I are congruent to integers $x = 0, 1,$ or 2, modulus 3. For example,

$$0(\text{mod } 3) = 0 \qquad 4(\text{mod } 3) = 1$$
$$1(\text{mod } 3) = 1 \qquad 5(\text{mod } 3) = 2$$
$$2(\text{mod } 3) = 2 \qquad 6(\text{mod } 3) = 0$$
$$3(\text{mod } 3) = 0 \qquad 7(\text{mod } 3) = 1$$
$$\text{etc.}$$

It can also be shown that all integers are congruent to 0 or 1, modulus 2.

$$0(\text{mod } 2) = 0$$
$$1(\text{mod } 2) = 1$$
$$2(\text{mod } 2) = 0$$
$$\text{etc.}$$

Similarly, all integers are congruent to 0, 1, 2, 3, or 4, modulus 5.

MODULAR ADDITION AND MULTIPLICATION

Two operations of modular arithmetic are used in constructing confounded designs, addition and multiplication. The operation of addition is illustrated by the following examples:

$$x_1 + x_2 = I(\text{mod } m)$$
$$1 + 0 = 1(\text{mod } 3)$$
$$1 + 1 = 2(\text{mod } 3)$$
$$2 + 2 = 1(\text{mod } 3)$$

$$1 + 3 = 4(\text{mod } 5)$$
$$2 + 3 = 0(\text{mod } 5)$$
$$3 + 2 = 0(\text{mod } 5).$$

Thus, to add two integers x_1 and x_2, one obtains their sum and expresses it as an integer I modulus m. The latter part of this section describes procedures whereby treatment levels are assigned to blocks by letting x_1, x_2, I, and m correspond to properties of an experimental design as follows:

$$x_1 \text{ and } x_2 = \text{levels of treatments } A \text{ and } B$$

$$I = \text{a particular block}$$

$$m = \text{the number of levels of each treatment.}$$

The second operation of modular arithmetic that is used, multiplication, is illustrated by the following examples:

$$1 \cdot 2 = 2(\text{mod } 3)$$
$$2 \cdot 2 = 1(\text{mod } 3)$$

$$4 \cdot 3 = 2(\text{mod } 5)$$

$$0 \cdot 4 = 0(\text{mod } 5).$$

To multiply two integers x_1 and x_2, one obtains their product and then expresses it as an integer I modulus m.

MODIFIED NOTATION SYSTEM FOR TREATMENT LEVELS

Designs described in the first part of this chapter are limited to factorial experiments of the form p^k, where p, the number of levels of each treatment, is a prime number. A prime number is any number divisible by no number smaller than itself other than one. Examples of prime numbers are 1, 2, 3, 5, 7, 11, etc. In order to take full advantage of modular arithmetic, a modified designation system for treatment levels must be used. According to this system, the first level of any treatment is designated by the subscript 0 instead of the usual 1. For example, the treatment levels of a type RBF-33 design would be designated as a_0, a_1, a_2, b_0, b_1, and b_2. The nine treatment combinations and their corresponding designations appear in Table 9.2-1. The digit in the first position indicates the level of treatment A, while the digit in the second position indicates the level of treatment B. An experiment having three treatments requires three digits to describe any combination of levels. The notation system described above, in which the first level is designated by 0, is also used for designating blocks, replications, and subjects.

TABLE 9.2-1   Modified Notation System for Type RBCF and RBPF Designs

a_0	a_0	a_0	a_1	a_1	a_1	a_2	a_2	a_2
b_0	b_1	b_2	b_0	b_1	b_2	b_0	b_1	b_2
00	01	02	10	11	12	20	21	22

ASSIGNMENT OF TREATMENT LEVELS TO BLOCKS

Assume that an experimenter desires to carry out an experiment having two treatments, each at three levels. In order to use a randomized block factorial design, n blocks of size nine ($3 \times 3 = 9$) would be required. It is often difficult in the behavioral sciences to secure blocks of nine homogeneous subjects. An alternative experimental procedure is to confound blocks with the AB interaction. If this is done, the experiment can be carried out with blocks containing only three subjects each. Of course, this kind of confounding would not be appropriate if the experimenter is particularly interested in evaluating the AB interaction.

Modular arithmetic is used to determine which of the nine treatment combinations are assigned to each block of subjects. Let x_1 stand for the ith level of treatment A and x_2 stand for the jth level of treatment B. All treatment combinations satisfying the equation

$$x_1 + x_2 = 0(\text{mod } 3)$$

are assigned to the same block. Modulus three is employed because A and B each have three levels. It can be shown that the treatment combinations 00, 12, and 21 satisfy the equation. If 0 is substituted for x_1 and 0 for x_2, the equation is

$$0 + 0 = 0(\text{mod } 3).$$

Similarly, if 12 and 21 are substituted in the equation, their respective sums are equal to 0(mod 3):

$$1 + 2 = 0(\text{mod } 3) \quad \text{and} \quad 2 + 1 = 0(\text{mod } 3).$$

Thus block 0 is composed of treatment combinations ab_{00}, ab_{12}, and ab_{21}.

The interaction of A and B can be partitioned into two nonoverlapping components as shown below:

SS	df
AB	4
(AB)	2
(AB^2)	2

The two orthogonal components (AB) and (AB^2) have no special significance apart from their convenience in partitioning the interaction. Treatment combinations that satisfy the equations

$$[x_1 + x_2 = 0(\text{mod } 3)] \text{ designated by } (AB)_0$$
$$[x_1 + x_2 = 1(\text{mod } 3)] \text{ designated by } (AB)_1$$
$$[x_1 + x_2 = 2(\text{mod } 3)] \text{ designated by } (AB)_2$$

comprise the (AB) component of the interaction. We have just seen that treatment combinations ab_{00}, ab_{12} and ab_{21} satisfy the equation $x_1 + x_2 = 0(\text{mod } 3)$ and are therefore assigned to subjects in block 0, which is designated by $(AB)_0$. The (AB^2) interaction component is composed of treatment combinations that satisfy the equations

$$[x_1 + 2x_2 = 0(\text{mod } 3)] \text{ designated by } (AB^2)_0$$
$$[x_1 + 2x_2 = 1(\text{mod } 3)] \text{ designated by } (AB^2)_1$$
$$[x_1 + 2x_2 = 2(\text{mod } 3)] \text{ designated by } (AB^2)_2.$$

The powers of the interaction components (AB) and (AB^2) are used as the coefficients of x_1 and x_2. The power of A, by convention, is always equal to one. If this convention is not followed, the notation system for inter-action components is not unique. This results from the fact that (A^2B) and (AB^2) define the same treatment combinations. That is,

$$2x_1 + x_2 = i(\text{mod } 3)$$

defines the same nine treatment combinations as

$$x_1 + 2x_2 = i(\text{mod } 3).$$

Treatment combinations satisfying the family of equations

$$x_1 + x_2 = i(\text{mod } 3), \qquad i = 0, 1, 2$$

and

$$x_1 + 2x_2 = i(\text{mod } 3), \qquad i = 0, 1, 2$$

are shown in Table 9.2-2.

TABLE 9.2-2   Arrangement of Treatment Combinations in a Type RBPF-3^2 Design

			ab_{ij}	ab_{ij}	ab_{ij}
	Block 0	$(AB)_0$	00	12	21
Replication 0	Block 1	$(AB)_1$	01	10	22
	Block 2	$(AB)_2$	11	02	20
	Block 0	$(AB^2)_0$	00	11	22
Replication 1	Block 1	$(AB^2)_1$	10	02	21
	Block 2	$(AB^2)_2$	01	12	20

If treatments A and B represent *fixed effects*, it can be shown that each block in Table 9.2-2 is balanced with respect to main effects but not with respect to the AB interaction. Assume that the following linear model is appropriate for block 0 in replication 0:

$$X_{ijm} = \mu + \alpha_i + \beta_j + \alpha\beta_{ij} + \varepsilon_{m(ij)},$$

where, according to the assumptions of the model,

$$\sum_1^p \alpha_i = 0, \quad \sum_{1'}^q \beta_j = 0, \quad \sum_1^p (\alpha\beta_{ij}) = \sum_1^q (\alpha\beta_{ij}) = 0.$$

Observations in block 0 are estimates of the following parameters:

$$00 \rightarrow \mu + \alpha_0 + \beta_0 + \alpha\beta_{00} + \varepsilon_{m(00)}$$

$$12 \rightarrow \mu + \alpha_1 + \beta_2 + \alpha\beta_{12} + \varepsilon_{m(12)}$$

$$\underline{21 \rightarrow \mu + \alpha_2 + \beta_1 + \alpha\beta_{21} + \varepsilon_{m(21)}}$$

$$3\mu + 0 + 0 + (\alpha\beta_{00} + \alpha\beta_{12} + \alpha\beta_{21}) + (\varepsilon_{m(00)} + \varepsilon_{m(12)} + \varepsilon_{m(21)})$$

According to the assumptions of the linear model, the sum of terms $\alpha_0 + \alpha_1 + \alpha_2 = 0$ and $\beta_0 + \beta_1 + \beta_2 = 0$. Interaction terms of the form $\Sigma_1^p \alpha \beta_{i0}$, $\Sigma_1^p \alpha \beta_{i1}$, and $\Sigma_1^p \alpha \beta_{i2}$ as well as $\Sigma_1^q \alpha \beta_{0j}$, $\Sigma_1^q \alpha \beta_{1j}$, and $\Sigma_1^q \alpha \beta_{2j} = 0$. However, the sum $\alpha \beta_{00} + \alpha \beta_{12} + \alpha \beta_{21} \neq 0$. Thus observations satisfying the equation

$$x_1 + x_2 = 0(\text{mod } 3)$$

are balanced with respect to main effects but not with respect to inter-action effects. This is true for each equation in the family of equations satisfying the relationship

$$x_1 + bx_2 = i(\text{mod } 3),$$

where $b = 1$ or 2 and is the power of B in the (AB) and (AB^2) interaction components. From the preceding discussion it should be apparent that treatments are assumed to be fixed effects for all randomized block con-founded factorial designs. In Table 9.2-2, variation between blocks 0 through 2 in replication zero and 0 through 2 in replication one account for two degrees of freedom each. The former variation comprises the (AB) interaction component; the latter variation comprises the (AB^2) component. Note that all nine combinations of treatments A and B are contained in replication zero. This is also true for replication one. However, each block contains only one-third of the nine treatment combinations. A replication in a confounded factorial design always contains all of the treatment combinations in the experiment; however, a block contains only a fraction of the combinations.

9.3   COMPLETE VERSUS PARTIAL CONFOUNDING

The type RBPF-3^2 design illustrated in Table 9.2-2 is an example of a *partially* confounded design. In this design, the (AB) interaction com-ponent is confounded with between-block variation in replication 0 and the (AB^2) component is confounded in replication 1. This arrangement permits an experimenter to compute within-block estimates of (AB) and (AB^2) from replications 1 and 0, respectively. Hence partial information with respect to the AB interaction is available from one-half of the repli-cations. An alternative arrangement is to confound either (AB) or (AB^2) in all replications. If this procedure of confounding the same interaction or interaction components in all replications is followed, the design is a *completely* confounded design. If complete confounding is used, no within-block estimate of the confounded effects can be computed. This is a con-sequence of the fact that only a portion of the treatment combinations comprising the effects are included within any one block.

In designs having more than two treatments, a type RBPF-2^3 design, for example, a different interaction can be confounded with between-block variation in each replication. For instance, in a three-treatment partially confounded design, the AB interaction can be confounded in the first replication, AC in the second, BC in the third, and ABC in the fourth replication. The advantage of this procedure is that partial information ($\frac{3}{4}$) is available with respect to all interactions because each interaction is confounded in only one of the four replications. If an experimenter knows that an interaction, say the ABC interaction, is insignificant, complete confounding in which ABC is confounded in all four replications is preferable to partial confounding.

Federer (1955, 230) distinguishes between *balanced partial* confounding and *unbalanced partial* confounding. The former designation refers to designs in which all effects of a particular order, for example, all first-order interactions, are confounded with blocks an equal number of times. The type RBPF-2^3 design described above, in which AB, AC, and BC were each confounded in one replication, illustrates balanced partial confounding. If all effects of a particular order are confounded with between-block variation an unequal number of times, the arrangement is described as unbalanced partial confounding.

9.4   COMPUTATIONAL PROCEDURES FOR TYPE RBPF-3^2 DESIGN

Assume that an experiment has been designed to evaluate the relative effectiveness of several procedures for using programmed instruction material. The programmed material has been prepared to acquaint electronic technicians with servicing procedures for a new satellite tracking system. The criterion used to assess the effectiveness of the instruction material was the number of simulated equipment malfunctions in the tracking system that trainees were able to detect. The programmed material was presented to the trainees by means of teaching machines. Treatment A consisted of three presentation rates for the material. One rate is designated as an unpaced presentation, for each trainee pressed a lever when he was ready to view the next frame of the program. This condition is treatment level a_0. Treatment levels a_1 and a_2 consisted of 40 seconds and 20 seconds, respectively, between presentation of the program frames. A second variable investigated was the type of response that the trainees were required to make to each frame of the program. The three types of responses were $b_0 =$ frame read but no overt response made, $b_1 =$ response spoken aloud, and $b_2 =$ response written down. Both treatments A and B represent fixed effects; that is, all treatment levels about which inferences are to be made are included in the experiment. It is assumed in type RBPF and RBCF designs that blocks represent a random variable.

Aptitude test data were used to assign trainees to six sets of three homogeneous subjects each. The six sets of trainees were randomly assigned to the six blocks of the type RBPF design shown in Table 9.2-2. Each subject in a block was assigned randomly to one of the three AB treatment combinations for that block. The research hypotheses leading to this experiment can be evaluated by means of statistical tests of the following null hypotheses:

$$H_0 : \alpha_i = 0 \qquad \text{for all } i$$
$$H_1 : \alpha_i \neq 0 \qquad \text{for some } i$$

$$H_0 : \beta_j = 0 \qquad \text{for all } j$$
$$H_1 : \beta_j \neq 0 \qquad \text{for some } j.$$

The level of significance adopted for all tests is .05.

The layout of the type RBPF-3^2 design, computational tables, and formulas are shown in Table 9.4-1. The analysis for this design is similar to the analysis for any factorial design. However, special computational procedures are required to partition the AB interaction into (AB) and (AB^2) components. These procedures are discussed in some detail following the presentation of the general analysis. The following notation is used in Table 9.4-1:

$$p \text{ levels of } a_i, \text{ where } p = 3$$
$$q \text{ levels of } b_j, \text{ where } q = 3$$
$$v \text{ levels of } X \text{ (observations/block), where } v = 3$$
$$w \text{ levels of } f_h \text{ (replications), where } w = 2$$
$$z \text{ levels of } g_t \text{ (blocks), where } z = 3$$
$$\sum_1^N = \sum_1^v \sum_1^w \sum_1^z.$$

The interaction of treatments A and B is confounded with blocks through the use of the family of relations

$$x_1 + x_2 = i(\text{mod } 3), \qquad i = 0, 1, 2$$

and

$$x_1 + 2x_2 = i(\text{mod } 3), \qquad i = 0, 1, 2.$$

All treatment combinations satisfying the former relation are assigned to blocks zero through two in replication zero. Treatment combinations satisfying the latter relation are assigned to blocks zero through two in replication one.

The results of the analysis procedures illustrated in Table 9.4-1 are summarized in Table 9.4-2. On the basis of this analysis, the null hypothesis can be rejected for treatment B, but not for treatment A. The next step is to determine which differences among population means for treatment B are significant. Before turning to this question, several points concerning the analysis procedures require further explication.

TABLE 9.4-1 Layout of Type RBPF-3² Design and Computational Procedures

(i) Data:

ABFG Summary Table

		ab_{ij}	ab_{ij}	ab_{ij}	$\sum\limits_{1}^{v}FG$
		00	12	21	
g_0	$(AB)_0$	3	7	4	14
		01	10	22	
f_0 g_1	$(AB)_1$	4	3	6	13
		11	02	20	
g_2	$(AB)_2$	3	7	3	13
		00	11	22	
g_0	$(AB^2)_0$	2	4	5	11
		10	02	21	
f_1 g_1	$(AB^2)_1$	1	5	3	9
		01	12	20	
g_2	$(AB^2)_2$	2	6	2	10

AB Summary Table

	b_0	b_1	b_2	$\sum\limits_{1}^{q}A$
	$w = 2$			
a_0	5	6	12	23
a_1	4	7	13	24
a_2	5	7	11	23
$\sum\limits_{1}^{p}B =$	14	20	36	

Note: $ab_{00} = abfg_{00..} = 00 + 00$
$= 3 + 2 = 5$
$ab_{01} = 01 + 01 = 4 + 2 = 6$
$ab_{22} = 22 + 22 = 6 + 5 = 11$

AF Summary Table

	f_0	f_1
	$v = 3$	
a_0	14	9
a_1	13	11
a_2	13	10
$\sum\limits_{1}^{p}F =$ 40		30

BF Summary Table

	f_0	f_1
	$v = 3$	
b_0	9	5
b_1	11	9
b_2	20	16

Note: $af_{00} = abfg_{0.0.} = 00 + 01 + 02 = 3 + 4 + 7 = 14$
$af_{10} = abfg_{1.0.} = 10 + 11 + 12 = 3 + 3 + 7 = 13$
$af_{01} = abfg_{0.1.} = 00 + 01 + 02 = 2 + 2 + 5 = 9$

(ii) Computational symbols:

$$\sum\limits_{1}^{N}ABFG = 3 + 4 + 3 + \cdots + 2 = 70.00$$

$$\sum\limits_{1}^{N}(ABFG)^2 = [ABFG] = (3)^2 + (4)^2 + (3)^2 + \cdots + (2)^2 = 326.00$$

$$\frac{\left(\sum\limits_{1}^{N}ABFG\right)^2}{N} = [X] = \frac{(70)^2}{18} = 272.22$$

$$\sum\limits_{1}^{w}\frac{\left(\sum\limits_{1}^{p}F\right)^2}{vp} = [F] = \frac{(40)^2}{(3)(3)} + \frac{(30)^2}{(3)(3)} = 277.78$$

TABLE 9.4-1 (continued)

$$\frac{\left(\sum\limits_{1}^{p} F_0\right)^2}{vp} = [F_0] = \frac{(40)^2}{(3)(3)} = 177.78$$

$$\frac{\left(\sum\limits_{1}^{p} F_1\right)^2}{vp} = [F_1] = \frac{(30)^2}{(3)(3)} = 100.00$$

$$\sum\limits_{1}^{w}\sum\limits_{1}^{z} \frac{\left(\sum\limits_{1}^{v} FG\right)^2}{v} = [FG] = \frac{(14)^2}{3} + \frac{(13)^2}{3} + \cdots + \frac{(10)^2}{3} = 278.67$$

$$\sum\limits_{1}^{p} \frac{\left(\sum\limits_{1}^{q} A\right)^2}{qw} = [A] = \frac{(23)^2}{(3)(2)} + \frac{(24)^2}{(3)(2)} + \frac{(23)^2}{(3)(2)} = 272.33$$

$$\sum\limits_{1}^{q} \frac{\left(\sum\limits_{1}^{p} B\right)^2}{pw} = [B] = \frac{(14)^2}{(3)(2)} + \frac{(20)^2}{(3)(2)} + \frac{(36)^2}{(3)(2)} = 315.33$$

$$\sum\limits_{1}^{p}\sum\limits_{1}^{w} \frac{(AF)^2}{v} = [AF] = \frac{(14)^2}{3} + \frac{(13)^2}{3} + \cdots + \frac{(10)^2}{3} = 278.67$$

$$\sum\limits_{1}^{q}\sum\limits_{1}^{w} \frac{(BF)^2}{v} = [BF] = \frac{(9)^2}{3} + \frac{(11)^2}{3} + \cdots + \frac{(16)^2}{3} = 321.33$$

(iii) Computational formulas:

$$\text{SS}_{\text{total}} = [ABFG] - [X] = 53.78$$
$$\text{SS}_{\text{between blocks and reps}} = [FG] - [X] = 6.45$$
$$\text{SS}_{\text{replications}} = [F] - [X] = 5.56$$
$$\text{SS}'_{AB(\text{between})} = [FG] - [F] = .89$$
$$\text{SS}_{\text{within blocks and reps}} = [ABFG] - [FG] = 47.33$$
$$\text{SS}_A = [A] - [X] = .11$$
$$\text{SS}_B = [B] - [X] = 43.11$$
$$\text{SS}'_{AB(\text{within})} = [ABFG] - [AF] - [BF] - [FG] + 2[F] = 2.89$$
$$\text{SS}_{AF} = [AF] - [A] - [F] + [X] = .78$$
$$\text{SS}_{BF} = [BF] - [B] - [F] + [X] = .44$$
$$\text{SS}_{\text{residual}} = \text{SS}_{AF} + \text{SS}_{BF} = 1.22$$

DIRECT COMPUTATION OF
INTERACTION SUM OF SQUARES

The computational formulas for $\text{SS}'_{AB(\text{between})}$ and $\text{SS}'_{AB(\text{within})}$ represent relatively simple analysis procedures, but they throw little light on

**TABLE 9.4-2   Analysis of Variance Table for
Type RBPF-3² Design**

	Source	SS	df	MS	F	E(MS) Model III (A and B Fixed Effects)
1	Between blocks and reps	6.45	$wz - 1 = 5$			
2	Replications	5.56	$w - 1 = 1$			
3	AB' (between)	.89	$(p - 1)(q - 1) = 4$			
4	Within blocks and reps	47.33	$wz(v - 1) = 12$			
5	A	.11	$p - 1 = 2$	.055	$[\frac{5}{8}]$ = N.S.	$\sigma_\varepsilon^2 + qw\sigma_\alpha^2$
6	B	43.11	$q - 1 = 2$	21.555	$[\frac{6}{8}]$ = 70.67*	$\sigma_\varepsilon^2 + pw\sigma_\beta^2$
7	AB' (within)	2.89	$(p - 1)(q - 1) = 4$	.722	$[\frac{7}{8}]$ = 2.37	$\sigma_\varepsilon^2 + (\frac{1}{2})w\sigma_{\alpha\beta}^2$
8	Residual	1.22	$= 4$	.305		σ_ε^2
9	AF	.78	$(p - 1)(w - 1) = 2$			
10	BF	.44	$(q - 1)(w - 1) = 2$			
11	Total	53.78	$vwz - 1 = 17$			

*$p < .01$.

the nature of these terms. Actually, both sums of squares are pooled terms. For example,

$$SS'_{AB(\text{between})} = SS_{(AB) \text{ from rep } 0} + SS_{(AB^2) \text{ from rep } 1}$$

$$SS'_{AB(\text{within})} = SS_{(AB^2) \text{ from rep } 0} + SS_{(AB) \text{ from rep } 1}.$$

The between-block interaction components are given by

$$SS_{(AB)\text{between}} = \frac{(AB)_0^2 + (AB)_1^2 + (AB)_2^2}{v} - \frac{\left(\sum_1^p F_0\right)^2}{vp}$$

$$SS_{(AB^2)\text{between}} = \frac{(AB^2)_0^2 + (AB^2)_1^2 + (AB^2)_2^2}{v} - \frac{\left(\sum_1^p F_1\right)^2}{vp},$$

where $(AB)_i$ and $(AB^2)_i$ satisfy the relations

$$x_1 + x_2 = i(\text{mod } 3) \quad \text{and} \quad x_1 + 2x_2 = i(\text{mod } 3),$$

respectively. Treatment combinations satisfying the above relations appear below.

Replication 0
$(AB)_0 = ab_{00} + ab_{12} + ab_{21} = 3 + 7 + 4 = 14$
$(AB)_1 = ab_{01} + ab_{10} + ab_{22} = 4 + 3 + 6 = 13$
$(AB)_2 = ab_{11} + ab_{02} + ab_{20} = 3 + 7 + 3 = 13$

Replication 1
$(AB^2)_0 = ab_{00.} + ab_{11} + ab_{22} = 2 + 4 + 5 = 11$
$(AB^2)_1 = ab_{10} + ab_{02} + ab_{21} = 1 + 5 + 3 = 9$
$(AB^2)_2 = ab_{01} + ab_{12} + ab_{20} = 2 + 6 + 2 = 10$

Computation of the between-block components of the AB interaction, using the above totals, gives

$$SS_{(AB)\text{between}} = \frac{(14)^2 + (13)^2 + (13)^2}{3} - \frac{(40)^2}{(3)(3)} = .22$$

$$SS_{(AB^2)\text{between}} = \frac{(11)^2 + (9)^2 + (10)^2}{3} - \frac{(30)^2}{(3)(3)} = .67.$$

The sum of these two components is equal to $SS'_{AB(\text{between})}$. These two interaction components are completely confounded with block effects. The reader can easily verify this fact by comparing the source of variation that comprises $SS_{(AB)}$ and $SS_{(AB^2)}$ with the source of variation that would be used to compute the sum of squares between blocks. Because of this confounding, an unambiguous interpretation of a significant $MS'_{AB(\text{between})}$ could not be made even if it were possible to test this mean square. In this example, differences between blocks represent different levels of aptitude for learning servicing procedures.

The within-block components of the AB interaction are given by

$$SS_{(AB^2)\text{within}} = \frac{(AB^2)_0^2 + (AB^2)_1^2 + (AB^2)_2^2}{v} - \frac{\left(\sum_1^p F_0\right)^2}{vp}$$

$$SS_{(AB)\text{within}} = \frac{(AB)_0^2 + (AB)_1^2 + (AB)_2^2}{v} - \frac{\left(\sum_1^p F_1\right)^2}{vp}.$$

The components $SS_{(AB)}$ and $SS_{(AB^2)}$ are computed from treatment combinations that (1) satisfy the relations

$$x_1 + x_2 = i(\text{mod } 3) \quad \text{and} \quad x_1 + 2x_2 = i(\text{mod } 3),$$

respectively, and (2) are not confounded with block effects. Treatment totals satisfying both requirements are shown below.

Replication 0
$(AB^2)_0 = ab_{00} + ab_{11} + ab_{22} = 3 + 3 + 6 = 12$
$(AB^2)_1 = ab_{10} + ab_{02} + ab_{21} = 3 + 7 + 4 = 14$
$(AB^2)_2 = ab_{01} + ab_{12} + ab_{20} = 4 + 7 + 3 = 14$

Replication 1
$(AB)_0 = ab_{00} + ab_{12} + ab_{21} = 2 + 6 + 3 = 11$
$(AB)_1 = ab_{01} + ab_{10} + ab_{22} = 2 + 1 + 5 = 8$
$(AB)_2 = ab_{11} + ab_{02} + ab_{20} = 4 + 5 + 2 = 11$

Computation of the two within-block components of the AB interaction gives

$$SS_{(AB^2)\text{within}} = \frac{(12)^2 + (14)^2 + (14)^2}{3} - \frac{(40)^2}{(3)(3)} = .89$$

and

$$SS_{(AB)\text{within}} = \frac{(11)^2 + (8)^2 + (11)^2}{3} - \frac{(30)^2}{(3)(3)} = 2.00.$$

It is customary to pool the two components as was done in Table 9.4-2 in carrying out a test of significance. If it is desirable to test either $SS_{(AB)\text{within}}$ or $SS_{(AB^2)\text{within}}$ separately, the procedure described above rather than the short-cut procedure in Table 9.4-1 must be used.

RELATIVE INFORMATION ON CONFOUNDED EFFECTS

The experimental design summarized in Table 9.4-2 provides within-block information on treatments A and B from both replications. Within-block information on the (AB^2) and (AB) components is available from replications 0 and 1, respectively. Thus only one-half as much information is available on the within-block interaction components as is available on the main effects. The ratio $\frac{1}{2}$ is called the *relative information* on the confounded effects (Yates, 1937).

ASSUMPTIONS OF THE MODEL FOR TYPE RBPF-3^2 DESIGN

Let $X_{ijt(h)}$ be a measure for a randomly selected observation in treatment population ab_{ij}. Under the mixed linear model,

$$X_{ijt(h)} = \mu + \pi_h + \theta_{t(h)} + \alpha_i + \beta_j + \alpha\beta_{ij} + \varepsilon_{ijt(h)},$$

where μ = grand mean of treatment populations.

π_h = effect of replication h.

$\theta_{t(h)}$ = effect of block t, which is nested within replication h.

α_i = effect of treatment i, which is a constant for all observations within treatment population i.

β_j = effect of treatment j, which is a constant for all observations within treatment population j.

$\alpha\beta_{ij}$ = effect that represents nonadditivity of effects α_i and β_j.

$\varepsilon_{ijt(h)}$ = experimental error, which is NID with mean = 0 and variance $= \sigma_\varepsilon^2$.

The F ratios in Table 9.4-2 are distributed as the F distribution under the conditions that (1) the v subjects in each of the wz blocks constitute random samples from a common population, (2) treatments A and B represent fixed effects, blocks are assumed to be random, (3) all pqw populations are normal, (4) the variances of each of the pqw populations are equal, and (5) block and treatment effects are additive. The assumption of equal covariances that is required if a design involves matched subjects or repeated measurements is discussed in detail in Sections 5.3 and 8.5.

COMPOSITION OF RESIDUAL ERROR TERM

The error term for testing "within" effects is MS_{res}. This error term is composed of two pooled interactions. It is assumed that the interaction components σ_{AF}^2 and σ_{BF}^2 are zero, and thus both interaction mean squares are estimates of σ_ε^2. If a test for homogeneity of variance, such as the F_{max} test, is insignificant, it lends some credence to this assumption. If the population variances estimated by MS_{AF} and MS_{BF} are not homogeneous, the two MS's should not be pooled. In this case MS_A can be tested by using MS_{AF} as an estimate of experimental error and MS_B by using MS_{BF}.

The computational formulas for MS_{AF} and MS_{BF} tend to obscure the nature of the sources which are pooled and which must be homogeneous. It can be shown that

$$MS_{AF} = \text{ave } \hat{\sigma}_i^2 - \text{ave } \hat{\rho\sigma}_{ii'}^2$$

and

$$MS_{BF} = \text{ave } \hat{\sigma}_j^2 - \text{ave } \hat{\rho\sigma}_{jj'}^2.$$

The terms ave $\hat{\sigma}_i^2$ and ave $\hat{\sigma}_j^2$ are averages of p and q unbiased estimates respectively of the population treatment variances. The covariances, ave $\hat{\rho\sigma}_{ii'}^2$ and ave $\hat{\rho\sigma}_{jj'}^2$, are averages of $[p(p-1)]/2$ and $[q(q-1)]/2$ unbiased estimates respectively of the population covariances. These terms can be computed from the AF and BF Summary Tables in Table 9.4-1. It is assumed that the population variances are homogeneous and that the population covariances are homogeneous. Procedures for determining if the variance-covariance matrices have the required symmetry are described in Sections 5.3 and 8.5.

The analysis in Table 9.4-2 provides only four degrees of freedom for experimental error. Alternative layouts providing a larger number of degrees of freedom for experimental error are described in Section 9.5.

Procedures for determining the gain in precision that results from confounding are described by Cochran and Cox (1957, 229), who present formulas for estimating the residual error term as if the experiment had been laid out in a randomized block factorial design. These procedures can be used to assess the relative efficiency of any confounded factorial design.

COMPARISONS AMONG MEANS

Comparisons among treatment means can be made using techniques described previously for factorial experiments. These procedures are illustrated for a type CRF-pq design in Section 7.6. Comparisons among means for main effects do not involve any new procedures because these means are free of block effects. If an experimenter wishes to make comparisons among means for simple main effects, he must first adjust the means for block effects. Cell totals in the AB Summary Table can be adjusted for block effects by

$$AB'_{ij} = \frac{\Sigma A_i + \Sigma B_j}{z} + \frac{\Sigma(AB)'_{i+j} + \Sigma(AB^2)'_{i+2j}}{z/w} - \frac{\Sigma ABFG}{z},$$

where ΣA_i = sum of all observations at level a_i.

$\quad\ \Sigma B_j$ = sum of all observations at level b_j.

$\Sigma(AB)'_{i+j}$ = sum of all observations that satisfy the relation $x_1 + x_2 = i + j$ (mod 3) and are free of block effects.

$\Sigma(AB^2)'_{i+2j}$ = sum of all observations that satisfy the relation $x_1 + 2x_2 = i + 2j$ (mod 3) and are free of block effects.

$\quad \Sigma ABFG$ = sum of all observations.

An adjustment for block effects is illustrated for treatment combinations AB_{00} and AB_{02}.

$$AB'_{00} = \frac{\Sigma A_0 + \Sigma B_0}{z} + \frac{(AB)'_{0+0} + (AB^2)'_{0+2(0)}}{z/w} - \frac{\Sigma ABFG}{z}$$

$$= \frac{23 + 14}{3} + \frac{11 + 12}{3/2} - \frac{70}{3} = 4.333$$

$$AB'_{02} = \frac{\Sigma A_0 + \Sigma B_2}{z} + \frac{(AB)'_{0+2} + (AB^2)'_{0+2(2)}}{z/w} - \frac{\Sigma ABFG}{z}$$

$$= \frac{23 + 36}{3} + \frac{11 + 14}{3/2} - \frac{70}{3} = 13.001.$$

In practice, it is customary to obtain the adjusted means by dividing the treatment combination totals by w replications as shown below.

$$\overline{AB}'_{00} = \frac{AB'_{00}}{w} = \frac{4.333}{2} = 2.17 \quad \text{and} \quad \overline{AB}'_{02} = \frac{AB'_{02}}{w} = \frac{13.001}{2} = 6.50.$$

It should be noted that the effective number of replications is actually less than w, for the (AB) and (AB^2) within-block components of the AB interaction are based on only one-half of the replications.

A t ratio for the comparison of two means based on adjusted totals has the general form described in Section 3.2.

$$t = \frac{C_j(\overline{AB}'_{ij}) + C_{j'}(\overline{AB}'_{ij'})}{\sqrt{2MS_{res}/w}}.$$

For example, a comparison of $\overline{AB}'_{00}$ with $\overline{AB}'_{02}$ is given by

$$t = \frac{2.17 - 6.50}{\sqrt{2(.305)/2}} = \frac{-4.33}{.55} = -7.87.$$

$$t_{.05/2,4} = 2.78.$$

9.5   COMPUTATIONAL PROCEDURES
FOR TYPE RBPF-3² DESIGN WITH
REPEATED MEASUREMENTS

The design described in Section 9.4 employed matched subjects. Each of the v subjects participated under only one treatment combination within a block. The v observations could also represent litter mates or v observations on the same subject. In this latter case, each block would correspond to a single subject who is observed under all treatment combinations in the block. If repeated measures are appropriate for the experiment, an alternative analysis for a type RBPF-3² design is possible. This analysis requires wz random samples of n subjects each. The wz samples of subjects are randomly assigned to blocks. Each subject participates under all treatment combinations within an incomplete block. The order of administration of treatment combinations is randomized independently for each subject. A block diagram for this design is shown in Figure 9.5-1.

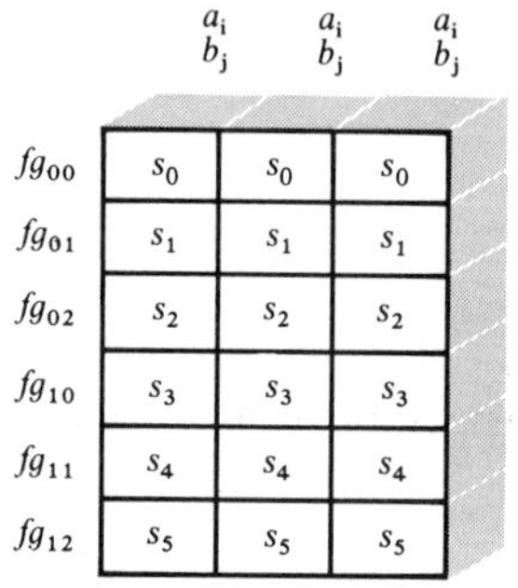

Figure 9.5-1 Block diagram of type RBPF-3² design. s_m refers to sets of n subjects who participate under all treatment combinations in the incomplete block.

The notation scheme for a type RBPF-3² design is described in Section 9.4. In addition to this notation, there are n levels of s_m, where for purposes of illustration $n = 3$ and $\Sigma_1^N = \Sigma_1^n \Sigma_1^v \Sigma_1^w \Sigma_1^z$. A total variance breakdown, degrees of freedom, and computational formulas for this design are given in Table 9.5-1. This particular example, with three subjects

TABLE 9.5-1　Analysis of Variance Table and Computational Formulas for Type RBPF-3² Design with Repeated Measures

	Source	df	Computational Formulas	F Ratio, E(MS) Model III (A and B Fixed Effects)
1	Between subjects	$nwz - 1 = 17$	$[FGS] - [X]$	
2	Between blocks and reps	$wz - 1 = 5$	$[FG] - [X]$	
3	Replications	$w - 1 = 1$	$[F] - [X]$	
4	AB' (between)	$(p-1)(q-1) = 4$	$[FG] - [F]$	
5	Subjects w.blocks and reps	$wz(n-1) = 12$	$[FGS] - [FG]$	
6	Within subjects	$nwz(v-1) = 36$	$[ABFGS] - [FGS]$	
7	A	$p - 1 = 2$	$[A] - [X]$	$\left[\frac{7}{10}\right]$　$\sigma_\varepsilon^2 + qw\sigma_\alpha^2$
8	B	$q - 1 = 2$	$[B] - [X]$	$\left[\frac{8}{10}\right]$　$\sigma_\varepsilon^2 + pw\sigma_\beta^2$
9	AB' (within)	$(p-1)(q-1) = 4$	$[ABFG] - [AF] - [BF] - [FG] + 2[F]$	$\left[\frac{9}{10}\right]$　$\sigma_\varepsilon^2 + (\frac{1}{2})w\sigma_{\alpha\beta}^2$
10	Residual	$= 28$	$SS_{AF} + SS_{BF} + SS_{AB \times \text{subj w.blocks}}$	σ_ε^2
11	AF	$(p-1)(w-1) = 2$	$[AF] - [A] - [F] + [X]$	
12	BF	$(q-1)(w-1) = 2$	$[BF] - [B] - [F] + [X]$	
13	$AB_{ij} \times$ subj w.block (f_0)	$z(n-1)(v-1) = 12$		
14	$AB_{ij} \times$ subj w.block (f_1)	$z(n-1)(v-1) = 12$	$[ABFGS] - [ABFG] - [FGS] + [FG]$	
15	Total	$nvwz - 1 = 53$	$[ABFGS] - [X]$	

assigned to each block, has 28 degrees of freedom for experimental error. The computational procedures are almost identical to the procedures illustrated in Table 9.4-1. The analysis involving repeated measurements on sets of subjects requires, in addition to the summary tables in Table 9.4-1, an *ABFGS* Summary Table. A slight modification of the computational symbols is required because each block corresponds to n subjects. For example,

$$\sum_{1}^{N}(ABFGS)^2 = [ABFGS], \quad \sum_{1}^{n}\sum_{1}^{w}\sum_{1}^{z}\frac{\left(\sum_{1}^{v}FGS\right)^2}{v} = [FGS],$$

$$\sum_{1}^{v}\sum_{1}^{w}\sum_{1}^{z}\frac{(ABFG)^2}{n} = [ABFG], \quad \sum_{1}^{p}\frac{\left(\sum_{1}^{q}A\right)^2}{nqw} = [A].$$

The MS_{res} is composed of pooled interactions. It is assumed that these interactions are each estimates of experimental error and hence that the interaction terms are zero. If a test for homogeneity of variance for these interactions is insignificant, it lends some credence to this assumption. If any of the interaction terms are greater than zero, tests of MS_A, MS_B, and MS'_{AB} are negatively biased. Procedures for testing the assumption of homogeneity are described in Section 2.6.

OTHER PLANS FOR 3² CONFOUNDED FACTORIAL DESIGN

The modification of the type RBPF-3^2 design described is useful when repeated measures can be obtained. Another modification of the basic design in Table 9.4-1 involves using more than two replications. This modification requires that the number of replications must be a multiple of two. A design using four replications is described by Federer (1955, 251). The residual error term for the case in which four replications are used can be broken down as follows:

SS	df
Residual	$= 16$
AF	$(p-1)(w-1) = 6$
BF	$(q-1)(w-1) = 6$
$(AB) \times F$	$(v-1)(w'-1) = 2$
$(AB^2) \times F$	$(v-1)(w'-1) = 2$

where $w' = 2$. The analysis of this design presents no new computational problems.

A completely confounded 3^2 design (type RBCF-3^2 design) can be used with any number of replications. The design is constructed by confounding either (AB) or (AB^2) in all replications. A disadvantage of this design is that it does not provide within-block information on both components of the AB interaction. If two, or a multiple of two, replications are used, a type RBPF-33 design is preferable to this one. For a description of this completely confounded design, see Cochran and Cox (1957, 193), Federer (1955, 239), and Hicks (1965, 213).

9.6 COMPUTATIONAL PROCEDURES FOR TYPE RBCF-2³ DESIGN

A 2^2 experiment in which both treatments have only two levels can be laid out in complete blocks of size four. Since the block is already small, there is no point in using confounding to reduce the size of the block further. For this reason, a 3^2 example, instead of a 2^2 example, was used to introduce the concept of confounding in this chapter. A type RBPF-3^2 design is the smallest two-treatment design for which confounding is useful.

A completely confounded 2^3 design is described in this section. If each of the three treatments has two levels, there are eight treatment combinations. Since in the behavioral sciences it is difficult to secure sets of eight homogeneous subjects, obtaining repeated measures on the same subjects is an alternative approach to achieving homogeneity. However, this is not always feasible because of the nature of the treatments used in the experiment. If an experimenter is willing to sacrifice within-block information on the ABC interaction or one of the first-order interactions, a 2^3 experiment can be laid out in incomplete blocks of size four.

As in the earlier confounded designs, modular arithmetic is used to determine which treatment combinations are assigned to each block. Let x_1, x_2, and x_3 refer to the levels of treatments A, B, and C, respectively. Because each treatment has two levels, the modulus 2 is used. All treatment combinations satisfying the relation

$$(ABC)_0 \quad \text{or} \quad [x_1 + x_2 + x_3 = 0(\text{mod } 2)]$$

are assigned to one block. Treatment combinations satisfying the relation

$$(ABC)_1 \quad \text{or} \quad [x_1 + x_2 + x_3 = 1(\text{mod } 2)]$$

are assigned to the other block. Table 9.6-1 shows the treatment combinations that satisfy the above two relations.

The example illustrating the computation for this design used four replications of the two blocks in Table 9.6-1. This was done to facilitate the comparison of this analysis with the analysis of a balanced partially confounded design described in Section 9.7. Any number of replications can be used with a type RBCF-2^3 design. If less than three replications

TABLE 9.6-1   **Treatment Combinations That Satisfy the Relations** $x_1 + x_2 + x_3 = i \pmod 2$, $i = 0, 1$

	abc_{ijk}	abc_{ijk}	abc_{ijk}	abc_{ijk}
Block $(ABC)_0$	000	011	101	110
Block $(ABC)_1$	001	010	100	111

are used, the number of degrees of freedom for experimental error is very small. For example, with two replications there are $2(4 - 1)(2 - 1) = 6$ degrees of freedom for evaluating main effects and unconfounded interactions. If three replications are used, there are $2(4 - 1)(3 - 1) = 12$ degrees of freedom. If more than one replication of the two blocks in Table 9.6-1 is obtained, a test of the completely confounded ABC interaction can be made. This test is relatively insensitive. An example illustrating the computational procedures for a type RBCF-2^3 design is shown in Table 9.6-2. The results of the analysis are summarized in Table 9.6-3. The following notation is used in the tables:

$$p \text{ levels of } a_i, \text{ where } p = 2$$

$$q \text{ levels of } b_j, \text{ where } q = 2$$

$$r \text{ levels of } c_k, \text{ where } r = 2$$

$$v \text{ levels of } X \text{ (observations/block), where } v = 4$$

$$w \text{ levels of } f_h \text{ (replications), where } w = 4$$

$$z \text{ levels of } g_t \text{ (blocks), where } z = 2$$

$$\sum_1^N = \sum_1^v \sum_1^w \sum_1^z.$$

According to the summary in Table 9.6-3, all within-block main effects and interactions are significant. Because the first-order interactions are significant, the next step in analyzing the data is to make comparisons among simple effects means. However, first several additional comments concerning a type RBCF-2^3 design are in order. The reader has probably already noted from Table 9.6-3 that the $MS_{res(between)}$ is based on only 3 df, while $MS_{res(within)}$ has 18 df. In this example, an experimenter sacrifices precision in evaluating MS_{ABC} in order to achieve a smaller size block and greater precision in evaluating other effects. The disadvantage of loss of precision in evaluating MS_{ABC} is not as great as it might first appear because an experimenter can choose the interaction to confound with blocks. If, for example, it is anticipated that the AC interaction is zero, this interaction, rather than the ABC interaction, can be confounded with blocks by using the family of relations:

$$x_1 + x_3 = i \pmod 2, \qquad i = 0, 1.$$

**TABLE 9.6-2　Layout of Type RBCF-2³ Design
and Computational Procedures**

(i) Data:

ABCFG Summary Table

		abc_{ijk}	abc_{ijk}	abc_{ijk}	abc_{ijk}
		000	011	101	110
	g_0	3	7	2	5
f_0		001	010	100	111
	g_1	4	7	1	10
		000	011	101	110
	g_0	6	8	3	6
f_1		001	010	100	111
	g_1	5	8	2	10
		000	011	101	110
	g_0	3	9	4	5
f_2		001	010	100	111
	g_1	4	7	2	9
		000	011	101	110
	g_0	3	8	3	6
f_3		001	010	100	111
	g_1	3	6	2	11

AB Summary Table

	b_0	b_1	$\overset{q}{\underset{1}{\sum}}A$
a_0	$wz = 8$ 31	60	91
a_1	19	62	81

$$\overset{p}{\underset{1}{\sum}}B = 50 \qquad 122$$

AC Summary Table

	c_0	c_1
a_0	$wz = 8$ 43	48
a_1	29	52

$$\overset{p}{\underset{1}{\sum}}C = 72 \qquad 100$$

BC Summary Table

	c_0	c_1
b_0	$wz = 8$ 22	28
b_1	50	72

FG Summary Table

	g_0	g_1	$\overset{z}{\underset{1}{\sum}}F$
f_0	$v = 4$ 17	22	39
f_1	23	25	48
f_2	21	22	43
f_3	20	22	42

$$\overset{w}{\underset{1}{\sum}}G = 81 \qquad 91$$

TABLE 9.6-2 (continued)

(ii) Computational symbols:

$$\sum_{1}^{N} ABCFG = 3 + 4 + \cdots + 11 = 172.000$$

$$\sum_{1}^{N} (ABCFG)^2 = [ABCFG] = (3)^2 + (4)^2 + \cdots + (11)^2 = 1160.000$$

$$\frac{\left(\sum_{1}^{N} ABCFG\right)^2}{N} = [X] = \frac{(172)^2}{32} = 924.500$$

$$\sum_{1}^{w} \frac{\left(\sum_{1}^{z} F\right)^2}{vz} = [F] = \frac{(39)^2}{(4)(2)} + \frac{(48)^2}{(4)(2)} + \cdots + \frac{(42)^2}{(4)(2)} = 929.750$$

$$\sum_{1}^{z} \frac{\left(\sum_{1}^{w} G\right)^2}{vw} = [G] = \frac{(81)^2}{(4)(4)} + \frac{(91)^2}{(4)(4)} = 927.625$$

$$\sum_{1}^{w} \sum_{1}^{z} \frac{\left(\sum_{1}^{v} FG\right)^2}{v} = [FG] = \frac{(17)^2}{4} + \frac{(22)^2}{4} + \cdots + \frac{(22)^2}{4} = 934.000$$

$$\sum_{1}^{p} \frac{\left(\sum_{1}^{q} A\right)^2}{qwz} = [A] = \frac{(91)^2}{(2)(4)(2)} + \frac{(81)^2}{(2)(4)(2)} = 927.625$$

$$\sum_{1}^{q} \frac{\left(\sum_{1}^{p} B\right)^2}{pwz} = [B] = \frac{(50)^2}{(2)(4)(2)} + \frac{(122)^2}{(2)(4)(2)} = 1086.500$$

$$\sum_{1}^{r} \frac{\left(\sum_{1}^{p} C\right)^2}{pwz} = [C] = \frac{(72)^2}{(2)(4)(2)} + \frac{(100)^2}{(2)(4)(2)} = 949.000$$

$$\sum_{1}^{p} \sum_{1}^{q} \frac{(AB)^2}{wz} = [AB] = \frac{(31)^2}{(4)(2)} + \cdots + \frac{(62)^2}{(4)(2)} = 1095.750$$

$$\sum_{1}^{p} \sum_{1}^{r} \frac{(AC)^2}{wz} = [AC] = \frac{(43)^2}{(4)(2)} + \cdots + \frac{(52)^2}{(4)(2)} = 962.250$$

$$\sum_{1}^{q} \sum_{1}^{r} \frac{(BC)^2}{wz} = [BC] = \frac{(22)^2}{(4)(2)} + \cdots + \frac{(72)^2}{(4)(2)} = 1119.000$$

(iii) Computational formulas:

$$SS_{total} = [ABCFG] - [X] = 235.500$$

$$SS_{between\ blocks\ and\ reps} = [FG] - [X] = 9.500$$

$$SS_{replications} = [F] - [X] = 5.250$$

$$SS_{ABC\ or\ blocks} = [G] - [X] = 3.125$$

$$SS_{residual(between)} = [FG] - [F] - [G] + [X] = 1.125$$

$$SS_{within\ blocks\ and\ reps} = [ABCFG] - [FG] = 226.000$$

TABLE 9.6-2 (continued)

$$SS_A = [A] - [X] = 3.125$$
$$SS_B = [B] - [X] = 162.000$$
$$SS_C = [C] - [X] = 24.500$$
$$SS_{AB} = [AB] - [A] - [B] + [X] = 6.125$$
$$SS_{AC} = [AC] - [A] - [C] + [X] = 10.125$$
$$SS_{BC} = [BC] - [B] - [C] + [X] = 8.000$$
$$SS_{residual(within)} = [ABCFG] - [AB] - [AC] - [BC] - [FG] + [A] + [B] + [C]$$
$$= 12.125$$

COMPOSITION OF ERROR TERMS

The composition of the two residual error terms in Table 9.6-3 is not readily apparent. However, it is not difficult to understand the nature of these sources of variation if the data in Table 9.6-2 are recast in a different form. For example, the $MS_{res(between)}$ is the interaction of *replications* × *ABC interaction*. It should be noted that the *ABC* interaction is indistinguishable from block effects because of the way in which the treatment combinations were assigned to blocks. If the relation

$$x_1 + x_3 = i(\bmod 2), \qquad i = 0, 1$$

had been used to determine which treatment combinations were assigned to each block, the *AC* interaction would have been confounded with blocks and MS_{ABC} would have been a within-block term. The *between-block* terms with seven degrees of freedom can be conceived of as comprising a randomized block design. This analogy is illustrated in Figure 9.6-1. Here variation between columns corresponds to the *ABC* interaction (or sum of squares for blocks) and variation between rows corresponds to the sum of squares for replications. It will be recalled that the error term for evaluating row and column mean squares in a randomized block design is the interaction of rows × columns. In this case, this interaction is analogous to $F \times ABC$, with df $= (4 - 1)(2 - 1) = 3$. The total degrees of freedom for between-block terms is equal to seven. The remaining four degrees of freedom are accounted for by the rows and columns with $4 - 1$ and $2 - 1$ degrees of freedom, respectively.

TABLE 9.6-3 Analysis of Variance Table for Type RBCF-2^3 Design

	Source	SS	df	MS	F	E(MS) Model III
1	Between blocks and reps	9.500	$wz - 1 = 7$			
2	Replications	5.250	$w - 1 = 3$			
3	ABC (Blocks)	3.125	$(z - 1) = 1$	3.125	$\left[\frac{3}{4}\right] = 8.33$	$\sigma_\varepsilon^2 + v\sigma_\pi^2 + w\sigma_{\alpha\beta\gamma}^2$
4	Residual (between)	1.125	$(w - 1)(z - 1) = 3$	.375		$\sigma_\varepsilon^2 + v\sigma_\pi^2$
5	Within blocks and reps	226.000	$wz(v - 1) = 24$			
6	A	3.125	$p - 1 = 1$	3.125	$\left[\frac{6}{12}\right] = 4.64^*$	$\sigma_\varepsilon^2 + qrw\sigma_\alpha^2$
7	B	162.000	$q - 1 = 1$	162.000	$\left[\frac{7}{12}\right] = 240.36^{**}$	$\sigma_\varepsilon^2 + prw\sigma_\beta^2$
8	C	24.500	$r - 1 = 1$	24.500	$\left[\frac{8}{12}\right] = 36.35^{**}$	$\sigma_\varepsilon^2 + pqw\sigma_\gamma^2$
9	AB	6.125	$(p - 1)(q - 1) = 1$	6.125	$\left[\frac{9}{12}\right] = 9.09^{**}$	$\sigma_\varepsilon^2 + rw\sigma_{\alpha\beta}^2$
10	AC	10.125	$(p - 1)(r - 1) = 1$	10.125	$\left[\frac{10}{12}\right] = 15.02^{**}$	$\sigma_\varepsilon^2 + qw\sigma_{\alpha\gamma}^2$
11	BC	8.000	$(q - 1)(r - 1) = 1$	8.000	$\left[\frac{11}{12}\right] = 11.87^{**}$	$\sigma_\varepsilon^2 + pw\sigma_{\beta\gamma}^2$
12	Residual (within)	12.125	$z(v - 1)(w - 1) = 18$	.674		σ_ε^2
13	$ABC_{ijk} \times F(g_0)$	7.0625	$(v - 1)(w - 1) = 9$			
14	$ABC_{ijk} \times F(g_1)$	5.0625	$(v - 1)(w - 1) = 9$			
15	Total	235.500	$vwz - 1 = 31$			

$^*p < .05.$

$^{**}p < .01.$

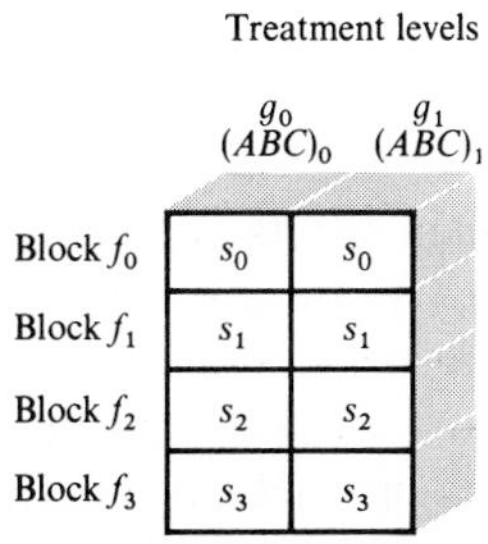

Treatment levels

g_0 g_1
$(A\hat{B}C)_0$ $(A\hat{B}C)_1$

Block f_0	s_0	s_0
Block f_1	s_1	s_1
Block f_2	s_2	s_2
Block f_3	s_3	s_3

Figure 9.6-1 *Between-block* terms of type RBCF-2^3 design recast in form of type RB-2 design.

The $MS_{res(within)}$ can also be understood by breaking it down into its underlying building block design. This error term corresponds to the pooled interaction of *replications × treatment combinations* at each level of *G*. The meaning of this statement can be clarified by examining the two type RB-4 designs in Figure 9.6-2. The building block design for

Treatment combinations

abc_{000} abc_{011} abc_{101} abc_{110}

Block fg_{00}	s_0	s_0	s_0	s_0
Block fg_{10}	s_1	s_1	s_1	s_1
Block fg_{20}	s_2	s_2	s_2	s_2
Block fg_{30}	s_3	s_3	s_3	s_3

Treatment combinations

abc_{001} abc_{010} abc_{100} abc_{111}

Block fg_{01}	s_0	s_0	s_0	s_0
Block fg_{11}	s_1	s_1	s_1	s_1
Block fg_{21}	s_2	s_2	s_2	s_2
Block fg_{31}	s_3	s_3	s_3	s_3

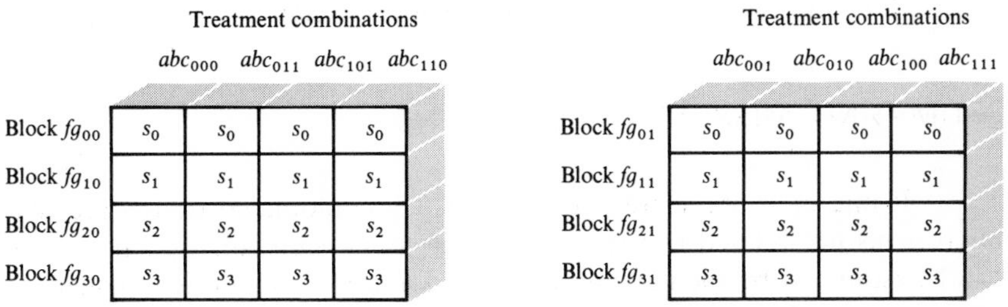

Figure 9.6-2 *Within-block* terms of type RBCF-2^3 design recast in form of two type RB-4 designs.

the *within-block* terms is a randomized block design. The interaction of rows and columns of the two type RB-4 designs is pooled in forming the $MS_{res(within)}$. This analogy is further clarified in Table 9.6-4. The computation of the sum of squares for *F × treatment combinations* is not illustrated. It can easily be computed by inserting the appropriate numbers in Figure 9.6-2 and computing the row × column interaction sum of squares.

TABLE 9.6-4 Breakdown of SS $_{residual\ (within)}$

Source	SS	df
Residual(within)	12.125	$z(v-1)(w-1) = 18$
Block 0 *F* × treatment combinations	7.0625	$(v-1)(w-1) = 9$
Block 1 *F* × treatment combinations	5.0625	$(v-1)(w-1) = 9$

In order for the *F* ratio to be distributed as the *F* distribution, the two interactions that are pooled to form $MS_{res(within)}$ must be homogeneous. There is no reason, in the behavioral sciences, to expect that these two sources of variance are heterogeneous, and thus a test of the assumption is not made routinely. The assumption can be evaluated by means of an F_{max} ratio or other test for homogeneity of variance.

COMPARISONS AMONG MEANS

For a $2 \times 2 \times 2$ design, F ratios for main effects are analogous to t ratios. Thus if interactions among treatments are insignificant, there is no need for further tests. If any of the first-order interactions are significant, comparisons among simple-effects means are useful in interpreting the data. Computational procedures for making these comparisons are identical, except for the error term, with procedures described in Section 7.6. This follows from the fact that main effects and first-order interactions are not confounded with blocks.

It is unlikely that MS_{ABC} or any other interaction that is confounded with blocks will be significant in a type RBCF-2^3 design. The reason is that an experimenter only confounds interactions that he anticipates are insignificant. Treatment totals can be adjusted for differences among blocks, but this procedure is not recommended (Federer; 1955, 238).

ESTIMATING MISSING OBSERVATIONS

If one or more scores in a completely confounded design are lost for reasons not related to the nature of the treatments, the missing scores can be estimated by the formula for a randomized block design. A general description of this procedure appears in Section 5.6. In order to estimate ABC_{ijk}, the term ΣB_j in Section 5.6 is redefined as the sum of observations in all blocks that contain ABC_{ijk}. ΣBS is defined as the sum of all observations in blocks that are designated to include ABC_{ijk}.

If missing observations occur in partially confounded experiments, estimation procedures are more complex. The reader is referred to Cochran and Cox (1957, 227) for a discussion of this problem.

USE OF REPEATED MEASUREMENTS
IN TYPE RBCF-2^3 DESIGN

The wz blocks of a type RBCF-2^3 design may consist of sets of matched subjects or litter mates. Alternatively, the blocks may contain one subject in each block who is observed under all treatment combinations in that block. If sufficient subjects are available, n subjects may be assigned to each block, thereby increasing the number of degrees of freedom for experimental error. A type RBCF-2^3 design can be easily modified for this situation. The design requires wz sets of n subjects ($n > 1$) who are observed under v treatment combinations. The order in which the treatment combinations are presented should be randomized independently for each subject.

Table 9.6-5 presents a breakdown of total variance, degrees of freedom, and computational formulas for this modified design. In addition to the notation scheme given at the beginning of this section, one additional

TABLE 9.6-5   Analysis of Variance Table and Computational Formulas for Type RBCF-2³ Design with Repeated Measures

	Source	df	Computational Formulas	F	E(MS) Model III
1	Between subjects	$nwz - 1 = 15$	$[FGS] - [X]$		
2	Between blocks and reps	$wz - 1 = 7$	$[FG] - [X]$		
3	Replications	$w - 1 = 3$	$[F] - [X]$		
4	Blocks × reps	$(w - 1)(z - 1) = 3$	$[FG] - [F] - [G] + [X]$		
5	ABC	$(z - 1) = 1$	$[G] - [X]$	$\left[\frac{5}{6}\right]$	$\sigma_\varepsilon^2 + v\sigma_\pi^2 + n\sigma_{\alpha\beta\gamma}^2$
6	Subj w.blocks and reps	$wz(n - 1) = 8$	$[FGS] - [FG]$		$\sigma_\varepsilon^2 + v\sigma_\pi^2$
7	Within subjects	$nwz(v - 1) = 48$	$[ABCFGS] - [FGS]$		
8	A	$p - 1 = 1$	$[A] - [X]$	$\left[\frac{8}{14}\right]$	$\sigma_\varepsilon^2 + nqrw\sigma_\alpha^2$
9	B	$q - 1 = 1$	$[B] - [X]$	$\left[\frac{9}{14}\right]$	$\sigma_\varepsilon^2 + nprw\sigma_\beta^2$
10	C	$r - 1 = 1$	$[C] - [X]$	$\left[\frac{10}{14}\right]$	$\sigma_\varepsilon^2 + npqw\sigma_\gamma^2$
11	AB	$(p - 1)(q - 1) = 1$	$[AB] - [A] - [B] + [X]$	$\left[\frac{11}{14}\right]$	$\sigma_\varepsilon^2 + nrw\sigma_{\alpha\beta}^2$
12	AC	$(p - 1)(r - 1) = 1$	$[AC] - [A] - [C] + [X]$	$\left[\frac{12}{14}\right]$	$\sigma_\varepsilon^2 + nqw\sigma_{\alpha\gamma}^2$
13	BC	$(q - 1)(r - 1) = 1$	$[BC] - [B] - [C] + [X]$	$\left[\frac{13}{14}\right]$	$\sigma_\varepsilon^2 + npw\sigma_{\beta\gamma}^2$
14	Residual (within)	$z(v - 1)(nw - 1) = 42$	$[ABCFGS] - [ABCG] - [FGS] + [G]$		σ_ε^2
15	$ABC \times F$ for g_0	$(v - 1)(w - 1) = 9$	$[ABCF] - [ABC] - [F] + [X]$ for g_0		
16	$ABC \times F$ for g_1	$(v - 1)(w - 1) = 9$	$[ABCF] - [ABC] - [F] + [X]$ for g_1		
17	$ABC \times$ subj w.reps for g_0	$w(n - 1)(v - 1) = 12$	$[ABCFS] - [ABCF] - [FS] + [F]$ for g_0		
18	$ABC \times$ subj w.reps for g_1	$w(n - 1)(v - 1) = 12$	$[ABCFS] - [ABCF] - [FS] + [F]$ for g_1		
19	Total	$nvwz - 1 = 63$	$[ABCFGS] - [X]$		

term is used in this design. This term is n and designates the number of subjects assigned to the wz blocks. For purposes of this example, assume that $n = 2$.

9.7   COMPUTATIONAL PROCEDURES
FOR TYPE RBPF-2^3 DESIGN

The $2 \times 2 \times 2$ design described in Section 9.6 is an example of a *completely* confounded design. In this design, the ABC interaction was confounded with between-block variation in each replication. Whenever complete confounding is used, within-block information is lost with respect to the interaction (component) that is confounded with blocks. An alternative procedure is to confound a different interaction in each replication. For example, in a $2 \times 2 \times 2$ design, the AB interaction can be confounded in the first replication, AC in the second, BC in the third, and ABC in the fourth replication. If this is done, within-block information for each interaction can be obtained from three of the four replications. Of course, within-block information with respect to the three treatments is available from all four replications. A design in which all effects of a particular order are confounded with blocks an equal number of times is called a balanced partially confounded design and designated by the letters RBPF.

This section describes a type RBPF-2^3 design. The same set of data used to illustrate a type RBCF-2^3 design are also used for this type RBPF-2^3 design. In order to confound the AB interaction with blocks in the first replication (f_0), treatment combinations that satisfy the relations

$$[x_1 + x_2 = 0(\text{mod } 2)] = (AB)_0 = 00, 11$$

and

$$[x_1 + x_2 = 1(\text{mod } 2)] = (AB)_1 = 01, 10$$

must be assigned to blocks fg_{00} and fg_{01}, respectively. The two levels of treatment C can be included in the two blocks in a balanced manner by the addition of 0 and 1 to the above ab treatment combinations. Thus block fg_{00} consists of treatment combinations

$$000, 001, 110, \text{ and } 111,$$

where the first, second, and third numbers designate the level of treatments A, B, and C, respectively. Similarly, block fg_{01} consists of treatment combinations

$$010, 011, 100, \text{ and } 101.$$

It should be apparent that the difference between the above two blocks is free of variation due to A, B, C, AC, BC, and ABC.

In order to confound the AC interaction with blocks in the second replication (f_1), all treatment combinations satisfying the relations

$$[x_1 + x_3 = 0(\text{mod } 2)] = (AC)_0 = 00, \; 11$$

and

$$[x_1 + x_3 = 1(\text{mod } 2)] = (AC)_1 = 01, \; 10$$

are assigned to blocks fg_{10} and fg_{11}, respectively. Treatment B can be included in these blocks in a balanced manner by inserting 0 and 1 between the ac treatment level designations. The resulting blocks are

$$000, \, 010, \, 101, \, 111$$

and

$$001, \, 011, \, 100, \, 110.$$

The BC and ABC interactions can be confounded with between-block variation in the third and fourth replications (f_2 and f_3), respectively, by means of the family of relations

$$[x_2 + x_3 = i(\text{mod } 2)] = (BC)_i \quad \text{and} \quad [x_1 + x_2 + x_3 = i(\text{mod } 2)] = (ABC)_i,$$

where i assumes values of 0 and 1. Treatment combinations satisfying these relations appear in the $ABCFG$ Summary Table of Table 9.7-1.

TABLE 9.7-1   Layout of Type RBPF-2^3 Design and Computational Procedures

(i) Data:

ABCFG Summary Table

			abc	abc	abc	abc
f_0	$(AB)_0$	g_0	000	001	110	111
			3	4	5	10
	$(AB)_1$	g_1	010	011	100	101
			7	7	1	2
f_1	$(AC)_0$	g_0	000	010	101	111
			6	8	3	10
	$(AC)_1$	g_1	001	011	100	110
			5	8	2	6
f_2	$(BC)_0$	g_0	000	011	100	111
			3	9	2	9
	$(BC)_1$	g_1	001	010	101	110
			4	7	4	5
f_3	$(ABC)_0$	g_0	000	011	101	110
			3	8	3	6
	$(ABC)_1$	g_1	001	010	100	111
			3	6	2	11

TABLE 9.7-1 (continued)

AB′ Summary Table
(based on rep $f_1 + f_2 + f_3$)

	b_0	b_1	$\sum_1^q A'_{AB}$
a_0	$rw' = 6$ 24	46	70
a_1	16	47	63
$\sum_1^p B'_{AB} = 40$		93	

AC′ Summary Table
(based on rep $f_0 + f_2 + f_3$)

	c_0	c_1	$\sum_1^r A'_{AC}$
a_0	$qw' = 6$ 29	35	64
a_1	21	39	60
$\sum_1^p C'_{AC} = 50$		74	

BC′ Summary Table
(based on rep $f_0 + f_1 + f_3$)

	c_0	c_1	$\sum_1^r B'_{BC}$
b_0	$pw' = 6$ 17	20	37
b_1	38	54	92
$\sum_1^q C'_{BC} = 55$		74	

AB Summary Table
(based on all reps)

	b_0	b_1	$\sum_1^q A$
a_0	$rw = 8$ 31	60	91
a_1	19	62	81
$\sum_1^p B = 50$		122	

ABC″ Summary Table
(based on rep $f_0 + f_1 + f_2$)

	b_0 c_0	b_0 c_1	b_1 c_0	b_1 c_1	$\sum_1^q \sum_1^r A''_{ABC}$
a_0	$w' = 3$ 12	13	22	24	71
a_1	5	9	16	29	59
$\sum_1^p B''_{ABC} = 39$			91		
$\sum_1^p C''_{ABC} = 55$			75		

AC Summary Table
(based on all reps)

	c_0	c_1
a_0	$qw = 8$ 43	48
a_1	29	52
$\sum_1^p C = 72$		100

FG Summary Table

	g_0	g_1	$\sum_1^z F$
f_0	$v = 4$ 22	17	39
f_1	27	21	48
f_2	23	20	43
f_3	20	22	42
$\sum_1^w G = 81$		91	

TABLE 9.7-1 (continued)

AB" Summary Table
(based on rep $f_0 + f_1 + f_2$)

	b_0	b_1
	$rw' = 6$	
a_0	25	46
a_1	14	45

AC" Summary Table
(based on rep $f_0 + f_1 + f_2$)

	c_0	c_1
	$qw' = 6$	
a_0	34	37
a_1	21	38

BC" Summary Table
(based on rep $f_0 + f_1 + f_2$)

	c_0	c_1
	$pw' = 6$	
b_0	17	22
b_1	38	53

(ii) Computational symbols:

$$\sum_1^N ABCFG = 3 + 7 + 6 + \cdots + 11 = 172.000$$

$$\sum_1^N (ABCFG)^2 = [ABCFG] = (3)^2 + (7)^2 + (6)^2 + \cdots + (11)^2 = 1160.000$$

$$\frac{\left(\sum_1^N ABCFG\right)^2}{N} = [X] = \frac{(172)^2}{32} = 924.500$$

$$\sum_1^w \frac{\left(\sum_1^z F\right)^2}{vz} = [F] = \frac{(39)^2}{(4)(2)} + \frac{(48)^2}{(4)(2)} + \cdots + \frac{(42)^2}{(4)(2)} = 929.750$$

$$\frac{\left(\sum_1^z F_0\right)^2}{vz} = [F_0] = \frac{(39)^2}{(4)(2)} = 190.125$$

$$\frac{\left(\sum_1^z F_1\right)^2}{vz} = [F_1] = \frac{(48)^2}{(4)(2)} = 288.000$$

$$\frac{\left(\sum_1^z F_2\right)^2}{vz} = [F_2] = \frac{(43)^2}{(4)(2)} = 231.125$$

$$\frac{\left(\sum_1^z F_3\right)^2}{vz} = [F_3] = \frac{(42)^2}{(4)(2)} = 220.500$$

$$\sum_1^w \sum_1^z \frac{(FG)^2}{v} = [FG] = \frac{(22)^2}{4} + \frac{(27)^2}{4} + \cdots + \frac{(22)^2}{4} = 939.000$$

$$\sum_1^z \frac{(FG_{0.})^2}{v} = [FG_{0.}] = \frac{(22)^2}{4} + \frac{(17)^2}{4} = 193.250$$

$$\sum_1^z \frac{(FG_{1.})^2}{v} = [FG_{1.}] = \frac{(27)^2}{4} + \frac{(21)^2}{4} = 292.500$$

$$\sum_1^z \frac{(FG_{2.})^2}{v} = [FG_{2.}] = \frac{(23)^2}{4} + \frac{(20)^2}{4} = 232.250$$

$$\sum_1^z \frac{(FG_{3.})^2}{v} = [FG_{3.}] = \frac{(20)^2}{4} + \frac{(22)^2}{4} = 221.000$$

$$\sum_1^p \frac{\left(\sum_1^q A\right)^2}{qrw} = [A] = \frac{(91)^2}{(2)(4)(2)} + \frac{(81)^2}{(2)(4)(2)} = 927.625$$

TABLE 9.7-1 (continued)

$$\sum_{1}^{p} \frac{\left(\sum_{1}^{q} A'_{AB}\right)^2}{qrw'} = [A'_{AB}] = \frac{(70)^2}{(2)(3)(2)} + \frac{(63)^2}{(2)(3)(2)} = 739.083$$

$$\sum_{1}^{p} \frac{\left(\sum_{1}^{r} A'_{AC}\right)^2}{qrw'} = [A'_{AC}] = \frac{(64)^2}{(2)(3)(2)} + \frac{(60)^2}{(2)(3)(2)} = 641.333$$

$$\sum_{1}^{p} \frac{\left(\sum_{1}^{q}\sum_{1}^{r} A''_{ABC}\right)^2}{qrw'} = [A''_{ABC}] = \frac{(71)^2}{(2)(2)(3)} + \frac{(59)^2}{(2)(2)(3)} = 710.167$$

$$\sum_{1}^{q} \frac{\left(\sum_{1}^{p} B\right)^2}{prw} = [B] = \frac{(50)^2}{(2)(4)(2)} + \frac{(122)^2}{(2)(4)(2)} = 1086.500$$

$$\sum_{1}^{q} \frac{\left(\sum_{1}^{p} B'_{AB}\right)^2}{prw'} = [B'_{AB}] = \frac{(40)^2}{(2)(3)(2)} + \frac{(93)^2}{(2)(3)(2)} = 854.083$$

$$\sum_{1}^{q} \frac{\left(\sum_{1}^{r} B'_{BC}\right)^2}{prw'} = [B'_{BC}] = \frac{(37)^2}{(2)(3)(2)} + \frac{(92)^2}{(2)(3)(2)} = 819.417$$

$$\sum_{1}^{q} \frac{\left(\sum_{1}^{p} B''_{ABC}\right)^2}{prw'} = [B''_{ABC}] = \frac{(39)^2}{(2)(2)(3)} + \frac{(91)^2}{(2)(2)(3)} = 816.833$$

$$\sum_{1}^{r} \frac{\left(\sum_{1}^{p} C\right)^2}{pqw} = [C] = \frac{(72)^2}{(2)(4)(2)} + \frac{(100)^2}{(2)(4)(2)} = 949.000$$

$$\sum_{1}^{r} \frac{\left(\sum_{1}^{p} C'_{AC}\right)^2}{pqw'} = [C'_{AC}] = \frac{(50)^2}{(2)(3)(2)} + \frac{(74)^2}{(2)(3)(2)} = 664.667$$

$$\sum_{1}^{r} \frac{\left(\sum_{1}^{q} C'_{BC}\right)^2}{pqw'} = [C'_{BC}] = \frac{(55)^2}{(2)(3)(2)} + \frac{(74)^2}{(2)(3)(2)} = 708.417$$

$$\sum_{1}^{r} \frac{\left(\sum_{1}^{p} C''_{ABC}\right)^2}{pqw'} = [C''_{ABC}] = \frac{(55)^2}{(2)(2)(3)} + \frac{(75)^2}{(2)(2)(3)} = 720.833$$

$$\sum_{1}^{p}\sum_{1}^{q} \frac{(AB')^2}{rw'} = [AB'] = \frac{(24)^2}{(3)(2)} + \cdots + \frac{(47)^2}{(3)(2)} = 859.500$$

$$\sum_{1}^{p}\sum_{1}^{q} \frac{(AB'')^2}{rw'} = [AB''_{ABC}] = \frac{(25)^2}{(2)(3)} + \cdots + \frac{(45)^2}{(2)(3)} = 827.000$$

$$\sum_{1}^{p}\sum_{1}^{r} \frac{(AC')^2}{qw'} = [AC'] = \frac{(29)^2}{(3)(2)} + \cdots + \frac{(39)^2}{(3)(2)} = 671.333$$

$$\sum_{1}^{p}\sum_{1}^{r} \frac{(AC'')^2}{qw'} = [AC''_{ABC}] = \frac{(34)^2}{(2)(3)} + \cdots + \frac{(38)^2}{(2)(3)} = 735.000$$

$$\sum_{1}^{q}\sum_{1}^{r} \frac{(BC')^2}{pw'} = [BC'] = \frac{(17)^2}{(3)(2)} + \cdots + \frac{(54)^2}{(3)(2)} = 841.500$$

$$\sum_{1}^{q}\sum_{1}^{r} \frac{(BC'')^2}{pw'} = [BC''_{ABC}] = \frac{(17)^2}{(2)(3)} + \cdots + \frac{(53)^2}{(2)(3)} = 837.667$$

TABLE 9.7-1 (continued)

$$\sum_1^p\sum_1^q\sum_1^r \frac{(ABC'')^2}{w'} = [ABC''] = \frac{(12)^2}{3} + \frac{(13)^2}{3} + \cdots + \frac{(29)^2}{3} = 858.667$$

$$\frac{\left(\sum_1^p\sum_1^q AB'\right)^2}{pqrw'} = [X'_{AB}] = \frac{(133)^2}{24} = 737.042$$

$$\frac{\left(\sum_1^p\sum_1^r AC'\right)^2}{pqrw'} = [X'_{AC}] = \frac{(124)^2}{24} = 640.667$$

$$\frac{\left(\sum_1^q\sum_1^r BC'\right)^2}{pqrw'} = [X'_{BC}] = \frac{(129)^2}{24} = 693.375$$

$$\frac{\left(\sum_1^p\sum_1^q\sum_1^r ABC''\right)^2}{pqrw'} = [X''_{ABC}] = \frac{(130)^2}{24} = 704.167$$

(iii) Computational formulas:

$$SS_{total} = [ABCFG] - [X] = 235.500$$
$$SS_{between\ blocks\ and\ reps} = [FG] - [X] = 14.500$$
$$SS_{replications} = [F] - [X] = 5.250$$
$$SS_{between\ blocks\ w.reps} = [FG] - [F] = 9.250$$
$$SS'_{AB(between)} = [FG_0.] - [F_0] = 3.125$$
$$SS'_{AC(between)} = [FG_1.] - [F_1] = 4.500$$
$$SS'_{BC(between)} = [FG_2.] - [F_2] = 1.125$$
$$SS'_{ABC(between)} = [FG_3.] - [F_3] = .500$$
$$SS_{within\ blocks\ and\ reps} = [ABCFG] - [FG] = 221.000$$
$$SS_A = [A] - [X] = 3.125$$
$$SS_B = [B] - [X] = 162.000$$
$$SS_C = [C] - [X] = 24.500$$
$$SS'_{AB} = [AB'] - [A'_{AB}] - [B'_{AB}] + [X'_{AB}] = 3.376$$
$$SS'_{AC} = [AC'] - [A'_{AC}] - [C'_{AC}] + [X'_{AC}] = 6.000$$
$$SS'_{BC} = [BC'] - [B'_{BC}] - [C'_{BC}] + [X'_{BC}] = 7.041$$
$$SS'_{ABC} = [ABC''] - [AB''_{ABC}] - [AC''_{ABC}] - [BC''_{ABC}] + [A''_{ABC}] + [B''_{ABC}]$$
$$+ [C''_{ABC}] - [X''_{ABC}] = 2.666$$
$$SS_{res} = SS_{within\ blocks\ and\ reps} - SS_A - SS_B - SS_C - SS'_{AB} - SS'_{AC} - SS'_{BC}$$
$$- SS'_{ABC} = 12.292$$

Designs using partial confounding require more computation than designs involving complete confounding. Computational procedures for a type RBPF-2^3 design are shown in Table 9.7-1. The notation scheme used in the table is described in Section 9.6. The analysis is summarized in Table 9.7-2.

TABLE 9.7-2   Analysis of Variance Table for Type RBPF-2³ Design

	Source	SS	df	MS	F	E(MS) Model III (A, B, and C, Fixed Effects)
1	Between blocks and reps	14.500	$wz - 1 = 7$			
2	Replications	5.250	$w - 1 = 3$			
3	Between blocks w.reps	9.250	$w(z - 1) = 4$			
4	AB'(between)	3.125	$(p - 1)(q - 1) = 1$			
5	AC'(between)	4.500	$(p - 1)(r - 1) = 1$			
6	BC'(between)	1.125	$(q - 1)(r - 1) = 1$			
7	ABC'(between)	.500	$(p - 1)(q - 1)(r - 1) = 1$			
8	Within blocks and reps	221.000	$wz(v - 1) = 24$			
9	A	3.125	$p - 1 = 1$	3.125	$\left[\frac{9}{16}\right] = 4.32$	$\sigma_\varepsilon^2 + qrw\sigma_\alpha^2$
10	B	162.000	$q - 1 = 1$	162.000	$\left[\frac{10}{16}\right] = 224.07^{**}$	$\sigma_\varepsilon^2 + prw\sigma_\beta^2$
11	C	24.500	$r - 1 = 1$	24.500	$\left[\frac{11}{16}\right] = 33.89^{**}$	$\sigma_\varepsilon^2 + pqw\sigma_\gamma^2$
12	AB'	3.376	$(p - 1)(q - 1) = 1$	3.376	$\left[\frac{12}{16}\right] = 4.67^{*}$	$\sigma_\varepsilon^2 + (\tfrac{3}{4})rw\sigma_{\alpha\beta}^2$
13	AC'	6.000	$(p - 1)(r - 1) = 1$	6.000	$\left[\frac{13}{16}\right] = 8.30^{*}$	$\sigma_\varepsilon^2 + (\tfrac{3}{4})qw\sigma_{\alpha\gamma}^2$
14	BC'	7.041	$(q - 1)(r - 1) = 1$	7.041	$\left[\frac{14}{16}\right] = 9.74^{**}$	$\sigma_\varepsilon^2 + (\tfrac{3}{4})pw\sigma_{\beta\gamma}^2$
15	ABC'	2.666	$(p - 1)(q - 1)(r - 1) = 1$	2.666	$\left[\frac{15}{16}\right] = 3.69$	$\sigma_\varepsilon^2 + (\tfrac{3}{4})w\sigma_{\alpha\beta\gamma}^2$
16	Residual(within)	12.292	$= 17$	.723		σ_ε^2
17	AF	4.125	$(p - 1)(w - 1) = 3$			
18	BF	1.250	$(q - 1)(w - 1) = 3$			
19	CF	1.750	$(r - 1)(w - 1) = 3$			
20	$(AB)_h \times (\tfrac{3}{4})F$	3.250	$(z - 1)(w' - 1) = 2$			
21	$(AC)_h \times (\tfrac{3}{4})F$	.250	$(z - 1)(w' - 1) = 2$			
22	$(BC)_h \times (\tfrac{3}{4})F$	.583	$(z - 1)(w' - 1) = 2$			
23	$(ABC)_h \times (\tfrac{3}{4})F$	1.084	$(z - 1)(w' - 1) = 2$			
24	Total	235.500	$vwz - 1 = 31$			

$^{*}p < .05.$
$^{**}p < .01.$

The analysis in Table 9.7-2 can be compared with the analysis in Table 9.6-3, which is for a completely confounded design. The advantage of the analysis in Table 9.7-2 is that a within-block estimate of the ABC interaction can be computed. The reader has undoubtedly noted that this advantage is gained at the price of greater complexity in the analysis of the data. Furthermore, the AB, AC, BC, and ABC interactions are computed from only three-fourths of the replications. The choice between a completely confounded or partially confounded design rests in part on the experimenter's expectations with respect to the interactions. If one interaction is known to be insignificant, a completely confounded design is the better choice.

Numerous design possibilities are inherent in partial confounding for the experimenter who wishes to utilize his knowledge of a research area. For example, an experimenter could choose to confound the AB interaction in replications f_0 and f_1 and the ABC interaction in replications f_2 and f_3. This is an example of an unbalanced partially confounded design, which was described in Section 9.3. If sufficient subjects are available for five replications, an experimenter could choose to confound AB, AC, and BC in replications f_0 through f_2, respectively, and ABC in replications f_3 and f_4. This design provides as much information on the AB, AC, and BC interactions as the completely confounded design summarized in Table 9.6-2. In addition, it provides three-fifths *relative information* on the ABC interaction.

A type RBPF-2³ design can be easily modified for the case in which each block contains n subjects who are observed under v treatment combinations. The modification follows the general pattern illustrated for a type RBCF-2³ design in Table 9.6-5.

COMPARISONS AMONG MEANS

If one or more interactions in a type RBPF-2³ design are significant, an experimenter generally proceeds to comparisons among means for simple main effects. Before this can be done, it is necessary to compute adjusted cell totals based on replications in which effects are not confounded with blocks. An adjusted cell total is given by

$$ABC'_{ijk} = \frac{\Sigma A_i + \Sigma B_j + \Sigma C_k}{4}$$

$$+ \frac{\Sigma(AB)'_{i+j} + \Sigma(AC)'_{i+k} + \Sigma(BC)'_{j+k} + \Sigma(ABC)'_{i+j+k}}{3} - \frac{3(\Sigma ABCFG)}{4},$$

where ΣA_i = sum of all observations at level a_i.

ΣB_j = sum of all observations at level b_j.

ΣC_k = sum of all observations at level c_k.

$\Sigma(AB)'_{i+j}$ = sum of all observations that satisfy the relation $x_1 + x_2 = i + j$ (mod 2) and are free of block effects.

$\Sigma(AC)'_{i+k}$ = sum of all observations that satisfy the relation $x_1 + x_3 = i + k$ (mod 2) and are free of block effects.

$\Sigma(BC)'_{j+k}$ = sum of all observations that satisfy the relation $x_2 + x_3 = j + k$ (mod 2) and are free of block effects.

$\Sigma(ABC)'_{i+j+k}$ = sum of all observations that satisfy the relation $x_1 + x_2 + x_3 = i + j + k$ (mod 2) and are free of block effects.

$\Sigma ABCFG$ = sum of all observations.

Comparisons among means for simple main effects follow the general procedures described in Section 7.6. These comparisons use means based on adjusted cell totals.

9.8   GENERAL DESCRIPTION OF ANALYSIS PROCEDURES FOR HIGHER-ORDER CONFOUNDED DESIGNS

So far in this chapter we have described designs for 3×3 and $2 \times 2 \times 2$ experiments. The principles discussed in connection with these designs can be readily extended to any experiment of the form p^k, in which p is a prime number. Experiments involving mixed prime numbers, such as $3 \times 2 \times 2$ and $3 \times 3 \times 2$, are more difficult to lay out and analyze than unmixed experiments. A computational example for a $3 \times 2 \times 2$ design is given in Section 9.10. The purpose of this section is to extend the principles described earlier in connection with 3×3 and $2 \times 2 \times 2$ designs to other unmixed designs.

A type RBCF-2^4 design in which the $ABCD$ interaction is confounded with between-block variation can be laid out by means of the family of relations

$$(ABCD)_i = x_1 + x_2 + x_3 + x_4 = i(\text{mod } 2), \qquad i = 0, 1.$$

Treatment combinations assigned to blocks $(ABCD)_0$ and $(ABCD)_1$ are

$$(ABCD)_0 = \text{0000, 0011, 0101, 0110, 1001, 1010, 1100, 1111}$$

$$(ABCD)_1 = \text{0001, 0010, 0100, 1000, 1110, 1101, 1011, 0111.}$$

A complete block design, such as a type RBF-2222 design, requires blocks of size sixteen. By confounding the $ABCD$ interaction with incomplete blocks, the block size can be reduced to eight. It should be noted that an experimenter can choose to confound an interaction other than $ABCD$ with between-block variation if this suits his purpose. Generally, the highest-order interaction is confounded because it is of less interest to an experimenter and is less likely to be significant.

A 3×3 design was described in Section 9.4. Treatment combinations were assigned to blocks according to the relations

$$(AB)_i = x_1 + x_2 = i(\text{mod } 3), \qquad i = 0, 1, 2$$

$$(AB^2)_i = x_1 + 2x_2 = i(\text{mod } 3), \qquad i = 0, 1, 2.$$

If the design involves three treatments each at three levels, treatment combinations can be assigned to blocks according to the following relations:

$$(ABC)_i = x_1 + x_2 + x_3 = i(\text{mod } 3), \qquad i = 0, 1, 2$$

$$(ABC^2)_i = x_1 + x_2 + 2x_3 = i(\text{mod } 3), \qquad i = 0, 1, 2$$

$$(AB^2C)_i = x_1 + 2x_2 + x_3 = i(\text{mod } 3), \qquad i = 0, 1, 2$$

$$(AB^2C^2)_i = x_1 + 2x_2 + 2x_3 = i(\text{mod } 3), \qquad i = 0, 1, 2.$$

Here each of the four orthogonal components of the ABC interaction is used to determine the treatment combinations that are assigned to blocks. The design layout has the form shown in Table 9.8-1. The layout in this table provides within-block information on treatments A, B, C, and the AB, AC, BC interactions from all four replications. Within-block

TABLE 9.8-1   Layout of Type RBPF-3^3 Design in Blocks of Size Nine

			Treatment Combinations								
			abc	*abc*	*abc*	*abc*	*abc*	*abc*	*abc*	*abc*	*abc*
	g_0	$(ABC)_0$	000	012	021	102	111	120	201	210	222
f_0	g_1	$(ABC)_1$	001	010	022	100	112	121	202	211	220
	g_2	$(ABC)_2$	002	011	020	101	110	122	200	212	221
	g_0	$(ABC^2)_0$	000	011	022	101	112	120	202	210	221
f_1	g_1	$(ABC^2)_1$	002	010	021	100	111	122	201	212	220
	g_2	$(ABC^2)_2$	001	012	020	102	110	121	200	211	222
	g_0	$(AB^2C)_0$	000	011	022	102	110	121	201	212	220
f_2	g_1	$(AB^2C)_1$	001	012	020	100	111	122	202	210	221
	g_2	$(AB^2C)_2$	002	010	021	101	112	120	200	211	222
	g_0	$(AB^2C^2)_0$	000	012	021	101	110	122	202	211	220
f_3	g_1	$(AB^2C^2)_1$	002	011	020	100	112	121	201	210	222
	g_2	$(AB^2C^2)_2$	001	010	022	102	111	120	200	212	221

information is available on each of the ABC interaction components from three of the four replications. For example, information on the $(ABC)_i$ component is available from replications f_1, f_2, and f_3, and information on the $(ABC^2)_i$ component is available from replications f_0, f_2, and f_3.

The design shown in Table 9.8-1 requires blocks of size nine. If this block size is considered too large, further confounding can be used to reduce the block size to three. This is accomplished by assigning treatment combinations to blocks that satisfy two defining relations instead of only one. For example, two defining relations might be

$$(ABC)_i = x_1 + x_2 + x_3 = i(\text{mod } 3)$$

$$(AB^2)_i = x_1 + 2x_2 = i(\text{mod } 3).$$

If these two relations are confounded with between-block variation, it can be shown that their two *generalized interactions* are also confounded with blocks. The generalized interactions for any two relations symbolized by (X) and (Y) are given by the product $(X)(Y)^{m-i}$, where m is the modulus and i assumes values $m - 1, m - 2, \ldots, m - (m - 1)$. For treatments with three levels, the modulus is equal to 3 and $i = 2$ and 1. Thus, when two interaction components symbolized by (X) and (Y) are confounded in a $3 \times 3 \times 3$ design, the two generalized interactions that are also confounded are given by

$$(X)(Y)^{3-2} \quad \text{and} \quad (X)(Y)^{3-1} \qquad \text{or} \qquad (X)(Y) \quad \text{and} \quad (X)(Y)^2.$$

If (ABC) is substituted for (X) and (AB^2) for (Y), the two generalized interactions are

$$(ABC)(AB^2) = A^2B^3C = (A^2B^3C)^2 = A^4B^6C^2 = AC^2 \text{ reduced modulo } 3$$

$$(ABC)(AB^2)^2 = (ABC)(A^2B^4) = A^3B^5C = BC^2 \text{ reduced modulo } 3.$$

The computation of generalized interactions follows the simple rules of modular arithmetic described in Section 9.2. The product of (ABC) and (AB^2), as indicated above, is A^2B^3C, but the family of relations is not unique unless the power of the first letter is one. This can be achieved simply by squaring the term A^2B^3C, thus getting $(A^2B^3C)^2 = A^4B^6C^2$, which, when reduced modulo 3 is equal to AC^2. Hence, if both (ABC) and (AB^2) are confounded with between-block variation, two other components (AC^2) and (BC^2) are also confounded with between-block variation. Consequently, care must be taken in choosing the confounding relations used to assign treatment combinations to blocks in order not to confound main effects. Kempthorne (1952, 299) lists 13 systems for confounding a $3 \times 3 \times 3$ design in blocks of size three; only four of these systems do not confound a treatment with between-block variation. One layout for a type RBPF-3^3 design in blocks of size three that provides within-block information on all main effects and interaction components is shown in Table 9.8-2.

TABLE 9.8-2   Layout of Type RBPF-3³ Design in Blocks of Size Three

				abc	*abc*	*abc*
	g_0	$(ABC)_0$	$(AB^2)_0$	000	111	222
	g_1	$(ABC)_0$	$(AB^2)_1$	021	102	210
	g_2	$(ABC)_0$	$(AB^2)_2$	012	120	201
	g_3	$(ABC)_1$	$(AB^2)_0$	001	112	220
f_0	g_4	$(ABC)_1$	$(AB^2)_1$	022	100	211
	g_5	$(ABC)_1$	$(AB^2)_2$	010	121	202
	g_6	$(ABC)_2$	$(AB^2)_0$	002	110	221
	g_7	$(ABC)_2$	$(AB^2)_1$	020	101	212
	g_8	$(ABC)_2$	$(AB^2)_2$	011	122	200
	g_0	$(ABC^2)_0$	$(AB^2)_0$	000	112	221
	g_1	$(ABC^2)_0$	$(AB^2)_1$	022	101	210
	g_2	$(ABC^2)_0$	$(AB^2)_2$	011	120	202
	g_3	$(ABC^2)_1$	$(AB^2)_0$	002	111	220
f_1	g_4	$(ABC^2)_1$	$(AB^2)_1$	021	100	212
	g_5	$(ABC^2)_1$	$(AB^2)_2$	010	122	201
	g_6	$(ABC^2)_2$	$(AB^2)_0$	001	110	222
	g_7	$(ABC^2)_2$	$(AB^2)_1$	020	102	211
	g_8	$(ABC^2)_2$	$(AB^2)_2$	012	121	200
	g_0	$(AB^2C)_0$	$(AB)_0$	000	121	212
	g_1	$(AB^2C)_0$	$(AB)_1$	011	102	220
	g_2	$(AB^2C)_0$	$(AB)_2$	022	110	201
	g_3	$(AB^2C)_1$	$(AB)_0$	001	122	210
f_2	g_4	$(AB^2C)_1$	$(AB)_1$	012	100	221
	g_5	$(AB^2C)_1$	$(AB)_2$	020	111	202
	g_6	$(AB^2C)_2$	$(AB)_0$	002	120	211
	g_7	$(AB^2C)_2$	$(AB)_1$	010	101	222
	g_8	$(AB^2C)_2$	$(AB)_2$	021	112	200
	g_0	$(AB^2C^2)_0$	$(AB)_0$	000	122	211
	g_1	$(AB^2C^2)_0$	$(AB)_1$	012	101	220
	g_2	$(AB^2C^2)_0$	$(AB)_2$	021	110	202
	g_3	$(AB^2C^2)_1$	$(AB)_0$	002	121	210
f_3	g_4	$(AB^2C^2)_1$	$(AB)_1$	011	100	222
	g_5	$(AB^2C^2)_1$	$(AB)_2$	020	112	201
	g_6	$(AB^2C^2)_2$	$(AB)_0$	001	120	212
	g_7	$(AB^2C^2)_2$	$(AB)_1$	010	102	221
	g_8	$(AB^2C^2)_2$	$(AB)_2$	022	111	200

A comparison of Tables 9.8-1 and 9.8-2 reveals that the treatment combinations in block fg_{00} of the former table are contained in blocks fg_{00}, fg_{01}, and fg_{02} of the latter table. An analysis of variance table that includes computational formulas for this design is presented in Table 9.8-3. Computation of SS'_{AB}, SS'_{AC}, SS'_{BC}, and SS'_{ABC} follows the procedure outlined in Section 9.4 for a type RBPF-3^2 design. For example, the $(AB)_i$ component is computed from the two replications in which it is not confounded with between-block variation. These replications are f_0 and f_1.

$$SS'_{(AB)} = \frac{(AB)_0^2 + (AB)_1^2 + (AB)_2^2}{18} - \frac{(F_0 + F_1)^2}{54}.$$

The $(ABC^2)_i$ component is computed from replications f_0, f_2, and f_3 according to the formula

$$SS'_{(ABC^2)} = \frac{(ABC^2)_0^2 + (ABC^2)_1^2 + (ABC^2)_2^2}{27} - \frac{(F_0 + F_2 + F_3)^2}{81}.$$

Adjusted treatment totals for the ABC Summary Table are given by

$$ABC'_{ijk} = \frac{\Sigma A_i + \Sigma B_j + \Sigma C_k}{9}$$

$$+ \frac{2[\Sigma(AB)'_{i+j} + \Sigma(AB^2)'_{i+2j} + \Sigma(AC)'_{i+k} + \Sigma(AC^2)'_{i+2k} + \Sigma(BC)'_{j+k} + \Sigma(BC^2)'_{j+2k}]}{9}$$

$$+ \frac{4[\Sigma(ABC)'_{i+j+k} + \Sigma(ABC^2)'_{i+j+2k} + \Sigma(AB^2C)'_{i+2j+k} + \Sigma(AB^2C^2)'_{i+2j+2k}]}{27}$$

$$- \frac{4(\Sigma ABCFG)}{9}.$$

Adjusted treatment totals for a two-way summary table, for example AB, have the form

$$AB'_{ij} = \frac{\Sigma A_i + \Sigma B_j}{3} + \frac{2[\Sigma(AB)'_{i+j} + \Sigma(AB^2)'_{i+2j}]}{3} - \frac{\Sigma ABCFG}{3}.$$

The symbols in the above formulas are defined in Section 9.7.

PLANS FOR TYPE RBCF-5^2
AND RBPF-5^2 DESIGNS

The procedures that have been described for type RBCF-p^k and RBPF-p^k designs where $p = 2$ or 3 are applicable to designs in which p is any prime number. If $p = 5$, the AB interaction degrees of freedom for type RBCF-5^2 and RBPF-5^2 designs can be partitioned as follows:

TABLE 9.8-3   Analysis of Variance Table for Type RBPF-3³ Design in Blocks of Size Three

	Source	df	Computational Formulas	F	E(MS) Model III (A, B, and C, Fixed Effects)
1	Between blocks and reps	$wz - 1 = 35$	$[FG] - [X]$		
2	Replications	$w - 1 = 3$	$[F] - [X]$		
3	Between blocks w.reps	$w(z - 1) = 32$	$[FG] - [F]$		
4	Within blocks and reps	$wz(v - 1) = 72$	$[ABCFG] - [FG]$		
5	A	$p - 1 = 2$	$[A] - [X]$	$\left[\frac{5}{12}\right]$	$\sigma_\varepsilon^2 + qrw\sigma_\alpha^2$
6	B	$q - 1 = 2$	$[B] - [X]$	$\left[\frac{6}{12}\right]$	$\sigma_\varepsilon^2 + prw\sigma_\beta^2$
7	C	$r - 1 = 2$	$[C] - [X]$	$\left[\frac{7}{12}\right]$	$\sigma_\varepsilon^2 + pqw\sigma_\gamma^2$
8	$AB' = (AB + AB^2)$	$(p-1)(q-1) = 4$	*	$\left[\frac{8}{12}\right]$	$\sigma_\varepsilon^2 + (\frac{1}{2})rw\sigma_{\alpha\beta}^2$
9	$AC' = (AC + AC^2)$	$(p-1)(r-1) = 4$	*	$\left[\frac{9}{12}\right]$	$\sigma_\varepsilon^2 + (\frac{1}{2})qw\sigma_{\alpha\gamma}^2$
10	$BC' = (BC + BC^2)$	$(q-1)(r-1) = 4$	*	$\left[\frac{10}{12}\right]$	$\sigma_\varepsilon^2 + (\frac{1}{2})rw\sigma_{\beta\gamma}^2$
11	$ABC' = (ABC + ABC^2 + AB^2C + AB^2C^2)$	$(p-1)(q-1)(r-1) = 8$	*	$\left[\frac{11}{12}\right]$	$\sigma_\varepsilon^2 + (\frac{3}{4})w\sigma_{\alpha\beta\gamma}^2$
12	Residual	$= 46$	$\begin{cases} SS_{\text{within blocks and reps}} - SS_A - SS_B \\ - SS_C - SS'_{AB} - SS'_{AC} - SS'_{BC} - SS'_{ABC} \end{cases}$		σ_ε^2
13	AF	$(p-1)(w-1) = 6$			
14	BF	$(q-1)(w-1) = 6$			
15	CF	$(r-1)(w-1) = 6$			
16	$(AB)_i \times (\frac{1}{2})F$	$(v-1)(w'-1) = 2$			
17	$(AB^2)_i \times (\frac{1}{2})F$	$(v-1)(w'-1) = 2$			
18	$(AC)_i \times (\frac{1}{2})F$	$(v-1)(w'-1) = 2$			
19	$(AC^2)_i \times (\frac{1}{2})F$	$(v-1)(w'-1) = 2$			
20	$(BC)_i \times (\frac{1}{2})F$	$(v-1)(w'-1) = 2$			
21	$(BC^2)_i \times (\frac{1}{2})F$	$(v-1)(w'-1) = 2$			
22	$(ABC)_i \times (\frac{3}{4})F$	$(v-1)(w''-1) = 4$			
23	$(ABC^2)_i \times (\frac{3}{4})F$	$(v-1)(w''-1) = 4$			
24	$(AB^2C)_i \times (\frac{3}{4})F$	$(v-1)(w''-1) = 4$			
25	$(AB^2C^2)_i \times (\frac{3}{4})F$	$(v-1)(w''-1) = 4$			
26	Total	$vwz - 1 = 107$	$[ABCFG] - [X]$		

*See text

	Degrees of Freedom
SS_{AB}	$(5 - 1)(5 - 1) = 16$
$SS_{(AB)}$	$= 4$
$SS_{(AB^2)}$	$= 4$
$SS_{(AB^3)}$	$= 4$
$SS_{(AB^4)}$	$= 4$

A balanced partially confounded design can be laid out in four or a multiple of four replications. Combinations of treatments A and B are assigned to blocks within each of the four replications by means of the following relations:

$$\text{Rep 0} \quad (AB)_i = x_1 + x_2 = i(\text{mod } 5) \quad i = 0, \ldots, 4$$

$$\text{Rep 1} \quad (AB^2)_i = x_1 + 2x_2 = i(\text{mod } 5) \quad i = 0, \ldots, 4$$

$$\text{Rep 2} \quad (AB^3)_i = x_1 + 3x_2 = i(\text{mod } 5) \quad i = 0, \ldots, 4$$

$$\text{Rep 3} \quad (AB^4)_i = x_1 + 4x_2 = i(\text{mod } 5) \quad i = 0, \ldots, 4.$$

Each replication in this design contains five blocks because $i = 0, 1, 2, 3,$ and 4.

A completely confounded design can be constructed by using any *one* of the four relations defined above to assign treatment combinations to blocks. The five blocks that satisfy one of the above relations can be replicated as many times as desired.

It is not possible to describe in this chapter all or even a majority of the designs for which the principle of confounding is useful. The approach that has been adopted is to present selected numerical examples illustrating basic principles and procedures applicable to a broad range of designs. A listing of confounded designs, together with pertinent information, is given in Table 9.8-4. The table includes references that describe the layout and main features of each design. Many of the designs listed in Table 9.8-4 are described by Yates (1937).

9.9   ALTERNATIVE NOTATION
AND COMPUTATIONAL SYSTEMS

There are almost as many notation systems in experimental design as there are books on the subject. Fortunately, a common thread runs through most systems. A reader can, with a little effort, learn to be comfortable with each system. One specialized notation system, however, would be difficult to follow without a brief note of explanation. This system is widely used in designating treatment combinations when each treatment has only two levels. In this system the symbol for a treatment combination contains only those letters for which the treatment is at the higher level. The absence of a letter indicates that the treatment is at the lower level. If all treatments are at the lower level, the symbol (1) is used. The terms *lower* or *higher* may refer to positions on a scale or may be an arbitrary distinction between levels. A comparison of this specialized notation with the notation used in this chapter appears below.

Treatment combination = 000   100   010   001   110   101   011   111

Specialized notation = (1)   *a*   *b*   *c*   *ab*   *ac*   *bc*   *abc*

Although this notation system has certain advantages over the notation used in this chapter, it has not been used here because it is appropriate only for treatments having two levels. The notation in this chapter is a more general system in that it is appropriate for treatments with any number of levels. Furthermore, the notation in this chapter lends itself to the application of modular arithmetic.

Section 9.2 described a notation system for designating components of an interaction. An alternative scheme used by Yates (1937) and other writers is as follows:

$$(AB^2) = AB(I), \quad (AB^2C^2) = ABC(W), \quad (ABC^2) = ABC(Y)$$
$$(AB) = AB(J), \quad (AB^2C) = ABC(X), \quad (ABC) = ABC(Z).$$

This alternative system is widely used but is less descriptive than the system used in this chapter.

The computational procedures introduced in Chapter 4 have been adhered to throughout this book. These procedures were chosen not because they are the most efficient, but because they are simple, they illustrate fundamental principles clearly, and they are easily adapted to the designs described in this book. This practice appears to the author to be pedagogically sound, particularly in view of the level of mathematical sophistication assumed on the part of the reader. It should be emphasized that other computational schemes may be more efficient for the reader's purpose. Yates (1937) has devised a simplified technique for obtaining treatment and interaction sums of squares for experiments in which all treatments have the same number of levels. He has also devised a simplified

TABLE 9.8-4 Reference Information for Confounded Factorial Designs

Type Design	Number of Treatment Combinations	Number of Observations per Block	Number of Replications for Balanced Design*	Interaction(s) Confounded and Relative Information†	Reference‡
§RBCF-2^3	8	4	x	any interaction	(1) p.220, (3) p. 233, (2) p. 427, (8) p. 394
§RBCF-2^3 (block $n > 1$)	8	4	x	any interaction	(8) p. 409
RBCF-2^3	8	2	x	AB, AC, BC	(5) p. 262
§RBPF-2^3	8	4	4	$AB(\frac{3}{4})$, $AC(\frac{3}{4})$, $BC(\frac{3}{4})$, $ABC(\frac{3}{4})$	(1) p. 220, (5) p. 275, (3) p. 244, (4) p. 201, (8) p. 395
RBPF-2^3 (block $n > 1$)	8	4	4	$AB(\frac{3}{4})$, $AC(\frac{3}{4})$, $BC(\frac{3}{4})$, $ABC(\frac{3}{4})$	(8) p. 397
§RBCF-2^4	16	8	x	any interaction	(1) p. 220, (2) p. 429 (4) p. 193
RBCF-2^4	16	4	x	AB, ACD, BCD; or $AB, CD, ABCD$	(1) p. 220, (2) p. 428, (4) p. 194
RBPF-2^4	16	4	6	all two-factor interactions ($\frac{5}{6}$), all three-factor interactions ($\frac{1}{2}$)	(1) p. 220
RBCF-2^4	16	2	x	$AB, AC, BC, AD, BD, CD, ABCD$	(5) p. 261
RBPF-2^4	16	2	4	main effects ($\frac{3}{4}$), two-factor interactions ($\frac{1}{2}$), three-factor interactions ($\frac{1}{4}$)	(5) p. 278
RBCF-2^5	32	16	x	any interaction	(2) p. 430
RBCF-2^5	32	8	x	$ABC, ADE, BCDE$; or $AB, CDE, ABCDE$	(1) p. 220, (2) p. 429
RBPF-2^5	32	8	5	all three-factor interactions ($\frac{4}{5}$), all four-factor interactions ($\frac{4}{5}$)	(1) p. 220
RBCF-2^5	32	4	x	$AB, AC, BC, DE, ABDE, ACDE, BCDE$; or $AB, CD, ACE, BDE, ADE, BCE, ABCD$	(2) p. 428
RBCF-3^2	9	3	x	AB or AB^2	(3) p. 239, (2) p. 435

TABLE 9.8-4 (continued)

Type Design	Number of Treatment Combinations	Number of Observations per Block	Number of Replications for Balanced Design*	Interaction(s) Confounded and Relative Information†	Reference‡
§RBPF-3^2	9	3	2	AB components ($\frac{1}{2}$)	(5) p. 300, (3) p. 251, (8) p. 412
RBPF-3^2 (block $n > 1$)	9	3	2	AB components ($\frac{1}{2}$)	(8) p. 414
§RBPF-3^3	27	9	4	ABC components ($\frac{3}{4}$)	(1) p. 222, (5) p. 302, (3) p. 251, (2) p. 438, (8) p. 423
§RBPF-3^3	27	3	4	all two-factor interactions ($\frac{1}{2}$), ABC ($\frac{3}{4}$)	(3) p. 252, (2) p. 436, (8) p. 426
RBPF-3^4	81	9	4	all three-factor interactions ($\frac{3}{4}$)	(1) p. 223, (5) p. 306
RBPF-4^2	16	4	3	AB components ($\frac{2}{3}$)	(1) p. 225
RBCF-4^3	64	16	x	ABC interaction	(6) p. 121
RBPF-5^2	25	5	4	AB components ($\frac{3}{4}$)	(7) p. 57

*The symbol x indicates that any number of replicates can be used; for a balanced design, replicates should be a multiple of the number that appears in the column.

†If a fraction does not follow the interaction, it is completely confounded with between-block variation.

‡Information about a design can be found in the following references: (1) Cochran and Cox (1957), (2) Davies (1956), (3) Federer (1955), (4) Johnson and Leone (1964), (5) Kempthorne (1952), (6) Nair (1938), (7) Nair (1940), and (8) Winer (1962).

§Design described in this chapter.

procedure for computing I and J interaction components. This procedure is described by Kempthorne (1952, 307) and Winer (1962, 387). Computational schemes using matrix operations are widely used for analyses performed with the aid of a computer. An elementary introduction to computer programs for analysis of variance is presented by Cooley and Lohnes (1962) and by Veldman (1967).

9.10 LAYOUT AND COMPUTATIONAL PROCEDURES FOR TYPE RBPF-32^2 DESIGN

Confounded designs in which the number of levels of each treatment are not equal are called *mixed* designs. Examples of mixed designs are $3 \times 2 \times 2$, $3 \times 3 \times 2$, and $4 \times 3 \times 2$ designs. These designs generally entail a more complex analysis than unmixed designs. The choice of block size is much more restricted for mixed designs than for unmixed ones. In order not to confound main effects, the block size must be a multiple of the number of levels of each treatment. Thus, for a $3 \times 2 \times 2$ design, the block size must equal six. This permits a_0, a_1, and a_2 to each occur twice in a block and b_0, b_1 and c_0, c_1 to occur three times. All twelve treatment combinations of a $3 \times 2 \times 2$ design can be assigned to two blocks, as shown in the following illustration:

Block 0	abc_{000}	abc_{011}	abc_{101}	abc_{110}	abc_{201}	abc_{210}
Block 1	abc_{001}	abc_{010}	abc_{100}	abc_{111}	abc_{200}	abc_{211}

A tabulation of the frequency of occurrence of ab_{ij}, ac_{ik}, and bc_{jk} combinations in the two blocks is as follows:

	Blocks			*Blocks*			*Blocks*	
	0	1		0	1		0	1
ab_{00}	1	1	ac_{00}	1	1	bc_{00}	1	2
ab_{01}	1	1	ac_{01}	1	1	bc_{01}	2	1
ab_{10}	1	1	ac_{10}	1	1	bc_{10}	2	1
ab_{11}	1	1	ac_{11}	1	1	bc_{11}	1	2

Each combination of ab_{ij} and ac_{ik} occurs equally often in blocks 0 and 1. This is not true for bc_{jk}. Since all combinations of bc_{jk} do not occur with equal frequency within each block, the BC interaction is partially confounded with between-block variation. Note also that the ABC interaction is confounded with between-block variation because different combinations of abc_{ijk} occur in the two blocks. Treatments A, B, and C are not confounded. It should be apparent to the reader that the BC interaction, which involves four treatment combinations, must be confounded in a $3 \times 2 \times 2$ design because the block size is not a multiple of four. Another mixed design, a type RBPF-$3^2 2$, is also laid out in blocks of size six. In this design it is the AB and ABC interactions that are confounded with blocks. The block size of six allows all six ac_{ik} and bc_{jk} treatment combinations to occur within a block but only six of the nine ab_{ij} combinations.

A balanced type RBPF-32² design can be laid out in three replications of two blocks. The general layout of the design is shown in Table 9.10-1. The symbol $a_0(BC)_0$ stands for treatment combinations 000 and 011, where

$$(BC)_0 = [x_2 + x_3 = 0 (\mathrm{mod}\ 2)] = 00 \text{ and } 11.$$

Treatment combinations designated by $a_1(BC)_1$ are 101 and 110, where

$$(BC)_1 = [x_2 + x_3 = 1 (\mathrm{mod}\ 2)] = 01 \text{ and } 10.$$

An examination of Table 9.10-1 shows that variation between block g_0 and block g_1 is confounded with variation between $(BC)_0$ and $(BC)_1$, or the BC interaction as well as the ABC interaction. Thus the BC and ABC interactions must be adjusted for block effects. The rationale that underlies the adjustment of SS_{BC} and SS_{ABC} can only be touched on in this section. For a general discussion of this problem, see Federer (1955, 255), Kempthorne (1952, 348), Li (1944), Nair (1938), and Yates (1937).

TABLE 9.10-1   General Layout of Type RBPF-32² Design

	Replication f_0		*Replication f_1*		*Replication f_2*	
	Block g_0	*Block g_1*	*Block g_0*	*Block g_1*	*Block g_0*	*Block g_1*
a_0	$(BC)_0$	$(BC)_1$	$(BC)_1$	$(BC)_0$	$(BC)_1$	$(BC)_0$
a_1	$(BC)_1$	$(BC)_0$	$(BC)_0$	$(BC)_1$	$(BC)_1$	$(BC)_0$
a_2	$(BC)_1$	$(BC)_0$	$(BC)_1$	$(BC)_0$	$(BC)_0$	$(BC)_1$

Analysis procedures for a type RBPF-32² design are illustrated in Table 9.10-2, where the following notation is used:

p levels of a_i, where $p = 3$

q levels of b_j, where $q = 2$

r levels of c_k, where $r = 2$

v levels of X (observations/block), where $v = 6$

w levels of f_h, where $w = 3$

z levels of g_t, where $z = 2$.

TABLE 9.10-2 Layout of Type RBPF-32² Design and Computational Procedures

(i) Data:

ABCFG Summary Table

		abc	abc	abc	abc	abc	abc
f_0	g_0	000 3	011 7	101 4	110 7	201 3	210 6
	g_1	001 4	010 7	100 3	111 9	200 3	211 8
f_1	g_0	001 2	010 5	100 2	111 10	201 3	210 6
	g_1	000 1	011 10	101 3	110 6	200 2	211 11
f_2	g_0	001 3	010 6	101 4	110 7	200 2	211 9
	g_1	000 2	011 8	100 3	111 8	201 3	210 7

AB Summary Table

	b_0	b_1	$\overset{q}{\underset{1}{\sum}}A$
a_0	$wz = 6$ 15	43	58
a_1	19	47	66
a_2	16	47	63
$\overset{p}{\underset{1}{\sum}}B = 50$		137	

AC Summary Table

	c_0	c_1
a_0	$wz = 6$ 24	34
a_1	28	38
a_2	26	37
$\overset{p}{\underset{1}{\sum}}C = 78$		109

ABC Summary Table

	b_0 c_0	b_0 c_1	b_1 c_0	b_1 c_1
a_0	$w = 3$ 6	9	18	25
a_1	8	11	20	27
a_2	7	9	19	28

BC Summary Table

	c_0	c_1
b_0	$pw = 9$ 21	29
b_1	57	80

FG Summary Table

	g_0	g_1	$\overset{z}{\underset{1}{\sum}}F$
f_0	$v = 6$ 30	34	64
f_1	28	33	61
f_2	31	31	62
$\overset{w}{\underset{1}{\sum}}G = 89$		98	

TABLE 9.10-2 (continued)

(ii) Computational symbols:

$$\sum_1^N ABCFG = 3 + 4 + 2 + \cdots + 7 = 187.000$$

$$\sum_1^N (ABCFG)^2 = [ABCFG] = 1239.000$$

$$\frac{\left(\sum_1^N ABCFG\right)^2}{N} = [X] = \frac{(187)^2}{36} = 971.361$$

$$\sum_1^w \frac{\left(\sum_1^z F\right)^2}{vz} = [F] = \frac{(64)^2}{(6)(2)} + \frac{(61)^2}{(6)(2)} + \frac{(62)^2}{(6)(2)} = 971.750$$

$$\sum_1^z \frac{\left(\sum_1^w G\right)^2}{vw} = [G] = \frac{(89)^2}{(6)(3)} + \frac{(98)^2}{(6)(3)} = 973.611$$

$$\sum_1^w \sum_1^z \frac{(FG)^2}{v} = [FG] = \frac{(30)^2}{6} + \frac{(28)^2}{6} + \cdots + \frac{(31)^2}{6} = 975.167$$

$$\sum_1^p \frac{\left(\sum_1^q A\right)^2}{qwz} = [A] = \frac{(58)^2}{(2)(3)(2)} + \frac{(66)^2}{(2)(3)(2)} + \frac{(63)^2}{(2)(3)(2)} = 974.083$$

$$\sum_1^q \frac{\left(\sum_1^p B\right)^2}{pwz} = [B] = \frac{(50)^2}{(3)(3)(2)} + \frac{(137)^2}{(3)(3)(2)} = 1181.611$$

$$\sum_1^r \frac{\left(\sum_1^p C\right)^2}{pwz} = [C] = \frac{(78)^2}{(3)(3)(2)} + \frac{(109)^2}{(3)(3)(2)} = 998.056$$

$$\sum_1^p \sum_1^q \frac{(AB)^2}{wz} = [AB] = \frac{(15)^2}{(3)(2)} + \cdots + \frac{(47)^2}{(3)(2)} = 1184.833$$

$$\sum_1^p \sum_1^r \frac{(AC)^2}{wz} = [AC] = \frac{(24)^2}{(3)(2)} + \cdots + \frac{(37)^2}{(3)(2)} = 1000.833$$

$$\sum_1^q \sum_1^r \frac{(BC)^2}{pw} = [BC] = \frac{(21)^2}{(3)(3)} + \cdots + \frac{(80)^2}{(3)(3)} = 1214.556$$

$$\sum_1^p \sum_1^q \sum_1^r \frac{(ABC)^2}{w} = [ABC] = \frac{(6)^2}{3} + \cdots + \frac{(28)^2}{3} = 1218.333$$

(iii) Computational formulas:

$$\text{SS}_{\text{total}} = [ABCFG] - [X] = 267.639$$

$$\text{SS}_{\text{between blocks and reps}} = [FG] - [X] = 3.806$$

$$\text{SS}_{\text{replications}} = [F] - [X] = .389$$

$$\text{SS}_{\text{blocks w.reps}} = [FG] - [F] = 3.417$$

$$\text{SS}_{\text{within blocks and reps}} = [ABCFG] - [FG] = 263.833$$

$$\text{SS}_A = [A] - [X] = 2.722$$

$$\text{SS}_B = [B] - [X] = 210.250$$

$$\text{SS}_C = [C] - [X] = 26.695$$

$$\text{SS}_{AB} = [AB] - [A] - [B] + [X] = .500$$

TABLE 9.10-2 (continued)

$$SS_{AC} = [AC] - [A] - [C] + [X] = .055$$
$$SS_{BC} = [BC] - [B] - [C] + [X] = 6.250$$
$$SS_{BC(adj)} = \text{see text} = 4.500$$
$$SS_{ABC} = [ABC] - [AB] - [AC] - [BC] + [A] + [B] + [C] - [X] = .500$$
$$SS_{ABC(adj)} = \text{see text} = .033$$
$$SS_{res} = [ABCFG] - [ABC] - [FG] + [X] = 16.861$$
$$SS_{res(adj)} = SS_{res} + SS_{BC} + SS_{ABC} - SS_{BC(adj)} - SS_{ABC(adj)} = 19.078$$

Procedures for adjusting SS_{BC} and SS_{ABC} require special comment. If the BC effects were not confounded with blocks, they could be estimated by taking the difference between the two components $(BC)_0$ and $(BC)_1$:

$$BC = (BC)_0 - (BC)_1.$$

This estimate also includes experimental error, but this is not germane to the present discussion and will be ignored. The sum of squares for BC under the condition of no confounding is given by

$$SS_{BC} = \frac{(BC)^2}{pqrw} = \frac{[(21 + 80) - (29 + 57)]^2}{(3)(2)(2)(3)} = \frac{(15)^2}{36} = 6.25,$$

where 21, 80, 29, and 57 are obtained from the BC Summary Table in Table 9.10-2. The reader can verify that this is the same value that is obtained by using the more familiar formula

$$SS_{BC} = [BC] - [B] - [C] + [X] = 6.25.$$

The former formula is actually simpler to use when both treatments have only two levels. The BC effects can be adjusted for block effects by

$$BC_{adj} = [(BC)_0 - (BC)_1] + \frac{[(fg_{00} - fg_{01}) + (fg_{10} - fg_{11}) + (fg_{20} - fg_{21})]}{w}$$

$$= 15 + \frac{[(30 - 34) + (28 - 33) + (31 - 31)]}{3}$$

$$= 15 + \frac{[(-4) + (-5) + (0)]}{3} = 15 - \tfrac{9}{3} = 12.$$

$$SS_{BC(adj)} = \frac{(BC_{adj})^2}{32} = \frac{(12)^2}{32} = 4.5$$

BC_{adj} is based on 32 effective observations as opposed to 36 for BC_{unadj}. Federer (1955, 260) illustrates the calculation of the number of effective observations.

The same general procedures can be used to adjust the ABC interaction for block effects. If the ABC interaction were not confounded, one procedure for computing SS_{ABC} is as follows:

$$\sum_1^p \frac{[a_i(BC)_0 - a_i(BC)_1]^2}{12} - SS_{BC} = SS_{ABC}.$$

Computation of the ABC interaction by this formula is analogous to summing the BC interaction over the p levels of treatment A. The numbers required for this computation are obtained from the ABC Summary Table.

$$\sum_1^p \frac{[a_i(BC)_0 - a_i(BC)_1]^2}{12} = \frac{(4)^2}{12} + \frac{(4)^2}{12} + \frac{(7)^2}{12} = 6.75.$$

If the SS_{BC} is subtracted from 6.75, the remainder is equal to SS_{ABC}, which is

$$6.75 - 6.25 = .500.$$

The $SS_{ABC(adj)}$ can be obtained by adjusting $[a_i(BC)_0 - a_i(BC)_1]$ for block effects and subtracting $\boldsymbol{BC}_{adj}$.

$$3a_0\boldsymbol{BC}_{adj} = 3[a_0(BC)_0 - a_0(BC)_1] + [(fg_{01} - fg_{00}) + (fg_{10} - fg_{11})$$
$$+ (fg_{20} - fg_{21})]$$
$$= 3[(6 + 25) - (9 + 18)] + (4 - 5 + 0) = 3(4) - 1 = 11.$$

$$3a_1\boldsymbol{BC}_{adj} = 3[a_1(BC)_0 - a_1(BC)_1] + [(fg_{00} - fg_{01}) + (fg_{11} - fg_{10})$$
$$+ (fg_{20} - fg_{21})]$$
$$= 3[(8 + 27) - (11 + 20)] + (-4 + 5 + 0) = 3(4) + 1 = 13.$$

$$3a_2\boldsymbol{BC}_{adj} = 3[a_2(BC)_0 - a_2(BC)_1] + [(fg_{00} - fg_{01}) + (fg_{10} - fg_{11})$$
$$+ (fg_{21} - fg_{20})]$$
$$= 3[(7 + 28) - (9 + 19)] + (-4 - 5 + 0) = 3(7) - 9 = 12.$$

A check on the adjusted $a_i\boldsymbol{BC}$ components is given by

$$\sum_1^p (3a_i\boldsymbol{BC}_{adj}) = 3(\boldsymbol{BC}_{adj})$$

$$11 + 13 + 12 = 3(12) = 36.$$

$$SS_{ABC(adj)} = \frac{(3a_0\boldsymbol{BC}_{adj} - \boldsymbol{BC}_{adj})^2 + (3a_1\boldsymbol{BC}_{adj} - \boldsymbol{BC}_{adj})^2 + (3a_2\boldsymbol{BC}_{adj} - \boldsymbol{BC}_{adj})^2}{60}$$

$$= \frac{(11 - 12)^2 + (13 - 12)^2 + (12 - 12)^2}{60} = .033.$$

    The results of the analysis in Table 9.10-2 are summarized in Table 9.10-3. It is apparent from the analysis in Table 9.10-3 that the F ratios for MS_B, MS_C, and $MS_{BC(adj)}$ are significant. These findings are what one would expect from a visual examination of the summary tables in Table 9.10-2. In view of the significant BC interaction, the experimenter might wish to

TABLE 9.10-3 Analysis of Variance Table for Type RBPF-32² Design

	Source	SS	df	MS	F	E(MS) Model III (A, B, and C, Fixed Effects, Blocks Random)
1	Between blocks and reps	3.806	$wz - 1 = 5$			
2	Replications	.389	$w - 1 = 2$			
3	Blocks w.reps	3.417	$w(z - 1) = 3$			
4	Within blocks and reps	263.833	$wz(v - 1) = 30$			
5	A	2.722	$p - 1 = 2$	1.361	$\left[\frac{5}{12}\right]$ N.S.	$\sigma_\varepsilon^2 + qrw\sigma_\alpha^2$
6	B	210.250	$q - 1 = 1$	210.250	$\left[\frac{6}{12}\right] = 209.41**$	$\sigma_\varepsilon^2 + prw\sigma_\beta^2$
7	C	26.695	$r - 1 = 1$	26.695	$\left[\frac{7}{12}\right] = 26.59**$	$\sigma_\varepsilon^2 + pqw\sigma_\gamma^2$
8	AB	.500	$(p - 1)(q - 1) = 2$	.250	$\left[\frac{8}{12}\right]$ N.S.	$\sigma_\varepsilon^2 + rw\sigma_{\alpha\beta}^2$
9	AC	.055	$(p - 1)(r - 1) = 2$	.028	$\left[\frac{9}{12}\right]$ N.S.	$\sigma_\varepsilon^2 + qw\sigma_{\alpha\gamma}^2$
10	BC(adj)	4.500	$(q - 1)(r - 1) = 1$	4.500	$\left[\frac{10}{12}\right] = 4.48*$	$\sigma_\varepsilon^2 + \left(\frac{8}{9}\right)pw\sigma_{\beta\gamma}^2$
11	ABC(adj)	.033	$(p - 1)(q - 1)(r - 1) = 2$	.016	$\left[\frac{11}{12}\right]$ N.S.	$\sigma_\varepsilon^2 + \left(\frac{5}{9}\right)w\sigma_{\alpha\beta\gamma}^2$
12	Residual(adj)	19.078	$= 19$	1.004		σ_ε^2
13	Total	267.639	$vwz - 1 = 35$			

$*p < .05.$
$**p < .01.$

make comparisons among means for simple main effects. These comparisons should be carried out with adjusted bc_{ij} cell means in order to remove the effects of between-block variation. Procedures for adjusting the BC cell means are described in the next section.

COMPARISONS AMONG MEANS

In a type RBPF-32^2 design, treatments A, B, and C, as well as the AB and AC interactions, are not confounded with blocks. Therefore comparisons among means for these main effects and simple main effects follow procedures described previously for factorial designs. Because the BC interaction is partially confounded with between-block variation, cell means must be adjusted before comparisons are made. The required adjustment for $\overline{BC}_{00}$ and $\overline{BC}_{11}$ is given by

$$\text{adj } BC_{00} \text{ or } BC_{11} = \left[\tfrac{1}{6}(fg_{00} + fg_{10} + fg_{20}) + \tfrac{1}{3}(fg_{01} + fg_{11} + fg_{21}) \right]$$

$$- \frac{(BC_{\text{adj}})}{32} - \frac{(\Sigma ABCFG)}{4} = \left[\frac{89}{6} + \frac{98}{3} \right]$$

$$- \frac{12}{32} - \frac{187}{4} = .37.$$

The adjusted means are

$$\overline{BC}_{00} = \frac{BC_{00}}{pw} - \frac{\text{adj } BC_{00}}{pw} = \frac{21}{(3)(3)} - \frac{.37}{(3)(3)} = 2.29.$$

$$\overline{BC}_{11} = \frac{BC_{11}}{pw} - \frac{\text{adj } BC_{11}}{pw} = \frac{80}{(3)(3)} - \frac{.37}{(3)(3)} = 8.85.$$

The adjustment for $\overline{BC}_{01}$ and $\overline{BC}_{10}$ is numerically equal to the adjustment for $\overline{BC}_{00}$ and $\overline{BC}_{11}$ but opposite in sign.

The t ratio for adjusted bc_{jk} cell means, which takes into account the effective number of observations, has the following form:

$$t = \frac{C_j(\overline{BC}_{jk}) + C_{j'}(\overline{BC}_{jk'})}{\sqrt{\dfrac{2\text{MS}_{\text{res}}}{pw}\left(\dfrac{9}{8}\right)}}.$$

For a description of the adjustment procedure for simple-simple effects means, see Cochran and Cox (1957, 210).

OTHER MIXED DESIGNS

Mixed confounded factorial designs present many special computational problems. A complete presentation of these designs is beyond the

TABLE 9.10-4 Reference Information for Mixed Confounded Factorial Designs

Type Design	Number of Treatment Combinations	Number of Observations per Block	Number of Replications for Balanced Design	Interaction(s) Confounded and Relative Information*	Reference†
‡RBPF-32²	12	6	3	$BC(\frac{8}{9})$, $ABC(\frac{5}{9})$	(1) p. 224, (2) p. 253, (3) p. 348, (5) p. 433
RBPF-32³	24	6	3	$BC(\frac{8}{9})$, $BD(\frac{8}{9})$, $CD(\frac{8}{9})$, $ABC(\frac{5}{9})$, $ABD(\frac{5}{9})$, $ACD(\frac{5}{9})$	(1) p. 225
RBPF-3²2	18	6	4	$AB(\frac{7}{8})$, $ABC(\frac{5}{8})$	(1) p. 224, (2) p. 254, (3) p. 355
RBPF-3³2	54	6	4	$AB(\frac{7}{8})$, $AC(\frac{7}{8})$, $AD(\frac{7}{8})$, $ABD(\frac{5}{8})$, $ACD(\frac{5}{8})$, $BCD(\frac{5}{8})$, $ABC(\frac{3}{4})$	(6) p. 63
RBPF-42²	16	8	3	$ABC(\frac{1}{2})$	(1) p. 226, (4) p. 460
RBPF-432	24	12	9	$AC(\frac{26}{27})$, $AB(\frac{23}{27})$	(1) p. 227
RBPF-43²	36	12	2	$BC(\frac{7}{8})$, $ABC(\frac{5}{8})$	(4) p. 475
RBCF-4²2	32	16	x	ABC	(4) p. 465
RBPF-4²3	48	12	3	$AB(\frac{26}{27})$, $ABC(\frac{23}{27})$	(4) p. 486
RBPF-42³	32	8	3	$ABC(\frac{1}{2})$, $ABD(\frac{1}{2})$, $ACD(\frac{1}{2})$	(4) p. 467
RBPF-52²	20	10	5	$BC(\frac{24}{25})$, $ABC(\frac{19}{25})$	(4) p. 469

*If a fraction does not follow the interaction, it is completely confounded with between-block variation.

†Information about a design can be found in the following references: (1) Cochran and Cox (1957), (2) Federer (1955), (3) Kempthorne (1952), (4) Li (1944), (5) Winer (1962), and (6) Yates (1937).

‡Design described in this chapter.

scope of this book. General references include the classic monograph of Yates (1937) and the work of Li (1944). Additional references are cited in Table 9.10-4. This table presents relevant information for a variety of mixed confounded factorial designs.

9.11 BLOCK CONFOUNDING BY MEANS OF A LATIN SQUARE

An alternative confounding scheme that is much simpler than that already described uses a Latin square building block. Confounded factorial designs based on a Latin square are not limited to experiments in which the number of treatment levels is a prime number. This confounding scheme, however, does have other restrictions; these are described in subsequent paragraphs.

Consider the Latin square in Figure 9.11-1. A comparison of treatment combinations in this square with those shown in the lower half of

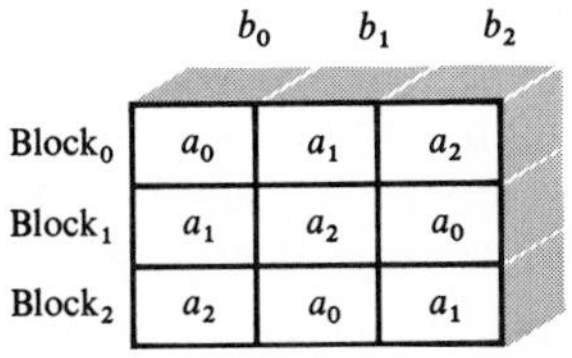

Figure 9.11-1   Block diagram of type LSCF-3^2 design.

Table 9.2-2, which forms a type RBCF-3^2 design, reveals that they are identical. The treatment combinations in the lower half of the design shown in Figure 9.2-2 are based on the relation $(AB^2)_i$. The general nature of the correspondence between these designs is discussed in some detail in Section 10.7. Although both designs use the same treatment combinations and reduce the block size of a 3×3 factorial design from nine to three, they require different assumptions and involve different analysis procedures. A confounded factorial design based on a Latin square is designated by the letters LSCF. The Latin square in Figure 9.11-1 is considered to have two treatments and one nuisance variable. A Latin square may be classified as a factorial design if the levels of either rows or columns correspond to an additional treatment instead of a nuisance variable. This point is developed further in Section 10.7.

The linear model for the design diagramed above is

$$X_{ijm(t)} = \mu + \theta_t + \pi_{m(t)} + \alpha_i + \beta_j + \alpha\beta'_{ij} + \varepsilon_{ijm(t)},$$

where μ = grand mean of treatment populations.

θ_t = effect of block t.

$\pi_{m(t)}$ = effect of subject m, who is nested within block θ_t.

α_i = effect of treatment i, which is a constant for all observations within treatment population i.

β_j = effect of treatment j, which is a constant for all observations within treatment population j.

$\alpha\beta'_{ij}$ = effect that represents nonadditivity of effects α_i and β_j.

$\varepsilon_{ijm(t)}$ = experimental error, which is NID with mean = 0 and variance = σ_ε^2.

The reader has probably noted an unusual feature of this model—the presence of an AB' interaction component in a design developed from a Latin square building block. This interaction component corresponds to $SS'_{(AB)within}$ described in Section 9.4. The (AB^2) component of the AB interaction is confounded with between-block variation of the Latin square. It is assumed that the remaining interactions of the Latin square are zero; that is, $\alpha\theta$, $\beta\theta$, and $\alpha\beta\theta = 0$. Benjamin (1965) has explored in some detail the assumptions underlying this design.

    In laying out the design, the z blocks, which contain n subjects, should represent random samples from a common population. The blocks are randomly assigned to the rows of the Latin square. General procedures for randomization of a Latin square are described in Section 6.2 and should be followed for a Latin square confounded factorial design. The sequence of administration of treatment combinations within a block is randomized independently for each subject. A type LSCF-p^2 design is restricted to experiments with two treatments. Any number of levels can be used in the design if the number is the same for blocks and treatments. The designation LSCF-3^2 instead of LSCF-33, for example, is used to convey this information.

    For purposes of comparison, the data in Table 9.4-1 will be analyzed by means of a type LSCF-3^2 design. It is assumed in Latin square confounded factorial designs that treatments represent fixed effects and blocks are random effects. The layout and computational procedures are presented in Table 9.11-1. The results of the analysis are summarized in Table 9.11-2, where the following notation is used:

$$p \text{ levels of } a_i, \text{ where } p = 3$$

$$q \text{ levels of } b_j, \text{ where } q = 3$$

$$z \text{ levels of } g_t, \text{ where } z = 3$$

$$n \text{ levels of } s_m, \text{ where } n = 2$$

$$\sum_1^N = \sum_1^q \sum_1^z \sum_1^n.$$

TABLE 9.11-1   Layout of Type LSCF-3^2 Design and Computational Procedures

(i) Data:

ABGS Summary Table

		b_0	b_1	b_2
g_0	s_0	a_0	a_1	a_2
		3	3	6
	s_1	2	4	5
g_1	s_0	a_1	a_2	a_0
		3	4	7
	s_1	1	3	5
g_2	s_0	a_2	a_0	a_1
		3	4	7
	s_1	2	2	6

AB Summary Table

	b_0	b_1	b_2	$\sum_1^q A$
a_0	$n = 2$			
	5	6	12	23
a_1	4	7	13	24
a_2	5	7	11	23
$\sum_1^p B =$	14	20	36	

GS Summary Table

	s_0	s_1	$\sum_1^n G$
g_0	$p = 3$		
	12	11	23
g_1	14	9	23
g_2	14	10	24

(ii) Computational symbols:

$$\sum_1^N ABGS = 3 + 2 + \cdots + 6 = 70.00$$

$$\sum_1^N (ABGS)^2 = [ABGS] = (3)^2 + (2)^2 + \cdots + (6)^2 = 326.00$$

$$\frac{\left(\sum_1^N ABGS\right)^2}{N} = [X] = \frac{(70)^2}{18} = 272.22$$

$$\sum_1^p \frac{\left(\sum_1^q A\right)^2}{nq} = [A] = \frac{(23)^2}{(2)(3)} + \frac{(24)^2}{(2)(3)} + \frac{(23)^2}{(2)(3)} = 272.33$$

$$\sum_1^q \frac{\left(\sum_1^p B\right)^2}{np} = [B] = \frac{(14)^2}{(2)(3)} + \frac{(20)^2}{(2)(3)} + \frac{(36)^2}{(2)(3)} = 315.33$$

$$\sum_1^z \frac{\left(\sum_1^n G\right)^2}{np} = [G] = \frac{(23)^2}{(2)(3)} + \frac{(23)^2}{(2)(3)} + \frac{(24)^2}{(2)(3)} = 272.33$$

$$\sum_1^p \sum_1^q \frac{(AB)^2}{n} = [AB] = \frac{(5)^2}{2} + \frac{(6)^2}{2} + \cdots + \frac{(11)^2}{2} = 317.00$$

$$\sum_1^n \sum_1^z \frac{(GS)^2}{p} = [GS] = \frac{(12)^2}{3} + \frac{(11)^2}{3} + \cdots + \frac{(10)^2}{3} = 279.33$$

TABLE 9.11-1 (continued)

(iii) Computational formulas:

$$SS_{total} = [ABGS] - [X] = 53.78$$
$$SS_{between\ blocks\ and\ subj} = [GS] - [X] = 7.11$$
$$SS_G = [G] - [X] = .11$$
$$SS_{subj\ w.blocks} = [GS] - [G] = 7.00$$
$$SS_{within\ blocks\ and\ subj} = [ABGS] - [GS] = 46.67$$
$$SS_A = [A] - [X] = .11$$
$$SS_B = [B] - [X] = 43.11$$
$$SS'_{AB(within)} = [AB] - [A] - [B] - [G] + 2[X] = 1.45$$
$$SS_{AB \times subj\ w.blocks} = [ABGS] - [AB] - [GS] + [G] = 2.00$$

According to the summary in Table 9.11-2, the null hypothesis can be rejected for treatment B. The same decision was reached using a type RBPF-3^2 design, which is summarized in Table 9.4-2. Both designs require the same number of observations. On what basis can an experimenter decide which design is most appropriate for his experiment? The answer requires a comparison of the respective degrees of freedom for $SS'_{AB(within)}$ and experimental error. The required information from Tables 9.4-2 and 9.11-2 is summarized below.

Source	df for Type RBPF-3^2 Design	df for Type LSCF-3^2 Design
$SS'_{AB(within)}$	$(p-1)(q-1) = 4$	$(p-1)(p-2) = 2$
$SS_{error(within)}$	$2(p-1)(w-1) = 4$	$p(n-1)(p-1) = 6$
	$F_{05;4,4} = 6.39$	$F_{05;2,6} = 5.14$

The type LSCF-3^2 design provides more degrees of freedom for experimental error but, unlike the RBPF-3^2 design, does not provide information on the (AB) interaction component from two replications. An experimenter who is particularly interested in the AB interaction and who is willing to sacrifice information on treatment A can use a third design. A type SPF-3.3 design, diagramed in Figure 9.11-2, requires the same number of observa-

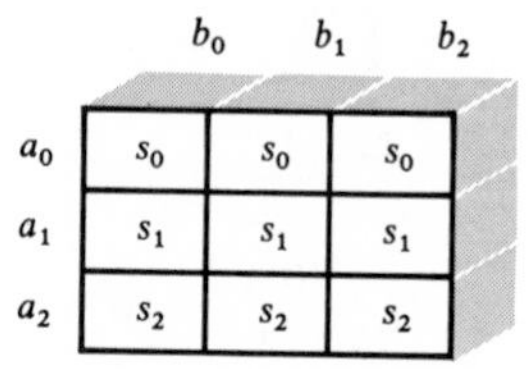

Figure 9.11-2 Block diagram of type SPF-3.3 design.

TABLE 9.11-2　Analysis of Variance Table for Type LSCF-3² Design

	Source	SS	df	MS	F	E(MS) Model III (A and B Fixed Effects, Blocks Random)
1	Between blocks and subj	7.11	$np - 1 = 5$			
2	G	.11	$p - 1 = 2$	.06	$[\frac{2}{3}]$ N.S.	$\sigma_\varepsilon^2 + p\sigma_\pi^2 + np\sigma_\theta^2$
3	Subj w.blocks	7.00	$p(n - 1) = 3$	2.33		$\sigma_\varepsilon^2 + p\sigma_\pi^2$
4	Within blocks and subj	46.67	$np(p - 1) = 12$			
5	A	.11	$p - 1 = 2$	.06	$[\frac{5}{8}]$ N.S.	$\sigma_\varepsilon^2 + np\sigma_\alpha^2$
6	B	43.11	$p - 1 = 2$	21.56	$[\frac{6}{8}] = 65.33*$	$\sigma_\varepsilon^2 + np\sigma_\beta^2$
7	AB'(within)	1.45	$(p - 1)(p - 2) = 2$	.72	$[\frac{7}{8}] = 2.18$	$\sigma_\varepsilon^2 + n\sigma_{\alpha\beta}^2$
8	$AB \times$ subj w.blocks	2.00	$p(n - 1)(p - 1) = 6$	.33		σ_ε^2
9	Total	53.78	$np^2 - 1 = 17$			

$*p < .01$.

tions as the two preceding designs. In this split-plot design, treatment A is confounded with between-block variation. Type RBPF and LSCF designs confound the AB interaction with between-block variation. It should be apparent to the reader that subtle variations in the layout of a design can markedly affect the power of significance tests.

COMPUTATIONAL PROCEDURES
FOR TYPE LSCF-$r.p^2$ DESIGN

The versatility of a Latin square in constructing confounded factorial designs is shown in Figure 9.11-3. This design is composed of two LSCF-p^2 designs. The levels of treatment C are assigned to different balanced squares. Assumptions appropriate for a type LSCF-p^2 design also apply to this design. There are no restrictions on the number of levels of treatment C, and interactions of C with A and B are permissible. Computational formulas for this design are shown in Table 9.11-3. The E(MS) in Table 9.11-3 are appropriate for an experiment in which treatments A, B, and C are fixed effects. Blocks are assumed to be random. The (AB) component of the AB interaction can be tested separately for squares one and two or pooled prior to a test. If the components are pooled, the resulting sum of squares represent a component of the ABC interaction.

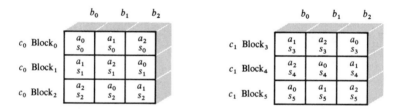

Figure 9.11-3   Block diagram of type LSCF-2.3² design.

9.12   DOUBLE CONFOUNDING

It is possible to arrange treatment combinations in a Latin square in such a way that unimportant interactions are confounded with between-row variation and between-column variation. This procedure is called *double confounding*. Yates (1937) proposed the name *quasi-latin squares* for these designs. These designs are useful for situations in which it is desirable to eliminate row and column variation from the experimental error and at the same time use relatively small rows and columns. They differ from a regular Latin square design in that each treatment combination does not appear once in each row and column. For a discussion of these designs, see Cochran and Cox (1957, 317), Federer (1955, 472), and Yates (1937).

TABLE 9.11-3   Analysis of Variance Table and Computational Formulas for Type LSCF-$r.p^2$ Design

	Source	df	Computational Formulas	F	E(MS) Model III (A, B, and C Fixed Effects, Blocks Random)
1	Between blocks and subj	$npr - 1$	$[CGS] - [X]$		
2	C	$r - 1$	$[C] - [X]$	$\left[\frac{2}{3}\right]$	$\sigma_\varepsilon^2 + p\sigma_\pi^2 + np\sigma_\theta^2 + np^2\sigma_\gamma^2$
3	Blocks w.C	$r(p - 1)$	$[CG] - [C]$	$\left[\frac{3}{4}\right]$	$\sigma_\varepsilon^2 + p\sigma_\pi^2 + np\sigma_\theta^2$
4	Subj w.blocks	$pr(n - 1)$	$[CGS] - [CG]$		$\sigma_\varepsilon^2 + p\sigma_\pi^2$
5	Within blocks and subj	$npr(p - 1)$	$[ABCGS] - [CGS]$		
6	A	$p - 1$	$[A] - [X]$	$\left[\frac{6}{12}\right]$	$\sigma_\varepsilon^2 + npr\sigma_\alpha^2$
7	B	$p - 1$	$[B] - [X]$	$\left[\frac{7}{12}\right]$	$\sigma_\varepsilon^2 + npr\sigma_\beta^2$
8	AC	$(p - 1)(r - 1)$	$[AC] - [A] - [C] + [X]$	$\left[\frac{8}{12}\right]$	$\sigma_\varepsilon^2 + np\sigma_{\alpha\gamma}^2$
9	BC	$(p - 1)(r - 1)$	$[BC] - [B] - [C] + [X]$	$\left[\frac{9}{12}\right]$	$\sigma_\varepsilon^2 + np\sigma_{\beta\gamma}^2$
10	AB'(square I)	$(p - 1)(p - 2)$	$[AB] - [A] - [B] - [G] + 2[X]$ terms computed from square I	$\left[\frac{10}{12}\right]$	$\sigma_\varepsilon^2 + n\sigma_{\alpha\beta}^2$
11	AB'(square II)	$(p - 1)(p - 2)$	$[AB] - [A] - [B] - [G] + 2[X]$ terms computed from square II	$\left[\frac{11}{12}\right]$	$\sigma_\varepsilon^2 + n\sigma_{\alpha\beta}^2$
12	$AB \times$ subj w.blocks	$pr(n - 1)(p - 1)$	$[ABCGS] - [ABC] - [CGS] + [CG]$		σ_ε^2
13	Total	$np^2r - 1$	$[ABCGS] - [X]$		

9.13   ADVANTAGES AND DISADVANTAGES OF CONFOUNDING IN FACTORIAL DESIGNS

An examination of current research literature in the behavioral sciences reveals an almost total absence of experiments utilizing the confounded factorial designs described in this chapter. This observation is in sharp contrast to the observation that a split-plot design, which involves a different form of confounding, is one of the most popular designs. How can one account for the relative popularity of these two designs, both of which accomplish the same objective of reducing block size? The answer to this question is probably to be found in an examination of the relative merits of the two designs and in the gradual evolution that is taking place in design sophistication among experimenters. Experimenters today are well aware of the potential advantage of a randomized block factorial design in reducing residual error variation by minimizing the effects of subject heterogeneity. As pointed out previously, however, type RBF-pq designs of only modest size may require a prohibitively large block size. For example, a type RBF-33 design requires blocks of size nine. A split-plot design provides a solution to this problem by confounding treatment A with between-block variation. Thus a type SPF-3.3 design requires blocks of size three. An alternative solution is provided by type RBPF-3^2 and LSCF-3^2 designs. These designs confound the AB interaction with between-block variation in order to achieve a block size of three. In all three designs, the advantage of reduced block size is achieved at a price. In the case of a SPF-3.3 design, the price an experimenter pays is loss of power in evaluating a treatment; in the case of type RBPF-3^2 and LSCF-3^2 designs, power is lost in evaluating an interaction. The particular research application will determine which kind of information can be sacrificed and, indeed, if either form of confounding is appropriate. This discussion serves to emphasize a theme that runs throughout this book. The selection of the *best* design requires an intimate knowledge of a research area as well as a knowledge of the advantages and disadvantages of alternative designs.

With the foregoing discussion as a general frame of reference, the advantages and disadvantages of confounding interactions with between-block variation can be stated as follows:

The advantages of type RBCF, RBPF, and LSCF designs are

1. These designs can be used in experiments in which it is not possible to administer all treatment combinations within each block. This condition may exist because of lack of sufficient homogeneous subjects to form complete blocks or because only a portion of the treatment combinations

can be administered in a relatively homogeneous time interval. If repeated observations are obtained on subjects, the sheer number of treatment combinations may preclude administration of all combinations to each subject.

2. All main effects can be evaluated with equal precision in these designs.

3. An experimenter is able to tailor his experimental design so that only interactions believed to be insignificant are partially or completely sacrificed.

The disadvantages of type RBCF, RBPF, and LSCF designs are

1. Information is lost with respect to one or more interactions.

2. The general layout and analysis of type RBCF and RBPF designs are more complex than the analysis of type SPF and RBF designs. This is also true in making comparisons among means when partially confounded interactions are significant and in estimating missing observations.

3. Type RBCF, RBPF, and LSCF designs, with their greater complexity of layout and analysis, may actually involve more work for the experimenter than designs using more subjects, such as a completely randomized factorial design. The availability of subjects, cost of assigning homogeneous subjects to blocks, and cost of running subjects must be taken into account in the choice of a design.

9.14   REPRESENTATIVE APPLICATIONS OF CONFOUNDED FACTORIAL DESIGNS IN THE RESEARCH LITERATURE

The following references illustrate a variety of applications of confounded factorial designs.

Conrad, R. Accuracy of recall using keyset and telephone dail, and the effect of a prefix digit. *Journal of Applied Psychology*, 1958, **42**, 285–288. Type LSCF-4^2 design.

Hunt, Earl B. Memory effects in concept learning. *Journal of Experimental Psychology*, 1961, **62**, 598–604. Type LSCF-4^2 design.

Martindale, Robert S., and William F. Lowe. Use of television for remote control: a preliminary study. *Journal of Applied Psychology*, 1959, **43**, 122–124. Type LSCF-5^2 design.

Staats, Arthur W., Carolyn K. Staats, and William G. Heard. Language conditioning of meaning to meaning using a semantic generalization paradigm. *Journal of Experimental Psychology*, 1959, **57**, 187–192. Type LSCF-2^2 design.

10 / FRACTIONAL FACTORIAL DESIGNS—

FACTORIAL DESIGNS WITH TREATMENT-INTERACTION CONFOUNDING

10.1 INTRODUCTION TO FRACTIONAL FACTORIAL DESIGNS

The main properties of factorial experiments were considered in Chapters 7, 8, and 9. One of the characteristics of the designs discussed is that *all* treatment combinations appear in the experiment. Fractional factorial designs described in this chapter represent a departure from this characteristic. These designs include only a *fraction*; for example, $\frac{1}{2}$, or $\frac{1}{3}$, $\frac{1}{4}$, etc., of the treatment combinations of a complete factorial design. A $3 \times 3 \times 3 \times 3$ completely randomized factorial design has 81 treatment combinations. By using a one-third fractional replication, only 27 of these combinations need be included in the experiment.

Fractional factorial designs represent a relatively recent development in the evolution of experimental designs. The theory of fractional replication was developed for 2^k and 3^k designs by Finney (1945, 1946a) and extended by Kempthorne (1947) to designs of the type p^k, where p is any prime number and k designates the number of treatments. Fractional factorial designs have found their greatest use in industrial research. Only limited application of these designs has been made in agricultural research, which historically has provided the impetus for the development of most designs in use today.

Fractional factorial designs have much in common with confounded factorial designs. This latter design achieves a reduction in the number of treatment combinations that must be included within blocks. A fractional factorial design extends this principle to the entire experiment. The reduction in size of an experiment is not obtained without paying a price, however. Considerable ambiguity may exist in interpreting the results of fractionally replicated experiments. This arises because every sum of squares can be given two or more designations. For example, a sum of squares might be attributed to the effects of treatment A and the $BCDE$ interaction. The two or more designations given to the same sum of squares are called *aliases*. In a one-half fractional replication of a 2^k factorial design, all sums of squares have two aliases; a one-fourth fractional replication results in all sums of squares having four aliases. This means, in the case of a one-fourth replication, that four names can be given to the same sum of squares. It is imperative that careful attention be given to the alias pattern of a proposed design in order to minimize confusion in interpreting tests of significance. Treatments are customarily aliased with higher-order interactions that are assumed to equal zero. This helps to minimize but does not eliminate ambiguity in interpreting the outcome of an experiment.

A fractional factorial design is appropriate for experiments that meet, in addition to the general assumptions of the analysis of variance model, the following conditions:

1. The experiment contains many treatments that result in a prohibitively large number of treatment combinations. Fractional replication is rarely used for experiments with less than four or five treatments.

2. The number of treatment levels should, if possible, be equal for all treatments. With the exception of fractional factorial experiments utilizing a Latin square building block design, analysis procedures for experiments involving mixed treatment levels are relatively complex.

3. An experimenter should have some *a priori* reason for believing that a number of higher-order interactions are zero or small relative to main effects. In practice, fractional factorial designs, with the exception of those based on a Latin square, are most often used with treatments having either two or three levels. The use of a restricted number of levels increases the likelihood that interactions will be insignificant.

4. Fractional factorial designs are most useful for exploratory research and for situations that permit *follow-up* experiments to be performed. Thus a large number of treatments can be investigated efficiently in an initial experiment, with subsequent experiments designed to focus on the most promising lines of investigation or to clarify the interpretation of the original analysis.

Among the disadvantages of a complete factorial design listed in Section 7.17 was the fact that the design committed an experimenter to a relatively large experiment. In many research situations, a sequence of relatively small experiments, each based on the results of the preceding experiment, is more efficient than a single experiment in determining optimum levels of treatments. A fractional factorial design lends itself to this kind of sequential experimentation. Fractional factorial experiments using three *building block* designs are described in this chapter. The building block designs are completely randomized, randomized block, and Latin square designs. These fractional factorial designs are designated by the letters CRFF, RBFF, and LSFF, respectively.

The use of a fractional factorial design can lead to a sizable reduction in the number of treatment combinations that must be included in an experiment. This is accomplished by *confounding* main effects with higher-order interactions. This form of confounding completes a cycle that began in Chapter 8. That chapter described split-plot designs that involve *block-*

treatment confounding. Chapter 9 presented confounded factorial designs involving *block-interaction* confounding. Here we shall discuss *treatment-interaction* confounding. It should be noted that whenever confounding is used, some information is lost.

However, if certain information concerning the outcome of the experiment is of negligible interest, an experimenter can employ confounding so as to sacrifice only this information. The advantage of confounding in terms of a reduction in experimental effort may more than compensate for the lost information.

10.2 GENERAL PROCEDURES FOR CONSTRUCTING TYPE CRFF-2^k DESIGNS

ONE-HALF REPLICATION DESIGNS

Procedures for constructing fractional factorial designs are closely related to those for confounded factorial designs. It will be recalled that the treatment combinations in a 2^4 completely confounded factorial design can be assigned to two blocks by means of the family of relations $(ABCD)_i$ modulo 2, where $i = 0, 1$. A 2^4 one-half fractional factorial design consists of the treatment combinations contained in either block $(ABCD)_0$ or $(ABCD)_1$. The interaction used to divide the treatment combinations into the two blocks is called the *defining contrast*.

ALIAS PATTERN FOR FRACTIONAL FACTORIAL DESIGNS

All effects in a fractional factorial design have two or more aliases. The alias pattern for a one-half fractional factorial design can be determined by multiplying each of the effects in the experiment by the defining contrast and expressing the product modulo m. Computation of the alias pattern for a type CRFF-2^4 design is shown in Table 10.2-1. It is apparent from this table that all main effects have three-factor interactions as aliases and that two-factor interactions have other two-factor interactions as aliases. This particular design is not very satisfactory because of the ambiguity associated with interpreting significant two-factor interactions. It is not possible to determine from this design whether a significant two-factor interaction is associated with, for example, the *AB* or *CD* interaction. This question can be answered by conducting a second experiment that includes the treatment combinations not included in the first experiment. If the two experiments are combined, a regular type CRF-2222 design is obtained.

**TABLE 10.2-1   Alias Pattern for Type CRFF-2^4 Design
with Defining Contrast $= ABCD$**

(1) Source	(2) Defining Contrast	(3) Product (1) × (2)	(4) Alias (mod 2)
A	ABCD	A^2BCD	BCD
B	ABCD	AB^2CD	ACD
C	ABCD	ABC^2D	ABD
D	ABCD	$ABCD^2$	ABC
AB	ABCD	A^2B^2CD	CD
AC	ABCD	A^2BC^2D	BD
AD	ABCD	A^2BCD^2	BC
BC	ABCD	AB^2C^2D	AD
BD	ABCD	AB^2CD^2	AC
CD	ABCD	ABC^2D^2	AB
ABC	ABCD	$A^2B^2C^2D$	D
ABD	ABCD	$A^2B^2CD^2$	C
ACD	ABCD	$A^2BC^2D^2$	B
BCD	ABCD	$AB^2C^2D^2$	A

ONE-FOURTH REPLICATION DESIGNS
AND ASSOCIATED ALIAS PATTERN

A one-fourth fractional replication can be obtained by using two defining contrasts to select treatment combinations that are included in an experiment. In this case, effects have four aliases. Two of the aliases are associated with the product of a treatment and the two defining contrasts. The third alias is associated with the product of a treatment and the *generalized interaction* of the two defining contrasts. The fourth alias is the treatment itself. Assume that the two defining contrasts are ABC and ACD. The generalized interaction of ABC and ACD, following procedures described in Section 9.8, is given by

$$(ABC)(ACD) = A^2BC^2D = BD \, (\text{mod } 2).$$

Aliases of effects for a type CRFF-2^4 design are shown in Table 10.2-2.

A one-fourth replication of a type CRFF-2^4 design is an unsatisfactory design, for some main effects are aliased with other main effects. In this example, the alias of treatment B is treatment D. If an experiment contains a large number of treatments, a one-fourth replication is a practical design. For example, an experiment with eight treatments at two levels each can be designed for a one-fourth replication so that no treatments or two factor-interactions are aliased with lower-order interactions. The

**TABLE 10.2-2   Alias Pattern for One-fourth Type CRFF-2^4
Design with Defining Contrasts $= ABC$ and ACD**

Source	Defining Contrasts and Generalized Interaction	Products	Aliases (mod 2)
A	ABC, ACD, BD	A^2BC, A^2CD, ABD	BC, CD, ABD
B	ABC, ACD, BD	$AB^2C, ABCD, B^2D$	$AC, ABCD, D$
C	ABC, ACD, BD	ABC^2, AC^2D, BCD	AB, AD, BCD
D	ABC, ACD, BD	$ABCD, ACD^2, BD^2$	$ABCD, AC, B$
.	. . .	. . .	. . .
.	. . .	. . .	. . .
.	. . .	. . .	. . .
BCD	ABC, ACD, BD	$AB^2C^2D, ABC^2D^2, B^2CD^2,$	AD, AB, C

number of treatment combinations can be reduced from 256 to 64 by this procedure. Care must be used in the selection of defining contrasts so as to avoid aliasing main effects with other main effects.

RELATION BETWEEN ONE-HALF
REPLICATION OF 2^4 DESIGN AND
COMPLETE 2^3 DESIGN

A careful examination of the alias pattern in Table 10.2-1 reveals an interesting feature of this one-half fractional factorial design. The incomplete four-treatment design contains all of the treatment combinations of a complete three-treatment design. That is, if any one of the four treatments is ignored, the experiment becomes a complete three-treatment factorial design. This point can be made clearer by a rearrangement of Table 10.2-1. For purposes of illustration, the effects associated with treatment D are ignored in the following source column.

Source	Alias
A	BCD
B	ACD
C	ABD
AB	CD
AC	BD
BC	AD
ABC	D

An examination of the source column reveals that all treatments and interactions of a type CRF-222 design are present. The significance of the above arrangement will become apparent in the following section, which describes general analysis procedures for fractional factorial designs.

10.3 COMPUTATIONAL PROCEDURES FOR TYPE CRFF-2^4 DESIGN

Computational procedures for a one-half replication of a 2^4 design are identical to those for a complete replication of a 2^3 design. This means that, by ignoring one of the treatments, the analysis of an incomplete design can be carried out as if all the treatment combinations were included in the experiment. This procedure can be extended to one-fourth and one-eighth replications. Thus a 2^k incomplete design is analogous to a 2^{k-1} complete design, where k refers to the number of treatments. Similarly, one-fourth and one-eighth incomplete designs are analogous to 2^{k-2} and 2^{k-3} complete designs, respectively.

The first step in laying out a type CRFF-2^4 design is to determine the treatment combinations to be included in the experiment. This is facilitated by the use of modular arithmetic. The convention adopted in Chapter 9 of using the subscript zero to designate the first level of a treatment will be followed in this chapter. It is customary in laying out a fractional factorial design to use the highest-order interaction as the defining contrast because it is less likely to be significant than lower-order interactions. Treatment combinations satisfying either $(ABCD)_0$ or $(ABCD)_1$ can be used as the defining contrast. Assume that $(ABCD)_0$ is selected by a toss of a coin. Treatment combinations that satisfy this relation are as follows:

$$[x_1 + x_2 + x_3 + x_4 = 0 \,(\text{mod } 2)] = 0000, \; 1100, \; 1010, \; 1001, \; 0110,$$

$$0101, \; 0011, \; 1111.$$

The successive numbers refer to the level of treatments A, B, C, and D, respectively. Thus 1010 stands for $A_1 \, B_0 \, C_1 \, D_0$.

General procedures for analyzing fractional factorial designs are illustrated in Table 10.3-1. This example has the virtue of simplicity, but, as noted previously, a type CRFF-2^4 design is unsatisfactory because of ambiguity in interpreting two-factor interactions. It is assumed that the following linear model is appropriate for this design:

$$X_{ijklm} = \mu + \alpha_i + \beta_j + \gamma_k + \delta_l + \alpha\beta_{ij}(\gamma\delta_{kl}) + \alpha\gamma_{ik}(\beta\delta_{jl})$$

$$+ \beta\gamma_{jk}(\alpha\delta_{il}) + \varepsilon_{m(ijkl)}.$$

The notation $\alpha\beta_{ij}(\gamma\delta_{kl})$ indicates that these two interactions are aliases which cannot be differentiated in this design. A fixed-effects model is assumed to be appropriate for the CRFF designs described in this chapter.

The following notation is used in Table 10.3-1:

$$p \text{ levels of } a_i, \text{ where } p = 2$$
$$q \text{ levels of } b_j, \text{ where } q = 2$$
$$r \text{ levels of } c_k, \text{ where } r = 2$$
$$u \text{ levels of } d_l, \text{ where } u = 2$$
$$n \text{ levels of } s_m, \text{ where } n = 2$$
$$\sum_{1}^{N} = \sum_{1}^{p}\sum_{1}^{q}\sum_{1}^{r}\sum_{1}^{n}.$$

TABLE 10.3-1 Layout of Type CRFF-2⁴ Design and Computational Procedures

(i) Data:

$ABCS = (\frac{1}{2} ABCDS)$ Summary Table

a_0	a_1	a_1	a_1	a_0	a_0	a_0	a_1
b_0	b_1	b_0	b_0	b_1	b_1	b_0	b_1
c_0	c_0	c_1	c_0	c_1	c_0	c_1	c_1
d_0	d_0	d_0	d_1	d_0	d_1	d_1	d_1
3	5	2	2	7	7	4	9
6	6	3	2	8	6	3	11

ABC Summary Table

	b_0	b_0	b_1	b_1
	c_0	c_1	c_0	c_1
a_0	$n = 2$			
	9	7	13	15
a_1	4	5	11	20

AB Summary Table

	b_0	b_1	$\sum_{1}^{q} A$
a_0	$nr = 4$		
	16	28	44
a_1	9	31	40
$\sum_{1}^{p} B = 25$		59	

AC Summary Table

	c_0	c_1
a_0	$nq = 4$	
	22	22
a_1	15	25
$\sum_{1}^{p} C = 37$		47

BC Summary Table

	c_0	c_1
b_0	$np = 4$	
	13	12
b_1	24	35

(ii) Computational symbols:

$$\sum_{1}^{N} ABCS = 3 + 6 + 5 + \cdots + 11 = 84.00$$

$$\sum_{1}^{N} (ABCS)^2 = [ABCS] = (3)^2 + (6)^2 + (5)^2 + \cdots + (11)^2 = 552.00$$

$$\frac{\left(\sum_{1}^{N} ABCS\right)^2}{N} = [X] = \frac{(84)^2}{16} = 441.00$$

$$\sum_{1}^{p} \frac{\left(\sum_{1}^{q} A\right)^2}{nqr} = [A] = \frac{(44)^2}{(2)(2)(2)} + \frac{(40)^2}{(2)(2)(2)} = 442.00$$

TABLE 10.3-1 (continued)

$$\sum_{1}^{q} \frac{\left(\sum_{1}^{p} B\right)^2}{npr} = [B] = \frac{(25)^2}{(2)(2)(2)} + \frac{(59)^2}{(2)(2)(2)} = 513.25$$

$$\sum_{1}^{r} \frac{\left(\sum_{1}^{p} C\right)^2}{npq} = [C] = \frac{(37)^2}{(2)(2)(2)} + \frac{(47)^2}{(2)(2)(2)} = 447.25$$

$$\sum_{1}^{p}\sum_{1}^{q} \frac{(AB)^2}{nr} = [AB] = \frac{(16)^2}{(2)(2)} + \cdots + \frac{(31)^2}{(2)(2)} = 520.50$$

$$\sum_{1}^{p}\sum_{1}^{r} \frac{(AC)^2}{nq} = [AC] = \frac{(22)^2}{(2)(2)} + \cdots + \frac{(25)^2}{(2)(2)} = 454.50$$

$$\sum_{1}^{q}\sum_{1}^{r} \frac{(BC)^2}{np} = [BC] = \frac{(13)^2}{(2)(2)} + \cdots + \frac{(35)^2}{(2)(2)} = 528.50$$

$$\sum_{1}^{p}\sum_{1}^{q}\sum_{1}^{r} \frac{(ABC)^2}{n} = [ABC] = \frac{(9)^2}{2} + \cdots + \frac{(20)^2}{2} = 543.00$$

(iii) Computational formulas:

$\text{SS}_{\text{total}} = [ABCS] - [X] = 111.00$ $\text{SS}_{AB} = [AB] - [A] - [B] + [X] = 6.25$

$\text{SS}_A = [A] - [X] = 1.00$ $\text{SS}_{AC} = [AC] - [A] - [C] + [X] = 6.25$

$\text{SS}_B = [B] - [X] = 72.25$ $\text{SS}_{BC} = [BC] - [B] - [C] + [X] = 9.00$

$\text{SS}_C = [C] - [X] = 6.25$ $\text{SS}_{ABC} = [ABC] - [AB] - [AC] - [BC] + [A]$

$$+ [B] + [C] - [X] = 1.00$$

$$\text{SS}_{\text{w.cell}} = [ABCS] - [ABC] = 9.00$$

For computational purposes, treatment D is ignored. The choice of which treatment to ignore is arbitrary. The analysis is summarized in Table 10.3-2. According to the analysis of variance table, the null hypothesis for treatments B and C can be rejected. The summary in Table 10.3-2 illustrates a major problem inherent in fractional factorial designs—how to interpret significant MS's that are aliased with other MS's of the same order. There is no way to determine from the analysis just performed whether, for example, the AB or CD interaction is significant or whether both are significant. The experiment provides only one mean square that is a linear function of AB and CD. Confusion with respect to AB and CD can be resolved by carrying out the other half of the experiment and combining it with the first half. Davies (1956, 471) and Daniel (1956) discuss the general problem of carrying out follow-up experiments to clarify the interpretation of fractional factorial experiments. Bennett and Franklin (1954, 597) introject a word of caution concerning *combined* experiments. They point out that some bias is introduced in the significance test for combined experiments if a decision to carry out the second half of an experiment is based on results obtained in the first half. The discussion in Section 7.12 concerning preliminary tests on the model and pooling procedures is relevant to this issue. In actual practice, it is customary to combine fractional factorial experiments as if no test of significance had preceded the joint analysis. Finney (1960, 139) states, "Undoubtedly the danger of bias arises, although the nature of this cannot be made clear without much fuller consideration of sequential experimentation, but many experimenters will, probably rightly, regard the risk as a reasonable price to pay for the advantages and economies gained."

It can be shown that the sums of squares computed for the AB and ABC interactions, for example, are indistinguishable from the sums of squares computed for the CD interaction and treatment D. The information contained in the $ABCS$ Summary Table can be used to construct the following CD Summary Table.

CD Summary Table

	d_0	d_1	$\overset{u}{\underset{1}{\sum}} C$
c_0 $\quad np = 4$	20	17	37
c_1	20	27	47

$\overset{r}{\underset{1}{\sum}} D = 40 \qquad 44$

$$[D] = \frac{(40)^2}{(2)(2)(2)} + \frac{(44)^2}{(2)(2)(2)} = 442.00$$

$$[CD] = \frac{(20)^2}{(2)(2)} + \cdots + \frac{(27)^2}{(2)(2)} = 454.50$$

$$SS_D = [D] - [X] = 1.00 = SS_{ABC}$$

$$SS_{CD} = [CD] - [C] - [D] + [X] = 6.25 = SS_{AB}$$

A comparison of SS_D with SS_{ABC} and of SS_{CD} with SS_{AB} shows that the alias pairs are equal. This example could be extended to all alias pairs in Table 10.3-2.

TABLE 10.3-2   Analysis of Variance Table for Type CRFF-2⁴ Design

Source and Alias		SS	df	MS	F (Model I)
1	A (BCD)	1.00	$p - 1 = 1$	1.000	$\left[\frac{1}{8}\right]$ N.S.
2	B (ACD)	72.25	$q - 1 = 1$	72.250	$\left[\frac{2}{8}\right] = 64.22**$
3	C (ABD)	6.25	$r - 1 = 1$	6.250	$\left[\frac{3}{8}\right] = 5.56*$
4	D (ABC)	1.00	$u - 1 = 1$	1.000	$\left[\frac{4}{8}\right]$ N.S.
5	AB (CD)	6.25	$(p - 1)(q - 1) = 1$	6.250	$\left[\frac{5}{8}\right] = 5.56*$
6	AC (BD)	6.25	$(p - 1)(r - 1) = 1$	6.250	$\left[\frac{6}{8}\right] = 5.56*$
7	BC (AD)	9.00	$(q - 1)(r - 1) = 1$	9.000	$\left[\frac{7}{8}\right] = 8.00*$
8	W.cell	9.00	$pqr(n - 1) = 8$	1.125	
9	Total	111.00	$npqr - 1 = 15$		

$*p < .05.$

$**p < .01.$

Each sum of squares in a fractional design can be given two or more names. In practice, an experimenter attempts to arrange the alias pattern so that one name is a more reasonable designation for effects than the other alias name. This is accomplished by aliasing main effects and lower-order interactions with higher-order interactions.

The example in Table 10.3-1 contains a total of 16 subjects with two observations in each cell. This was necessary in order to provide an estimate of experimental error. In larger fractional factorial designs, it is customary to obtain only one observation under the treatment combinations. The higher-order interactions are pooled in order to obtain an estimate of experimental error. A complete factorial design could be carried out with the same number of subjects used in this fractional factorial design. If, for example, 16 subjects were used in a type CRF-2222 design, it would not be possible to compute a within-cell error term. Under these conditions, the second- and third-order interactions could be pooled to form a residual error term. If these pooled interactions are insignificant, a complete factorial design would have been a better design choice for the data in Table 10.3-1 than the fractional factorial design. On the other hand, if some of the interactions are significant, the present analysis offers the advantage of a larger number of degrees of freedom for experimental error and a within-cell error term.

Extensive tables of plans (Davies; 1956, 484 and Cochran and Cox; 1957, 276) are available for $\frac{1}{2}, \frac{1}{4}, \frac{1}{8}$, etc. fractional factorial designs minimizing undesirable alias patterns. Of particular interest are the extensive tables published by the National Bureau of Standards (1957). This latter publication provides plans for 1/2 through 1/256 replication of experiments with up to 16 treatments.

10.4   COMPUTATIONAL PROCEDURES FOR TYPE CRFF-3^4 DESIGN

If each treatment has three instead of two levels, the experiment can be designed so that only $\frac{1}{3}$ or $\frac{1}{9}$ or $\frac{1}{27}$, etc. of the treatment combinations must be run. Computational procedures described in previous sections of this chapter are applicable to these experiments. However, the analysis and interpretation of fractional factorial designs are more complicated for the 3^k series than for the 2^k series. Effects have three aliases in a one-third replication, instead of two as in a one-half replication of the 2^k series. If a one-ninth replication is used, effects have nine aliases; whereas in a one-fourth replication of the 2^k series, effects have only four aliases. In general, fractional replication is less satisfactory for 3^k experiments than for 2^k experiments. One reason, in addition to greater complexity, is that a 3^k experiment must have a relatively large number of treatments ($k \geq 5$) in order to provide useful estimates of two-factor interactions.

Another problem with 3^k experiments that is not present in 2^k experiments concerns the interpretation of interactions. In a 3^k experiment, the AB interaction, for example, is partitioned into two components (AB) and (AB^2). It is customary in 3^k confounded factorial designs to pool these two estimates. This is rarely possible in a fractional factorial design because the components have different aliases. Thus, although the (AB) and (AB^2) components are orthogonal in the sense of representing nonoverlapping portions of the AB interaction, their physical interpretation is unclear. Extensive tables of fractional factorial designs for the 3^k series have been prepared by Connor and Zelen (1959).

Assume that an experimenter wants to carry out a one-third replication of a type CRFF-3^4 design. One of the components of the $ABCD$ interaction can be selected as the defining contrast. This interaction, which has 16 degrees of freedom, can be partitioned according to procedures described in Section 9.2 as follows:

Interaction	df
$ABCD$	16
$(ABCD)$	2
$(ABCD^2)$	2
(ABC^2D)	2
(AB^2CD)	2
(ABC^2D^2)	2
(AB^2CD^2)	2
(AB^2C^2D)	2
$(AB^2C^2D^2)$	2

Any one of the eight components of the interaction can be used to partition the treatment combinations into three sets. If the $(ABCD^2)$ component is selected as the defining contrast, three sets of treatment combinations are given by

$$x_1 + x_2 + x_3 + 2x_4 = i(\text{mod } 3), \qquad i = 0, 1, 2.$$

Only one of the sets of relations, $(ABCD^2)_0$, $(ABCD^2)_1$, or $(ABCD^2)_2$, is used in the experiment. A table of random numbers can be employed to determine which of these three sets is adopted. Let us assume that the relation $(ABCD^2)_0$ has been selected. A complete experiment has 81 treatment combinations, but this number can be reduced to 27 by the use of the relation $(ABCD^2)_0$ modulo 3.

The pattern of aliases for treatments having three levels can be determined by procedures similar to those discussed in Section 9.8. If X and Y symbolize the defining contrast and treatment (or interaction), respectively, the alias pattern is given by $(X)(Y)$ and $(X)(Y^2)$, modulo 3. For example, the aliases of treatment A are

$$(ABCD^2) \times A = A^2BCD^2 = (A^2BCD^2)^2 = AB^2C^2D \text{ (mod 3)}$$

$$(ABCD^2) \times A^2 = A^3BCD^2 = BCD^2 \text{ (mod 3)}.$$

The aliases associated with effects are given in Table 10.4-1 for a type CRFF-3^4 design in which $(ABCD^2)$ is the defining contrast. Treatments and two-factor interaction components that are not aliased with other treatments or two-factor interaction components are considered *measurable*. An asterisk designates the measurable effects in the type CRFF-3^4 design of Table 10.4-1.

TABLE 10.4-1   Alias Pattern for Type CRFF-3^4 Design with Defining Contrast = $(ABCD^2)$

Source		Aliases			df
$A*$	$=$	(AB^2C^2D)	$=$	(BCD^2)	$p - 1 = 2$
$B*$	$=$	(AB^2CD^2)	$=$	(ACD^2)	$q - 1 = 2$
$C*$	$=$	(ABC^2D^2)	$=$	(ABD^2)	$r - 1 = 2$
(AB)	$=$	(ABC^2D)	$=$	(CD^2)	$(p - 1)(q - 1)/2 = 2$
$(AB^2)*$	$=$	(AC^2D)	$=$	(BC^2D)	$(p - 1)(q - 1)/2 = 2$
(AC)	$=$	(AB^2CD)	$=$	(BD^2)	$(p - 1)(r - 1)/2 = 2$
$(AC^2)*$	$=$	(AB^2D)	$=$	(BC^2D^2)	$(p - 1)(r - 1)/2 = 2$
(BC)	$=$	$(AB^2C^2D^2)$	$=$	(AD^2)	$(q - 1)(r - 1)/2 = 2$
$(BC^2)*$	$=$	(AB^2D^2)	$=$	(AC^2D^2)	$(q - 1)(r - 1)/2 = 2$
(ABC)	$=$	$(ABCD)$	$=$	$D*$	$(p - 1)(q - 1)(r - 1)/4 = 2$
(ABC^2)	$=$	(ABD)	$=$	$(CD)*$	$(p - 1)(q - 1)(r - 1)/4 = 2$
(AB^2C)	$=$	(ACD)	$=$	$(BD)*$	$(p - 1)(q - 1)(r - 1)/4 = 2$
(AB^2C^2)	$=$	$(AD)*$	$=$	(BCD)	$(p - 1)(q - 1)(r - 1)/4 = 2$

*Effects that are considered measurable.

The layout and computational procedures for the design are simplified by ignoring one of the treatments, say treatment D. It should be apparent from Table 10.4-1 that all main effects and interaction components can be obtained from summary tables that involve only treatments A, B, and C. The procedures described in Section 9.4 must be used to compute the *interaction component* sum of squares. The example used to illustrate the computation in Table 10.4-2 has one observation under each of the 27 treatment combinations. The levels of treatment D occurring in each cell of the ABC Summary Table are included for illustrative purposes only; this information is not used in the analysis. The reader can verify that the treatment combinations in the 27 cells satisfy the relation

$$x_1 + x_2 + x_3 + 2x_4 = 0 \text{(mod 3)}.$$

This example does not provide for a within-cell error term. If higher-order interaction components can be assumed insignificant, they can be pooled to form a residual error term. The following notation is used in Table 10.4-2:

$$p \text{ levels of } a_i, \text{ where } p = 3$$

$$q \text{ levels of } b_j, \text{ where } q = 3$$

$$r \text{ levels of } c_k, \text{ where } r = 3$$

$$u \text{ levels of } d_l, \text{ where } u = 3$$

$$\sum_{1}^{N} = \sum_{1}^{p}\sum_{1}^{q}\sum_{1}^{r}.$$

TABLE 10.4-2 Layout of Type CRFF-3^4 Design and Computational Procedures

(i) Data:

$ABC = (\frac{1}{3} ABCD)$ *Summary Table*

		b_0	b_0	b_0	b_1	b_1	b_1	b_2	b_2	b_2
		c_0	c_1	c_2	c_0	c_1	c_2	c_0	c_1	c_2
a_0	$n = 1$	d_0	d_1	d_2	d_1	d_2	d_0	d_2	d_0	d_1
		3	4	3	3	5	10	5	9	11
a_1		d_1	d_2	d_0	d_2	d_0	d_1	d_0	d_1	d_2
		4	3	5	4	6	10	5	8	12
a_2		d_2	d_0	d_1	d_0	d_1	d_2	d_1	d_2	d_0
		3	3	7	6	7	8	6	9	13

AB Summary Table

	b_0	b_1	b_2	$\sum_{1}^{q} A$
a_0	$r = 3$ 10	18	25	53
a_1	12	20	25	57
a_2	13	21	28	62
$\sum_{1}^{p} B =$ 35	59	78		

TABLE 10.4-2 (continued)

	c_0	c_1	c_2
a_0	$q = 3$ 11	18	24
a_1	13	17	27
a_2	15	19	28
$\sum_1^p C =$ 39	54	79

AC Summary Table

	c_0	c_1	c_2
b_0	$p = 3$ 10	10	15
b_1	13	18	28
b_2	16	26	36

BC Summary Table

(ii) Computational symbols:

$$\sum_1^N ABC = 3 + 4 + \cdots + 13 = 172.00$$

$$\sum_1^N (ABC)^2 = [ABC] = (3)^2 + (4)^2 + \cdots + (13)^2 = 1332.00$$

$$\frac{\left(\sum_1^N ABC\right)^2}{N} = [X] = \frac{(172)^2}{27} = 1095.70$$

$$\sum_1^p \frac{\left(\sum_1^q A\right)^2}{qr} = [A] = \frac{(53)^2}{(3)(3)} + \frac{(57)^2}{(3)(3)} + \frac{(62)^2}{(3)(3)} = 1100.22$$

$$\sum_1^q \frac{\left(\sum_1^p B\right)^2}{pr} = [B] = \frac{(35)^2}{(3)(3)} + \frac{(59)^2}{(3)(3)} + \frac{(78)^2}{(3)(3)} = 1198.89$$

$$\sum_1^r \frac{\left(\sum_1^p C\right)^2}{pq} = [C] = \frac{(39)^2}{(3)(3)} + \frac{(54)^2}{(3)(3)} + \frac{(79)^2}{(3)(3)} = 1186.44$$

$$[D] = \frac{[\sum(ABC)_0]^2}{(3)(3)} + \frac{[\sum(ABC)_1]^2}{(3)(3)} + \frac{[\sum(ABC)_2]^2}{(3)(3)} = \frac{(60)^2}{(3)(3)} + \frac{(60)^2}{(3)(3)} + \frac{(52)^2}{(3)(3)}$$
$$= 1100.44, \text{ where } (ABC)_i = [x_1 + x_2 + x_3 = i \text{ (mod 3)}]$$

$$[(AB^2)] = \frac{[\sum(AB^2)_0]^2}{(3)(3)} + \frac{[\sum(AB^2)_1]^2}{(3)(3)} + \frac{[\sum(AB^2)_2]^2}{(3)(3)} = \frac{(58)^2}{(3)(3)} + \frac{(58)^2}{(3)(3)} + \frac{(56)^2}{(3)(3)}$$
$$= 1096.00, \text{ where } (AB^2)_i = [x_1 + 2x_2 = i \text{ (mod 3)}]$$

$$[(AC^2)] = \frac{[\sum(AC^2)_0]^2}{(3)(3)} + \frac{[\sum(AC^2)_1]^2}{(3)(3)} + \frac{[\sum(AC^2)_2]^2}{(3)(3)} = \frac{(56)^2}{(3)(3)} + \frac{(60)^2}{(3)(3)} + \frac{(56)^2}{(3)(3)}$$
$$= 1096.89, \text{ where } (AC^2)_i = [x_1 + 2x_3 = i \text{ (mod 3)}]$$

$$[(AD)] = \frac{[\sum(AB^2C^2)_0]^2}{(3)(3)} + \frac{[\sum(AB^2C^2)_1]^2}{(3)(3)} + \frac{[\sum(AB^2C^2)_2]^2}{(3)(3)} = \frac{(61)^2}{(3)(3)} + \frac{(57)^2}{(3)(3)} + \frac{(54)^2}{(3)(3)}$$
$$= 1098.44, \text{ where } (AB^2C^2)_i = [x_1 + 2x_2 + 2x_3 = i \text{ (mod 3)}]$$

$$[(BC^2)] = \frac{[\sum(BC^2)_0]^2}{(3)(3)} + \frac{[\sum(BC^2)_1]^2}{(3)(3)} + \frac{[\sum(BC^2)_2]^2}{(3)(3)} = \frac{(64)^2}{(3)(3)} + \frac{(54)^2}{(3)(3)} + \frac{(54)^2}{(3)(3)}$$
$$= 1103.11, \text{ where } (BC^2)_i = [x_2 + 2x_3 = i \text{ (mod 3)}]$$

TABLE 10.4-2 (continued)

$$[(BD)] = \frac{[\sum(AB^2C)_0]^2}{(3)(3)} + \frac{[\sum(AB^2C)_1]^2}{(3)(3)} + \frac{[\sum(AB^2C)_2]^2}{(3)(3)} = \frac{(53)^2}{(3)(3)} + \frac{(63)^2}{(3)(3)} + \frac{(56)^2}{(3)(3)}$$

$$= 1101.56, \text{ where } (AB^2C)_i = [x_1 + 2x_2 + x_3 = i \text{ (mod 3)}]$$

$$[(CD)] = \frac{[\sum(ABC^2)_0]^2}{(3)(3)} + \frac{[\sum(ABC^2)_1]^2}{(3)(3)} + \frac{[\sum(ABC^2)_2]^2}{(3)(3)} = \frac{(59)^2}{(3)(3)} + \frac{(54)^2}{(3)(3)} + \frac{(59)^2}{(3)(3)}$$

$$= 1097.56, \text{ where } (ABC^2)_i = [x_1 + x_2 + 2x_3 = i \text{ (mod 3)}]$$

(iii) Computational formulas:

$$SS_{total} = [ABC] - [X] = 236.30 \qquad SS_{(AC^2)} = [(AC^2)] - [X] = 1.19$$

$$SS_A = [A] - [X] = 4.52 \qquad SS_{(AD)} = [(AD)] - [X] = 2.74$$

$$SS_B = [B] - [X] = 103.19 \qquad SS_{(BC^2)} = [(BC^2)] - [X] = 7.41$$

$$SS_C = [C] - [X] = 90.74 \qquad SS_{(BD)} = [(BD)] - [X] = 5.86$$

$$SS_D = [D] - [X] = 4.74 \qquad SS_{(CD)} = [(CD)] - [X] = 1.86$$

$$SS_{(AB^2)} = [(AB^2)] - [X] = .30 \qquad SS_{res} = SS_{total} - SS_A - SS_B - SS_C$$

$$- \cdots - SS_{(CD)} = 13.75$$

The results of the analysis are summarized in Table 10.4-3. The residual error term is based on only six degrees of freedom. If a larger number of degrees of freedom is desired, all of the remaining two- and three-factor interaction components, with the exception of those aliased with treatments, namely, (BCD^2), (ACD^2), (ABD^2), and (ABC), can be

TABLE 10.4-3   Analysis of Variance Table for Type CRFF-3⁴ Design

	Source	SS	df	MS	F (Model I)
1	A	4.52	2	2.26	$[\frac{1}{11}]$
2	B	103.19	2	51.60	$[\frac{2}{11}] = 7.50^*$
3	C	90.74	2	45.37	$[\frac{3}{11}] = 6.59^*$
4	D	4.74	2	2.37	$[\frac{4}{11}]$
5	(AB^2)	.30	2	.15	$[\frac{5}{11}]$
6	(AC^2)	1.19	2	.60	$[\frac{6}{11}]$
7	(AD)	2.74	2	1.37	$[\frac{7}{11}]$
8	(BC^2)	7.41	2	3.70	$[\frac{8}{11}]$
9	(BD)	5.86	2	2.93	$[\frac{9}{11}]$
10	(CD)	1.86	2	.93	$[\frac{10}{11}]$
11	Residual	13.75	6	6.88	
12	Total	236.30	$N - 1 = 26$		

$^*p < .05.$

pooled with the residual error term under the assumption that they are insignificant. If 54 subjects are available for the experiment, a within-cell error term can be computed. This requires two observations under each of the 27 treatment combinations. None of the interaction components in Table 10.4-3 is significant. This lends support to the assumption that the residual error term is an estimate only of random error.

If the (CD) component, for example, had been significant, an experimenter would be faced with the problem of how to interpret this result. Several courses of action can be pursued in carrying out follow-up experiments designed to clarify the interpretation of aliased effects. The experimenter might choose to *complete* the experiment by running the remaining two-thirds of the treatment combinations. Another alternative would be to carry out a complete factorial experiment involving only treatments B, C, D under the assumption, supported by this analysis, that treatment A is of no consequence.

Comparisons among means in a fractional factorial design can be carried out following procedures described in Section 7.6 for a complete factorial design.

An alternative design for this 3^4 experiment uses a Latin square as the building block design. This design, which is described by Winer (1962, 532), uses three balanced Latin squares, with n subjects assigned to each cell. Fractional factorial designs based on a Latin square are described in Sections 10.7 through 10.12.

10.5   GENERAL PROCEDURES FOR CONSTRUCTING TYPE RBFF-2^k DESIGNS

The *building block* for fractional factorial designs described in the previous sections is a completely randomized design. Designs described here use a randomized block design as the building block and are designated by the letters RBFF. A one-half fractional factorial design, for example, can be laid out in two blocks, four blocks, etc., by means of confounding procedures described in Chapter 9. No new principles are involved in these designs. The assumptions underlying a type RBF-pq design (Section 7.16) are also required for a type RBFF-2^k design.

General procedures for laying out fractional factorial designs in blocks will be illustrated by means of a one-half replication of a type RBFF-2^5 design. The first step is to choose a defining contrast. Let the $ABCDE$ interaction be the defining contrast. The 32 treatment combinations of a complete factorial design can be reduced to 16 by the use of either relation $(ABCDE)_0$ or $(ABCDE)_1$. In order to assign the 16 treatment combinations to two blocks of eight combinations each, it is necessary to confound an interaction other than the defining contrast with between-block variation. The interaction selected as the confounding interaction should be one considered to be insignificant. Procedures for confounding an interaction with blocks are described in Section 9.2. If the AB interaction is confounded with between-block variation and $(ABCDE)_0$ is used as the defining contrast, one obtains the design shown in Table 10.5-1. In this design, treatment combinations in block 0 satisfy both relations

$$(ABCDE)_0 = [x_1 + x_2 + x_3 + x_4 + x_5 = 0(\text{mod } 2)]$$

and $$(AB)_0 = [x_1 + x_2 = 0(\text{mod } 2)].$$

Treatment combinations in block 1 satisfy the relations

$$(ABCDE)_0 = [x_1 + x_2 + x_3 + x_4 + x_5 = 0(\text{mod } 2)]$$

and $$(AB)_1 = [x_1 + x_2 = 1(\text{mod } 2)].$$

TABLE 10.5-1   Layout of Type RBFF-2^5 Design in Two Blocks

				Treatment Combinations				
	abcde	*abcde*	*abcde*	*abcde*	*abcde*	*abcde*	*abcde*	*abcde*
Block 0	00000	00110	00101	00011	11000	11110	11101	11011
Block 1	01111	01100	01010	01001	10100	10010	10001	10111

All treatments and interactions except AB, its alias CDE, and the defining contrast $ABCDE$ are within-block effects. The analysis of the experiment is carried out as if the experiment were a complete four-treatment experiment. The alias pattern and computational formulas for this design appear in Table 10.5-2. For purposes of computation, treatment E can be ignored. Only summary tables involving treatments A, B, C, and D are required for the analysis. All main effects are aliased with four-factor interactions. If it can be assumed that the two- and three-factor interactions are insignificant, they can be pooled to form a residual error term with nine degrees of freedom. This design is not satisfactory if an experimenter is interested in evaluating two-factor interactions.

If an experiment contains six treatments, a one-half replication can be laid out in blocks of size eight. In this design, only 32 of the 64 treatment combinations are included in the experiment. This design permits an experimenter to evaluate all two-factor interactions except one. Higher-order interactions are pooled to form a residual error term. In order to lay out the 32 treatment combinations in blocks of size eight, it is necessary to confound two interactions as described in Section 9.8 with between-block variation.

TABLE 10.5-2 Alias Pattern and Computational Formulas for Type RBFF-2⁵ Design

Source	Alias	df	Computational Formulas	F (Model I)
1 Blocks (AB)	CDE	1	$[AB] - [A] - [B] + [X]$	$[\frac{2}{16}]$
2 A	BCDE	1	$[A] - [X]$	$[\frac{3}{16}]$
3 B	ACDE	1	$[B] - [X]$	$[\frac{4}{16}]$
4 C	ABDE	1	$[C] - [X]$	$[\frac{5}{16}]$
5 D	ABCE	1	$[D] - [X]$	$[\frac{6}{16}]$
6 E	ABCD	1	$[ABCD] - [ABC] - [ABD] - [ACD] - [BCD] + [AB] + [AC]$ $+ [AD] + [BC] + [BD] + [CD] - [A] - [B] - [C] - [D] + [X]$	
7 AC	BDE	1	$[AC] - [A] - [C] + [X]$	
8 AD	BCE	1	$[AD] - [A] - [D] + [X]$	
9 BC	ADE	1	$[BC] - [B] - [C] + [X]$	
10 BD	ACE	1	$[BD] - [B] - [D] + [X]$	
11 CD	ABE	1	$[CD] - [C] - [D] + [X]$	
12 ABC	DE	1	$[ABC] - [AB] - [AC] - [BC] + [A] + [B] + [C] - [X]$	
13 ABD	CE	1	$[ABD] - [AB] - [AD] - [BD] + [A] + [B] + [D] - [X]$	
14 ACD	BE	1	$[ACD] - [AC] - [AD] - [CD] + [A] + [C] + [D] - [X]$	
15 BCD	AE	1	$[BCD] - [BC] - [BD] - [CD] + [B] + [C] + [D] - [X]$	
16 Residual = pooled two- and three-factor interactions				
17 Total		$N - 1 = 15$	$[ABCD] - [X]$	

A procedure for estimating missing observations in fractional factorial designs was described by Draper and Stoneman (1964), who illustrate the estimating procedure for one, two, and three missing observations.

10.6   OTHER TYPES OF CRFF AND RBFF DESIGNS

Fractional factorial designs in which all treatments are at four levels can be easily constructed from 2^k plans. Cochran and Cox (1957) describe procedures for laying out these designs. Johnson and Leone (1964, 216) described a 4×2^k fractional factorial design.

Designs with mixed treatments at two and three levels present special problems with respect to layout and analysis. Kempthorne (1952, 419) discusses some of the problems inherent in these designs. Connor and Young (1961) present plans for $2^k \times 3^l$ experiments, with k and l equal to one through nine treatments. Addelman (1963) has described general procedures for constructing complex fractional factorial designs.

10.7   INTRODUCTION TO LATIN SQUARE FRACTIONAL FACTORIAL DESIGN

LATIN SQUARE DESIGN AS A $1/p$ FRACTIONAL FACTORIAL DESIGN

The classic application of a Latin square design in agricultural research involves one treatment with *nuisance* variables assigned to rows and columns of the square. If the Latin square contains two treatments and one nuisance variable, it is called a Latin square confounded factorial design. If both variables assigned to rows and columns represent treatments instead of nuisance variables, the design is described as a fractional factorial design (type LSFF design). It will be recalled that the term *factorial experiment* refers to the simultaneous evaluation in an experiment of two or more *crossed* treatments. Thus the Latin square in Figure 10.7-1 may be designated as a Latin square design or as a Latin square confounded factorial design or as a Latin square fractional factorial design, depending on the nature of the variables assigned to the rows and columns.

If a_i, b_j, and c_k in Figure 10.7-1 represent three treatments, it can be shown that this Latin square is equivalent to a one-third replication of a 3^3 factorial experiment. Assume that the $(ABC^2)_0$ component has been

Figure 10.7-1   3 × 3 standard Latin square.

selected as the defining contrast for a 3^3 experiment. The treatment combinations are as follows:

$$(ABC^2)_0 = [x_1 + x_2 + 2x_3 = 0 \, (\text{mod } 3)] = \text{000, 011, 022, 101,}$$

$$\text{112, 120, 202, 210, 221,}$$

where the numbers refer to the level of treatments A, B, and C, respectively. A comparison of these treatment combinations with those in Figure 10.7-1 reveals that they are identical. Thus a standard 3 × 3 Latin square corresponds to the treatment combinations in a one-third replication of a 3^3 factorial experiment, with $(ABC^2)_0$ as the defining contrast. A complete 3^3 factorial experiment contains 27 treatment combinations. The Latin square, or one-third replication, contains only nine of these combinations.

In Section 6.2 it was noted that a 3 × 3 Latin square has twelve arrangements. These twelve arrangements can be generated by the family of relations

$$
\begin{array}{ll}
(ABC)_0 & (ABC^2)_2 \\
(ABC)_1 & (AB^2C)_0 \\
(ABC)_2 & \cdot \\
(ABC^2)_0 & \cdot \\
(ABC^2)_1 & (AB^2C^2)_2.
\end{array}
$$

A 2 × 2 Latin square has two arrangements. These correspond to the relation $(AB)_0$ and $(AB)_1$. A 2 × 2 Latin square is analogous to a one-half replication of a 2^3 experiment.

If a one-third replication of a 3^3 experiment corresponds to a 3 × 3 Latin square, the reader may wonder where $\frac{1}{9}$, $\frac{1}{27}$, etc. replications fit into the scheme. A $\frac{1}{9}$ replication of a 3^4 experiment is a 3 × 3 Graeco-Latin square, and a $\frac{1}{27}$ replication of a 3^5 experiment is a 3 × 3 hyper-Graeco-Latin square. The use of hyper-squares, where the maximum number of orthogonal squares have been superimposed on a Latin square, is an extreme form of fractionation. It can be shown that these designs represent the smallest fractional replication in which main effects are not aliased with one another.

THE IMPORTANCE OF ADDITIVITY OF ROW, COLUMN, AND SQUARE EFFECTS

In order to draw valid inferences from experimental designs constructed from Latin squares, interactions among row, column, and square variables must be zero. This requirement is much more likely to be met if the row and column variables represent nuisance or classification variables than if they represent additional treatments, as in the case of a fractional factorial design. In Chapter 6, which deals with Latin square designs, this *additivity requirement* was stated without explanation. A clearer presentation of the problem associated with nonadditivity of effects can be made by using the alias concept developed for fractional factorial designs. Consider the 3×3 Latin square in Figure 10.7-1. This square can be constructed by using the $(ABC^2)_0$ component of the three-factor interaction as the defining contrast. The aliases associated with treatment A are given by

$$(ABC^2)\,A = A^2BC^2 = (A^2BC^2)^2 = AB^2C(\mathrm{mod}\ 3)$$

$$(ABC^2)\,A^2 = A^3BC^2 = BC^2(\mathrm{mod}\ 3).$$

Treatment A is aliased with the (BC^2) and (AB^2C) components of the two- and three-factor interactions, respectively. Similarly, it can be shown that

$$B = (AC^2) = (AB^2C^2)$$

$$C = (AB) = (ABC).$$

Hence in a 3×3 Latin square design or a one-third replication of a 3^3 design, A, B, and C are indistinguishable from components of the two- and three-factor interactions. It can also be shown that the components of the two-factor interactions not aliased with main effects are aliased with each other. That is,

$$(AB^2) = (AC) = (BC).$$

A general principle can be stated with respect to the use of Latin square designs or Latin squares as building blocks for more complex designs. Main effects will always be aliased with interaction effects. Thus in order to interpret F ratios for main effects that are significant, it is necessary to assume that the aliased interactions (or components) are zero.

In large Latin squares, a relatively small portion of all two-factor interaction components are aliased with treatments. Therefore, if a within-cell error term is available, the presence of significant two-factor interaction effects biases main effects tests less in large Latin squares than in small Latin squares. The situation is more complex if a within-cell error term is not available. Under these conditions, a residual error term is sometimes obtained by pooling all interaction MS's not aliased with main effects. If the pooled two- and three-factor interaction components are not zero, they will negatively bias tests of main effects.

GENERAL INTRODUCTION TO
TYPE LSFF-p^k DESIGNS

Subsequent sections of this chapter describe a number of complex designs that utilize a Latin square as the building block design. For convenience, these designs are designated as type LSFF designs. Additional examples of Latin square fractional factorial designs can be found in the thorough coverage by Winer (1962, Ch. 10).

The layout of type LSFF designs is much simpler than the layout of fractional factorial designs based on completely randomized and randomized block designs. The latter designs are generally restricted to experiments having two or three levels of each treatment; type LSFF designs do not have this restriction. In addition, type LSFF designs are not limited to experiments in which the number of levels of each treatment are prime numbers. The use of mixed levels for treatments poses no computational problem if, of course, at least three of the treatments or classification variables have the same number of levels. The number of levels of rows, columns, and Latin letters comprising the square must be equal. It should be emphasized again that the use of a Latin square as a building block design requires a highly restrictive set of assumptions with respect to interactions. If interactions among variables that comprise the Latin square are not zero, main effects will be aliased with interaction effects.

10.8   COMPUTATIONAL PROCEDURES
FOR TYPE LSFF-$p.p^2$ DESIGN

If the design illustrated in Figure 10.7-1 of the previous section contains three treatments, it can be classified as a fractional factorial design. A confounded factorial design based on a Latin square that contains two treatments was described in Section 9.11. It is assumed that the $p^2 = 9$ cells of the square in Figure 10.7-1 contain nine random samples of n subjects ($n \geq 1$) from a common population. Computational procedures for this type LSFF-p^3 are identical to those for a regular Latin square design and have been described in Section 6.3.

A type LSFF-p^3 design can be easily modified for research situations in which it is possible to use matched subjects or repeated measures on the same subjects. The modified design is diagramed in Figure 10.8-1 and is designated by the letters LSFF-$p.p^2$. In this design, treatment A is a between-block treatment, whereas B and C are within-block treatments. This is indicated in the designation scheme by placing a dot after the between-block treatment. This same procedure was followed in the designation scheme for split-plot designs. The use of the letter p in the designation for this design indicates that treatments A, B, and C must have the

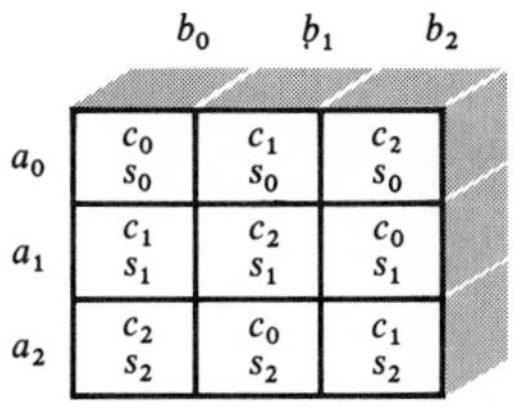

Figure 10.8-1   Block diagram of type LSFF-3.3^2 design.

same number of levels. If repeated measurements are obtained, the design requires p random samples of n subjects from a common population. The p samples are randomly assigned to the levels of treatment A. The sequence of administration of the bc_{jk} treatment combinations is randomized independently for each subject. If matched subjects are used, p random samples of n sets of p matched subjects are required. The p subjects within each matched set are randomly assigned to the bc_{jk} treatment combinations.

The model for this design is

$$X_{ijkm} = \mu + \alpha_i + \pi_{m(i)} + \beta_j + \gamma_k + \text{res} + \beta\gamma\pi_{jkm(i)} + \varepsilon_{ijkm},$$

where μ = grand mean.

α_i = effect of treatment i, which is a constant for all subjects within treatment population i.

$\pi_{m(i)}$ = constant associated with person m, who is nested under level α_i.

β_j = effect of treatment j, which is a constant for all subjects within treatment population j.

γ_k = effect of treatment k, which is a constant for all subjects within treatment population k.

residual = effect that represents nonadditivity of effects α_i, β_j, and γ_k.

$\beta\gamma\pi_{jkm(i)}$ = effect that represents nonadditivity of effects $\beta\gamma_{jk}$ and $\pi_{m(i)}$. It is assumed that $\beta\gamma\pi_{jkm(i)}$ provides an estimate of σ_ε^2.

ε_{ijkm} = experimental error, which is NID with mean = 0 and variance = σ_ε^2.

It is assumed that treatments A, B, and C represent fixed effects. Special assumptions—for example, the assumption of equal covariances as well as other assumptions required for designs involving matched subjects or repeated measurements—are described in Chapters 5 and 8.

The layout of the type LSFF-3.3^2 design, computational tables, and formulas are shown in Table 10.8-1, where the following notation is used:

$$p \text{ levels of } a_i, \text{ where } p = 3$$

$$q \text{ levels of } b_j, \text{ where } q = 3$$

$$r \text{ levels of } c_k, \text{ where } r = 3$$

$$n \text{ levels of } s_m, \text{ where } n = 2$$

$$\sum_1^N = \sum_1^p \sum_1^q \sum_1^n.$$

TABLE 10.8-1 Layout of Type LSFF-3.3² Design and Computational Procedures

(i) Data:

ABCS Summary Table

		b_0	b_1	b_2	$\sum_1^q AS$
		c_0	c_1	c_2	
a_0	s_0	3	4	6	13
	s_1	1	4	6	11
		c_2	c_0	c_1	
a_1	s_0	7	3	3	13
	s_1	5	2	3	10
		c_1	c_2	c_0	
a_2	s_0	4	7	3	14
	s_1	2	5	2	9

ABC Summary Table

	b_0	b_1	b_2	$\sum_1^q A$
	$n = 2$			
	c_0	c_1	c_2	
a_0	4	8	12	24
	c_2	c_0	c_1	
a_1	12	5	6	23
	c_1	c_2	c_0	
a_2	6	12	5	23

BC Summary Table

	b_0	b_1	b_2	$\sum_1^q C$
	$np = 6$			
c_0	4	5	5	14
c_1	6	8	6	20
c_2	12	12	12	36
$\sum_1^r B =$	22	25	23	

(ii) Computational symbols:

$$\sum_1^N ABCS = 3 + 1 + 7 + \cdots + 2 = 70.00$$

$$\sum_1^N (ABCS)^2 = [ABCS] = (3)^2 + (1)^2 + (7)^2 + \cdots + (2)^2 = 326.00$$

TABLE 10.8-1 (continued)

$$\frac{\left(\sum_{1}^{N} ABCS\right)^2}{N} = [X] = \frac{(70)^2}{18} = 272.22$$

$$\sum_{1}^{p} \frac{\left(\sum_{1}^{q} A\right)^2}{nq} = [A] = \frac{(24)^2}{(2)(3)} + \frac{(23)^2}{(2)(3)} + \frac{(23)^2}{(2)(3)} = 272.33$$

$$\sum_{1}^{q} \frac{\left(\sum_{1}^{r} B\right)^2}{nr} = [B] = \frac{(22)^2}{(2)(3)} + \frac{(25)^2}{(2)(3)} + \frac{(23)^2}{(2)(3)} = 273.00$$

$$\sum_{1}^{r} \frac{\left(\sum_{1}^{q} C\right)^2}{nq} = [C] = \frac{(14)^2}{(2)(3)} + \frac{(20)^2}{(2)(3)} + \frac{(36)^2}{(2)(3)} = 315.33$$

$$\sum_{1}^{p} \sum_{1}^{q} \frac{(ABC)^2}{n} = [ABC] = \frac{(4)^2}{2} + \frac{(8)^2}{2} + \cdots + \frac{(5)^2}{2} = 317.00$$

$$\sum_{1}^{p} \sum_{1}^{n} \frac{\left(\sum_{1}^{q} AS\right)^2}{q} = [AS] = \frac{(13)^2}{3} + \frac{(11)^2}{3} + \cdots + \frac{(9)^2}{3} = 278.67$$

(iii) Computational formulas:

$$SS_{total} = [ABCS] - [X] = 53.78$$
$$SS_{between\ subj} = [AS] - [X] = 6.45$$
$$SS_A = [A] - [X] = .11$$
$$SS_{subj\ w.groups} = [AS] - [A] = 6.34$$
$$SS_{within\ subj} = [ABCS] - [AS] = 47.33$$
$$SS_B = [B] - [X] = .78$$
$$SS_C = [C] - [X] = 43.11$$
$$SS_{res} = [ABC] - [A] - [B] - [C] + 2[X] = .78$$
$$SS_{BC \times subj\ w.groups} = [ABCS] - [ABC] - [AS] + [A] = 2.66$$

The analysis of the data is summarized in Table 10.8-2. According to this summary, the null hypothesis can be rejected for treatment C but not for treatments A and B. A partial check on the assumption that all interactions among treatments are insignificant is given by the ratio

$$F = \frac{MS_{res}}{MS_{BC \times subj\ w.groups}}.$$

In this example, it seems safe to conclude that interactions among treatments are zero. Under this condition, the experimenter may wish to pool MS_{res} with $MS_{BC \times subj\ w.groups}$ in order to obtain a better estimate of experimental error. It should be noted that the test of treatment A is less powerful than the tests of treatments B and C. This same point has been made repeatedly with respect to between-groups (block) treatments of a split-plot design.

TABLE 10.8-2 Analysis of Variance Table for Type LSFF-3.3² Design

	Source	SS	df	MS	F	E(MS) Model III
1	Between subjects	6.45	$np - 1 = 5$			
2	A	.11	$p - 1 = 2$	.06	$[\frac{2}{3}]$ N.S.	$\sigma_\varepsilon^2 + p\sigma_\pi^2 + np\sigma_\alpha^2$
3	Subj w.groups	6.34	$p(n - 1) = 3$	2.11		$\sigma_\varepsilon^2 + p\sigma_\pi^2$
4	Within subjects	47.33	$np(p - 1) = 12$			
5	B	.78	$p - 1 = 2$	.39	$[\frac{5}{8}]$ N.S.	$\sigma_\varepsilon^2 + np\sigma_\beta^2$
6	C	43.11	$p - 1 = 2$	21.56	$[\frac{6}{8}] = 49.00^*$	$\sigma_\varepsilon^2 + np\sigma_\gamma^2$
7	Residual	.78	$(p - 1)(p - 2) = 2$	.39	$[\frac{7}{8}]$ N.S.	$\sigma_\varepsilon^2 + n\sigma_{res}^2$
8	$BC \times$ subj w.groups	2.66	$p(n - 1)(p - 1) = 6$	.44		σ_ε^2
9	Total	53.78	$np^2 - 1 = 17$			

$^*p < .01.$

COMPOSITION OF ERROR TERMS

The error terms, $MS_{\text{subj w.groups}}$ and $MS_{BC \times \text{subj w.groups}}$, represent pooled terms that must be homogeneous in order for the associated F ratios to be distributed as the F distribution. Moderate departure from homogeneity probably has little effect on the respective significance levels. The composition of these two error terms can be understood by breaking them down into more familiar terms. Let us consider the between-subjects terms of the experiment as consisting of three type CR-2 designs corresponding to the three levels of treatment A. This is shown in the following example:

Type CR-2 *Design at* a_0		*Type CR-2* *Design at* a_1		*Type CR-2* *Design at* a_2	
s_0	s_1	s_0	s_1	s_0	s_1
3	1	7	5	4	2
4	4	3	2	7	5
6	6	3	3	3	2
$\Sigma = 13$	11	$\Sigma = 13$	10	$\Sigma = 14$	9
$SS_{\text{between subj}} = .67$		$SS_{\text{between subj}} = 1.50$		$SS_{\text{between subj}} = 4.16$	

The sum of squares between subjects at each level of treatment A is given by $[S] - [X]$. This is the variation between the two subjects (s_0, s_1) at each level of a_i. If the two subjects are considered to be a group, this variation is analogous to *within-group* variation in a type CR-k design. If this variation is pooled over the three levels of treatment A, it is equal to $SS_{\text{subj w.groups}}$. That is,

$$.67 + 1.50 + 4.16 = SS_{\text{subj w.groups}} = 6.33.$$

Thus the sum of squares for subjects within groups represents *between-subject* or, alternatively, *within-group* variation pooled over each level of treatment A. Another approach to understanding the nature of $SS_{\text{subj w.groups}}$ is presented in Section 8.4; there an analogy is drawn between

$$F = \frac{MS_{BG}}{MS_{WG}} \quad \text{and} \quad F = \frac{MS_A}{MS_{B \times \text{subj w.groups}}}.$$

The within-subjects terms of the experiment can be seen as consisting of three type RB-3 designs, as shown in the following example:

Type RB-3 design at a_0				*Type RB-3 design at* a_1				*Type RB-3 design at* a_2			
	bc_{00}	bc_{11}	bc_{22}		bc_{02}	bc_{10}	bc_{21}		bc_{01}	bc_{12}	bc_{20}
s_0	3	4	6 13	s_0	7	3	3 13	s_0	4	7	3 14
s_1	1	4	6 11	s_1	5	2	3 10	s_1	2	5	2 9
	4	8	12		12	5	6		6	12	5
$SS_{\text{rows} \times \text{cols}} = 1.33$				$SS_{\text{rows} \times \text{cols}} = 1.00$				$SS_{\text{rows} \times \text{cols}} = .34$			

The interaction of rows and columns is given by $[(BC)S] - [(BC)] - [S] + [X]$. If this variation is pooled over the three levels of treatment A, it is equal to $SS_{BC \times subj\ w.groups}$.

$$1.33 + 1.00 + .34 = SS_{BC \times subj\ w.groups} = 2.67.$$

Thus the error term for testing within-subjects effects is the BC treatments $\times$ subjects interaction pooled over the levels of treatment A.

Comparisons among means follow the procedures described in Section 8.7.

10.9   COMPUTATIONAL PROCEDURES FOR TYPE LSFF-p^3u DESIGN

In Section 6.3 an example involving a road test of four automobile tires was used to illustrate a possible application of a Latin square design. The levels of A, B, and C corresponded, respectively, to automobiles, wheel positions, and rubber compounds used in the tire construction. Two road tests using the same four automobiles were run one after the other. In the analysis described in Section 6.3, the data were treated as if the two replications of the experiment were carried out under identical conditions. This is unrealistic because the two tests were separated by an interval of time and the cars were older during the second test. The within-cell error term that was computed included not only random error but also variation attributable to temperature and other climatic changes as well as variation associated with mechanical wear of the automobiles. An alternative design described in this section treats the two replications of the road test as two levels of a nuisance variable (D).

A type LSFF-$4^3 2$ design, in which treatment D corresponds to replications, is diagramed in Figure 10.9-1. The linear model for this design is

$$X_{ijkl} = \mu + \alpha_i + \beta_j + \gamma_k + \delta_l + \alpha\delta_{il} + \beta\delta_{jl} + \gamma\delta_{kl} + res + \varepsilon_{ijkl}.$$

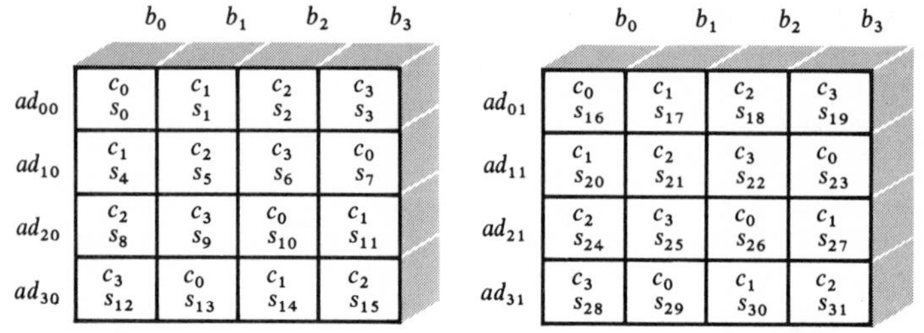

Figure 10.9-1   Block diagram of type LSFF-$4^3 2$ design.

The terms in the model, with the exception of δ_l, $\alpha\delta_{il}$, $\beta\delta_{jl}$, and $\gamma\delta_{kl}$, are defined in Section 10.8. δ_l refers to the effect of treatment l, which is a constant for all subjects within population l. This design permits an experimenter to evaluate the AD, BD, and CD interactions. Each cell of the design diagramed in Figure 10.9-1 contains one observation. This design can be easily modified for the case in which each cell contains n observations. The required modifications are described in a subsequent paragraph.

    The layout of the type LSFF-4^32 design, computational tables, and formulas are shown in Table 10.9-1. The analysis is summarized in Table 10.9-2. The following notation is used in the table:

$$p \text{ levels of } a_i, \text{ where } p = 4$$

$$q \text{ levels of } b_j, \text{ where } q = 4$$

$$r \text{ levels of } c_k, \text{ where } r = 4$$

$$u \text{ levels of } d_l, \text{ where } u = 2$$

$$\sum_1^N = \sum_1^p \sum_1^q \sum_1^u.$$

TABLE 10.9-1   Layout of Type LSFF-4^32 Design and Computational Procedures

(i) Data:

ABCD Summary Table

		b_0	b_1	b_2	b_3
	a_0	c_0	c_1	c_2	c_3
		3	4	7	7
	a_1	c_1	c_2	c_3	c_0
d_0		5	8	8	6
	a_2	c_2	c_3	c_0	c_1
		7	9	3	4
	a_3	c_3	c_0	c_1	c_2
		8	3	3	6
	a_0	c_0	c_1	c_2	c_3
		1	2	5	10
	a_1	c_1	c_2	c_3	c_0
d_1		3	6	10	2
	a_2	c_2	c_3	c_0	c_1
		5	9	2	4
	a_3	c_3	c_0	c_1	c_2
		11	2	3	6

AD Summary Table

	d_0	d_1	$\sum_1^u A$
	$q = 4$		
a_0	21	18	39
a_1	27	21	48
a_2	23	20	43
a_3	20	22	42
$\sum_1^p D =$ 91		81	

BD Summary Table

	d_0	d_1	$\sum_1^u B$
	$p = 4$		
b_0	23	20	43
b_1	24	19	43
b_2	21	20	41
b_3	23	22	45

CD Summary Table

	d_0	d_1	$\sum_1^u C$
	$p = 4$		
c_0	15	7	22
c_1	16	12	28
c_2	28	22	50
c_3	32	40	72

TABLE 10.9-1 (continued)

(ii) Computational symbols:

$$\sum_{1}^{N} ABCD = 3 + 5 + 7 + \cdots + 6 = 172.000$$

$$\sum_{1}^{N}(ABCD)^2 = [ABCD] = (3)^2 + (5)^2 + (7)^2 + \cdots + (6)^2 = 1160.000$$

$$\frac{\left(\sum_{1}^{N} ABCD\right)^2}{N} = [X] = \frac{(172)^2}{32} = 924.500$$

$$\sum_{1}^{p} \frac{\left(\sum_{1}^{u} A\right)^2}{qu} = [A] = \frac{(39)^2}{(4)(2)} + \frac{(48)^2}{(4)(2)} + \cdots + \frac{(42)^2}{(4)(2)} = 929.750$$

$$\sum_{1}^{q} \frac{\left(\sum_{1}^{u} B\right)^2}{pu} = [B] = \frac{(43)^2}{(4)(2)} + \frac{(43)^2}{(4)(2)} + \cdots + \frac{(45)^2}{(4)(2)} = 925.500$$

$$\sum_{1}^{r} \frac{\left(\sum_{1}^{u} C\right)^2}{pu} = [C] = \frac{(22)^2}{(4)(2)} + \frac{(28)^2}{(4)(2)} + \cdots + \frac{(72)^2}{(4)(2)} = 1119.000$$

$$\sum_{1}^{u} \frac{\left(\sum_{1}^{p} D\right)^2}{pq} = [D] = \frac{(91)^2}{(4)(4)} + \frac{(81)^2}{(4)(4)} = 927.625$$

$$\sum_{1}^{p}\sum_{1}^{u} \frac{(AD)^2}{q} = [AD] = \frac{(21)^2}{4} + \frac{(27)^2}{4} + \cdots + \frac{(22)^2}{4} = 937.000$$

$$\sum_{1}^{q}\sum_{1}^{u} \frac{(BD)^2}{p} = [BD] = \frac{(23)^2}{4} + \frac{(24)^2}{4} + \cdots + \frac{(22)^2}{4} = 930.000$$

$$\sum_{1}^{r}\sum_{1}^{u} \frac{(CD)^2}{p} = [CD] = \frac{(15)^2}{4} + \frac{(16)^2}{4} + \cdots + \frac{(40)^2}{4} = 1141.500$$

(iii) Computational formulas:

$$SS_{total} = [ABCD] - [X] = 235.500$$
$$SS_A = [A] - [X] = 5.250$$
$$SS_B = [B] - [X] = 1.000$$
$$SS_C = [C] - [X] = 194.500$$
$$SS_D = [D] - [X] = 3.125$$
$$SS_{AD} = [AD] - [A] - [D] + [X] = 4.125$$
$$SS_{BD} = [BD] - [B] - [D] + [X] = 1.375$$
$$SS_{CD} = [CD] - [C] - [D] + [X] = 19.375$$
$$SS_{res} = [ABCD] - [AD] - [BD] - [CD] + 2[D] = 6.750$$

**TABLE 10.9-2 Analysis of Variance Table
for Type LSFF-$4^3 2$ Design**

	Source	SS	df	MS	F	E(MS) Model I
1	A	5.250	$p - 1 = 3$	1.750	$[\frac{1}{8}] =$ 3.11	$\sigma_\varepsilon^2 + pu\sigma_\alpha^2$
2	B	1.000	$p - 1 = 3$	.333	$[\frac{2}{8}]$ N.S.	$\sigma_\varepsilon^2 + pu\sigma_\beta^2$
3	C	194.500	$p - 1 = 3$	64.833	$[\frac{3}{8}] = 115.36**$	$\sigma_\varepsilon^2 + pu\sigma_\gamma^2$
4	D	3.125	$u - 1 = 1$	3.125	$[\frac{4}{8}] =$ 5.56*	$\sigma_\varepsilon^2 + p^2\sigma_\delta^2$
5	AD	4.125	$(p - 1)(u - 1) = 3$	1.375	$[\frac{5}{8}] =$ 2.45	$\sigma_\varepsilon^2 + p\sigma_{\alpha\delta}^2$
6	BD	1.375	$(p - 1)(u - 1) = 3$	.458	$[\frac{6}{8}]$ N.S.	$\sigma_\varepsilon^2 + p\sigma_{\beta\delta}^2$
7	CD	19.375	$(p - 1)(u - 1) = 3$	6.458	$[\frac{7}{8}] =$ 11.49**	$\sigma_\varepsilon^2 + p\sigma_{\gamma\delta}^2$
8	Residual	6.750	$u(p - 1)(p - 2) = 12$	.562		σ_ε^2
9	Total	235.500	$p^2u - 1 = 31$			

*$p < .05$.

**$p < .01$.

According to the analysis in Table 10.9-2, the effects of rubber compounds, replications, and the interaction of rubber compounds with replications are significant. An examination of the CD Summary Table suggests that there was less difference among the tires and corresponding rubber compounds during the first road test than during the second road test (an interesting finding, one an experimenter would want to follow up). The superiority of the present analysis, in which the two road tests were treated as a fourth variable, compared to the analysis summarized in Table 6.3-3 is readily apparent. In the latter analysis, the within-cell variation included, in addition to random error, the effects of treatment D and the CD interaction.

A type LSFF-$4^3 2$ design corresponds to a one-fourth replication of a type CRF-4442 design. If only one subject is assigned to each treatment combination, the latter design requires 128 subjects compared with 32 for the fractional factorial design. For research situations in which an experimenter believes that only one treatment is likely to interact with the other treatments, a type LSFF-p^3u design is a better choice than a complete factorial design. The example that was presented employed the same Latin square for both levels of treatment D. If it suits the experimenter's purpose, balanced sets of squares or independently randomized squares can be used. The number of levels of treatments A, B, and C must be equal. The only restriction on the number of levels of treatment D is that there must be at least two levels.

Comparisons among means follow the general procedures described in Section 7.6.

TYPE LSFF-p^3u DESIGN WITH
MORE THAN ONE SCORE PER CELL

The analysis shown in Table 10.9-1 can be modified for the case in which more than one observation is obtained within each cell. An $ABCDS$ Summary Table must be constructed. The following modifications of the computational symbols as illustrated for $[A]$, $[CD]$, and $[ABCD]$ are required:

$$[A] = \sum_1^p \frac{\left(\sum_1^u A\right)^2}{nqu}, \quad [CD] = \sum_1^r \sum_1^u \frac{(CD)^2}{np}, \quad [ABCD] = \sum_1^p \sum_1^q \sum_1^u \frac{(ABCD)^2}{n}.$$

A within-cell error term is used as the denominator of F ratios. The formula is

$$SS_{w.cell} = [ABCDS] - [ABCD]$$

with degrees of freedom equal to $up^2(n-1)$.

COMPUTATIONAL PROCEDURES FOR
TYPE LSFF-$pu.p^2$ DESIGN

The design that has been described can be modified for the case in which matched subjects or repeated measures on the same subjects are obtained. A diagram of this design is shown in Figure 10.9-2. s_m refers to

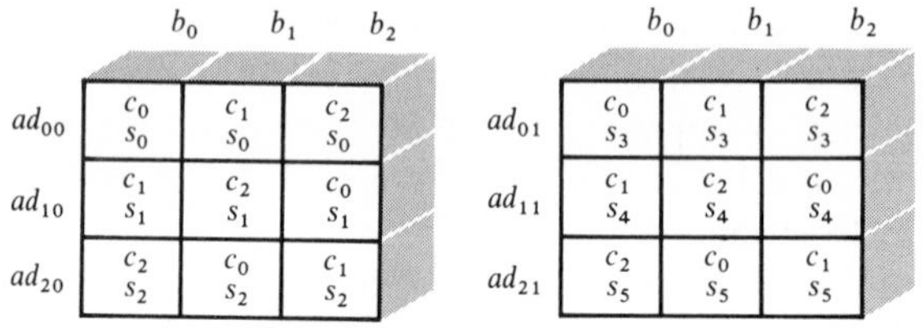

Figure 10.9-2 Block diagram of type LSFF-32.3^2 design.

pu random samples of n subjects if repeated measures are obtained or np subjects if matched subjects are used. In the former case, administration of the bc_{jk} combinations is randomized independently for each subject.

The linear model for this design is

$$X_{ijklm} = \mu + \alpha_i + \delta_l + \alpha\delta_{il} + \pi_{m(il)} + \beta_j + \gamma_k + \beta\delta_{jl} + \gamma\delta_{kl}$$
$$+ \text{res} + \beta\gamma\pi_{jkm(il)} + \varepsilon_{ijklm}.$$

Computational formulas and degrees of freedom for this design appear in Table 10.9-3.

TABLE 10.9-3 Computational Formulas for Type LSFF-$pu.p^2$ Design

	Source	df	Computational Formulas	F	E(MS) Model III (A, B, C, and D Fixed Effects, Subjects Random)
1	Between subjects	$npu - 1$			
2	A	$p - 1$	$[A] - [X]$	$[\frac{2}{5}]$	$\sigma_\varepsilon^2 + p\sigma_\pi^2 + npu\sigma_\alpha^2$
3	D	$u - 1$	$[D] - [X]$	$[\frac{3}{5}]$	$\sigma_\varepsilon^2 + p\sigma_\pi^2 + np^2\sigma_\delta^2$
4	AD	$(p-1)(u-1)$	$[AD] - [A] - [D] + [X]$	$[\frac{4}{5}]$	$\sigma_\varepsilon^2 + p\sigma_\pi^2$
5	Subject w.groups	$pu(n-1)$	$[ADS] - [AD]$		
6	Within subjects	$npu(p-1)$	$[ABCDS] - [ADS]$		
7	B	$p - 1$	$[B] - [X]$	$[\frac{7}{12}]$	$\sigma_\varepsilon^2 + npu\sigma_\beta^2$
8	C	$p - 1$	$[C] - [X]$	$[\frac{8}{12}]$	$\sigma_\varepsilon^2 + npu\sigma_\gamma^2$
9	BD	$(p-1)(u-1)$	$[BD] - [B] - [D] + [X]$	$[\frac{9}{12}]$	$\sigma_\varepsilon^2 + np\sigma_{\beta\delta}^2$
10	CD	$(p-1)(u-1)$	$[CD] - [C] - [D] + [X]$	$[\frac{10}{12}]$	$\sigma_\varepsilon^2 + np\sigma_{\gamma\delta}^2$
11	Residual	$u(p-1)(p-2)$	$[ABCD] - [AD] - [BD] - [CD] + 2[D]$	$[\frac{11}{12}]$	$\sigma_\varepsilon^2 + \text{res}$
12	BC × subj w.groups	$pu(n-1)(p-1)$	$[ABCDS] - [ABCD] - [ADS] + [AD]$		σ_ε^2
13	Total	$np^2u - 1$	$[ABCDS] - [X]$		

10.10   COMPUTATIONAL PROCEDURES FOR TYPE LSFF-p^4v DESIGN

The design described in this section is appropriate for experiments having five treatments. If four of the treatments have p levels each, the fifth treatment must have p^2 levels. For example, if the four treatments have two levels each, then the fifth treatment must have $2^2 = 4$ levels. A block diagram for a type LSFF-$2^4 4$ design is shown in Figure 10.10-1.

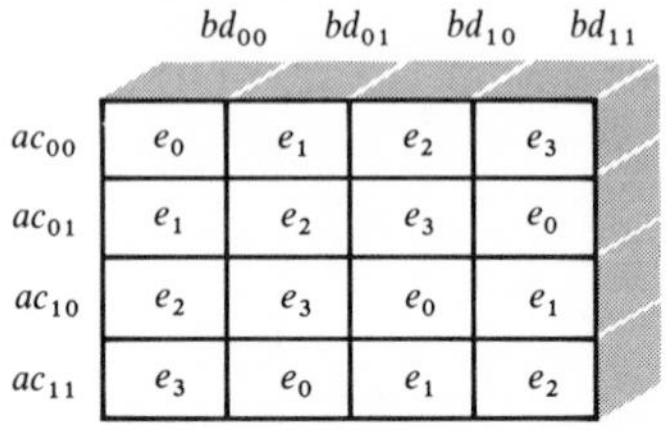

Figure 10.10-1   Block diagram of type LSFF-$2^4 4$ design.

This design corresponds to a one-fourth replication of a type CRF-22224 design.

The linear model for this design is

$$X_{ijklmo} = \mu + \alpha_i + \gamma_k + \alpha\gamma_{ik} + \beta_j + \delta_l + \beta\delta_{jl} + \zeta_o + \text{res} + \varepsilon_{m(ijklo)}.$$

The Greek letter ζ_o designates one of the v levels of treatment E. It is assumed that all interactions not appearing in the model are zero. The design requires np^4 subjects who are randomly assigned to the p^4 cells. Computational formulas and degrees of freedom for this design appear in Table 10.10-1.

TABLE 10.10-1   Computational Formulas for Type LSFF-p^4v Design

Source	df	Computational Formulas	F	E(MS) Model I
1 A	$p - 1$	$[A] - [X]$	$[\frac{1}{9}]$	$\sigma_\varepsilon^2 + np^2\sigma_\alpha^2$
2 C	$p - 1$	$[C] - [X]$	$[\frac{2}{9}]$	$\sigma_\varepsilon^2 + np^2\sigma_\gamma^2$
3 AC	$(p-1)(p-1)$	$[AC] - [A] - [C] + [X]$	$[\frac{3}{9}]$	$\sigma_\varepsilon^2 + np\sigma_{\alpha\gamma}^2$
4 B	$p - 1$	$[B] - [X]$	$[\frac{4}{9}]$	$\sigma_\varepsilon^2 + np^2\sigma_\beta^2$
5 D	$p - 1$	$[D] - [X]$	$[\frac{5}{9}]$	$\sigma_\varepsilon^2 + np^2\sigma_\delta^2$
6 BD	$(p-1)(p-1)$	$[BD] - [B] - [D] + [X]$	$[\frac{6}{9}]$	$\sigma_\varepsilon^2 + np\sigma_{\beta\delta}^2$
7 E	$v - 1$	$[E] - [X]$	$[\frac{7}{9}]$	$\sigma_\varepsilon^2 + np^2\sigma_\zeta^2$
8 Residual	$(p^2-1)(p^2-2)$	$[ABCDE] - [AC] - [BD] - [E]$ $+ 2[X]$	$[\frac{8}{9}]$	$\sigma_\varepsilon^2 + n\sigma_{\text{res}}^2$
9 W.cell	$p^4(n-1)$	$[ABCDES] - [ABCDE]$		σ_ε^2
10 Total	$np^4 - 1$	$[ABCDES] - [X]$		

TABLE 10.11-1　Computational Formulas for Type GLSFF-p^3 Design

Source	df	Computational Formulas	F	E(MS) Model III (A, B, and C Fixed Effects, Subjects Random)
1 Between subjects	$np - 1$	$[GS] - [X]$		
2 Groups	$p - 1$	$[G] - [X]$	$[\frac{2}{3}]$	$\sigma_\varepsilon^2 + p\sigma_\pi^2 + np\sigma_\theta^2$
3 Subj w.groups	$p(n - 1)$	$[GS] - [G]$		$\sigma_\varepsilon^2 + p\sigma_\pi^2$
4 Within subjects	$np(p - 1)$	$[ABCGS] - [GS]$		
5 A	$p - 1$	$[A] - [X]$	$[\frac{5}{9}]$	$\dot\sigma_\varepsilon^2 + np\sigma_\alpha^2$
6 B	$p - 1$	$[B] - [X]$	$[\frac{6}{9}]$	$\sigma_\varepsilon^2 + np\sigma_\beta^2$
7 C	$p - 1$	$[C] - [X]$	$[\frac{7}{9}]$	$\sigma_\varepsilon^2 + np\sigma_\gamma^2$
8 Residual	$(p - 1)(p - 3)$	$[ABCG] - [A] - [B] - [C] - [G] + 3[X]$	$[\frac{8}{9}]$	$\sigma_\varepsilon^2 + n\sigma_{\text{res}}^2$
9 $ABC \times$ subj w.groups	$p(n - 1)(p - 1)$	$[ABCGS] - [ABCG] - [GS] + [G]$		σ_ε^2
10 Total	$np^2 - 1$	$[ABCGS] - [X]$		

10.11 COMPUTATIONAL PROCEDURES FOR TYPE GLSFF-p^3 DESIGN

A Graeco-Latin square can be used as a building block for fractional factorial designs. The type GLSFF-3^3 design diagramed in Figure 10.11-1 is appropriate for experiments that use repeated measures or matched subjects. The letter g designates a group of subjects who are

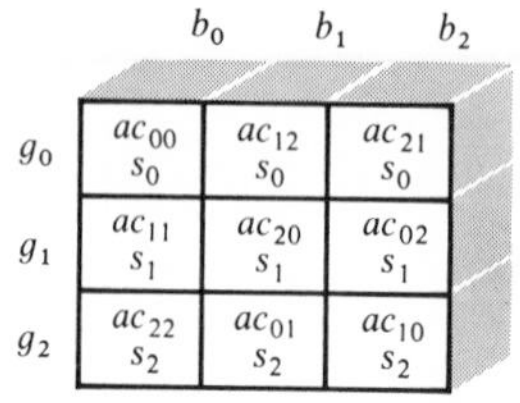

Figure 10.11-1 Block diagram of type GLSFF-3^3 design.

randomly assigned to rows of the square. There are z levels of g_t. This design requires z random samples of n subjects if repeated measures are obtained or nz sets of p matched subjects if matching is used. In the latter case, the matched subjects are randomly assigned to the ac_{ik} treatment combinations. If repeated measures are obtained, the sequence of administration of the ac_{ik} combinations is randomized independently for each subject.

The linear model for this design is

$$X_{ijkmt} = \mu + \theta_t + \pi_{m(t)} + \alpha_i + \beta_j + \gamma_k + \text{res} + \alpha\beta\gamma\pi_{ijkm(t)} + \varepsilon_{ijkm(t)},$$

where θ_t and $\pi_{m(t)}$ designate the effect of group t and the effect of person m who is nested within group t, respectively. This design requires the same number of observations as the type LSFF-$p.p^2$ design summarized in Table 10.8-2. The advantage of a type GLSFF-p^3 design relative to a type LSFF-$p.p^2$ design is that all treatment effects in the former design are within-subjects effects. Computational formulas for a type GLSFF-p^3 design are presented in Table 10.11-1. It is assumed that the treatments represent fixed effects and that the blocks are random effects.

10.12 ADVANTAGES AND DISADVANTAGES OF FRACTIONAL FACTORIAL DESIGNS

This chapter has described fractional factorial designs based on three building block designs—completely randomized, randomized block, and Latin square designs. Their chief advantages are

1. They permit the evaluation of a large number of treatments but employ only a fraction of the total possible number of treatment combinations.

2. Fractional factorial designs lend themselves to sequential research programs in which flexibility in the pursuit of promising lines of investigation is essential.

The chief disadvantages of these designs are

1. Interpretation of the statistical analysis is complicated by the fact that treatments are aliased with interactions. These designs require the assumption of zero interactions among some or all treatments. This assumption is often unrealistic in the behavioral sciences.

2. The requirement of these designs that all or most treatments have the same number of levels restricts their usefulness.

3. The layout and computational procedures are more complex for fractional factorial designs than for conventional factorial designs.

10.13   REPRESENTATIVE APPLICATIONS OF FRACTIONAL FACTORIAL DESIGNS IN THE RESEARCH LITERATURE

The following references illustrate a variety of applications of fractional factorial designs.

Adams, Jack A., and Sanne Dijkstra. Short-term memory for motor responses. *Journal of Experimental Psychology*, 1966, **71**, 314–318. Type GLSFF-3.7³ design.

Kaufman, Herbert, and Gordon M. Becker. The empirical determination of game-theoretical strategies. *Journal of Experimental Psychology*, 1961, **61**, 462–468. Type LSFF-5.5² design.

Sidowski, Joseph B, and Robert G. Eason. Drive, verbal performance, and muscle action potential. *Journal of Experimental Psychology*, 1960, **60**, 365–370. Type GLSFF-2.4³ design.

11 / INCOMPLETE BLOCK DESIGNS

11.1 INTRODUCTION TO INCOMPLETE BLOCK DESIGNS

The name *incomplete block design* refers to a large class of designs in which q treatment levels of a single-treatment experiment are assigned to blocks of size k, where k is less than q. These designs resemble randomized block and Latin square building block designs. A diagram of a balanced incomplete block design, designated by the letters BIB-t, appears in Figure 11.1-1. Here t_j designates any one of seven treatment levels. This particular balanced incomplete block design enables an experimenter to investigate

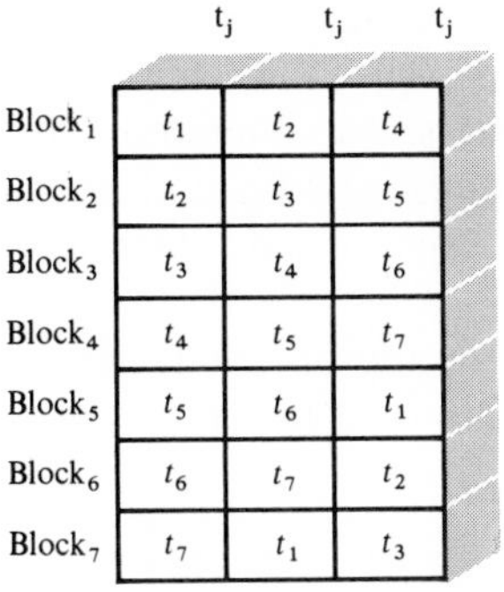

	t_j	t_j	t_j
Block$_1$	t_1	t_2	t_4
Block$_2$	t_2	t_3	t_5
Block$_3$	t_3	t_4	t_6
Block$_4$	t_4	t_5	t_7
Block$_5$	t_5	t_6	t_1
Block$_6$	t_6	t_7	t_2
Block$_7$	t_7	t_1	t_3

Figure 11.1-1 Block diagram of type BIB-7 design.

seven treatment levels using blocks of size three. A block can consist of one subject who receives all three treatment levels in a random sequence or three matched subjects. If repeated measures are obtained, the assumptions presented in Section 5.3 concerning the variance-covariance matrix must be tenable. A randomized block design for this same experiment would require blocks of size seven.

The technique of confounding, which was described in Chapters 8, 9, and 10, also produces designs with incomplete blocks. For example, each block of a type SPF-$p.q$ design contains only q of the pq treatment combinations. However, the designs in Chapters 8 through 10 are not included in the general category of incomplete block designs, for they contain more than one treatment and have a factorial structure.

Incomplete block designs have been widely used in agricultural research and, to a lesser extent, in industrial research. Since their introduction by Yates (1936b), many different kinds of incomplete block designs have been developed by mathematical statisticians. These can, for classification purposes, be divided into two categories: balanced designs and partially balanced designs. This chapter describes two types of balanced designs: a balanced incomplete block design and a Youden square incomplete block design. Each has broad applicability and each illustrates general principles common to many incomplete block designs. A brief survey of other incomplete block designs appears in Section 11.12.

Incomplete block designs are little used in the behavioral sciences, partly because they are more difficult to lay out and analyze than the complete block designs. Another reason for this lack of use concerns the research orientation and philosophy that characterize behavioral scientists. An examination of current journals in the behavioral sciences suggests that experimenters can be divided into two groups in terms of the kinds of experiments that they design. Many behavioral scientists design experiments having numerous independent variables, each with relatively few levels. Other behavioral scientists, who comprise a minority group, use a limited number of treatments in an experiment (frequently only one) but employ many levels of each treatment. The latter group is interested in determining the functional relationship that exists between dependent and independent variables for as wide a range of the manipulated variable(s) as possible. Incomplete block designs are well suited to this research orientation. The former group of experimenters, whose interest is in testing interaction and multitreatment effects, requires experimental designs with a factorial structure. A single-treatment design is not suitable for this research orientation.

Balanced incomplete block designs are appropriate for experiments that meet, in addition to the general assumptions of the analysis of variance model, the following conditions:

1. One treatment with q levels. The q levels are assigned to blocks of size k, where $k < q$. The size of the blocks may be limited, for example, by the availability of subjects, equipment, facilities, or time.

2. Each possible pair of treatment levels occurs together within some block an equal number of times.

11.2   ENUMERATION OF PLANS
FOR BALANCED INCOMPLETE
BLOCK DESIGNS

NOTATION SCHEME AND
FUNDAMENTAL RELATIONS FOR
BALANCED INCOMPLETE BLOCK DESIGNS

Statisticians who write about incomplete block designs have, for the most part, adhered to the notation scheme introduced by Yates (1936b).

Consequently, to help the reader who may wish to read the basic references concerning these designs, we shall use Yates's symbols in this chapter. This requires a modification of the notation scheme employed in previous chapters. The amalgamation of the two notation schemes leads to some redundancy but is reasonably clear.

Plans for balanced incomplete block designs are generally described by the following letters:

t = number of treatment levels in experiment

b = number of blocks

k = number of treatment levels assigned to each block

r = number of replications of each treatment level

λ = number of times each pair of treatment levels occurs together within some block.

It follows from the above definitions that the total number of observations, N, is given by

$$N = bk = rt.$$

For any treatment level, t_j, there are $(t - 1)$ possible treatment pairs that contain t_j. If each pair occurs λ times, the total number of times a treatment pair containing t_j occurs in the experiment is

$$\lambda(t - 1).$$

It can also be shown that

$$\lambda(t - 1) = r(k - 1)$$

because each block in which t_j occurs provides $k - 1$ pairs involving t_j, and t_j is replicated r times in the experiment. Thus

$$\lambda = \frac{r(k - 1)}{t - 1}.$$

For a design to be a balanced incomplete block design, it is necessary that $\lambda(t - 1) = r(k - 1)$ and that t, b, k, r, and λ be integers. By definition, the efficiency factor of a balanced incomplete block design is

$$E = \frac{t(k - 1)}{k(t - 1)}.$$

This indicates the *lower limit* of the efficiency of a balanced incomplete block design relative to the use of a complete block design. In general, the efficiency of a balanced incomplete block design is not as low as E, for the blocks are relatively more homogeneous than complete blocks, thus producing a smaller residual error term.

PLANS FOR BALANCED INCOMPLETE BLOCK DESIGNS

For the design diagramed in Figure 11.1-1,

$$t = 7, \quad b = 7, \quad k = 3, \quad r = 3, \quad \text{and} \quad \lambda = 1.$$

Once an experimenter has specified the number of treatment levels and the block size, his choice of values for b and r is limited. The smallest number of blocks that can be used in an experiment can be determined by substitution in the formula

$$b = \frac{tr}{k}$$

subject to the restrictions that $t, b, k, r,$ *and* λ are integers and that $\lambda(t - 1)$

TABLE 11.2-1   Partial List of Available Balanced Incomplete Block Designs

t	k	r	b	λ	E
4	2	3	6	1	.67
	3	3	4	2	.89*
5	2	4	10	1	.62
	3	6	10	3	.83
	4	4	5	3	.94*
6	2	5	15	1	.60*
	3	5	10	2	.80*
	3	10	20	4	.80
	4	10	15	6	.90
	5	5	6	4	.96
7	2	6	21	1	.58
	3	3	7	1	.78*
	4	4	7	2	.88
	6	6	7	5	.97
8	2	7	28	1	.57
	4	7	14	3	.86
	7	7	8	6	.98
9	2	8	36	1	.56
	4	8	18	3	.84
	5	10	18	5	.90
	6	8	12	5	.94
	8	8	9	7	.98
10	2	9	45	1	.56
	3	9	30	2	.74
	4	6	15	2	.83
	5	9	18	4	.89
	6	9	15	5	.93
	9	9	10	8	.99
11	2	10	55	1	.55
	5	5	11	2	.88
	6	6	11	3	.92
	10	10	11	9	.99

*Designs described in this chapter.

$= r(k - 1)$. If $t = 7$ and $k = 3$, one can determine by trial and error that the smallest number of blocks for this design is seven.

Lists of available designs have been prepared to help an experimenter select a balanced incomplete block design. Cochran and Cox (1957, 469) and Fisher and Yates (1963) give extensive lists of such designs. Cochran and Cox also provide the layout of each design included in their list. A partial list of balanced incomplete block designs appears in Table 11.2-1. An experimenter who wants to use an incomplete block design should first determine if there is a design that fits his research requirements. If a design is available, he should then determine the proper layout for the design by referring to the book by Cochran and Cox (1957) or to any other standard reference book. Unfortunately, no single technique exists for determining the layout of all balanced incomplete block designs. Kempthorne (1952) suggests that when the number of treatment levels is small, the layout can be obtained by the simple expedient of determining the smallest possible value of r and then enumerating the design by trial and error. Bose (1939) and Rao (1947) give a detailed discussion of methods of enumeration.

11.3   LAYOUT AND COMPUTATIONAL PROCEDURES FOR TYPE BIB-6 DESIGN

Assume that an experimenter wants to evaluate six types of over-the-ear protection devices (earmuffs) for use by ground aircraft-maintenance personnel. A device that provides the greatest noise attenuation must be selected because these personnel are exposed to intense noise from jet airplanes. Ten men representing a random sample from a population of maintenance personnel are available to participate in the experiment. The evaluation procedure consists of exposing each man to a simulated jet aircraft noise having an over-all sound pressure level of 120 db. The noise that penetrates the earmuff is measured by means of a probe microphone inserted under the earmuff and positioned one-eighth of an inch in front of the subject's eardrum. Because of the tediousness of the experimental procedure, it is believed that a maximum of three observations can be obtained for each subject. According to Table 11.2-1, an incomplete block design is available for six treatment levels in blocks of size three, with b equal to ten. In this plan each treatment level is replicated five times, and each pair of treatment levels occurs twice. The research hypothesis leading to this experiment can be evaluated by means of statistical tests of the following null hypothesis:

$$H_0 : \tau_j = 0 \qquad \text{for all } j$$

$$H_1 : \tau_j \neq 0 \qquad \text{for some } j.$$

TABLE 11.3-1   Layout of Type BIB-6 Design and Computational Procedures

(i) Data:

BT Summary Table

	t_1	t_2	t_3	t_4	t_5	t_6	$\sum\limits_1^{q'} B$
b_1	1	1			5		7
b_2	2	3				9	14
b_3	3		4	4			11
b_4	5		8			13	26
b_5	4			7	7		18
b_6		5	7	8			20
b_7		4	5		6		15
b_8		3		5		13	21
b_9			4		5	8	17
b_{10}				5	9	9	23
$\sum\limits_1^{p'} T = $	15	16	28	29	32	52	

Adjustment Summary Table*

$$W_j = (t - k)\sum_1^{p'} T_j$$
$$- (t - 1)\sum_1^{p'}\sum_1^{q'} B_{(j)}$$
$$+ (k - 1)\sum_1^{N} BT$$

t_j	$\sum\limits_1^{p'} T_j$	$\sum\limits_1^{p'}\sum_1^{q'} B_{(j)}$	$Q_j = k\sum\limits_1^{p'} T_j - \sum\limits_1^{p'}\sum_1^{q'} B_{(j)}$	W_j	$T'_j = \sum\limits_1^{p'} T_j + \mu W_j$
1	15	76	-31	9	15.603
2	16	77	-29	7	16.469
3	28	·89	-5	-17	26.861
4	29	93	-6	-34	26.722
5	32	80	16	40	34.680
6	52	101	55	-5	51.665

$\Sigma = 172$ $\Sigma = 516 = (k)(\Sigma BT)$ $\Sigma = 0$ $\Sigma = 0$

*Terms not defined in the table are defined in part (ii).

(ii) Computational symbols:

$$\sum_1^N BT = 1 + 2 + \cdots + 9 = 172.000$$

$$\sum_1^N (BT)^2 = [BT] = (1)^2 + (2)^2 + \cdots + (9)^2 = 1244.000$$

$$\frac{\left(\sum\limits_1^N BT\right)^2}{rt} = [X] = \frac{(172)^2}{(5)(6)} = 986.133$$

TABLE 11.3-1 (continued)

$$\sum_{1}^{q} \frac{\left(\sum_{1}^{p'} T_j\right)^2}{r} = [T] = \frac{(15)^2}{5} + \cdots + \frac{(52)^2}{5} = 1166.800$$

$$\sum_{1}^{q} \frac{(T'_j)^2}{r} = [T'] = \frac{(15.603)^2}{5} + \cdots + \frac{(51.665)^2}{5} = 1164.447$$

$$\sum_{1}^{p} \frac{\left(\sum_{1}^{q'} B\right)^2}{k} = [B] = \frac{(7)^2}{3} + \cdots + \frac{(23)^2}{3} = 1083.333$$

$$\frac{\sum_{1}^{q}(Q_j)^2}{kt\lambda} = SS_{T(\text{adj for blocks})} = \frac{(-31)^2 + \cdots + (55)^2}{(3)(6)(2)} = 142.889$$

$$E_b = MS_{\text{blocks(adj for treats)}} = \frac{SS_{\text{blocks(adj for treats)}}}{b - 1} = 6.602 \quad [\text{see part (iii)}]$$

$$E_e = MS_{\text{intrablock error}} = \frac{SS_{\text{intrablock error}}}{rt - t - b + 1} = 1.185 \quad [\text{see part (iii)}]$$

$$\mu = \frac{(b-1)(E_b - E_e)}{t(k-1)(b-1)E_b + (t-k)(b-t)E_e}$$

$$= \frac{(10-1)(6.602 - 1.185)}{6(3-1)(10-1)6.602 + (6-3)(10-6)1.185} = .067$$

$$E'_e = E_e[1 + (t-k)\mu] = 1.185[1 + (6-3).067] = 1.423$$

(iii) Computational formulas:

$$SS_{\text{total}} = [BT] - [X] = 257.867$$

$$SS_{T(\text{unadj})} = [T] - [X] = 180.667$$

$$SS_{T(\text{adj})} = [T'] - [X] = 178.314$$

$$SS_{T(\text{adj for blocks})} = \frac{\sum_{1}^{q}(Q_j)^2}{kt\lambda} = 142.889$$

$$SS_{B(\text{unadj})} = [B] - [X] = 97.200$$

$$SS_{B(\text{adj for treats})} = [B] + SS_{T(\text{adj for blocks})} - [T] = 59.422$$

$$SS_{\text{intrablock error}} = [BT] - [B] - SS_{T(\text{adj for blocks})} = 17.778$$

The level of significance adopted for this test is .05.

The analysis of type BIB-t designs includes several computational procedures not previously described. These procedures appear in Table 11.3-1 without explanation. A discussion of the rationale behind these computational procedures is presented in Section 11.4. For convenience in presenting the computational formulas in Table 11.3-1, the following notation is used:

q levels of t_j, where $q = t = 6$

q' levels of $t_{(i)}$, where $q' = 3$ and refers to the treatment
levels that occur in the ith block

p levels of b_i, where $p = b = 10$

p' levels of $b_{(j)}$, where $p' = 5$ and refers to the blocks that contain the jth treatment level

k = number of treatment levels per block = 3

r = number of replications of each treatment level = 5

λ = number of times each pair of treatment levels occurs = 2

$$\sum_{1}^{N} = \sum_{1}^{p'}\sum_{1}^{q} \text{ or } \sum_{1}^{p}\sum_{1}^{q'}.$$

The analysis is summarized in Table 11.3-2. The practice initiated in Chapter 9 of identifying the first level of a treatment by the subscript zero instead of one will not be followed in this or subsequent chapters.

The analysis summarized in Table 11.3-2 is actually two analyses of the same data. In practice, only one of the analyses, as described below, is performed. The experiment provides two sources of information on treatment effects—intrablock information, which is derived from comparisons among treatment levels *within* blocks, and interblock information, which is derived from comparisons among treatment levels *between* blocks. If, as in the present example, blocks are random effects, interblock information in addition to intrablock information can be used. However, if blocks are fixed effects (Model I), only intrablock information is used, since such estimates are optimum (Scheffé; 1959, 170). It is customary to ignore the interblock information for designs in which $k < 5$ and $b < 10$. If only intrablock information is utilized, the analysis requires the computation of terms in rows 4 through 6 and row 9 of Table 11.3-2. The ratio

$$F = \frac{\text{MS}_{T(\text{adj for blocks})}}{E_e}$$

is distributed as the F distribution under the conditions described in Section 11.4.

Both inter- and intrablock information on treatment effects can be utilized for designs (Model III) in which $E_b > E_e$ and $k \geq 5$, $b \geq 10$. This analysis requires the computation of terms in rows 1 through 3 and 7 through 9 of Table 11.3-2.

If $E_b > E_e$ and $k < 5$, $b < 10$, the contribution of interblock information relative to intrablock information is small. Under these conditions the additional labor required to recover the interblock information is not justified. The F ratio that includes both inter- and intrablock information is given by

$$F = \frac{\text{MS}_{T(\text{adj})}}{E'_e}$$

and is approximately distributed as the F distribution under the conditions described in Section 11.4. Only intrablock information should be utilized

TABLE 11.3-2　Analysis of Variance Table for Type BIB-6 Design

Source	SS	df	MS	F	E(MS) Model III
1　$T_{(unadj)}$	180.667	$t-1=5$			
2　$B_{(adj\ for\ treats)}$	59.422	$b-1=9$	$6.602 = E_b$		$\sigma_\varepsilon^2 + \dfrac{bk-t}{b-1}\sigma_\beta^2$
3　Intrablock error	17.778	$rt-t-b+1=15$	$1.185 = E_e$		σ_ε^2
4　$T_{(adj\ for\ blocks)}$ Intrablock info. only	142.889	$t-1=5$	28.578	$\left[\frac{4}{6}\right] = 24.12^*$	$\sigma_\varepsilon^2 + r\sigma_\tau^2$
5　$B_{(unadj)}$	97.200	$b-1=9$			
6　Intrablock error	17.778	$rt-t-b+1=15$	$1.185 = E_e$		σ_ε^2
7　$T_{(adj)}$ Inter- and intrablock info.	178.314	$t-1=5$	35.663	$\left[\frac{7}{8}\right] = 25.06^*$	
8　Effective error		$rt-t-b+1=15$	$1.423 = E'_e$		
9　Total	257.867	$rt-1=29$			

$^*p < .01.$

for the design summarized in Table 11.3-2. A comparison of the F ratios for the two analyses shows that the addition of interblock information contributes little to the analysis. Seshadri (1963) has described a procedure for combining inter- and intrablock information that provides uniformly better estimates regardless of the size of the experiment. However, his analysis is relatively complex.

If $E_b \leq E_e$, the design should be analyzed as if it were a completely randomized design with six treatment levels and five subjects per level. An examination of Table 11.3-2 reveals the following relationship:

$$\text{SS}_{T(\text{unadj})} + \text{SS}_{\text{blocks(adj for } T)} = \text{SS}_{T(\text{adj for blocks})} + \text{SS}_{\text{blocks(unadj)}}.$$

11.4   ASSUMPTIONS OF THE MODEL
FOR TYPE BIB-t DESIGN

Let X_{ij} be a measure for a randomly selected subject i in treatment population j. The linear model for this design is

$$X_{ij} = \mu + \beta_i + \tau_j + \varepsilon_{ij},$$

where μ = grand mean of treatment population.

β_i = effect of block i; in the population of blocks, β is assumed to be NID with mean = 0 and variance = σ_β^2.

τ_j = effect of treatment j, which is a constant for all subjects within treatment population j, $\Sigma_{j=1}^q \tau_j = 0$.

ε_{ij} = experimental error, which is NID with mean = 0 and variance = σ_ε^2.

The ratio $\text{MS}_{T(\text{adj for blocks})}/E_e$ is distributed as the F distribution, and $\text{MS}_{T(\text{adj})}/E_e'$ is approximately distributed as the F distribution under the conditions that (1) the subjects assigned to blocks constitute random samples from a common population, (2) treatment levels represent fixed effects, (3) all bt populations are normal, (4) the variances of the bt populations are homogeneous, and (5) block and treatment effects are additive.

NONORTHOGONALITY OF TREATMENT
AND BLOCK EFFECTS

The linear model for a balanced incomplete block design has the same form as the model for a randomized block design. Computational procedures for the former design are much more complex because treatment and block effects are not orthogonal. The nature of this nonorthogonality can be seen by examining the type BIB-4 design in Table 11.4-1. Each cell is an estimate of the parameters shown in the table. For convenience, the

TABLE 11.4-1   Type BIB-4 Design

	t_1	t_2	t_3	t_4	$\sum\limits_{1}^{q'}$
b_1	$\mu + \tau_1 + \beta_1$		$\mu + \tau_3 + \beta_1$	$\mu + \tau_4 + \beta_1$	$3\mu + 3\beta_1 + \tau_1 + \tau_3 + \tau_4$
b_2		$\mu + \tau_2 + \beta_2$	$\mu + \tau_3 + \beta_2$	$\mu + \tau_4 + \beta_2$	$3\mu + 3\beta_2 + \tau_2 + \tau_3 + \tau_4$
b_3	$\mu + \tau_1 + \beta_3$	$\mu + \tau_2 + \beta_3$	$\mu + \tau_3 + \beta_3$		$3\mu + 3\beta_3 + \tau_1 + \tau_2 + \tau_3$
b_4	$\mu + \tau_1 + \beta_4$	$\mu + \tau_2 + \beta_4$		$\mu + \tau_4 + \beta_4$	$3\mu + 3\beta_4 + \tau_1 + \tau_2 + \tau_4$

$$\sum_{1}^{p'} = \begin{array}{llll} 3\mu + 3\tau_1 + \beta_1 & 3\mu + \tau_2 + \beta_2 & 3\mu + \tau_3 + \beta_1 & 3\mu + \tau_3 + \beta_1 \\ + \beta_3 + \beta_4 & + \beta_3 + \beta_4 & + \beta_2 + \beta_3 & + \beta_2 + \beta_4 \end{array}$$

error components are not included in the table, for it can be assumed that $\Sigma\varepsilon_{ij} = 0$ whether summation is with respect to blocks or to treatment levels. The sum of observations in treatment levels 1 and 2 are estimates of the following parameters as shown in Table 11.4-1:

$$\Sigma T_1 \doteq 3\mu + 3\tau_1 + \beta_1 + \beta_3 + \beta_4$$

$$\Sigma T_2 \doteq 3\mu + 3\tau_2 + \beta_2 + \beta_3 + \beta_4.$$

For the jth level,

$$\Sigma T_j \doteq r\mu + r\tau_j + \Sigma\beta_{(j)}.$$

It is apparent that the difference between ΣT_1 and ΣT_2 is simultaneously a comparison between treatment effects τ_1 versus τ_2 and block effects β_1 versus β_2. This problem was not present in a randomized block design because each ΣT_j contained an estimate of the same block effects. In order to test the hypothesis that $\tau_j = 0$ for all j in a type **BIB**-t design, the effects of blocks must be removed from the treatment sums.

RATIONALE UNDERLYING ADJUSTMENT
OF TREATMENT LEVEL SUMS

The adjustment of treatment level sums so as to eliminate the confounding effects of blocks was accomplished in Table 11.3-1 by computing $Q_j = k\Sigma T_j - \Sigma B_{(j)}$. A treatment sum of squares that is adjusted so as to remove block effects is given by $\Sigma Q_j^2/kt\lambda$. The rationale underlying this adjustment can be readily shown. For example, treatment level 1 occurs in blocks 1, 3, and 4. The sum of these blocks is

$$\Sigma B_1 \doteq 3\mu + 3\beta_1 + \tau_1 + \tau_3 + \tau_4$$

$$\Sigma B_3 \doteq 3\mu + 3\beta_3 + \tau_1 + \tau_2 + \tau_3$$

$$\underline{\Sigma B_4 \doteq 3\mu + 3\beta_4 + \tau_1 + \tau_2 + \tau_4}$$

$$\Sigma B_{(1)} \doteq 9\mu + 3(\beta_1 + \beta_3 + \beta_4) + \tau_1 + 2(\tau_1 + \tau_2 + \tau_3 + \tau_4).$$

According to the assumptions of the linear model, $\Sigma_{j=1}^{q} \tau_j = 0$. Thus

$$2(\tau_1 + \tau_2 + \tau_3 + \tau_4) = 0.$$

The sum of blocks that contains treatment level 1, therefore, is equal to

$$\Sigma B_{(1)} \doteq 9\mu + 3(\beta_1 + \beta_3 + \beta_4) + \tau_1.$$

The symbol $\Sigma B_{(j)}$ designates the sum of blocks that contains the jth treatment level. For the jth treatment level,

$$\Sigma B_{(j)} \doteq kr\mu + k\Sigma \beta_{(j)} + (r - \lambda)\tau_j.$$

By subtracting $\Sigma B_{(1)}$ from $k\Sigma T_1$, one obtains an estimate of τ_1 that is not confounded with block effects. The computation of this estimate, which is designated Q_1, is as follows:

$$\begin{aligned}
3T_1 &\doteq & 9\mu + 9\tau_1 + 3(\beta_1 + \beta_3 + \beta_4) \\
-\Sigma B_{(1)} &\doteq & -9\mu - \tau_1 - 3(\beta_1 + \beta_3 + \beta_4) \\
\hline
Q_1 &\doteq & 8\tau_1
\end{aligned}.$$

For the general case $Q_j \doteq (t\lambda)\tau_j$. This can also be written $Q_j \doteq krE\tau_j$, where

$$E = \frac{t(k-1)}{k(t-1)} = \frac{t\lambda}{rk}.$$

If there was no confounding with block effects, Q_j would estimate $kr\tau_j$. The efficiency factor E is the proportion of treatment information retained in the adjusted sum of squares for treatments.

We noted earlier that interblock treatment information can be recovered if $k \geq 5$ and $b \geq 10$. An estimate containing both inter- and intrablock information is given by

$$\Sigma T_{j'} = \Sigma T_j + \mu W_j.$$

This treatment sum weights the inter- and intrablock estimates inversely as their variances. The reader interested in the derivation of this weighted treatment sum should refer to the original paper by Yates (1940) or Anderson and Bancroft (1952, Chap. 24).

11.5 COMPARISONS AMONG MEANS FOR TYPE BIB-6 DESIGN

Table 11.5-1 shows two formulas for computing treatment means. The first formula uses both inter- and intrablock information. If the analysis of variance is carried out using only intrablock information, the second formula should be used to compute means. The two sets of means do not differ appreciably. This will be the case whenever E_b is large relative

TABLE 11.5-1　Computation of Adjusted Treatment Means

Treatment Level	$\bar{T}'_j = T'_j/r$	$\bar{T}_j = Q_j/t\lambda + \Sigma BT/N$
t_1	3.12	3.15
t_2	3.29	3.32
t_3	5.37	5.32
t_4	5.34	5.23
t_5	6.94	7.07
t_6	10.33	10.32

$\bar{T}'_j$ includes inter- and intrablock information.

$\bar{T}_j$ includes only intrablock information.

to E_e and indicates that the relative contribution of interblock information is small.

A PRIORI COMPARISONS

If all orthogonal comparisons among means have been specified prior to collection of the data, the t statistic has the form

$$t = \frac{C_j(\bar{T}'_j) + C_{j'}(\bar{T}'_{j'})}{\sqrt{2E'_e/r}} \quad \text{or} \quad t = \frac{C_j(\bar{T}_j) + C_{j'}(\bar{T}_{j'})}{\sqrt{2kE_e/t\lambda}}.$$

The first t ratio includes both inter- and intrablock information; the second ratio utilizes only intrablock information. A general discussion of procedures for carrying out comparisons among means is given in Sections 3.2 and 3.4.

A POSTERIORI TESTS

Tukey's test for carrying out *a posteriori* comparisons among means, using both inter- and intrablock information or only intrablock information respectively, is given by

$$q = \frac{C_j(\bar{T}'_j) + C_{j'}(\bar{T}'_{j'})}{\sqrt{E'_e/r}} \quad \text{or} \quad q = \frac{C_j(\bar{T}_j) + C_{j'}(\bar{T}_{j'})}{\sqrt{kE_e/t\lambda}}.$$

If the comparison involves more than two means, Scheffé's test can be used. This statistic has the form

$$F = \frac{[C_j(\bar{T}'_j) + C_{j'}(\bar{T}'_{j'})]^2}{E'_e\left(\frac{(C_j)^2}{r} + \frac{(C_{j'})^2}{r}\right)} \quad \text{or} \quad F = \frac{[C_j(\bar{T}_j) + C_{j'}(\bar{T}_{j'})]^2}{\frac{krE_e}{t\lambda}\left(\frac{(C_j)^2}{r} + \frac{(C_{j'})^2}{r}\right)},$$

where the second formula utilizes only intrablock information. The critical value of F is equal to $(t - 1) F_{\alpha; \nu_1, \nu_2}$.

11.6   ESTIMATING MISSING OBSERVATIONS IN TYPE BIB-t DESIGN

If one or more observations are lost during an experiment, an estimate of the missing values can be obtained by a formula given by Cornish (1940b).

$$X_{ij} = \frac{rt(k - 1)\Sigma B_i + k(t - 1)Q_j - (t - 1)\Sigma Q'_{j'}}{(k - 1)[rt(k - 1) - k(t - 1)]},$$

where ΣB_i = sum of remaining observations in block that contains missing score.

Q_j = Q value for treatment level containing missing score.

$\Sigma Q'_{j'}$ = sum of Q values for all treatment levels in the same block as missing score.

Assume that score X_{73} in Table 11.3-1 is missing. The absence of this score is reflected in the treatment and block sums shown in Table 11.6-1.

The missing score is estimated by

$$X_{73} = \frac{(5)(6)(3 - 1)\, 10 + 3(6 - 1)(-15) - (6 - 1)(-24 - 15 + 21)}{(3 - 1)\,[(5)(6)(3 - 1) - 3(6 - 1)]} = 5.17.$$

TABLE 11.6-1   Adjustment Summary Table

t_j	$\sum_1^{p'} T_j$	$\sum_1^{p'}\sum_1^{q'} B_{(j)}$	$Q = 3\sum_1^{p'} T_j - \sum_1^{p'}\sum_1^{q'} B_{(j)}$
1	15	76	-31
2	16	$72 + X$	$-24 - X$
3	$23 + X_{73}$	$84 + X$	$-15 + 2X$
4	29	93	-6
5	32	$75 + X$	$21 - X$
6	52	101	55

If more than one score is missing, the iterative process described in Section 5.6 can be used. One degree of freedom should be subtracted from the intrablock degrees of freedom for each estimated missing score. The formula given in this section provides an estimate of a missing score that minimizes the intrablock mean square. Cochran and Cox (1957, 400–403) present a brief discussion of alternative estimating formulas. Wilkinson (1958) gives a general survey of the problem of incomplete data.

11.7   TYPE BIB-t DESIGN IN DISTINCT REPLICATIONS

Some incomplete block designs can be arranged in distinct replications. An example of a BIB-6 design in five distinct replications, with $k = 2$ and $b = 15$, is shown in Figure 11.7-1. Computational procedures for this design are identical, with minor exceptions, to those for designs not having distinct replications. The required formulas appear in Table 11.7-1. The following new or modified computational symbols are required for this analysis:

$$[BR] = \sum_{1}^{p} \sum_{1}^{r} \frac{\left(\sum_{1}^{q'} BR\right)^2}{k}, \quad [R] = \sum_{1}^{r} \frac{\left(\sum_{1}^{q} R\right)^2}{t}, \quad [BRT] = \sum_{1}^{N}(BRT)^2,$$

$$\mu = \frac{r(E_b - E_e)}{rt(k - 1)E_b + k(b - r - t + 1)E_e}.$$

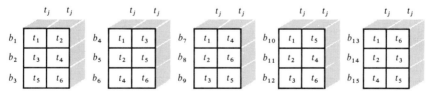

Figure 11.7-1 Type BIB-6 design in distinct replications.

The terms $[BR]$, $[R]$, and $[BRT]$ are computed from the *BRT*, *RT*, and *BRT* summary tables, respectively.

TABLE 11.7-1   Computational Formulas for Type BIB-t Design in Distinct Replications

	Source	df	Computational Formulas	F(Model III)
1	Replications	$r - 1$	$[R] - [X]$	
2	Treats(unadj)	$t - 1$	$[T] - [X]$	
3	Blocks w.reps(adj)	$b - r$	$SS_{blocks\ w.reps(unadj)} + SS_{T(adj\ for\ blocks)} - SS_{T(unadj)} = E_b$	
4	Intrablock error	$rt - t - b + 1$	$SS_{total} - SS_{reps} - SS_{T(unadj)} - SS_{blocks\ w.reps(adj)} = E_e$	
5	Treats(adj for blocks)	$t - 1$	$\sum_{1}^{q} Q^2/kt\lambda$	$[\frac{5}{7}]$
6	Blocks w.reps(unadj)	$b - r$	$[BR] - [R]$	
7	Intrablock error	$rt - t - b + 1$	E_e	
8	Treats(adj)	$t - 1$	$[T'] - [X]$	$[\frac{8}{9}]$
9	Effective error	$rt - t - b + 1$	$E_e[1 + (t - k)\mu_t] = E'_e$	
10	Total	$rt - 1$	$[BRT] - [X]$	

11.8 TYPE BIB-*t* DESIGN WITH *rw* REPLICATIONS

Small balanced incomplete block designs may provide insufficient degrees of freedom for experimental error. In that case it is possible to replicate the basic plan w times. The design will contain rw replications instead of r replications. A diagram of a BIB-5 design, with $k = 4$, $r = 4$, $b = 5$, $w = 2$, and $\lambda = 3$, appears in Figure 11.8-1.

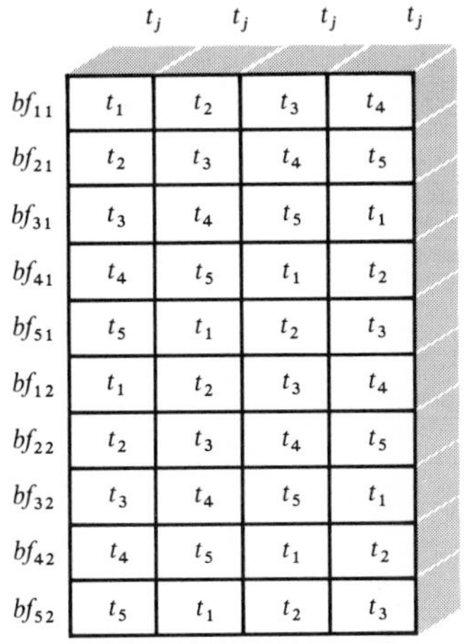

	t_j	t_j	t_j	t_j
bf_{11}	t_1	t_2	t_3	t_4
bf_{21}	t_2	t_3	t_4	t_5
bf_{31}	t_3	t_4	t_5	t_1
bf_{41}	t_4	t_5	t_1	t_2
bf_{51}	t_5	t_1	t_2	t_3
bf_{12}	t_1	t_2	t_3	t_4
bf_{22}	t_2	t_3	t_4	t_5
bf_{32}	t_3	t_4	t_5	t_1
bf_{42}	t_4	t_5	t_1	t_2
bf_{52}	t_5	t_1	t_2	t_3

Figure 11.8-1 Block diagram of type BIB-5 design

Computational formulas for this design are shown in Table 11.8-1. There are w levels of F_h, which designates the number of replications of the basic plan. The following terms illustrate the general nature of the modification that must be made to the computational symbols:

$$\sum_1^N = \sum_1^{p'} \sum_1^q \sum_1^w \text{ or } \sum_1^p \sum_1^{q'} \sum_1^w, \quad [BFT] = \sum_1^N (BFT)^2,$$

$$[BF] = \sum_1^p \sum_1^w \frac{(BF)^2}{k}, \quad [F] = \sum_1^w \frac{\left(\sum_1^p F\right)^2}{rt}$$

$$[X] = \frac{\left(\sum_1^N BFT\right)^2}{rtw}, \quad \lambda = \frac{rw(k-1)}{t-1},$$

$$\mu = \frac{w(b-1)(E_b - E_e)}{t(k-1)w(b-1)E_b + (t-k)(bw-t-w+1)E_e}.$$

The terms $[BFT]$ and $[X]$ are computed from a BFT Summary Table, $[BF]$ and $[F]$ from a BF Summary Table.

TABLE 11.8-1 Computational Formulas for Type BIB-t Design with rw Replications

	Source	df	Computational Formulas	F(Model III)
1	Replications	$w - 1$	$[F] - [X]$	
2	Treats(unadj)	$t - 1$	$[T] - [X]$	
3	Blocks w.reps(adj for T)	$w(b - 1)$	$SS_{\text{blocks w.reps(unadj)}} + SS_{T(\text{adj for blocks})} - SS_{T(\text{unadj})} = E_b$	
4	Intrablock error	$rtw - t - bw + 1$	$SS_{\text{total}} - SS_{\text{reps}} - SS_{T(\text{unadj})} - SS_{\text{blocks w.reps(adj)}} = E_e$	
5	Treats(adj for blocks)	$t - 1$	$\sum_1^4 Q^2/kt\lambda$	$\left[\frac{5}{7}\right]$
6	Blocks w.reps(unadj)	$w(b - 1)$	$[BF] - [F]$	
7	Intrablock error	$rtw - t - bw + 1$	E_e	
8	Treats(adj)	$t - 1$	$[T'] - [X]$	$\left[\frac{8}{9}\right]$
9	Effective error	$rtw - t - bw + 1$	$E_e[1 + (t - k)\mu] = E'_e$	
10	Total	$rtw - 1$	$[BFT] - [X]$	

11.9 INTRODUCTION TO YOUDEN SQUARES

A Youden square design, which combines features of balanced incomplete block and Latin square designs, was first introduced by Youden (1940) for use in agricultural research. The incomplete block designs described previously permit an experimenter to isolate variation associated with blocks. A Youden square is a special type of incomplete Latin square that permits an experimenter to isolate variation due to both blocks and columns.

A block diagram of a Youden square design, designated by the letters YBIB-t, is shown in Figure 11.9-1. In this design, $t = b = 4$, $r = k$

	k_1	k_2	k_3
b_1	t_1 s_1	t_2 s_1	t_3 s_1
b_2	t_2 s_2	t_3 s_2	t_4 s_2
b_3	t_3 s_3	t_4 s_3	t_1 s_3
b_4	t_4 s_4	t_1 s_4	t_2 s_4

Figure 11.9-1 Block diagram of type YBIB-4 design.

$= 3$, and $\lambda = 2$. This design corresponds to a standard 4×4 Latin square in which the last column has been omitted. For example, the treatment levels in a type LS-4 design are as follows:

$$\begin{matrix} 1 & 2 & 3 & 4 \\ 2 & 3 & 4 & 1 \\ 3 & 4 & 1 & 2 \\ 4 & 1 & 2 & 3. \end{matrix}$$

A comparison of the first three columns of this Latin square with those in Figure 11.9-1 reveals that they are identical. In general, the following relations hold for a Youden square: $t = b$ and $k = r$. Although a Youden square is always a Latin square from which *one or more* columns are omitted, the converse is not always true. A Latin square from which one or more columns have been deleted is not necessarily a Youden square.

CONSTRUCTION OF YOUDEN SQUARES

A Latin square can be constructed by a one-step cyclic permutation of a sequence of numbers. This involves moving the first letter in the sequence to the extreme right and simultaneously moving the remaining letters one position to the left. A Youden balanced incomplete block design can be constructed from any cyclic Latin square by deleting one of the columns. There is only one form of Youden square that can be constructed for $t = 4, 5, 6, 8, 9$, and 10. There are three forms of a type YBIB-7 design. This design can be constructed, for example, by omitting the last column of the following 7×7 Latin square:

$$
\begin{array}{ccccccc}
1 & 2 & 3 & 4 & 5 & 6 & 7 \\
2 & 3 & 4 & 5 & 6 & 7 & 1 \\
3 & 4 & 5 & 6 & 7 & 1 & 2 \\
4 & 5 & 6 & 7 & 1 & 2 & 3 \\
5 & 6 & 7 & 1 & 2 & 3 & 4 \\
6 & 7 & 1 & 2 & 3 & 4 & 5 \\
7 & 1 & 2 & 3 & 4 & 5 & 6.
\end{array}
$$

If one column is omitted, $t = b = 7$, $k = r = 6$, and $\lambda = 5$. Another plan for a type YBIB-7 design, with $k = r = 3$ and $\lambda = 1$, can be constructed by selecting any two adjacent columns of a 7×7 cyclic Latin square and a third column one step away. If columns 2, 3, and 5 are selected, the design has the following form:

$$
\begin{array}{ccc}
2 & 3 & 5 \\
3 & 4 & 6 \\
4 & 5 & 7 \\
5 & 6 & 1 \\
6 & 7 & 2 \\
7 & 1 & 3 \\
1 & 2 & 4.
\end{array}
$$

The remaining four columns of the 7×7 Latin square form the third Youden square with $k = r = 4$ and $\lambda = 2$. Smith and Hartley (1948)

TABLE 11.9-1 Partial List of Youden Squares

$t = b$	$k = r$	λ	E
4	3	2	.89
5	4	3	.94*
6	5	4	.96*
7	3	1	.78*
7	4	2	.88*
7	6	5	.97*
8	7	6	.98
9	8	7	.98
10	9	8	.99
11	5	2	.88
11	6	3	.92
11	10	9	.99

*Layout of design described in this chapter.

proved that Youden squares exist for all balanced incomplete block designs in which $t = b$ and $k = r$. They suggest a number of procedures for constructing Youden squares. These designs can be constructed by trial and error if a type BIB-t design is known to exist, with $t = b$ and $k = r$. Cochran and Cox (1957) give an extensive list of Youden squares as well as the layout for designs on their list. Preece (1966) presents an elaborate scheme for classifying Youden squares. Table 11.9-1 shows a partial list of Youden square designs.

11.10   LAYOUT AND COMPUTATIONAL PROCEDURES FOR TYPE YBIB-6 DESIGN

A type YBIB-t design is a special type of balanced incomplete block design. Analysis procedures described for the latter design generalize, with slight modification, to a Youden square. A Youden square design has the same relation to a balanced incomplete block design as a Latin square design has to a randomized block design. Both the Youden and Latin square designs enable an experimenter to isolate two nuisance variables.

The example used in Section 11.3 to illustrate the application of a type BIB-6 design involved the evaluation of six over-the-ear noise muffs. The effects of order of administration of the treatment levels within blocks were *controlled* in the example by randomization. Treatment order can also be controlled by assigning this nuisance variable to the columns of a Youden square. According to Table 11.9-1, a design is available with $t = b = 6$, $k = r = 5$, and $\lambda = 4$. A random sample of six subjects is required for the experiment. The Youden square should be randomized according to the procedures described in Section 6.2 for a Latin square. Subjects are randomly assigned to blocks of the square. Treatment levels are administered to the subjects according to the order specified within each block.

The layout of a type YBIB-6 design, computational tables, and formulas appear in Table 11.10-1. The analysis is summarized in Table 11.10-2. The following notation is used in the tables:

q levels of t_j, where $q = t = 6$

p levels of b_i, where $p = b = 6$

p' levels of $b_{(j)}$, where $p' = 5$ and refers to the blocks that contain the jth treatment level

v levels of k_l, where $v = k = 5$

r = number of replications of each treatment level = 5

TABLE 11.10-1   Layout of Type YBIB-6 Design and Computational Procedures

(i) Data:

BKT Summary Table

	k_1	k_2	k_3	k_4	k_5	$\sum_{1}^{v}B$
b_1	t_3 4	t_5 5	t_1 1	t_4 4	t_2 1	15
b_2	t_4 5	t_6 8	t_2 3	t_5 5	t_3 4	25
b_3	t_5 6	t_1 2	t_3 5	t_6 9	t_4 5	27
b_4	t_6 9	t_2 3	t_4 7	t_1 3	t_5 7	29
b_5	t_1 4	t_3 7	t_5 9	t_2 4	t_6 13	37
b_6	t_2 5	t_4 8	t_6 13	t_3 8	t_1 5	39
$\sum_{1}^{p}K=$	33	33	38	33	35	

Adjustment Summary Table*

t_j	$\sum_{1}^{p'}T_j$	$\sum_{1}^{p'}\sum_{1}^{v}B_{(j)}$	W_j	Q_j	T'_j
1	15	147	-32	-72	13.688
2	16	145	-21	-65	15.139
3	28	143	1	-3	28.041
4	29	135	42	10	30.722
5	32	133	55	27	34.255
6	52	157	-45	103	50.155
	$\Sigma = 172$	$\Sigma = 860$	$\Sigma = 0$	$\Sigma = 0$	
		$= (k)(\Sigma BKT)$			

*Terms in this table are defined in part (ii).

(ii) Computational symbols:

$$W_j = (t-k)\sum_{1}^{p'}T_j - (t-1)\sum_{1}^{p'}\sum_{1}^{v}B_{(j)} + (k-1)\sum_{1}^{N}BKT, \qquad Q_j = k\sum_{1}^{p'}T_j - \sum_{1}^{p'}\sum_{1}^{v}B_{(j)},$$

$$T'_j = \sum_{1}^{p'}T_j + \mu W_j, \qquad \lambda = \frac{r(k-1)}{t-1}, \qquad \mu = \frac{(E_b - E_e)}{t(k-1)E_b} = .041,$$

$$E_b = \text{MS}_{B(\text{adj for } T)} = 13.800, \qquad E_e = \text{MS}_{\text{intrablock error}} = .333 \quad [\text{see part (iii)}]$$

$$\sum_{1}^{N}BKT = 4 + 5 + \cdots + 5 = 172.000$$

TABLE 11.10-1 (continued)

$$\sum_{1}^{N}(BKT)^2 = [BKT] = (4)^2 + (5)^2 + \cdots + (5)^2 = 1244.000$$

$$\frac{\left(\sum_{1}^{N}BKT\right)^2}{kt} = [X] = \frac{(172)^2}{(5)(6)} = 986.133$$

$$\sum_{1}^{q}\frac{\left(\sum_{1}^{p'}T_j\right)^2}{r} = [T] = \frac{(15)^2}{5} + \cdots + \frac{(52)^2}{5} = 1166.800$$

$$\sum_{1}^{q}\frac{(T'_j)^2}{r} = [T'] = \frac{(13.688)^2}{5} + \cdots + \frac{(50.155)^2}{5} = 1167.124$$

$$\sum_{1}^{q}\frac{Q_j^2}{kt\lambda} = SS_{T(\text{adj for }B)} = \frac{(-72)^2}{(5)(6)(4)} + \cdots + \frac{(103)^2}{(5)(6)(4)} = 173.800$$

$$\sum_{1}^{q}\frac{W_j^2}{kt(t-k)(k-1)} = SS_{B(\text{adj for }T)} = \frac{(-32)^2 + \cdots + (-45)^2}{(5)(6)(6-5)(5-1)} = 69.000$$

$$\sum_{1}^{p}\frac{\left(\sum_{1}^{v}B\right)^2}{k} = [B] = \frac{(15)^2}{5} + \cdots + \frac{(39)^2}{5} = 1062.000$$

$$\sum_{1}^{v}\frac{\left(\sum_{1}^{p}K\right)^2}{b} = [K] = \frac{(33)^2}{6} + \cdots + \frac{(35)^2}{6} = 989.333$$

(iii) Computational formulas:

$$SS_{\text{total}} = [BKT] - [X] = 257.867 \qquad SS_{T(\text{unadj})} = [T] - [X] = 180.667$$

$$SS_{T(\text{adj})} = [T'] - [X] = 180.991 \qquad SS_{T(\text{adj for }B)} = \frac{\sum_{1}^{q}Q_j^2}{kt\lambda} = 173.800$$

$$SS_{B(\text{unadj})} = [B] - [X] = 75.867 \qquad SS_{B(\text{adj for }T)} = 69.000$$

$$E_b = \frac{SS_{B(\text{adj for }T)}}{b-1} = 13.800 \qquad SS_K = [K] - [X] = 3.200$$

$$SS_{\text{intrablock error}} = SS_{\text{total}} - SS_K - SS_{T(\text{unadj})} - SS_{B(\text{adj for }T)} = 5.000$$

$$= SS_{\text{total}} - SS_K - SS_{T(\text{adj for }B)} - SS_{B(\text{unadj})} = 5.000$$

$$E_e = \frac{SS_{\text{intrablock error}}}{(k-2)(t-1)} = .333 \qquad E'_e = E_e\,[1 + (t-k)\mu] = .347$$

**TABLE 11.10-2 Analysis of Variance Table for
Type YBIB-6 Design**

	Source	SS	df	MS	F(Model III)
1	Columns	3.200	$k - 1 = 4$	.800	$\left[\frac{1}{4}\right] = \quad 2.40$
2	Treats (unadj)	180.667	$t - 1 = 5$		
3	Blocks (adj for T)	69.000	$b - 1 = 5$	$13.800 = E_b$	$\left[\frac{3}{4}\right] = \quad 41.44^*$
4	Intrablock error	5.000	$(k - 2)(t - 1) = 15$	$.333 = E_e$	
5	Columns	3.200	$k - 1 = 4$	.800	$\left[\frac{5}{8}\right] = \quad 2.40$
6	Treats (adj for B)	173.800	$t - 1 = 5$	34.760	$\left[\frac{6}{8}\right] = 104.38^*$
7	Blocks (unadj)	75.867	$b - 1 = 5$		
8	Intrablock error	5.000	$(k - 2)(t - 1) = 15$	$.333 = E_e$	
9	Treats (adj)	180.991	$t - 1 - 5$	36.198	$\left[\frac{9}{10}\right] = 104.32^*$
10	Effective error		$(k - 2)(t - 1) = 15$	$.347 = E_e'$	
11	Total	257.867	$kt - 1 = 29$		

$^*p < .01.$

λ = number of times each pair of treatment levels occurs = 4

$$\sum_1^N = \sum_1^p \sum_1^v.$$

Redundancy in this notation scheme results from an attempt to adhere not only to the notation used throughout this book but also to the specialized notation used by statisticians in connection with incomplete block designs.

It is customary to utilize only intrablock information if the design contains less than twelve treatment levels. A test of treatment effects using intrablock information is given by the ratio

$$F = \frac{\text{MS}_{T(\text{adj for } B)}}{\text{MS}_{\text{intrablock error}}}.$$

This analysis does not require the computation of all terms in Table 11.10-2, only those in rows 5 through 8 and row 11. According to this analysis, the null hypothesis that $\tau_j = 0$ for all j can be rejected. The analysis of a Youden balanced incomplete block design is simplified because $t = b$.

According to the analysis in Table 11.10-2, E_b is large relative to E_e, which indicates that the contribution of interblock information is relatively small compared to intrablock information. If $t > 12$ and an experimenter wishes to utilize both inter- and intrablock treatment information, an approximate test of treatment effects is given by

$$F = \frac{\text{MS}_{T(\text{adj})}}{\text{MS}_{\text{effective error}}}.$$

This analysis requires the computation of the terms in rows 1 through 4 and 9 through 11 in Table 11.10-2. The computation required for utilization of intrablock information or intra- and interblock information is illustrated in Tables 11.10-1 and 11.10-2. Normally an experimenter would utilize only intrablock information in an experiment such as the one described in Table 11.10-2.

COMPARISON AMONG MEANS

If inter- and intrablock information on treatment effects is utilized, an adjusted treatment mean is given by T'_j/r. The denominator of a t ratio is

$$\sqrt{\frac{2E'_e}{r}}.$$

An adjusted treatment mean utilizing only intrablock information is given by $Q/t\lambda + \Sigma BKT/N$. The denominator of a t ratio for this case in which only intrablock information is used is

$$\sqrt{\frac{2kE_e}{t\lambda}}.$$

ESTIMATING MISSING OBSERVATIONS
IN A TYPE YBIB-t DESIGN

The formula for estimating a missing observation in a type YBIB-t design is similar to the formula described in Section 11.6 for a balanced incomplete block design. In both designs the estimated value is that score which minimizes the intrablock error. A general discussion of a procedure for minimizing error is given in Section 7.9. The estimated value is correct for experiments involving less than twelve treatment levels and provides an approximate solution if interblock information is recovered. The formula is

$$X_{ijl} = \frac{\lambda\left[r\Sigma K_l + t\Sigma B_i + (t-1)Q_j - \Sigma BKT\right] - rQ'_{j'} - (r-1)\Sigma B_{(j)} + \Sigma B_{(j')}}{r(r-1)(r-2)},$$

where ΣK_l = sum of remaining observations in column that contains missing score.

ΣB_i = sum of remaining observations in block that contains missing score.

Q_j = sum of remaining observations in treatment level that contains missing score.

ΣBKT = sum of all remaining observations.

$Q'_{j'}$ = sum of all other treatment levels that appear in block containing the missing score.

$\Sigma B_{(j)}$ = sum of all blocks in which treatment level j occurs.

$\Sigma B_{(j')}$ = total of $B_{(j)}$ for all other treatment levels that occur in the block containing the missing score.

Assume that score X_{254} is missing in Table 11.10-1. The missing score is estimated by

$$X_{254} = \frac{4[5(28) + 6(20) + (6 - 1)(27) - 167] - 5(125) - (5 - 1)(128) + 560}{5(5 - 1)(5 - 2)}$$

$$= \frac{335}{60} = 5.58.$$

11.11   TYPE YBIB-t DESIGN WITH rw REPLICATIONS

The Youden square described in the preceding section provides r replications of each treatment level. If this number of replications is considered inadequate, the entire square can be replicated w times. The w Youden squares should be randomized independently for each replication.

Computational formulas for this design are shown in Table 11.11-1. Computational symbols must be modified to reflect the w levels of replications (F) of the Youden square. The following terms illustrate the general nature of the modification that must be made to the computational symbols:

$$[BFKT] = \sum_{1}^{N}(BFKT)^2, \quad [BF] = \sum_{1}^{p}\sum_{1}^{w}\frac{(BF)^2}{k}, \quad [B] = \sum_{1}^{p}\frac{\left(\sum_{1}^{w}B\right)^2}{kw},$$

$$[F] = \sum_{1}^{w}\frac{\left(\sum_{1}^{v}F\right)^2}{bk}, \quad [K] = \sum_{1}^{v}\frac{\left(\sum_{1}^{w}K\right)^2}{bw}, \quad [T] = \sum_{1}^{q}\frac{\left(\sum_{1}^{p'}T_j\right)^2}{rw},$$

$$[X] = \sum_{1}^{N}\frac{(BFKT)^2}{ktw}, \quad \mu = \frac{w(E_b - E_e)}{tw(k - 1)E_b + (t - k)(w - 1)E_e},$$

$$\lambda = \frac{rw(t - 1)}{t - 1}.$$

The terms $[BF]$ and $[B]$ are computed from a BF Summary Table, $[F]$ and $[K]$ from a FK Summary Table, and $[BFKT]$, $[T]$, and $[X]$ from a $BFKT$ Summary Table.

TABLE 11.11-1 Computational Formulas for Type YBIB-t Design with rw Replications

	Source	df	Computational Formulas	F(Model III)
1	Columns	$kw - 1$	$[K] - [X]$	
2	Treats(unadj)	$t - 1$	$[T] - [X]$	
3	Blocks w.reps(adj for T)	$w(b - 1)$	$[BF] - [B] - [F] + [X]$ $+ \Sigma W_j^2/ktw(t - k)(k - 1) = E_b$	
4	Intrablock error	$(t - 1)(kw - w - 1)$	$[BFKT] - [BF] + [B] + [F] - [K]$ $- [T] - \Sigma W_j^2/ktw(t - k)(k - 1) = E_e$	
5	Columns	$kw - 1$	$[K] - [X]$	
6	Treats(adj for B)	$t - 1$	$\sum_1^q Q_j^2/kt\lambda$	$\left[\frac{6}{8}\right]$
7	Blocks w.reps(unadj)	$w(b - 1)$	$[BF] - [F]$	
8	Intrablock error	$(t - 1)(kw - w - 1)$	$[BFKT] - [BF] + [F] - [K] - \sum_1^q Q_j^2/kt\lambda = E_e$	
9	Treats(adj)	$t - 1$	$[T'] - [X]$	$\left[\frac{9}{10}\right]$
10	Effective error	$(t - 1)(kw - w - 1)$	$E_e[1 + (t - k)\mu] = E_e'$	
11	Total	$ktw - 1$	$[BFKT] - [X]$	

COMPARISONS AMONG MEANS

If inter- and intrablock information on treatment effects is utilized, an adjusted treatment mean is given by T'_j/rw. The denominator of a t ratio is

$$\sqrt{\frac{2E'_e}{rw}}.$$

If only intrablock information is used, a treatment mean is given by $Q_j/t\lambda + \Sigma BFKT/N$. The denominator of a t ratio for the case in which only intrablock information is used is

$$\sqrt{\frac{2kE_e}{t\lambda}}.$$

11.12   OTHER INCOMPLETE BLOCK DESIGNS

Two types of incomplete block designs were described in previous sections of this chapter. Although not widely used in behavioral research, they are well suited to this research area. In addition, many other types of incomplete block designs are potentially useful in behavioral research. However, an examination of all these designs is beyond the scope of this book. Therefore we shall, in this section, describe briefly some of the better known designs. References describing the layout and computational procedures for each design are provided.

LATTICE DESIGNS

Lattice designs, which comprise a large group of incomplete block designs, are most useful for single-treatment experiments with sixteen or more levels. The designation *lattice design* is given to incomplete block designs in which the layout and analysis are facilitated by establishing a correspondence between the treatment levels of the experiment and the treatment combinations of a factorial experiment. The nature of the correspondence referred to above can be illustrated by the following example. Consider the treatment combinations of a type CRF-22 design. The four treatment combinations can be assigned to two blocks of two units each by means of the confounding procedures described in Chapter 9. This is illustrated in Figure 11.12-1. An examination of the three replications reveals that treatments A and B and the AB interaction are confounded with between-block variation in replications 1, 2, and 3, respectively. For example, in replication 1, treatment level a_2 occurs only in block 1

	Replication 1			Replication 2			Replication 3	
	ab_{ij}	ab_{ij}		ab_{ij}	ab_{ij}		ab_{ij}	ab_{ij}
Block 1	ab_{21}	ab_{22}	Block 1	ab_{12}	ab_{22}	Block 1	ab_{11}	ab_{22}
Block 2	ab_{11}	ab_{12}	Block 2	ab_{11}	ab_{21}	Block 2	ab_{21}	ab_{12}

A confounded with blocks B confounded with blocks AB confounded with blocks

Figure 11.12-1   Factorial design with treatments confounded with blocks.

and a_1 occurs only in block 2. However, treatments B and AB are not confounded with between-block variation in this first replication. The following correspondence can be arbitrarily established between the treatment combinations of the factorial design and the treatment levels of a lattice design with $t = 4$.

$$t_1 \quad ab_{11}$$

$$t_2 \quad ab_{21}$$

$$t_3 \quad ab_{12}$$

$$t_4 \quad ab_{22}$$

If the t_j treatment levels above are substituted for the ab_{ij} combinations in Figure 11.12-1, a lattice design is obtained. This design is shown in Figure 11.12-2.

	Replication 1			Replication 2			Replication 3	
	t_j	t_j		t_j	t_j		t_j	t_j
Block$_1$	t_2	t_4	Block$_1$	t_3	t_4	Block$_1$	t_1	t_4
Block$_2$	t_1	t_3	Block$_2$	t_1	t_2	Block$_2$	t_2	t_3

Figure 11.12-2   Balanced lattice design for $t = 4$ treatment levels.

In other incomplete block designs, such as type BIB and YBIB designs, factorial correspondence is of no help in laying out the design. This group of designs is generally referred to as incomplete block designs.

Lattice designs may be classified in terms of the number of restrictions imposed on the assignment of treatment levels to the experimental units. In Figure 11.12-2 randomization within each replication was restricted in one way—by blocks. Designs having this property are called *one-restrictional* lattices. If randomization is restricted with respect to both blocks and columns, as in a Latin square, the design is a *two-restrictional* lattice, and so on.

The categories one-, two-, . . . , s- restrictional lattices can be further subdivided according to (1) the number of treatment levels relative to the block size and (2) whether the design is *balanced*, *partially balanced*, or *unbalanced*. If the number of treatment levels, t, in the experiment is equal to the square of the block size ($t = k^2$), the design is two-dimensional. If $t = k^3$, the design is three-dimensional. For a n-dimensional lattice, $t = k^n$.

A one-restrictional, two-dimensional lattice is balanced if all confounding arrangements are used. The design in Figure 11.12-2 involves all three possible confounding arrangements. Thus this design is a *balanced lattice design*. A balanced lattice is distinguished from other lattices in that every pair of treatment levels occurs in some block an equal number of times. In other words, λ is the same for every pair of treatment levels, and all pairs of treatment levels are compared with the same degree of precision. Balanced lattice designs are available for all prime numbers or powers of prime numbers ($k = 3, 4, 5, 7, 8, 9$, etc.), plus some other integers. $k + 1$ replications are required for balance in a two-dimensional design. Three-dimensional and four-dimensional designs require $k^2 + k + 1$ and $k^3 + k^2 + k + 1$ replications, respectively, for balance.

A nonbalanced design results from the use of fewer replications than are required for balanced designs. If $r < k + 1$, a two-dimensional design is not balanced. (Partially balanced and unbalanced designs are defined in Section 9.3.) A one-restrictional, two-dimensional nonbalanced design that uses *two* replications is referred to as a *double lattice design* or *simple lattice design* (Federer; 1955, 318). If any two replicates in Figure 11.12-2 are selected, the design becomes a double lattice design. If three replicates are used and $r < k + 1$, the design is a triple lattice design, and so on.

The requirement that $t = k^2$ is somewhat restrictive. A *rectangular lattice* design is a one-restrictional, two-dimensional design in which $t = k(k + 1)$ treatment levels are assigned to blocks of size k. This design, which was introduced by Harshbarger (1947, 1949, 1951), is suitable for 12, 20, 30, 42, etc. treatment levels. Procedures for constructing rectangular lattice designs are described by Cochran and Cox (1957, 416–417) and Nair (1953). Another class of rectangular lattice designs has been proposed by Yates (1936b).

A one-restrictional, three-dimensional lattice design in which $t = k^3$ is a *cubic lattice design*. These designs, as well as higher-dimensional lattices, are not particularly useful in the behavioral sciences. A cubic lattice design is used for experiments involving 27, 64, or more treatment levels.

If randomization is restricted with respect to both blocks and columns and $t = k^2$, the design is a *lattice square*. A balanced lattice square for $t = 9$ is shown in Figure 11.12-3. Note that $t = k^2$ treatment levels are grouped into $k + 1$ replicates of $k \times k$ squares so that every pair of treatment levels occurs once in a row and once in a column. For example, t_1 occurs with t_2 through t_9, in rows 1, 3, 2, 2, and columns 1, 2, 1, 3 of the four replications, respectively. If $(k + 1)/2$ instead of $k + 1$ replicates are used, the design is a semibalanced lattice square. In this case, the treatment levels are grouped so that every pair of treatment levels occurs once in a row or column. Balanced lattice square designs are available

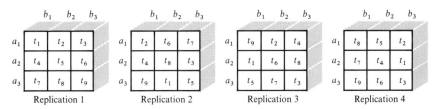

Figure 11.12-3　Balanced lattice square design for $t = 9$.

for blocks of size k, where k is a prime number or power of a prime number. In terms of the classification system used in this section, a lattice square design is a two-restrictional, two-dimensional lattice design. This design, like a Latin square design, enables an experimenter to isolate variation attributable to rows and columns of the square. Clem and Federer (1950) described the layout for balanced lattice square designs for blocks of size $k = 5, 7, 8,$ and 9.

If a lattice design seems appropriate for an experiment, the reader should consult the above references or the more general discussions by Cochran and Cox (1957, Chaps. 10 and 12), Federer (1955, Chaps. 11 and 12) and Kempthorne (1952, Chaps. 23, 24, and 25).

INCOMPLETE LATIN SQUARE DESIGNS

Another type of incomplete block design is the incomplete Latin square design. A Youden square, which is a special case of an incomplete Latin square design, was described in Section 11.9. An incomplete Latin square can be constructed by omitting one or more rows or columns of a Latin square. An example illustrating the computation for a Latin square with one missing row is given by Li (1964, Chap. 26). A general discussion of incomplete Latin square designs is given by Yates (1936a), Yates and Hale (1939), and Cochran and Cox (1957, Chap. 13). Pearce (1952, 1953) has described Latin square type designs that contain an additional column, an additional row and column, and an additional column with one row omitted.

PARTIALLY BALANCED INCOMPLETE BLOCK DESIGN

The type BIB-t designs described previously are balanced in the sense that every possible pair of treatment levels occurs within some block an equal number of times. Balanced incomplete block designs with many treatment levels may require a prohibitively large number of replicates. A smaller number of replicates can be used if the design is partially balanced. That is, some pairs of treatment levels occur within some block more often than other pairs. An example of a type PBIB-10 design appears in Figure 11.12-4. The analysis of partially balanced incomplete block designs is more complex than the analysis of balanced designs.

The development of type PBIB-t designs stems largely from the work of Bose and Nair (1939) and Rao (1947). Procedures for constructing these designs were summarized by Addelman and Bush (1963). A catalog of plans with computational procedures has been prepared by Bose, Clatworthy, and Shrikhande (1954). Computational examples for these designs are given by Cochran and Cox (1957, 453–463), Kempthorne (1952, 560–564), and Winer (1962, 506–511).

	t_j	t_j	t_j	t_j
Block_1	t_1	t_2	t_3	t_4
Block_2	t_1	t_5	t_6	t_7
Block_3	t_2	t_5	t_8	t_9
Block_4	t_3	t_6	t_8	t_{10}
Block_5	t_4	t_7	t_9	t_{10}

Figure 11.12-4 Type PBIB-10 design with $b = 5$, $k = 4$, and $r = 2$.

11.13 ADVANTAGES AND DISADVANTAGES OF INCOMPLETE BLOCK DESIGNS

Two incomplete block designs, a balanced incomplete block design and a Youden square, were described in some detail in this chapter. The principal advantages of these designs are

1. They permit an experimenter to evaluate many levels of a treatment using a blocking procedure that does not require the use of complete blocks.
2. In general, an incomplete block design with recovery of interblock information is more efficient than a randomized block design.

The principal disadvantages of these designs are

1. The layout of balanced incomplete block designs cannot be obtained by any formal procedure.
2. The layout and computational procedures for balanced incomplete block designs are considerably more complex than for randomized block designs.
3. The estimation of missing scores is relatively complex.

12 / ANALYSIS OF COVARIANCE

12.1 INTRODUCTION TO ANALYSIS OF COVARIANCE

The emphasis in previous chapters has been on the use of *experimental control* to reduce variability due to experimental error and to obtain unbiased estimates of treatment effects. Experimental control can take various forms, such as the random assignment of subjects to treatment levels, the stratification of subjects into homogeneous blocks, and the refinement of techniques for measuring a dependent variate. An alternative approach to reducing experimental error and obtaining unbiased estimates of treatment effects involves the use of *statistical control*. This latter approach also enables an experimenter to remove potential sources of bias from an experiment, biases that are difficult or impossible to eliminate by experimental control.

Statistical control, as described in this chapter, is referred to as analysis of covariance; it combines the advantages of regression analysis with analysis of variance. The procedure involves measuring one or more concomitant variates (also called covariates) in addition to the dependent variate. The concomitant variate represents a source of variation that has not been controlled in the experiment and that is believed to affect the dependent variate. Through analysis of covariance, the dependent variate can be adjusted so as to remove the effects of the uncontrolled source of variation represented by the concomitant variate.

APPLICATIONS OF ANALYSIS OF COVARIANCE IN THE BEHAVIORAL SCIENCES

Analysis of covariance may be particularly appropriate for three research situations. One of these involves the use of *intact groups*, a situation that is common in educational and industrial research. This situation can be illustrated by an experiment designed to evaluate four methods of teaching arithmetic. It is impractical for administrative reasons to assign four different teaching methods to the same classroom. The alternative is to assign the four teaching methods randomly to four different classrooms, an alternative design with a serious defect. If differences in learning ability or similar characteristics exist between the classes prior to the introduction of the four teaching methods, these extraneous variables will bias the evaluation. In this example, it is possible to administer a test of intelligence prior to the beginning of the experiment in order to obtain an estimate of learning ability. If the classes differ in intelligence, one can, if certain assumptions are tenable, adjust the dependent variable of achievement in arithmetic to account for differences in the concomitant variable, which is learning ability.

A note of caution concerning the use of *intact groups* is needed here. Experiments of this type are always subject to interpretation difficulties that are not present when random assignment is used in forming the experimental groups. Even when analysis of covariance is skillfully used, we can never be certain that some variable that has been overlooked will not bias the evaluation of an experiment. This problem is absent in properly randomized experiments because the effects of all uncontrolled variables are distributed among the groups in such a way that they can be taken into account in the test of significance. The use of intact groups removes this safeguard.

Analysis of covariance is not limited to the use of only one concomitant variable. In the teaching example, differences in arithmetic achievement may also exist among the children prior to the beginning of the experiment. If concomitant measures of arithmetic achievement and intelligence are obtained prior to the introduction of the treatment, the dependent variate can be adjusted for both potential sources of bias.

A second situation in which analysis of covariance may be appropriate is illustrated in the following example. It may become apparent during the course of an experiment that subjects assigned to k treatment groups were not equated on some relevant variable at the beginning of the experiment although randomization or matching was employed. For example, an experiment might be designed to evaluate the effects of different drugs on stimulus generalization in rats. At the beginning of the experiment the rats are randomly assigned to k experimental groups and a bar-pressing response is shaped by operant-conditioning procedures. If the k groups require different amounts of training to establish a stable bar-pressing response, this suggests that differences in learning ability exist between the groups. An experimenter may find, at the conclusion of the experiment, that amount of stimulus generalization is related to amount of training necessary to establish the stable bar-pressing response. If certain assumptions are tenable, the generalization scores of the groups can be adjusted for differences in learning ability. Thus unsuspected differences present at the beginning of the experiment can be controlled by analysis of covariance.

Analysis of covariance may be useful in yet another research situation. In the example concerning the evaluation of four methods of teaching arithmetic, a third variable may bias the evaluation. This variable is the number of hours spent in study by students in the four classrooms. Variations in the daily schedules of the classrooms may provide more study periods for students in one class than for students in other classes. It would be difficult to control experimentally the amount of time available for arithmetic study. A practical alternative is to record each day the amount of study time available to the students. This information can then be used to make appropriate adjustments in the dependent variable. In this example, variation in the concomitant variable of study time did not occur until after the beginning of the experiment. It is assumed that amount of study time available during school is not influenced by the treatment. A teacher might allocate additional study periods for arithmetic because students were unable to master the material using the assigned teaching method. Under this condition, it would be incorrect to adjust the dependent variable for this concomitant variable.

SELECTION OF CONCOMITANT VARIABLE

Concomitant variables in analysis of covariance should be selected with care. Effects eliminated by covariate adjustment must be irrelevant to the objectives of the experiment. It should be obvious that statistical control and experimental control are not mutually exclusive approaches for increasing precision. It may be convenient to control some variables by experimental control, some by statistical control, and still others by the joint use of experimental and statistical control. The last case is illustrated by the assignment of subjects to relatively homogeneous blocks and the measurement of a concomitant variable, which is then used to adjust for any residual variation associated with differences among the blocks. Section 12.10 discusses this point more fully. In general, an experimenter should attempt to use experimental control whenever possible. Statistical control is based on a series of assumptions, described in Section 12.4, that may prove untenable in a particular experiment.

Analysis of covariance can be used in conjunction with each of the experimental designs described in this book. Covariance adjustment is appropriate for experiments that meet, in addition to the assumptions described in Section 12.4, the following conditions:

1. The experiment contains one or more extraneous sources of variation believed to affect the dependent variable and considered irrelevant to the objectives of the experiment.

2. Experimental control of the extraneous sources of variation is either not possible or not feasible.

3. It is possible to obtain a measure of the extraneous variation that does not include effects attributable to the treatment. Any one of the following situations will generally meet this third condition:

(a) The concomitant observations are obtained prior to presentation of the treatment levels, or

(b) the concomitant observations are obtained after the presentation of the treatment levels but before the treatment levels have had an opportunity to affect the concomitant variate, or

(c) it can be assumed that the concomitant variable is unaffected by the treatment.

If the third condition is not satisfied and the concomitant variable is influenced by the treatment, the adjustment made on the dependent variable is biased. Consider the drug example cited previously. If administering the drug affected both the learning of the bar-pressing response (covariate) and the generalization (dependent variable), it would not be possible to adjust the generalization scores correctly. An adjustment of generalization scores for differences in learning of the bar-pressing response would remove the effects of drugs from the dependent variable. This follows because both covariate and dependent variate reflect the effects of the treatment.

Analysis of covariance can also be used as a general procedure for estimating missing observations. The rationale underlying this application of analysis of covariance is discussed by Coons (1957).

12.2   RATIONALE UNDERLYING COVARIATE ADJUSTMENT

If dependent and concomitant variates are designated by Y and X, respectively, how can Y be adjusted so as to be free of variation due to X? The adjustment used in analysis of covariance is based on regression analysis. Although the regression of Y on X need not be linear, only the linear case is considered. The discussion is limited to one covariate; multiple covariates are discussed in Section 12.6.

CALCULATION OF ADJUSTED TOTAL SUM OF SQUARES

The regression equation for predicting Y from X is

(1) $$Y'_{ij} = b_T(X_{ij} - \overline{X}..) + \overline{Y}..,$$

where Y'_{ij} = the predicted score, b_T = the linear regression coefficient computed for the entire set of N pairs of observations, X_{ij} = the covariate for subject i in treatment level j, $\overline{X}..$ = the mean of covariates, and $\overline{Y}..$ = the mean of dependent variates. The sum of squares of residuals about this regression line is equal to

(2) $$\sum_{1}^{k}\sum_{1}^{n}(Y_{ij} - Y'_{ij})^2,$$

where $(Y_{ij} - Y'_{ij})$ is the deviation of each score from the predicted score. This sum of squares represents the variation among the dependent scores which is *not* associated with the linear regression of Y on X. This is the sum of squares that is of interest in analysis of covariance. If $[b_T(X_{ij} - \bar{X}..) + \bar{Y}..]$ is substituted for Y'_{ij} in equation (2), the residual sum of squares can be shown to equal

$$\sum_1^k\sum_1^n (Y_{ij} - Y'_{ij})^2 = \sum_1^k\sum_1^n [(Y_{ij} - \bar{Y}..) - b_T(X_{ij} - \bar{X}..)]^2$$

$$= \sum_1^k\sum_1^n (Y_{ij} - \bar{Y}..)^2 - 2b_T\sum_1^k\sum_1^n (X_{ij} - \bar{X}..)(Y_{ij} - \bar{Y}..)$$

$$+ b_T^2\sum_1^k\sum_1^n (X_{ij} - \bar{X}..)^2$$

but

$$b_T = \frac{\sum_1^k\sum_1^n (X_{ij} - \bar{X}..)(Y_{ij} - \bar{Y}..)}{\sum_1^k\sum_1^n (X_{ij} - \bar{X}..)^2}$$

and

$$b_T\sum_1^k\sum_1^n (X_{ij} - \bar{X}..)^2 = \sum_1^k\sum_1^n (X_{ij} - \bar{X}..)(Y_{ij} - \bar{Y}..).$$

Thus

$$\sum_1^k\sum_1^n (Y_{ij} - Y'_{ij})^2 = \sum_1^k\sum_1^n (Y_{ij} - \bar{Y}..)^2 - 2b_T^2\sum_1^k\sum_1^n (X_{ij} - \bar{X}..)^2$$

$$+ b_T^2\sum_1^k\sum_1^n (X_{ij} - \bar{X}..)^2$$

$$(3) \qquad\qquad = \sum_1^k\sum_1^n (Y_{ij} - \bar{Y}..)^2 - b_T^2\sum_1^k\sum_1^n (X_{ij} - \bar{X}..)^2.$$

The term $[b_T^2\Sigma_1^k\Sigma_1^n(X_{ij} - \bar{X}..)^2]$ represents an adjustment that is made to the total sum of squares for Y, $[\Sigma_1^k\Sigma_1^n(Y_{ij} - \bar{Y}..)^2]$, which removes the linear effects of the covariate. This adjustment will always reduce the sum of squares for Y if $b_T \neq 0$. Consequently, the sum of squares on the right side of equation (3) is sometimes called the *reduced* sum of squares. This sum of squares will be referred to in this chapter as an *adjusted* total sum of squares and designated by the symbol $T_{yy(adj)}$, or T_{adj} when it is clear from the context that it refers to the dependent variable. Unadjusted sums of squares for Y and X are designated by the symbols T_{yy} and T_{xx}, respectively. The use of T_{yy}, T_{xx}, etc. instead of SS to stand for a sum of squares is common practice in discussions of analysis of covariance.

It can be shown that the slope, b_T, of the regression line used in predicting Y from X is given by

$$b_T = \frac{\sum\limits_{1}^{k}\sum\limits_{1}^{n}(X_{ij} - \bar{X}..)(Y_{ij} - \bar{Y}..)}{\sum\limits_{1}^{k}\sum\limits_{1}^{n}(X_{ij} - \bar{X}..)^2} = \frac{T_{xy}}{T_{xx}}.$$

The term T_{xy} is called the sum of squares for the cross product of X and Y. It can be shown that the coefficient b_T provides the best fitting line according to a least-squares criterion for the N pairs of observations. A brief discussion of the method of least-squares is given in Section 7.9. An adjusted *total sum of squares*, using the abbreviated notation described above, can be written

(4)
$$T_{yy(\text{adj})} = T_{yy} - b_T^2 T_{xx} = T_{yy} - \frac{T_{xy}^2}{T_{xx}}.$$

The degrees of freedom for $T_{yy(\text{adj})}$ are $N - 2$. One additional degree of freedom has been lost because of the linear restriction imposed on the sum of squares whereby the deviations are computed from the regression line.

CALCULATION OF ADJUSTED
WITHIN-GROUPS SUM OF SQUARES

The total sum of squares, $\Sigma_1^k \Sigma_1^n (Y_{ij} - \bar{Y}..)^2$, in a completely randomized design can be partitioned into between- and within-groups sums of squares, as shown in Section 2.2

$$\sum\limits_{1}^{k}\sum\limits_{1}^{n}(Y_{ij} - \bar{Y}..)^2 = \sum\limits_{1}^{k}\sum\limits_{1}^{n}(Y_{ij} - \bar{Y}._j)^2 + n\sum\limits_{1}^{k}(\bar{Y}._j - \bar{Y}..)^2$$

$$T_{yy} \qquad = \qquad S_{yy} \qquad + \qquad B_{yy}.$$

The abbreviated designation for each sum of squares appears below the formulas. Similarly, the total sum of squares for X and the cross product of X and Y can be partitioned into

$$\sum\limits_{1}^{k}\sum\limits_{1}^{n}(X_{ij} - \bar{X}..)^2 = \sum\limits_{1}^{k}\sum\limits_{1}^{n}(X_{ij} - \bar{X}._j)^2 + n\sum\limits_{1}^{k}(\bar{X}._j - \bar{X}..)^2$$

$$T_{xx} \qquad = \qquad S_{xx} \qquad + \qquad B_{xx}$$

and

$$\sum\limits_{1}^{k}\sum\limits_{1}^{n}(X_{ij} - \bar{X}..)(Y_{ij} - \bar{Y}..) = \sum\limits_{1}^{k}\sum\limits_{1}^{n}(X_{ij} - \bar{X}._j)(Y_{ij} - \bar{Y}._j)$$

$$+ n\sum\limits_{1}^{k}(X._j - \bar{X}..)(\bar{Y}._j - \bar{Y}..).$$

$$T_{xy} \qquad = \qquad S_{xy} \qquad + \qquad B_{xy}.$$

An adjusted within-groups sum of squares, following the procedure for computing $T_{yy(\text{adj})}$, is given by

$$S_{yy(\text{adj})} = S_{yy} - b_W^2 S_{xx} = S_{yy} - \frac{S_{xy}^2}{S_{xx}},$$

where b_W is the *within-groups* regression coefficient. The within-groups regression coefficient can be computed by

$$b_W = \frac{\sum\limits_{1}^{k}\sum\limits_{1}^{n}(X_{ij} - \overline{X}._j)(Y_{ij} - \overline{Y}._j)}{\sum\limits_{1}^{k}\sum\limits_{1}^{n}(X_{ij} - \overline{X}._j)^2} = \frac{S_{xy}}{S_{xx}}.$$

The degrees of freedom for $S_{yy(\text{adj})}$ are $N - k - 1$.

INTERPRETATION OF b_T, b_W, AND b_B

If data consist of N paired observations for k treatment levels, a number of different regression lines can be identified. Two regression lines, with slopes b_T and b_W, have been mentioned in this section. A third regression line can also be identified—a *between-groups* regression line with slope b_B. The interpretation of these three regression lines can be clarified by a simple numerical example and diagrams. The data in Table 12.2-1 will

TABLE 12.2-1   Data from Experiment

B_{y1}	B_{x1}	B_{y2}	B_{x2}	B_{y3}	B_{x3}
1.0	1.0	2.6	4.5	4.8	3.0
1.5	2.0	2.0	2.0	4.0	2.0
2.0	4.0	2.3	3.0	5.3	4.0
1.8	3.0	2.5	4.0	6.0	5.0
Mean = 1.6	2.5	2.4	3.4	5.0	3.5

Grand mean $\overline{Y}.. = 3.0$, $\overline{X}.. = 3.1$

be used for purposes of illustration. Data for the three treatment levels have been plotted in Figure 12.2-1. If all twelve points in Figure 12.2-1 are plotted as if they represent one treatment level instead of three levels, a single regression line with slope equal to b_T can be drawn. The slope b_T of this single line is given by

$$b_T = \frac{\sum\limits_{1}^{k}\sum\limits_{1}^{n}(X_{ij} - \overline{X}..)(Y_{ij} - \overline{Y}..)}{\sum\limits_{1}^{k}\sum\limits_{1}^{n}(X_{ij} - \overline{X}..)^2} = \frac{T_{xy}}{T_{xx}} = \frac{11.72}{16.00} = .73.$$

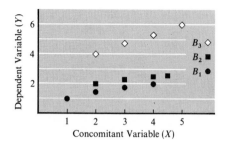

**Figure 12.2-1   Regression lines for three treat-
ment levels.**

This regression line is shown in Figure 12.2-2. For convenience the X and Y scores are expressed as deviations from their respective grand means; that is, $x = X - \overline{X}..$ and $y = Y - \overline{Y}..$.

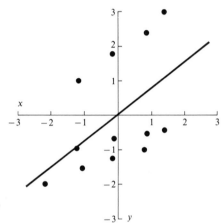

**Figure 12.2-2   Total over-all regression line
with $b_T = .73$.**

The within-group regression coefficient for each of the treatment levels shown in Figure 12.2-1 is given by

$$b_{Wj} = \frac{\sum_{1}^{n}(X_{ij} - \overline{X}._j)(Y_{ij} - \overline{Y}._j)}{\sum_{1}^{n}(X_{ij} - \overline{X}._j)^2} = \frac{S_{xyj}}{S_{xxj}}.$$

These three regression coefficients are, respectively,

$$b_{W1} = \frac{S_{xy1}}{S_{xx1}} = \frac{1.65}{5.00} = .33, \quad b_{W2} = \frac{S_{xy2}}{S_{xx2}} = \frac{.88}{3.69} = .24,$$

$$b_{W3} = \frac{S_{xy3}}{S_{xx3}} = \frac{3.25}{5.00} = .65.$$

By computing a weighted mean of these three coefficients, one obtains the within-groups regression coefficient b_W.

$$b_W = \frac{(S_{xx1})(b_{W1}) + (S_{xx2})(b_{W2}) + (S_{xx3})(b_{W3})}{S_{xx1} + S_{xx2} + S_{xx3}} = \frac{5.78}{13.69} = .42.$$

The weights in this formula are the corresponding values of S_{xxj}. The formula is less convenient for computational purposes than the formula $b_W = S_{xy}/S_{xx}$ given previously, but it helps to clarify the nature of b_W. The regression lines corresponding to b_{W1}, b_{W2}, b_{W3}, and b_W are plotted in Figure 12.2-3.

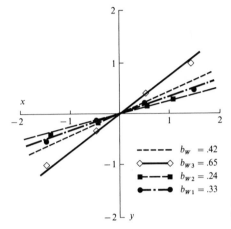

Figure 12.2-3 Regression lines corresponding to b_{w1}, b_{w2}, b_{w3}, and b_w.

One of the assumptions underlying the adjustment of the within-groups sum of squares is that the within-group regression coefficients are all estimates of the same common population regression coefficient. That is,

$$\beta'_{W1} = \beta'_{W2} = \beta'_{W3} = \beta'_W.$$

Section 12.4 describes procedures for testing this assumption.

The final regression coefficient that needs to be defined is b_B. This coefficient is given by $b_B = B_{xy}/B_{xx} = 2.51$ and refers to the line that fits the means of the three treatment levels. This regression line is shown in Figure 12.2-4, where the mean of each treatment level is expressed as a deviation from the grand mean; that is, $x_j = \overline{X}._j - \overline{X}..$ and $y_j = \overline{Y}._j - \overline{Y}..$.

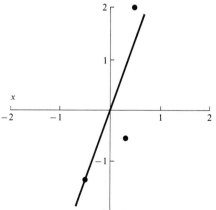

Figure 12.2-4 Regression line corresponding to b_B.

We noted that the total sum of squares for Y, X, and XY can be partitioned into between- and within-groups sums of squares. The total regression coefficient b_T is equal to the weighted mean of b_W and b_B, where the last two terms are weighted by the corresponding sum of squares for X. That is,

$$b_T = \frac{S_{xx}b_W + B_{xx}b_B}{S_{xx} + B_{xx}} = \frac{(13.69)(.42) + (2.37)(2.51)}{13.69 + 2.37} = .73.$$

CALCULATION OF ADJUSTED
BETWEEN-GROUPS SUM OF SQUARES

The adjusted between-groups sum of squares is given by

$$B_{yy(\text{adj})} = T_{yy(\text{adj})} - S_{yy(\text{adj})}.$$

The reader may wonder why $B_{yy(\text{adj})}$ is obtained by subtraction and not by

$$B_{yy(\text{adj})} = B_{yy} - b_B^2 B_{xx} = B_{yy} - \frac{B_{xy}^2}{B_{xx}}.$$

This latter formula is analogous to the formulas used to adjust $T_{yy(\text{adj})}$ and $S_{yy(\text{adj})}$. Upon reflection, it is apparent that b_B is affected by differences among the means for the dependent variable. The adjustment that is made to the dependent variable, however, must be independent of the differences to be tested. Consequently, b_B is unsatisfactory for making this adjustment. The coefficient b_W could be considered for this adjustment, for it is independent of the differences to be tested. However, b_W should not be used for adjusting both numerator and denominator of an F ratio. This is a consequence of the requirement that an F ratio must be the ratio of two *independent* chi-square variables, each divided by its respective degrees of freedom. The computation of $B_{yy(\text{adj})}$ by subtraction circumvents the above problems. The degrees of freedom for $B_{yy(\text{adj})}$ are $k - 1$, and not $k - 2$, because the between-groups regression line did not enter into the calculation of the adjusted sum of squares.

LINEAR MODEL FOR
ANALYSIS OF COVARIANCE

The linear model for a completely randomized analysis of covariance design is

(1) $$Y_{ij} = \mu + \beta_j + \beta_W'(X_{ij} - \overline{X}..) + \varepsilon_{i(j)},$$

where μ, β_j, and $\varepsilon_{i(j)}$ are the familiar terms for a completely randomized design. The terms β_W', X_{ij}, and $\overline{X}..$ refer, respectively, to the linear regression coefficient, the value of the covariate for subject i in treatment j, and the grand mean of the covariates. The difference between two observations

Y_{ij} and $Y_{ij'}$ is an estimate of

$$Y_{ij} - Y_{ij'} = [\mu + \beta_j + \beta'_W(X_{ij} - \overline{X}..) + \varepsilon_{i(j)}]$$

$$- [\mu + \beta_{j'} + \beta'_W(X_{ij'} - \overline{X}..) + \varepsilon_{i(j')}]$$

$$(2) \qquad = \beta_j - \beta_{j'} + \beta'_W(X_{ij} - X_{ij'}) + \varepsilon_{i(j)} - \varepsilon_{i(j')}.$$

It is apparent that unless the two covariates X_{ij} and $X_{ij'}$ are equal, the difference $(X_{ij} - X_{ij'})$ will affect the observed difference between Y_{ij} and $Y_{ij'}$. The terms in the linear model for analysis of covariance can be rearranged by subtracting $[\beta'_W(X_{ij} - \overline{X}..)]$ from Y_{ij}. The difference is an *adjusted score*. Thus

$$(3) \qquad Y_{ij(\text{adj})} = Y_{ij} - \beta'_W(X_{ij} - \overline{X}..) = \mu + \beta_j + \varepsilon_{i(j)}.$$

The adjusted score is free of the effects of the covariate. Furthermore, the adjusted score provides an estimate of the familiar terms of the linear model for a completely randomized design.

12.3 LAYOUT AND COMPUTATIONAL PROCEDURES FOR TYPE CRAC-*k* DESIGN

Assume that the experiment described in Section 12.1 for evaluating four methods of teaching arithmetic has been carried out. The teaching methods were randomly assigned to four classrooms containing eight students each. An intelligence test was administered to each student at the beginning of the experiment. These data are used to adjust arithmetic achievement scores obtained at the conclusion of the experiment for differences in intelligence among the students.

The research hypothesis can be evaluated by means of a statistical test of the following null hypothesis:

$$H_0 : \beta_j = 0 \qquad \text{for all } j$$

$$H_1 : \beta_j \neq 0 \qquad \text{for some } j.$$

The level of significance adopted for the test is .05.

The layout of the design, computational tables, and formulas are shown in Table 12.3-1. The analysis is summarized in Table 12.3-2. The sums of squares in Table 12.3-2 were adjusted for differences among the students. It is obvious that the null hypothesis cannot be rejected. The reader may wonder what conclusion would have been drawn if the arithmetic achievement scores had not been adjusted for the nuisance variable of intelligence. The required sums of squares for this test appear in Table 12.3-1. The F ratio is

TABLE 12.3-1   Layout of Type CRAC-4 Design and Computational Procedures

(i) Data:

BS Summary Table

B_{y1}	B_{x1}	B_{y2}	B_{x2}	B_{y3}	B_{x3}	B_{y4}	B_{x4}
3	42	4	47	7	61	7	65
6	57	5	49	8	65	8	74
3	33	4	42	7	64	9	80
3	47	3	41	6	56	8	73
1	32	2	38	5	52	10	85
2	35	3	43	6	58	10	82
2	33	4	48	5	53	9	78
2	39	3	45	6	54	11	89
$\sum_{1}^{n}B = 22$	318	28	353	50	463	72	626

(ii) Computational symbols:

$$\sum_{1}^{N}BS_y = 3 + 6 + 3 + \cdots + 11 = 172.00$$

$$\sum_{1}^{N}BS_y^2 = [BS_y] = (3)^2 + (6)^2 + (3)^2 + \cdots + (11)^2 = 1160.00$$

$$\frac{\left(\sum_{1}^{N}BS_y\right)^2}{N} = [Y] = \frac{(172)^2}{32} = 924.50$$

$$\sum_{1}^{k}\frac{\left(\sum_{1}^{n}B_y\right)^2}{n} = [B_y] = \frac{(22)^2}{8} + \frac{(28)^2}{8} + \cdots + \frac{(72)^2}{8} = 1119.00$$

$$\sum_{1}^{N}BS_x = 42 + 57 + 33 + \cdots + 89 = 1760.00$$

$$\sum_{1}^{N}BS_x^2 = [BS_x] = (42)^2 + (57)^2 + (33)^2 + \cdots + (89)^2 = 105202.00$$

$$\frac{\left(\sum_{1}^{N}BS_x\right)^2}{N} = [X] = \frac{(1760)^2}{32} = 96800.00$$

$$\sum_{1}^{k}\frac{\left(\sum_{1}^{n}B_x\right)^2}{n} = [B_x] = \frac{(318)^2}{8} + \frac{(353)^2}{8} + \cdots + \frac{(626)^2}{8} = 103997.25$$

$$\sum_{1}^{N}BS_yBS_x = [BS_{xy}] = (3)(42) + (6)(57) + (3)(33) + \cdots + (11)(89) = 10840.00$$

$$\frac{\left(\sum_{1}^{N}BS_y\right)\left(\sum_{1}^{N}BS_x\right)}{N} = [XY] = \frac{(172)(1760)}{32} = 9460.00$$

$$\sum_{1}^{k}\frac{\left(\sum_{1}^{n}B_y\right)\left(\sum_{1}^{n}B_x\right)}{n} = [B_{xy}] = \frac{(22)(318)}{8} + \cdots + \frac{(72)(626)}{8} = 10637.75$$

TABLE 12.3-1 (continued)

(iii) Computational formulas:

$$T_{yy} = [BS_y] - [Y] = 235.500 \qquad B_{xy} = [B_{xy}] - [XY] = 1177.750$$

$$B_{yy} = [B_y] - [Y] = 194.500 \qquad S_{xy} = [BS_{xy}] - [B_{xy}] = 202.250$$

$$S_{yy} = [BS_y] - [B_y] = 41.000 \qquad T_{\text{adj}} = T_{yy} - \frac{(T_{xy})^2}{T_{xx}} = 8.840$$

$$T_{xx} = [BS_x] - [X] = 8402.000$$

$$B_{xx} = [B_x] - [X] = 7197.250 \qquad S_{\text{adj}} = S_{yy} - \frac{(S_{xy})^2}{S_{xx}} = 7.047$$

$$S_{xx} = [BS_x] - [B_x] = 1204.750 \qquad B_{\text{adj}} = T_{\text{adj}} - S_{\text{adj}} = 1.793$$

$$T_{xy} = [BS_{xy}] - [XY] = 1380.000$$

**TABLE 12.3-2   Analysis of Covariance Table
for Type CRAC-4 Design**

Source	SS	df	MS	F	E(MS) *Model I*
1 Between groups, B_{adj}	1.793	$k - 1 = 3$	.598	$[\frac{1}{2}] = 2.29$ N.S.	$\sigma_\varepsilon^2 + n\sigma_\beta^2$
2 Within groups, S_{adj}	7.047	$N - k - 1 = 27$	.261		σ_ε^2
3 Total$_{\text{adj}}$	8.840	$N - 2 = 30$			

$$F = \frac{B_{yy}/(k - 1)}{S_{yy}/(N - k)} = \frac{194.5/3}{41.0/28} = 44.28.$$

$$F_{.05;3,28} = 2.95.$$

This F ratio is significant beyond the .05 level. Thus if the covariate adjustment had not been used, the experimenter would have drawn an erroneous conclusion with respect to the four teaching methods. We infer from the F ratio for adjusted mean squares that there are no differences in arithmetic achievement apart from differences in intelligence among the classes. A test of the hypothesis that the intelligence test scores of students in the four classes are equal is given by

$$F = \frac{B_{xx}/(k - 1)}{S_{xx}/(N - k)} = \frac{7197.250/3}{1204.75/28} = \frac{2399.08}{43.03} = 55.75$$

$$F_{.05;3,28} = 2.95.$$

The null hypothesis with respect to intelligence scores can be rejected beyond the .05 level.

CORRELATION COEFFICIENTS FOR BETWEEN, WITHIN, AND TOTAL SUM OF SQUARES

Three correlation coefficients can be computed for the paired observations in Table 12.3-1:

$$r_T = \frac{T_{xy}}{\sqrt{T_{xx}T_{yy}}} = \frac{1380.00}{\sqrt{(8402.00)(235.50)}} = .98$$

$$r_B = \frac{B_{xy}}{\sqrt{B_{xx}B_{yy}}} = \frac{1177.75}{\sqrt{(7197.25)(194.50)}} = .99$$

$$r_W = \frac{S_{xy}}{\sqrt{S_{xx}S_{yy}}} = \frac{202.25}{\sqrt{(1204.75)(41.00)}} = .91,$$

where r_T refers to the over-all correlation between X and Y, r_B refers to the correlation between the treatment level means for X and Y, and r_W is the weighted average correlation between X and Y for the three treatment levels.

If r_B is larger than r_W, the reduction in the variation attributable to the treatment can be large relative to the reduction in the error variation. Under this condition, the F ratio in analysis of covariance will be smaller than the corresponding F ratio in analysis of variance. The data summarized in Table 12.3-2 illustrate this situation. In general, if r_B is negative and r_W is positive, the F ratio in analysis of covariance will be larger than the corresponding F ratio in analysis of variance.

The reduction in the error term $MS_{S(adj)}$ that occurs from the use of analysis of covariance is determined by the size of r_W. The larger this correlation, the greater the reduction in the error term. An alternative method of computing an adjusted mean square for experimental error illustrates this fact. If σ_ε^2 is the experimental error when no covariance adjustment is used, this term reduces approximately to

$$\sigma_\varepsilon^2(1 - \rho_W^2)\left(1 + \frac{1}{f_e - 2}\right)$$

by the use of analysis of covariance. Here ρ_W^2 is the population within-groups correlation coefficient, and f_e is the degrees of freedom for estimation of σ_ε^2 (Cochran, 1957). For the data in Table 12.3-1, the above formula is

$$1.464[1 - (.91)^2]\left(1 + \frac{1}{28 - 2}\right) = 1.464(.1719)(1.0385) = .261,$$

which is equal to $MS_{S(adj)}$. It is apparent from the above formula that the reduction in the error term due to the covariance adjustment is primarily a function of the size of r_W.

12.4   ASSUMPTIONS OF THE MODEL
FOR TYPE CRAC-*k* DESIGN

Let Y_{ij} be a measure for a randomly selected subject in treatment population j. Under the fixed effects linear model, it is assumed that

$$Y_{ij(\text{adj})} = Y_{ij} - \beta'_W(X_{ij} - \overline{X}..) = \mu + \beta_j + \varepsilon_{i(j)},$$

where $Y_{ij(\text{adj})}$ = adjusted criterion measure.

Y_{ij} = unadjusted criterion measure.

β'_W = common population linear regression coefficient for treatment levels.

X_{ij} = covariate measure for subject i in treatment population j.

$\overline{X}..$ = covariate sample mean.

μ = grand mean of criterion treatment populations.

β_j = effect of treatment j, which is a constant for all subjects in treatment population j.

$\varepsilon_{i(j)}$ = experimental error, which is NID with mean = 0 and variance = σ_ε^2.

In order for the F ratio in Table 12.3-2 to be distributed as the F distribution, the assumptions of a completely randomized design described in Section 4.4 must be met. In addition to these assumptions, the following assumptions must also be tenable: (1) population within-group regression coefficients are homogeneous; that is $\beta'_1 \doteq \beta'_2 = \cdots = \beta'_k = \beta'_W$ for the k treatment levels, and (2) the residuals (deviations from regression) are NID with mean = 0 and common variance. This implies that the proper form of regression equation has been used. In the present example, it is assumed that the regression is linear. Of course, analysis of covariance is not appropriate unless the effects eliminated by covariate adjustment are irrelevant to the objectives of the experiment.

In general, tests of significance in the analysis of covariance are robust with respect to violation of the assumptions of normality and homogeneity of the residual variance. Little is known concerning the effect of violation of the assumption of homogeneity of within-group regression coefficients. A test of the hypothesis that

$$\beta'_1 = \beta'_2 = \cdots = \beta'_k$$

is given by

$$F = \frac{S_2/(k - 1)}{S_1/k(n - 2)},$$

which is distributed as the F distribution, with $k - 1$ and $k(n - 2)$ degrees of freedom. A numerically large level of significance ($\alpha = .10$ or $.25$) should be used for this test in order to avoid a type II error—that is, accepting the hypothesis of homogeneity of regression coefficients when, in fact, the hypothesis is false. The statistics S_1 and S_2 are computed as follows:

$$S_1 = S_{yy} - \sum_1^k \frac{(S_{xyj})^2}{S_{xxj}},$$

where

$$S_{xyj} = [BS_{xyj}] - [B_{xyj}] \quad \text{and} \quad S_{xxj} = [BS_{xj}] - [B_{xj}]$$

and

$$S_2 = \sum_1^k \frac{(S_{xyj})^2}{S_{xxj}} - \frac{(S_{xy})^2}{S_{xx}}.$$

Table 12.3-1 gives the data for the computation of S_1 and S_2.

$$S_1 = 41 - \left[\frac{(79.50)^2}{529.50} + \frac{(20.50)^2}{100.88} + \frac{(34.25)^2}{174.88} + \frac{(68.00)^2}{399.50} \right]$$

$$= 41 - 34.38 = 6.62$$

$$S_2 = 34.38 - 33.95 = .43.$$

The F ratio is equal to

$$F = \frac{.43/3}{6.62/24} = .52,$$

which is less than the tabled value, $F_{.10;3,24} = 2.33$. Thus the assumption of homogeneity of regression coefficients is tenable. The rationale underlying this test has been discussed by Kendall (1948a, 237–242). It can be shown that S_1 plus S_2 comprise the adjusted sum of squares for experimental error,

$$S_{adj} = 6.62 + .43 = 7.05.$$

S_1 corresponds to the variation of the individual observations around the unpooled within-group regression lines. S_2 is the variation of the k within-group regression coefficients around the pooled within-groups regression coefficient; that is, $\Sigma(b_{wj} - b_w)^2$. The larger this latter source of variation relative to S_1, the less tenable the assumption of homogeneity of the within-group regression coefficients.

The adjusted treatment sum of squares, like the adjusted error sum of squares, can be partitioned into two components. Tests associated with these components are described by Kendall (1948a, 237–242). A test of the hypothesis that the regression for the k treatment means is linear, assuming that the slopes within the groups are the same, is given by

$$F = \frac{S_3/(k-2)}{(S_1 + S_2)/(N - k - 1)}$$

with degrees of freedom equal to $k - 2$ and $N - k - 1$. S_3 is computed by

$$S_3 = B_{yy} - \frac{B_{xy}^2}{B_{xx}}.$$

An approximate test of the hypothesis that the over-all regression line is linear is given by

$$F = \frac{(S_2 + S_3 + S_4)/2(k - 1)}{S_1/k(n - 2)}$$

with degrees of freedom equal to $2(k - 1)$ and $k(n - 2)$. The terms S_2 and S_3 have already been defined; S_4 is given by

$$S_4 = \frac{B_{xy}^2}{B_{xx}} + \frac{S_{xy}^2}{S_{xx}} - \frac{T_{xy}^2}{T_{xx}}.$$

If the relationship between X and Y is not linear, it may be possible to transform the variates so that the resulting relationship is linear. Transformations are discussed in Section 2.7.

12.5   PROCEDURES FOR TESTING DIFFERENCES AMONG MEANS IN TYPE CRAC-k DESIGN

Before comparisons among means can be made, the means must be adjusted for the concomitant variable. An adjusted mean for treatment level j is given by

$$\bar{B}_{y(\text{adj } j)} = \bar{B}_{yj} - b_W(\bar{B}_{xj} - \overline{BS}_x),$$

where $b_W = S_{xy}/S_{xx}$ and $\overline{BS}_x$ = mean of all X observations. Although the treatment mean square in Table 12.3-2 is not significant, these data will be used to illustrate the computation of adjusted means. Adjusted means for levels b_1 and b_2 are given by

$$\bar{B}_{y(\text{adj } 1)} = \frac{22}{8} - \frac{202.25}{1204.75}\left(\frac{318}{8} - \frac{1760}{32}\right) = 5.312$$

$$\bar{B}_{y(\text{adj } 2)} = \frac{28}{8} - \frac{202.25}{1204.75}\left(\frac{353}{8} - \frac{1760}{32}\right) = 5.237.$$

The values required for the computation are contained in Table 12.3-1.

A PRIORI COMPARISONS

Comparisons among means that fall in the *a priori* category are given by

$$t = \frac{C_j(\bar{B}_{y(\text{adj } j)}) + C_{j'}(\bar{B}_{y(\text{adj } j')})}{\sqrt{\text{MS}_{S(\text{adj})}\left[2/n + (\bar{B}_{xj} - \bar{B}_{xj'})^2/S_{xx}\right]}}.$$

The degrees of freedom for this test and for Tukey's test, which is illustrated in the following paragraph, are equal to $N - k - 1$. The computation will be illustrated for the comparison of $\bar{B}_{y(\text{adj } 1)}$ with $\bar{B}_{y(\text{adj } 2)}$.

$$t = \frac{1(5.312) - 1(5.327)}{\sqrt{.261\left[2/8 + (39.750 - 44.125)^2/1204.75\right]}} = \frac{-.015}{\sqrt{.069}} = -.06$$

A POSTERIORI COMPARISONS

Comparisons among means, using Tukey's test, are given by

$$q = \frac{C_j(\bar{B}_{y(\text{adj } j)}) + C_{j'}(\bar{B}_{y(\text{adj } j')})}{\sqrt{\text{MS}_{\text{error}}/n}},$$

where

$$\text{MS}_{\text{error}} = \text{MS}_{S(\text{adj})}\left(1 + \frac{B_{xx}/(k-1)}{S_{xx}}\right).$$

MS_{error} represents the average effective error per unit (Finney, 1946b). If Scheffé's test is used, the formula is

$$F = \frac{\left[C_j(\bar{B}_{y(\text{adj } j)}) + C_{j'}(\bar{B}_{y(\text{adj } j')}) + \cdots + C_{j''}(\bar{B}_{y(\text{adj } j'')})\right]^2}{\text{MS}_{\text{error}}\left[\dfrac{(C_j)^2}{n_j} + \dfrac{(C_{j'})^2}{n_{j'}} + \cdots + \dfrac{(C_{j''})^2}{n_{j''}}\right]}.$$

The value of F that is significant is equal to $(k - 1)F_{\alpha;k,N-k-1}$.

12.6   ANALYSIS OF MULTIPLE COVARIANCE

The procedures described for one covariate can be extended to experiments containing two or more covariates. That is, if two covariates designated as X and Z are available, it is possible to adjust the dependent variate, Y, so as to remove the extraneous variation associated with X and Z. An example illustrating the use of two covariates is presented in this section. The computation for the two-covariate case is relatively simple. If more than two covariates are used, the computation is laborious but does not involve any new principles.

The model presented in Section 12.4 for a type CRAC-k design is

$$Y_{ij(\text{adj})} = Y_{ij} - \beta'_W(X_{ij} - \bar{X}..) = \mu + \beta_j + \varepsilon_{i(j)}.$$

This model can be generalized to two covariates as follows:

$$Y_{ij(\text{adj})} = Y_{ij} - \beta'_{W yx}(X_{ij} - \overline{X}..) - \beta'_{W yz}(Z_{ij} - \overline{Z}..) = \mu + \beta_j + \varepsilon_{i(j)}.$$

If the two covariates selected for measurement in the experiment represent good choices, the inclusion of a third covariate generally will not add appreciably to the precision of the experiment. The analogous situation occurs in multiple correlation in which the inclusion of additional predictors reaches a point of diminishing returns; that is, there is some point beyond which the addition of predictors to, say, a test battery, does not appreciably improve prediction.

Assume that in the experiment analyzed in Section 12.3, two covariates are measured prior to the beginning of the experiment—intelligence and arithmetic achievement. These covariates are designated by the letters X and Z, respectively. The layout of the design, computational tables, and formulas are shown in Table 12.6-1. The data in Table 12.6-1 for Y and X are identical to the data in Table 12.3-1. All the computational symbols in this latter table are required in the analysis. To simplify the presentation,

TABLE 12.6-1   Layout of Type CRAC-4 Design with Two Covariates

(i) Data:

BS Summary Table

B_{y1}	B_{x1}	B_{z1}	B_{y2}	B_{x2}	B_{z2}	B_{y3}	B_{x3}	B_{z3}	B_{y4}	B_{x4}	B_{z4}
3	42	3	4	47	4	7	61	5	7	65	2
6	57	5	5	49	6	8	65	7	8	74	4
3	33	4	4	42	5	7	64	5	9	80	5
3	47	4	3	41	2	6	56	4	8	73	5
1	32	0	2	38	1	5	52	2	10	85	6
2	35	1	3	43	2	6	58	3	10	82	6
2	33	0	4	48	5	5	53	3	9	78	5
2	39	2	3	45	3	6	54	4	11	89	7
$\sum_1^n B = 22$	318	19	28	353	28	50	463	33	72	626	40

(ii) Computational symbols:*

$$\sum_1^N BS_z = 3 + 5 + 4 + \cdots + 7 = 120.000$$

$$\sum_1^N BS_z^2 = [BS_z] = (3)^2 + (5)^2 + (4)^2 + \cdots + (7)^2 = 560.000$$

$$\frac{\left(\sum_1^N BS_z\right)^2}{N} = [Z] = \frac{(120)^2}{32} = 450.000$$

$$\sum_1^k \frac{\left(\sum_1^n B_z\right)^2}{N} = [B_z] = \frac{(19)^2}{8} + \frac{(28)^2}{8} + \cdots + \frac{(40)^2}{8} = 479.250$$

TABLE 12.6-1 (continued)

$$\sum_{1}^{N} BS_y BS_z = [BS_{yz}] = (3)(3) + (6)(5) + \cdots + (11)(7) = 768.000$$

$$\frac{\left(\sum_{1}^{N} BS_y\right)\left(\sum_{1}^{N} BS_z\right)}{N} = [YZ] = \frac{(172)(120)}{32} = 645.000$$

$$\sum_{1}^{k} \frac{\left(\sum_{1}^{n} B_y\right)\sum_{1}^{n} B_z}{n} = [B_{yz}] = \frac{(22)(19)}{8} + \cdots + \frac{(72)(40)}{8} = 716.500$$

$$\sum_{1}^{N} BS_x BS_z = [BS_{xz}] = (42)(3) + (57)(5) + \cdots + (89)(7) = 7280.000$$

$$\frac{\left(\sum_{1}^{N} BS_x\right)\left(\sum_{1}^{N} BS_z\right)}{N} = [XZ] = \frac{(1760)(120)}{32} = 6600.000$$

$$\sum_{1}^{k} \frac{\left(\sum_{1}^{n} B_x\right)\left(\sum_{1}^{n} B_z\right)}{n} = [B_{xz}] = \frac{(318)(19)}{8} + \cdots + \frac{(626)(40)}{8} = 7030.625$$

*Only symbols associated with Z are defined in this table. See Table 12.3-1 for other required symbols.

(iii) Computational formulas:

$$T_{yy} = [BS_y] - [Y] = 235.500 \qquad\qquad S_{yy} = [BS_y] - [B_y] = 41.000$$

$$T_{xx} = [BS_x] - [X] = 8402.000 \qquad\qquad S_{xx} = [BS_x] - [B_x] = 1204.750$$

$$T_{zz} = [BS_z] - [Z] = 110.000 \qquad\qquad S_{zz} = [BS_z] - [B_z] = 80.750$$

$$T_{xy} = [BS_{xy}] - [XY] = 1380.000 \qquad\qquad S_{xy} = [BS_{xy}] - [B_{xy}] = 202.250$$

$$T_{yz} = [BS_{yz}] - [YZ] = 123.000 \qquad\qquad S_{yz} = [BS_{yz}] - [B_{yz}] = 51.500$$

$$T_{xz} = [BS_{xz}] - [XZ] = 680.000 \qquad\qquad S_{xz} = [BS_{xz}] - [B_{xz}] = 249.375$$

$$b_{Tyx} = \frac{T_{zz}T_{xy} - T_{xz}T_{yz}}{T_{xx}T_{zz} - T_{xz}^2} = .148 \qquad\qquad b_{Wyx} = \frac{S_{zz}S_{xy} - S_{xz}S_{yz}}{S_{xx}S_{zz} - S_{xz}^2} = .099$$

$$b_{Tyz} = \frac{T_{xx}T_{yz} - T_{xz}T_{xy}}{T_{xx}T_{zz} - T_{xz}^2} = .206 \qquad\qquad b_{Wyz} = \frac{S_{xx}S_{yz} - S_{xz}S_{xy}}{S_{xx}S_{zz} - S_{xz}^2} = .331$$

$$T_{adj} = T_{yy} - b_{Tyx}T_{xy} - b_{Tyz}T_{yz} = 5.922 \qquad\qquad S_{adj} = S_{yy} - b_{Wyx}S_{xy} - b_{Wyz}S_{yz} = 3.931$$

$$B_{adj} = T_{adj} - S_{adj} = 1.991$$

only the new symbols required for the analysis appear in Table 12.6-1. The analysis of the experiment is summarized in Table 12.6-2. The inclusion of a second covariate in the experiment has reduced the experimental error and provided a better estimate of treatment effects relative to the use of only one covariate. As a result, the null hypothesis can be rejected. When both intelligence and initial arithmetic achievement are taken into account, the four teaching methods produce different results with respect to the dependent variable.

    The assumptions for this analysis are the same as the assumptions described in Section 12.4 for the case of one covariate.

TABLE 12.6-2   Analysis of Covariance Table for
Type CRAC-4 Design with Two Covariates

	Source	SS	df	MS	F
1	Between treatments, B_{adj}	1.991	$k - 1 = 3$	.664	$[\frac{1}{2}] = 4.40^*$
2	Within treatments, S_{adj}	3.931	$N - k - 2 = 26$	.151	
3	Total$_{adj}$	5.922	$N - 3 = 29$		

  *$p < .05$.

COMPARISONS AMONG MEANS

Comparisons among means are carried out with adjusted means. An adjusted mean for treatment j is given by

$$\bar{B}_{y(adj\ j)} = \bar{B}_{yj} - b_{Wyx}(\bar{X}_{\cdot j} - \bar{X}_{\cdot\cdot}) - b_{Wyz}(\bar{Z}_{\cdot j} - \bar{Z}_{\cdot\cdot}).$$

A priori comparisons among means use the formula

$$t = \frac{C_j(\bar{B}_{y(adj\ j)}) + C_{j'}(\bar{B}_{y(adj\ j')})}{\sqrt{MS_{S(adj)}\left[\dfrac{2}{n} + \dfrac{S_{zz}(\bar{X}_{\cdot j} - \bar{X}_{\cdot j'})^2 - 2S_{xz}(\bar{X}_{\cdot j} - \bar{X}_{\cdot j'})(\bar{Z}_{\cdot j} - \bar{Z}_{\cdot j'}) + S_{xx}(\bar{Z}_{\cdot j} - \bar{Z}_{\cdot j'})^2}{S_{xx}S_{zz} - S_{xz}^2}\right]}}.$$

Comparisons among means by Tukey's and Scheffé's tests are, respectively,

$$q = \frac{C_j(\bar{B}_{y(adj\ j)}) + C_{j'}(\bar{B}_{y(adj\ j')})}{\sqrt{MS_{error}/n}}$$

and

$$F = \frac{[C_j(\bar{B}_{y(adj\ j)}) + C_{j'}(\bar{B}_{y(adj\ j')}) + \cdots + C_{j''}(\bar{B}_{y(adj\ j'')})]^2}{MS_{error}\left[\dfrac{(C_j)^2}{n_j} + \dfrac{(C_{j'})^2}{n_{j'}} + \cdots + \dfrac{(C_{j''})^2}{n_{j''}}\right]},$$

where

$$MS_{error} = MS_{S(adj)}\left[1 + \frac{B_{xx}S_{zz} - 2B_{xz}S_{xz} + B_{zz}S_{xx}}{(k - 1)(S_{xx}S_{zz} - S_{xz}^2)}\right].$$

12.7   ANALYSIS OF COVARIANCE FOR RANDOMIZED BLOCK DESIGN

The computational procedures described for a type CRAC-k design can easily be extended to other experimental designs, such as the type RBAC-k design described here. The linear model for this design is

TABLE 12.7-1 Computational Procedures for Type RBAC-k Design

Source	Sum of Squares yy	xy	xx	df	Adjusted Sum of Squares	F
1 Treatment(B)	B_{yy}	B_{xy}	B_{xx}	$k-1$	$B_{adj} = (B_{yy} + E_{yy}) - \dfrac{(B_{xy} + E_{xy})^2}{B_{xx} + E_{xx}} - E_{adj}$	[1/3]
2 Blocks(S)	S_{yy}	S_{xy}	S_{xx}	$n-1$		
3 Residual(E)	E_{yy}	E_{xy}	E_{xx}	$(k-1)(n-1)-1$	$E_{adj} = E_{yy} - \dfrac{(E_{xy})^2}{E_{xx}}$	
4 Total	tot_{yy}	tot_{xy}	tot_{xx}	$N-2$		

$$Y_{ij(\text{adj})} = Y_{ij} - \beta'_W(X_{ij} - \overline{X}..) = \mu + \beta_j + \pi_i + \varepsilon_{ij}.$$

The main features of the analysis for a type RBAC-k design are presented in Table 12.7-1. The formulas for the unadjusted sums of squares are those for a randomized block design but follow the pattern shown in Table 12.3-1 for a completely randomized design. For example,

$$b_W = \frac{E_{xy}}{E_{xx}}, \quad B_{yy} = [B_y] - [Y], \quad S_{yy} = [S_y] - [Y],$$

$$E_{yy} = [BS_y] - [B_y] - [S_y] + [Y],$$

where

$$[B_y] = \sum_1^k \frac{\left(\sum_1^n B_y\right)^2}{n}, \quad [S_y] = \sum_1^n \frac{\left(\sum_1^k S_y\right)^2}{k}, \quad [Y] = \frac{\left(\sum_1^N BS_y\right)^2}{N},$$

$$[BS_y] = \sum_1^N (BS_y)^2.$$

The procedures shown in Table 12.7-1 are analogous to the adjustment procedures for a completely randomized design. This is more apparent if the adjustment procedure for a type CRAC-k design is presented in the following way:

$$B_{\text{adj}} = T_{\text{adj}} - S_{\text{adj}} = \left[T_{yy} - \frac{(T_{xy})^2}{T_{xx}}\right] - S_{\text{adj}} = (B_{yy} + S_{yy})$$

$$- \frac{(B_{xy} + S_{xy})^2}{B_{xx} + S_{xx}} - S_{\text{adj}}.$$

This follows because $T_{yy} = B_{yy} + S_{yy}$, $T_{xy} = B_{xy} + S_{xy}$, and $T_{xx} = B_{xx} + S_{xx}$, where B and S designate treatment and error sums of squares, respectively. The adjustment formula must be modified for a randomized block analysis of covariance, for in this design T_{yy} includes row sum of squares in addition to treatment and error sums of squares. We shall see in subsequent sections that whenever the total sum of squares contains variation other than treatment and error sums of squares, a subtotal consisting of only these latter sources of variation must be used in the analysis of covariance.

The assumptions associated with tests of significance are those for a randomized block design (Section 5.3) and the analysis of covariance (Section 12.4). Procedures for making comparisons among adjusted treatment means are, with one exception, identical to those described in Section 12.5 for a type CRAC-k design. The proper error term $MS_{E(\text{adj})}$ must be substituted for $MS_{S(\text{adj})}$.

Computational procedures for the case in which an observation for Y or X is missing are described by Bartlett (1936) and Federer (1955, 513–517).

TABLE 12.8-1 Computational Procedures for Type LSAC-k Design

Source	Sum of Squares yy	xy	xx	df	Adjusted Sum of Squares	F
1 Rows(A)	A_{yy}	A_{xy}	A_{xx}	$p - 1$		
2 Columns(B)	B_{yy}	B_{xy}	B_{xx}	$p - 1$		
3 Treatment(C)	C_{yy}	C_{xy}	C_{xx}	$p - 1$	$C_{\text{adj}} = (C_{yy} + E_{yy}) - \dfrac{(C_{xy} + E_{xy})^2}{C_{xx} + E_{xx}} - E_{\text{adj}}$	$\left[\frac{3}{4}\right]$
4 Residual(E)	E_{yy}	E_{xy}	E_{xx}	$(p - 1)(p - 2) - 1$	$E_{\text{adj}} = E_{yy} - \dfrac{(E_{xy})^2}{E_{xx}}$	
5 Total	tot_{yy}	tot_{xy}	tot_{xx}	$p^2 - 2$		

12.8 ANALYSIS OF COVARIANCE FOR LATIN SQUARE DESIGN

Computational procedures for a type LSAC-k design are shown in Table 12.8-1. The linear model for this design is

$$Y_{ijk(\text{adj})} = Y_{ijk} - \beta'_W(X_{ijk} - \overline{X}...) = \mu + \alpha_i + \beta_j + \gamma_k + \varepsilon_{ijk}.$$

The assumptions associated with this analysis are those for a Latin square design described in Section 6.4 and the analysis of covariance described in Section 12.4. Comparisons among adjusted means can be made following the procedures presented in Section 12.5 for a type CRAC-k design.

Chapter 6 describes a Latin square design that contains more than one observation per cell. The proper error term for testing treatment effects in this design is $MS_{w.cell}$ rather than MS_{res}. If more than one observation per cell is obtained in a type LSAC-k design, three terms are required in addition to those shown in Table 12.8-1. These are the within-cell sums of squares associated with Y, XY, and X. These sums of squares are used in computing an adjusted within-cell error term and in adjusting the treatment sum of squares.

Numerical examples illustrating the computation for a type LSAC-k design are given by Federer (1955, 489–495) and Snedecor (1956, 411–412).

12.9 ANALYSIS OF COVARIANCE FOR FACTORIAL EXPERIMENTS

The analysis of covariance for a factorial experiment is a straight-forward generalization of the procedures discussed in connection with a completely randomized analysis of covariance design. General analysis procedures for type CRFAC-pq and SPFAC-$p.q$ designs are presented in this section.

ANALYSIS OF COVARIANCE FOR TYPE CRFAC-pq DESIGN

Computational procedures for a type CRFAC-pq design appear in Table 12.9-1. The model for this design is

$$Y_{ijm(\text{adj})} = Y_{ijm} - \beta'_W(X_{ijm} - \overline{X}...) = \mu + \alpha_i + \beta_j + \alpha\beta_{ij} + \varepsilon_{m(ij)}.$$

It is apparent from this model that an adjusted observation estimates the parameters of a conventional analysis of variance. In order for the F ratios in Table 12.9-1 to be distributed as the F distribution, the assumptions of a type CRF-pq design described in Section 7.5 must be met. In

TABLE 12.9-1   Computational Procedures for Type CRFAC-*pq* Design

Source	Sum of Squares yy	xy	xx	df	Adjusted Sum of Squares	F (Model I)
1 A	A_{yy}	A_{xy}	A_{xx}	$p - 1$	$A_{\text{adj}} = (A_{yy} + E_{yy}) - \dfrac{(A_{xy} + E_{xy})^2}{A_{xx} + E_{xx}} - E_{\text{adj}}$	$\left[\frac{1}{4}\right]$
2 B	B_{yy}	B_{xy}	B_{xx}	$q - 1$	$B_{\text{adj}} = (B_{yy} + E_{yy}) - \dfrac{(B_{xy} + E_{xy})^2}{B_{xx} + E_{xx}} - E_{\text{adj}}$	$\left[\frac{2}{4}\right]$
3 AB	AB_{yy}	AB_{xy}	AB_{xx}	$(p - 1)(q - 1)$	$AB_{\text{adj}} = (AB_{yy} + E_{yy}) - \dfrac{(AB_{xy} + E_{xy})^2}{AB_{xx} + E_{xx}} - E_{\text{adj}}$	$\left[\frac{3}{4}\right]$
4 W.cell(E)	E_{yy}	E_{xy}	E_{xx}	$pq(n - 1) - 1$	$E_{\text{adj}} = E_{yy} - \dfrac{(E_{xy})^2}{E_{xx}}$	
5 Total	tot_{yy}	tot_{xy}	tot_{xx}	$npq - 2$		

addition, the following assumptions must also be tenable: (1) the ij population within-cell regression coefficients are homogeneous and (2) the residuals (deviations from regression) are NID with mean $= 0$ and common variance. A test of the hypothesis that

$$H_0: \beta'_{w\,ij} = \beta'_w \qquad \text{for all } ij$$

is given by

$$F = \frac{S_2/(pq - 1)}{S_1/pq(n - 2)},$$

where

$$S_1 = E_{yy} - \sum_{1}^{p}\sum_{1}^{q} \frac{(E_{xyij})^2}{E_{xxij}}$$

$$S_2 = \sum_{1}^{p}\sum_{1}^{q} \frac{(E_{xyij})^2}{E_{xxij}} - \frac{(E_{xy})^2}{E_{xx}}.$$

This F ratio is distributed as the F distribution with $pq - 1$ and $pq(n - 2)$ degrees of freedom. A numerically large level of significance should be used ($\alpha = .10$ or $.25$) in order to avoid a type II error.

A priori comparisons among means for main effects have the form

$$t = \frac{C_j(\bar{A}_{y(\text{adj } i)}) + C_{j'}(\bar{A}_{y(\text{adj } i')})}{\sqrt{\text{MS}_{\text{w.cell(adj)}}\left[\dfrac{2}{nq} + \dfrac{(\bar{A}_{xi} - \bar{A}_{xi'})^2}{E_{xx}}\right]}}$$

and

$$t = \frac{C_j(\bar{B}_{y(\text{adj } j)}) + C_{j'}(\bar{B}_{y(\text{adj } j')})}{\sqrt{\text{MS}_{\text{w.cell(adj)}}\left[\dfrac{2}{np} + \dfrac{(\bar{B}_{xj} - \bar{B}_{xj'})^2}{E_{xx}}\right]}}.$$

Comparisons among means for simple main effects have the form

$$t = \frac{C_j(\overline{AB}_{y(\text{adj } ij)}) + C_{j'}(\overline{AB}_{y(\text{adj } ij')})}{\sqrt{\text{MS}_{\text{w.cell(adj)}}\left[\dfrac{2}{n} + \dfrac{(\overline{AB}_{xij} - \overline{AB}_{xij'})^2}{E_{xx}}\right]}}.$$

Adjusted means for A_y, B_y, and AB_y are given by

$$\bar{A}_{y(\text{adj } i)} = \bar{A}_{yi} - b_w(\bar{A}_{xi} - \overline{ABS}_x)$$

$$\bar{B}_{y(\text{adj } i)} = \bar{B}_{yj} - b_w(\bar{B}_{xj} - \overline{ABS}_x)$$

$$\overline{AB}_{y(\text{adj } ij)} = \overline{AB}_{yij} - b_w(\overline{AB}_{xij} - \overline{ABS}_x),$$

where $b_w = E_{xy}/E_{xx}$.

A posteriori comparisons among means, using Tukey's or Scheffé's test statistics, are as follows:

$$q = \frac{C_j(\bar{A}_{y(\text{adj } i)}) + C_{j'}(\bar{A}_{y(\text{adj } i')})}{\sqrt{\text{MS}_{\text{error } 1}/nq}}$$

$$q = \frac{C_j(\bar{B}_{y(\text{adj } j)}) + C_{j'}(\bar{B}_{y(\text{adj } j')})}{\sqrt{\text{MS}_{\text{error } 2}/np}}$$

$$q = \frac{C_j(\overline{AB}_{y(\text{adj } ij)}) + C_{j'}(\overline{AB}_{y(\text{adj } ij')})}{\sqrt{\text{MS}_{\text{error } 3}/n}}$$

$$F = \frac{[C_j(\bar{A}_{y(\text{adj } i)}) + C_{j'}(\bar{A}_{y(\text{adj } i')}) + \cdots + C_{j''}(\bar{A}_{y(\text{adj } i'')})]^2}{\text{MS}_{\text{error } 1}\left[\dfrac{(C_j)^2}{nq} + \dfrac{(C_{j'})^2}{nq} + \cdots + \dfrac{(C_{j''})^2}{nq}\right]}$$

$$F = \frac{[C_j(\bar{B}_{y(\text{adj } j)}) + C_{j'}(\bar{B}_{y(\text{adj } j')}) + \cdots + C_{j''}(\bar{B}_{y(\text{adj } j'')})]^2}{\text{MS}_{\text{error } 2}\left[\dfrac{(C_j)^2}{np} + \dfrac{(C_{j'})^2}{np} + \cdots + \dfrac{(C_{j''})^2}{np}\right]}$$

$$F = \frac{[C_j(\overline{AB}_{y(\text{adj } ij)}) + C_{j'}(\overline{AB}_{y(\text{adj } ij')}) + \cdots + C_{j''}(\overline{AB}_{y(\text{adj } ij'')})]^2}{\text{MS}_{\text{error } 3}\left[\dfrac{(C_j)^2}{n} + \dfrac{(C_{j'})^2}{n} + \cdots + \dfrac{(C_{j''})^2}{n}\right]},$$

where

$$\text{MS}_{\text{error } 1} = \text{MS}_{\text{w.cell(adj)}}\left(1 + \frac{A_{xx}/(p-1)}{E_{xx}}\right)$$

$$\text{MS}_{\text{error } 2} = \text{MS}_{\text{w.cell(adj)}}\left(1 + \frac{B_{xx}/(q-1)}{E_{xx}}\right)$$

$$\text{MS}_{\text{error } 3} = \text{MS}_{\text{w.cell(adj)}}\left[1 + \frac{AB_{xx}/(p-1)(q-1)}{E_{xx}}\right].$$

The analysis of factorial experiments with unequal numbers of observations per cell has been discussed by Federer (1955, 515–517), Hazel (1946), and Das (1953). The computational procedures for this condition are relatively complex.

ANALYSIS OF COVARIANCE FOR
TYPE SPFAC-$p.q$ DESIGN

The collection of concomitant observations in a split-plot design can take one of two forms, as shown in Figure 12.9-1. In Figure 12.9-1a, a single covariate measure is associated with all the criterion measures for a subject. In this case it is assumed that the covariate is obtained prior to administration of any of the treatment combinations. In Figure 12.9-1b, each criterion measure for a subject is paired with a unique covariate measure. The design in part (a) can be considered a special case of part (b), where the covariate is identical for each criterion measure. For this reason, only computational procedures for the design in part (b) are given.

TABLE 12.9-2 Computational Procedures for Type SPFAC-$p.q$ Design

Source	Sum of Squares yy	Sum of Squares xy	Sum of Squares xx	df	Adjusted Sum of Squares	F(Model III) (A and B Fixed Effects, Subjects Random)
1 A	A_{yy}	A_{xy}	A_{xx}	$p - 1$	$A_{\text{adj}} = (A_{yy} + S_{yy}) - \dfrac{(A_{xy} + S_{xy})^2}{A_{xx} + S_{xx}} - S_{\text{adj}}$	$\left[\frac{1}{2}\right]$
2 Subj w.groups(S)	S_{yy}	S_{xy}	S_{xx}	$p(n - 1) - 1$	$S_{\text{adj}} = S_{yy} - \dfrac{(S_{xy})^2}{S_{xx}}$	
3 B	B_{yy}	B_{xy}	B_{xx}	$q - 1$	$B_{\text{adj}} = (B_{yy} + E_{yy}) - \dfrac{(B_{xy} + E_{xy})^2}{B_{xx} + E_{xx}} - E_{\text{adj}}$	$\left[\frac{3}{5}\right]$
4 AB	AB_{yy}	AB_{xy}	AB_{xx}	$(p - 1)(q - 1)$	$AB_{\text{adj}} = (AB_{yy} + E_{yy}) - \dfrac{(AB_{xy} + E_{xy})^2}{AB_{xx} + E_{xx}} - E_{\text{adj}}$	$\left[\frac{4}{5}\right]$
5 $B \times$ subj w.groups(E)	E_{yy}	E_{xy}	E_{xx}	$p(n - 1)(q - 1)$	$E_{\text{adj}} = E_{yy} - \dfrac{(E_{xy})^2}{E_{xx}}$	
6 Total	tot_{yy}	tot_{xy}	tot_{xx}	$npq - 3$		

		b_{x1}	b_{y1}	b_{y2}	b_{y3}
a_1	s_1	X_1	Y_{11}	Y_{12}	Y_{13}
	s_2	X_2	Y_{21}	Y_{22}	Y_{23}
a_2	s_3	X_3	Y_{31}	Y_{32}	Y_{33}
	s_4	X_4	Y_{41}	Y_{42}	Y_{43}

(a)

		b_{x1}	b_{y1}	b_{x2}	b_{y2}	b_{x3}	b_{y3}
a_1	s_1	X_{11}	Y_{11}	X_{12}	Y_{12}	X_{13}	Y_{13}
	s_2	X_{21}	Y_{21}	X_{22}	Y_{22}	X_{23}	Y_{23}
a_2	s_3	X_{31}	Y_{31}	X_{32}	Y_{32}	X_{33}	Y_{33}
	s_4	X_{41}	Y_{41}	X_{42}	Y_{42}	X_{43}	Y_{43}

(b)

Figure 12.9-1 Type SPFAC-2.3 designs illustrating two forms for the concomitant variable.

If the regression, β'_B, for between-subject variation is different from the regression, β'_W, for within-subject variation, the following model for the design in part (b) is appropriate:

(1) $Y_{ijm(\text{adj})} = Y_{ijm} - \beta'_B(\overline{X}_{ij\cdot} - \overline{X}...) - \beta'_W(X_{ijm} - \overline{X}_{ij\cdot}) =$

$$\mu + \alpha_i + \pi_{m(i)} + \beta_j + \alpha\beta_{ij} + \beta\pi_{jm(i)} + \varepsilon_{ijm}.$$

If $\beta'_B = \beta'_W = \beta'$, the model can be simplified as shown below.

(2) $Y_{ijm(\text{adj})} = Y_{ijm} - \beta'(X_{ijm} - \overline{X}...) = \mu + \alpha_i + \pi_{m(i)} + \beta_j + \alpha\beta_{ij}$

$$+ \beta\pi_{jm(i)} + \varepsilon_{ijm}.$$

Computational procedures for a SPFAC-$p.q$ design, in which linear model 1 above is assumed to be appropriate, are shown in Table 12.9-2. Adjusted means for A_i, B_j, and AB_{ij} are given by

$$\overline{A}_{y(\text{adj } i)} = \overline{A}_{yi} - b_B(\overline{A}_{xi} - \overline{ABS}_x)$$

$$\overline{B}_{y(\text{adj } j)} = \overline{B}_{yj} - b_W(\overline{B}_{xj} - \overline{ABS}_x)$$

$$\overline{AB}_{y(\text{adj } ij)} = \overline{AB}_{yij} - b_B(\overline{A}_{xi} - \overline{ABS}_x) - b_W(\overline{AB}_{xij} - \overline{A}_{xi}),$$

where $b_B = \dfrac{S_{xy}}{S_{xx}}$ and $b_W = \dfrac{E_{xy}}{E_{xx}}.$

Formulas for carrying out comparisons among adjusted means are similar to those for the type CRFAC-pq design described previously. The proper error term, $\text{MS}_{\text{subj w.groups(adj)}}$ or $\text{MS}_{B \times \text{subj w.groups(adj)}}$, must be inserted in the formulas. Comparisons among simple effects means that are at different levels of treatment A require a modified adjustment formula. The formula is described by Winer (1962, 610).

If it can be assumed that $\beta'_B = \beta'_W$, the latter regression coefficient can be used to make adjustments of between-subject and within-subject variation. The simplified linear model (2) described earlier is appropriate for this case. According to Winer (1962, 610), a test of the hypothesis that $\beta'_B = \beta'_W$ is given by

$$t' = \frac{b_B - b_W}{\sqrt{\dfrac{MS_{S(adj)}}{S_{xx}} + \dfrac{MS_{E(adj)}}{E_{xx}}}}$$

Because the variances in the denominator of this t' ratio are likely to be heterogeneous, t' is not distributed as the t distribution. The sampling distribution of t' is approximately distributed as the t distribution with

$$df = \frac{\left(\dfrac{MS_{S(adj)}}{S_{xx}} + \dfrac{MS_{E(adj)}}{E_{xx}}\right)^2}{\dfrac{\left(\dfrac{MS_{S(adj)}}{S_{xx}}\right)^2}{df_S} + \dfrac{\left(\dfrac{MS_{E(adj)}}{E_{xx}}\right)^2}{df_E}},$$

where df_S and df_E refer to the degrees of freedom for $MS_{S(adj)}$ and $MS_{E(adj)}$, respectively. A numerically large level of significance ($\alpha = .10$ or $.25$) should be used for this test in order to avoid a type II error. If the hypothesis that $\beta'_B = \beta'_W$ is tenable, the adjustment procedures shown in Table 12 9 2 for between-subject sums of squares can be modified to reflect this. The adjustment procedures for within-subject sums of squares are unchanged. Formulas for computing adjusted sums of squares for treatment A and subjects within groups are

$$A_{adj} = A_{yy} - 2b_W A_{xy} + b_W^2 A_{xx}$$
$$\text{subj w.groups } (S_{adj}) = S_{yy} - 2b_W A_{xy} + b_W^2 S_{xx}.$$

Adjusted means for treatment A_i and AB_{ij} are given by

$$\bar{A}_{y(adj\ i)} = \bar{A}_{yi} - b_W(\bar{A}_{xi} - \overline{ABS}_x)$$

and
$$\overline{AB}_{y(adj\ ij)} = \overline{AB}_{yij} - b_W(\overline{AB}_{xij} - \overline{ABS}_x).$$

Formulas for computing adjusted means for treatment B are unchanged.

We noted earlier that the design in Figure 12.9-1a, which involves a single covariate measure for all criterion measures, is a special case of the design in Figure 12.9-1b. Only the between-subject comparisons are adjusted for the covariate in part (a). This follows because the within-subject adjustments are equal to zero. That is, B_{xx}, AB_{xx}, E_{xx}, B_{xy}, AB_{xy}, and E_{xy} equal zero.

ANALYSIS OF COVARIANCE FOR OTHER TYPES OF DESIGNS

The general procedures involved in applying analysis of covariance to different experimental designs should be apparent to the reader. Limitations due to space prevent a discussion of all analysis of covariance designs. Federer (1955, Chap. 16) has described the application of analysis of covariance to a variety of different designs. The analysis for incomplete block designs has been discussed by Cornish (1940a) and Zelen (1957), and the analysis for lattice designs by Cornish (1940a), Kishen (1941), and Cochran (1940a).

12.10   COVARIANCE VERSUS STRATIFICATION

If concomitant variates are obtained prior to presentation of a treatment, several alternative research strategies should be considered by an experimenter. The alternative described in this chapter is to remove statistically the variation in the dependent variate that is associated with the variation in the covariate. Another alternative is to use the covariate to form homogeneous blocks by assigning subjects with the highest covariate to one block, subjects with a lower covariate to a different block, and so on. If this type of stratification is employed, the data are analyzed by means of a randomized block design in which variation associated with blocks is isolated from error variation. In general, this design strategy is preferable to analysis of covariance if an experimenter's principal interest is in reducing the experimental error rather than in removing bias from estimates of treatment effects. It is important to note that a randomized block analysis requires somewhat less restrictive assumptions than a covariance analysis. The analysis of covariance design assumes that the correct form of regression equation has been fitted and that the within-treatment regression coefficients are homogeneous. The analysis is greatly simplified if the relationship between Y and X is linear. A randomized block design is essentially a function-free regression scheme that is appropriate even though the relationship between Y and X is nonlinear. Of course, it is assumed that the interaction of blocks and treatment levels is zero in a randomized block design. This assumption is similar to the assumption of homogeneity of regression coefficients in a covariance analysis. According to Cochran (1957), covariance and stratification are almost equally effective in removing the effects of an extraneous source of variation from the experimental error if the relationship between X and Y is linear. If it is possible to assign subjects to blocks so that the X values are equal within a block, the use of stratification in a randomized block design reduces the error term to

$$\sigma_\varepsilon^2(1 - \rho_W^2),$$

where σ_ε^2 is the experimental error variance when no stratification is used and ρ_W is the within-groups correlation coefficient. The corresponding reduction due to analysis of covariance was given in Section 12.3 as

$$\sigma_\varepsilon^2(1 - \rho_W^2)\left(1 + \frac{1}{f_e - 2}\right).$$

A disadvantage of a randomized block design is that stratification of subjects into homogeneous blocks may not be feasible for administrative reasons or stratification may be impossible because the covariate is not available at the beginning of the experiment.

Another alternative research strategy is to use stratification of subjects with respect to X in addition to using analysis of covariance to adjust for any residual variation associated with X. It is doubtful if the increased precision of this procedure justifies the additional computational labor. The greatest gain from the simultaneous use of blocking and covariance occurs when the two techniques are used to control two different sources of variation, X and Z, which are believed to affect the dependent variate. The randomized block and Latin square analysis of covariance designs are normally used in this manner. Thus, in a type RBAC-k design, the variation associated with X can be removed by covariance adjustment, while Z is removed experimentally by forming homogeneous blocks based on this source of variation. A general discussion of the merits of stratification versus analysis of covariance appears in Finney (1957), Cox (1957), and Feldt (1958).

ANALYSIS OF DIFFERENCE MEASURES

In analysis of covariance, the relationship between Y and X is estimated from the data. As we noted, the computations required for analysis of covariance can be involved and laborious. Under certain conditions, the use of difference measures in a conventional analysis of variance achieves some of the same advantages as analysis of covariance without the laborious computations. This procedure is applicable to situations in which the concomitant variable is of the same nature as the dependent variable. For example, the covariate might be an initial score, (X_{ij}), on a test and the dependent variate a score, (Y_{ij}), obtained on the test following the introduction of a treatment. The difference measure is defined as

$$D_{ij} = Y_{ij} - X_{ij}$$

and reflects the change in a subject's test performance that is attributable to treatment j. The analysis of variance is performed with the difference measures. If the regression of Y on X is linear and $b_{yx} = 1.0$, the analysis of difference measures gives the same estimate of treatment effects as analysis of covariance. The use of a difference measure assumes a particular form for the residual relation between Y and X. This assumption may or may not be tenable for a particular experiment. The analysis of covariance does not require an *a priori* assumption concerning the value of b_{yx} but instead determines the most suitable value of b_{yx} from the data. According to Cox (1957) and Gourlay (1953), a moderate departure of b_{yx} from the required value of one does not result in a serious loss of precision when difference measures are used.

12.11 ADVANTAGES AND DISADVANTAGES OF ANALYSIS OF COVARIANCE

The major advantages of analysis of covariance are

1. Enables an experimenter to remove one or more potential sources of bias that are difficult or impossible to eliminate by experimental control from estimates of experimental effects.

2. Analysis of covariance provides approximately the same reduction in experimental error as the use of stratification of subjects. Covariance analysis can be used after the data have been collected. Stratification of subjects into homogeneous blocks must be carried out at the beginning of the experiment.

The major disadvantages of analysis of covariance are

1. Computations required are more laborious than for a corresponding analysis of variance.

2. Analysis of covariance requires a somewhat restrictive set of assumptions that may prove untenable in a particular research application.

3. Computational formulas for estimating missing observations and carrying out comparisons among means for some analysis of covariance designs are relatively complex.

12.12 REPRESENTATIVE APPLICATIONS OF ANALYSIS OF COVARIANCE IN THE RESEARCH LITERATURE

The following references illustrate a variety of applications of analysis of covariance.

Ausubel, David P., and Mohamed Youssef. Role of discriminability in meaningful parallel learning. *Journal of Educational Psychology.* 1963, **54**, 331–336. Type CRFAC-23 design.

Calabria, Frank M. Experimentally induced psyche- and socio-process in small groups. *Journal of Social Psychology.* 1963, **60**, 57–69. Type CRAC-2 design.

Fitzgerald, Donald, and David P. Ausubel. Cognitive versus affective factors in the learning and retention of controversial material. *Journal of Educational Psychology.* 1963, **54**, 73–84. Type CRFAC-232 design.

Lublin, Shirley Curran. Reinforcement schedules, scholastic aptitude, autonomy need, and achievement in a programed course. *Journal of Educational Psychology.* 1965, **56**, 295–302. Type CRFAC-43 design.

Rosnow, Ralph L. "Conditioning" the direction of opinion change in persuasive communication. *Journal of Social Psychology.* 1966, **69**, 291–303. Type CRFAC-323 design.

Satz, Paul. Specific and nonspecific effects of brain lesions in man. *Journal of Abnormal Psychology.* 1966, **71**, 65–70. Type CRAC-4 design.

Stone, J. Blair. The effects of learner characteristics on performance in programed text and conventional text formats. *Journal of Educational Research.* 1965, **59**, 122–127. Type CRFAC-22 design.

13 / NONPARAMETRIC ANALYSIS OF MULTIGROUP EXPERIMENTS

13.1 INTRODUCTION TO NONPARAMETRIC METHODS

Analysis of variance and related statistical procedures are used to estimate population parameters and to test hypotheses concerning these parameters. The statistics employed in the above procedures are called parametric statistics. As we noted, parametric statistics are based on the assumption, among others, that the variables have underlying normal distributions. In some research situations, however, it is not possible to specify the functional form of the population distribution. In many such cases, the only assumption that appears tenable is continuity of the underlying probability distribution. Statistical procedures that do not depend on a knowledge of population distributions and associated parameters are called nonparametric or distribution-free methods. These statistics are used to compare population *distributions* rather than *parameters*. Parametric and nonparametric methods do not provide tests of the same hypotheses. The procedures described in this chapter are used to test the hypothesis that $k \geq 2$ population distributions of *unspecified* form are exactly alike. If an experimenter is interested in making inferences concerning means, for example, additional assumptions are required. These assumptions are the same ones required for tests of significance using t and F ratios. If nonparametric methods are used, an experimenter is generally unable or unwilling to assume that the underlying populations are normal, have equal variances, and so forth.

The data collected in an experiment are usually expressed in the form of numbers. A number may represent a frequency count of the occurrence of some category, an ordinal relationship among the categories, or it may represent the magnitude of the categories relative to some arbitrary point and provide information regarding the size of differences among the categories. The assignment of numbers to categories as indicated above is referred to as nominal, ordinal, and interval measurement, respectively. Most elementary statistics books contain a discussion of *levels of measure-*

ment. Numbers as such can be subjected to arithmetic operations *without* regard to the level of measurement used. If no computational errors are made, the resulting numbers will be correct as *numbers*. The measurement process whereby numbers are assigned to categories is, in many experiments, such that the numbers contain no information apart from designating ordinal relations among the categories. This is true, for example, if the measurement process employed by an experimenter consists of rank ordering the categories according to some criterion. In this case, differences among the numbers assigned to the categories are not likely to correspond to true differences among the categories. It remains for an experimenter to determine the extent to which the numbers used in the measurement process are isomorphic with his categories. This is an important point because parametric analysis of variance methods treat numbers as if the *size* of differences among the numbers contains useful information regarding the categories. If this is not true, an experimenter may prefer to use a statistical procedure that uses only the information actually contained in the numbers and that disregards the irrelevant properties. Nonparametric methods utilizing either the nominal or the ordinal information contained in numbers are available. If a level of measurement greater than ordinal but less than interval is achieved, an experimenter may choose to use a parametric test in order to take advantage of the additional information that is available. The general issue of level of measurement as related to the choice of parametric or nonparametric tests has been discussed by Anderson (1961).

This chapter describes two nonparametric tests for $k \geq 3$ treatment levels. These tests are appropriate for experiments that meet the following conditions:

1. One treatment with three or more levels.
2. Random assignment of treatment levels to experimental units.
3. Underlying probability distribution is continuous.
4. Data (numbers) contain at least ordinal information concerning the effects of the independent variable.

Nonparametric methods, because of their less stringent assumptions, are applicable to experimental data for which parametric methods are inappropriate. It is important to note, however, that one pays a price in exchange for less-stringent assumptions. If the form of the underlying populations is known to be normal, for example, or if the numbers used to represent the dependent variable contain more information than ordinal relationship, nonparametric tests extract less information from the data than parametric tests and are generally less powerful. Some nonparametric methods, including those described in this chapter, compare favorably with parametric methods in terms of power if the assumptions required by the latter methods are fulfilled.

Nonparametric methods can be used in place of parametric methods if assumptions associated with the latter cannot be met. In general, however, parametric tests are robust with respect to departures from the assumptions of normality and homogeneity. Thus it is common practice in the behavioral sciences to use the more powerful parametric tests even though the assumptions are only approximately fulfilled.

The terms nonparametric and distribution-free are used synonymously, although this is a simplification. Most nonparametric statistics are intended to apply to a large class of distributions rather than to all possible distributions.

13.2 KRUSKAL-WALLIS ONE-WAY ANALYSIS OF VARIANCE BY RANKS

Kruskal and Wallis (1952) developed a nonparametric test based on ranks. Their one-way analysis of variance by ranks provides a test of the null hypothesis that k *independent* samples were drawn from k identically distributed populations. It is assumed that the data provide at least ordinal information and that the underlying probability distribution is continuous. This test can be regarded as an extension of the Mann-Whitney U test, which is described later in connection with individual comparisons among treatment populations. The analysis of variance analogue of the Kruskal-Wallis test is a completely randomized analysis of variance design.

Assume that we are interested in determining if there are differences in the incidence of articulatory defects, such as sound substitutions, omissions, and lisping among children from different socio-economic backgrounds. Children in the first grade are assigned to one of four socio-economic classifications, b_1, b_2, b_3, and b_4, on the basis of their parents' income, education, and occupational status. Treatment level b_1 corresponds to the highest classification, while b_4 is the lowest socio-economic classification. A random sample of eight first-grade children from each of the four populations is obtained. Each child's speech is rated on a twelve-point scale by three specially trained teachers. The median of the three ratings is shown in Table 13.2-1. The 32 scores are ranked with the smallest score assigned a rank (R) of 1 and the largest score assigned a rank of 32, as shown in Table 13.2-1. Ties are assigned the average rank for that set. The sum of the ranks and computational procedures are presented in Table 13.2-1. If no tied observations occur, H is referred to the chi-square distribution with $k - 1$ degrees of freedom. Percentage points for the chi-square distribution are given in Table D.6. If ties occur, as in the present example, H' is the test statistic. In this example, $H' > \chi^2_{.05,3}$. Thus the hypothesis that the four samples were drawn from identically distributed populations is rejected.

TABLE 13.2-1   Computational Procedures for Kruskal-Wallis One-Way Analysis of Variance by Ranks

(i) Data:

b_1	R_1	b_2	R_2	b_3	R_3	b_4	R_4
3	8.5	4	13.0	7	23.0	7	23.0
6	19.5	5	16.0	8	26.0	8	26.0
3	8.5	4	13.0	7	23.0	9	28.5
3	8.5	3	8.5	6	19.5	8	26.0
1	1.0	2	3.5	5	16.0	10	30.5
2	3.5	3	8.5	6	19.5	10	30.5
2	3.5	4	13.0	5	16.0	9	28.5
2	3.5	3	8.5	6	19.5	11	32.0

$$\sum_{i=1}^{n} R_{ij} = 56.5 \qquad\qquad 84.0 \qquad\qquad 162.5 \qquad\qquad 225.0$$

Computational check: $\displaystyle\sum_{1}^{k}\sum_{1}^{n} R_{ij} = \frac{N(N+1)}{2} = 56.5 + 84.0 + \cdots + 225.0$

$$= \frac{32(32+1)}{2} = 528.0$$

(ii) Computational formulas:

$$H = \frac{12}{N(N+1)}\left[\sum_{j=1}^{k}\frac{\left(\sum_{i=1}^{n} R_{ij}\right)^2}{n_j}\right] - 3(N+1)$$

$$= \frac{12}{32(32+1)}\left[\frac{(56.5)^2}{8} + \frac{(84.0)^2}{8} + \frac{(162.5)^2}{8} + \frac{(225.0)^2}{8}\right] - 3(32+1) = 25.37$$

$$C = 1 - \left[\frac{\Sigma(t^3 - t)}{N^3 - N}\right]$$

$$= 1 - \left[\frac{2[(2)^3 - 2] + 4[(3)^3 - 3] + 2[(4)^3 - 4] + [(6)^3 - 6]}{(32)^3 - 32}\right] = .99$$

t refers to the number of tied observations in a tied group of numbers. For example, there are two sets of tied observations containing two numbers, four sets containing three numbers, etc.

$$H' = \frac{H}{C} = \frac{25.37}{.99} = 25.63$$

$$\chi^2_{.05,3} = 7.82$$

MULTIPLE COMPARISONS AMONG SAMPLES

Following an over-all test of significance, an experimenter may wish to determine which comparisons among the k treatment populations are significant. Several procedures have been proposed for this purpose (Dunn, 1964; Nemenyi, 1963; Ryan, 1960; Steel, 1959, 1960, 1961). Two of these procedures are described here. The one proposed by Ryan (1960) is illustrated because it uses the familiar Mann-Whitney U test for two independent samples (Mann and Whitney, 1947). Ryan's procedure, which is called the *method of adjusted significance levels*, controls the experimentwise error rate at α.

The first step in Ryan's procedure is to arrange the samples in order, according to the sums of the ranks. This has been done in Table 13.2-1. The two extreme treatment levels are identified as b_1 and b_4. A Mann-Whitney U statistic is used to test the hypothesis that these two samples came from identically distributed populations. Computational procedures for the Mann-Whitney test appear in Table 13.2-2. The scores are ranked from 1 to 16, with the smallest score assigned a rank of 1. Table D.15 can be used if n_1 and n_2 are both ≤ 8 to determine the probabilities associated with values as small as U or U'. In order to provide an experimentwise error rate of α, the tables are entered for α'. α' is given by

$$\alpha' = \frac{2\alpha}{k(r-1)},$$

where α = experimentwise error rate, k = number of treatment levels, and r = number of steps between ordered treatment levels under test. For this first test,

$$\alpha' = \frac{2(.05)}{4(4-1)} = .009.$$

TABLE 13.2-2   Computational Procedures for Mann-Whitney U Test

(i) Data:

b_1	R_1	b_4	R_4
3	6.0	7	9.0
6	8.0	8	10.5
3	6.0	9	12.5
3	6.0	8	10.5
1	1.0	10	14.5
2	3.0	10	14.5
2	3.0	9	12.5
2	3.0	11	16.0
$\sum_{i=1}^{n} R_{ij} = 36.0$			100.0

Computational check: $\sum_{1}^{k}\sum_{1}^{n} R_{ij} = \dfrac{N(N+1)}{2} = 136$

(ii) Computational formulas:

$$U = n_1 n_2 + \frac{n_1(n_1+1)}{2} - \sum_{i=1}^{n} R_{i1} = (8)(8) + \frac{8(8+1)}{2} - 36 = 64$$

$$U' = n_1 n_2 - U = (8)(8) - 64 = 0$$

The test statistic is U or U', whichever is smaller.

In order for the comparison of b_1 and b_4 to be declared significant, the two-tailed probability associated with U' must be less than .009. According to Table D.15, the probability associated with U' is less than .009. Thus the null hypothesis for this comparison is rejected. If the comparison of b_1 versus b_4 had been insignificant, no further tests would be made. It would then be concluded that all other pairwise comparisons are also insignificant. A test of the largest comparison between ranks, using Ryan's procedure, provides an alternative to the Kruskal-Wallis over-all null hypothesis test. If Ryan's procedure shows this comparison to be significant, tests are carried out for the next most extreme samples. These comparisons are b_1 versus b_3 and b_4 versus b_2. The value of α' for these comparisons is

$$\alpha' = \frac{2(.05)}{4(3-1)} = .013.$$

The rule governing the sequence for carrying out tests is based on a stair-step principle. The samples having the largest and smallest sums of ranks, respectively, are tested first. Next, two subgroups are formed by eliminating first one and then the other extreme sample. For these tests, $r = 3$. If either test is insignificant, one concludes that all comparisons within the same subgroup are also insignificant. If, however, b_1 versus b_3 is significant, comparisons of b_1 versus b_2 and b_2 versus b_3 are made with

$$\alpha' = \frac{2(.05)}{4(2-1)} = .025.$$

Table 13.2-3 summarizes the test sequence and results.

TABLE 13.2-3   Summary of _A Posteriori_ Tests using the Method of Adjusted Significance Levels

Comparison	r	Required Probability for Significance α'	U or U'	Obtained Probability	Decision
b_1 versus b_4	4	.009	0	$<.001$	Reject H_0
b_1 versus b_3	3	.013	3.5	.001	Reject H_0
b_4 versus b_2	3	.013	0	$<.001$	Reject H_0
b_1 versus b_2	2	.025	17.0	.065	Do not reject H_0
b_4 versus b_3	2	.025	3.0	.001	Reject H_0
b_2 versus b_3	2	.025	1.0	$<.001$	Reject H_0

If n_1 or $n_2 > 8$, Table D.15 cannot be used. It has been shown that as n_1 and n_2 increase in size, the sampling distribution of the test statistic approaches the normal distribution with mean equal to

$$\mu_U = \frac{n_1 n_2}{2}$$

and variance equal to

$$\sigma_U^2 = \frac{n_1 n_2 (n_1 + n_2 + 1)}{12}.$$

Thus, for large samples, the hypothesis of no difference between the population distributions can be tested by

$$z = \frac{U - \mu_U}{\sigma_U}.$$

z is referred to the standardized normal distribution, which is tabulated in Table D.3. If ties occur, the variance of U is given by

$$\sigma_U^2 = \frac{n_1 n_2}{12} \left[n_1 + n_2 + 1 - \frac{\Sigma(t^3 - t)}{(n_1 + n_2)(n_1 + n_2 - 1)} \right],$$

where t is defined in Table 13.2-1.

The Mann-Whitney U statistic can be employed to make planned orthogonal comparisons among the k treatment populations. An overall test is not required for such tests, nor is Ryan's procedure. An experimenter interested in making a relative small number of planned comparisons among k treatment levels can use Dunn's procedure, which is described in Section 3.2. This procedure amounts to evaluating each Mann-Whitney test statistic at α/C level of significance, where C represents the number of comparisons performed. Dunn's procedure, utilizing a Mann-Whitney U test, sets the error rate per experiment at or less than α.

An alternative *a posteriori* procedure for determining which pairwise comparisons among k treatment populations are significant was proposed by Nemenyi (1963). This procedure, which involves less computational labor than Ryan's method, is based on the Kruskal-Wallis test. In order to reject the hypothesis that two samples j and j' were drawn from identically distributed populations, the absolute value of the difference d for ranks j and j' must exceed dKW, where

$$d = \left| \left(\frac{1}{n_j} \sum_{i=1}^{n} R_{ij} \right) - \left(\frac{1}{n_{j'}} \sum_{i=1}^{n} R_{ij'} \right) \right|$$

and

$$dKW = \sqrt{H_{\alpha, k-1}} \cdot \sqrt{\frac{N(N + 1)}{12}} \cdot \sqrt{\frac{1}{n_j} + \frac{1}{n_{j'}}}.$$

The terms in these formulas are defined in Table 13.2-1. For N large, $H_{\alpha, k-1}$ is approximately distributed as $\chi^2_{\alpha, k-1}$ in Table D.6. Nemenyi's procedure can be used to make all pairwise comparisons among the k populations with an experimentwise error rate less than α.

Nemenyi's test described above is extremely versatile and can be used when sample sizes are unequal. If all of the n's are equal and relatively large, an alternative test based on the studentized range will give a smaller value for dKW. This procedure, as well as other variations of the test—for example, the comparison of $k - 1$ treatment populations with a control population—are described by Miller (1966, 166–167).

13.3   FRIEDMAN TWO-WAY ANALYSIS OF VARIANCE BY RANKS

Friedman (1937) has developed a nonparametric test based on ranks that can be used when matched subjects are employed or when repeated measures on the same subjects are obtained. This test is an analogue of a randomized block analysis of variance design. If matched subjects are used, it is assumed that the subjects are randomly assigned to the k treatment levels. If repeated measures are obtained, it is assumed that the order of administration of the treatment levels is randomized independently for each subject. It is further assumed that the data provide at least ordinal information and that the underlying probability distribution is continuous. Friedman's two-way analysis of variance by ranks provides a test of the null hypothesis that k *related* samples were drawn from k identically distributed populations.

Let us assume that the data shown in Table 13.3-1 are from $n = 8$ sets of matched subjects. The first step in the analysis is to rank the observations within each row with the smallest score assigned a rank of one. For the case of tied observations, the ties are given the average of the ranks they would occupy. The computational procedures and formulas appear in Table 13.3-1. χ_r^2 is approximately distributed as chi square with $k - 1$ degrees of freedom. Percentage points for the chi-square distribution are given in Table D.6. Exact probabilities for this test for $k = 3$, $n = 2$ to 9, and for $k = 4$, $n = 2$ to 4, are contained in Friedman (1937) and Siegel (1956, 280–281). It is apparent from Table 13.3-1 that the hypothesis that the k samples are drawn from k identically distributed populations can be rejected.

MEASURES OF ASSOCIATION BASED ON k RELATED SAMPLES

An experimenter may wish to know the extent to which n rank orderings of k categories tend to be similar. An appropriate statistic for answering this question is Kendall's coefficient of concordance, W (Kendall; 1948b, 81). W is the ratio of the variance of k rank sums to the maximum possible variance of k rank sums. The limits for W are 0 and 1. If each of the n rank orderings of the k categories is identical, W is equal to 1. If there is maximum disagreement (lack of concordance), the value of W is 0.

The limits of $\bar{r}_s$ are $-1/(n-1)$ and 1. It can be concluded that, on the average, the rank orderings for pairs of subjects are almost identical. If Friedman's χ_r^2 is significant, it can be concluded that Kendall's coefficient of concordance is not equal to zero.

MULTIPLE COMPARISONS AMONG POPULATION DISTRIBUTIONS

A Wilcoxon matched-pairs signed-ranks test can be used for both *a priori* and *a posteriori* comparisons among k treatment populations (Wilcoxon; 1945, 1949). If an experimenter is interested in $k-1$ planned orthogonal comparisons, he can employ the Wilcoxon test statistic to evaluate each comparison at α level of significance. Alternatively, an experimenter may wish to set the error rate per experiment at or less than α for a collection of C comparisons. In this case, each Wilcoxon test statistic can be evaluated at α/C level of significance. If the number of comparisons to be performed is large, Ryan's procedure (see Section 13.2) for setting the error rate experimentwise at or less than α may lead to more powerful tests than Dunn's procedure.

Computational procedures for the Wilcoxon test are shown in Table 13.3-2. Since we have already illustrated Ryan's procedure in con-

TABLE 13.3-2   Computational Procedures for Wilcoxon Matched-Pairs Signed-Ranks Test

(1)	(2)	(3)	(4)	(5)
			Rank of	Rank associated with less frequent
b_1	b_2	d	$|d|$	sign in column 3
3	4	-1	3.5	
6	5	1	3.5	3.5
3	4	-1	3.5	
3	3	0	—	
1	2	-1	3.5	
2	3	-1	3.5	
2	4	-2	7.0	
2	3	-1	3.5	

$$T = 3.5$$

$$z = \frac{T - \mu_T}{\sigma_T} = \frac{T - \dfrac{n(n+1)}{4}}{\sqrt{\dfrac{n(n+1)(2n+1)}{24}}} = \frac{3.5 - \dfrac{7(7+1)}{4}}{\sqrt{\dfrac{7(7+1)[2(7)+1]}{24}}} = \frac{3.5 - 14.0}{\sqrt{35.0}}$$

$$= \frac{-10.5}{5.9} = -1.78$$

$$z_{.05/2} = 1.96$$

TABLE 13.3-1   Computational Procedures for Friedman Two-Way Analysis of Variance by Ranks

(i) Data:

	b_1	R_1	b_2	R_2	b_3	R_3	b_4	R_4
S_1	3	1	4	2	7	3.5	7	3.5
S_2	6	2	5	1	8	3.5	8	3.5
S_3	3	1	4	2	7	3	9	4
S_4	3	1.5	3	1.5	6	3	8	4
S_5	1	1	2	2	5	3	10	4
S_6	2	1	3	2	6	3	10	4
S_7	2	1	4	2	5	3	9	4
S_8	2	1	3	2	6	3	11	4

$$\sum_{i=1}^{n} R_{ij} = 9.5 \qquad\qquad 14.5 \qquad\qquad 25.0 \qquad\qquad 31.0$$

(ii) Computational formulas:

$$\chi_r^2 = \frac{12}{nk(k+1)}\left[\sum_{j=1}^{k}\left(\sum_{i=1}^{n} R_{ij}\right)^2\right] - 3n(k+1)$$

$$= \frac{12}{(8)(4)(4+1)}[(9.5)^2 + (14.5)^2 + (25.0)^2 + (31.0)^2] - 3(8)(4+1)$$

$$= .075(1886.50) - 120 = 21.49$$

$$df = k - 1$$

$$\chi_{.05,3}^2 = 7.82$$

Kendall's coefficient can be computed for the data in Table 13.3-1 The formula for W is

$$W = \frac{12\left[\sum_{j=1}^{k}\left(\sum_{i=1}^{n} R_{ij}\right)^2\right]}{n^2 k(k^2 - 1)} - \frac{3(k+1)}{k-1}$$

$$= \frac{12[(9.5)^2 + (14.5)^2 + \cdots + (31.0)^2]}{(8)^2 4[(4)^2 - 1]} - \frac{3(4+1)}{4-1} = .90.$$

The variance of the k rank sums is 90 percent of the maximum possible variance. This interpretation of W is somewhat obscure. A more meaningful interpretation is in terms of $\bar{r}_s$, the average rank correlation over all possible pairs of rank orders. This is given by

$$\bar{r}_s = \frac{nW - 1}{n - 1} = \frac{8(.90) - 1}{8 - 1} = .89.$$

The measure $\bar{r}_s$ is equivalent to computing the average rank correlation for $n(n-1)/2 = 28$ possible pairs of rankings among $n = 8$ sets of subjects nection with the Mann-Whitney U test, only one example with the Wilcoxon test is given here. The computational procedures shown in Table 13.3-2 are for the comparison of treatment levels b_1 and b_2.

The first step in the analysis is to compute the difference between the scores for the treatment levels b_1 and b_2. This is shown in column 3. Next, the differences are ranked without regard to the sign of the difference, as shown in column 4. Differences of -1 and $+1$ receive the same rank according to this procedure. This example has one pair of scores for which the difference is zero. This difference of zero is ignored, and n is reduced from 8 to 7. If an *even* number of zero differences occur, each zero difference is assigned the average rank for the set and then half are arbitrarily given positive signs and the other half negative signs. If an *odd* number of zeros occur, one randomly chosen zero difference is discarded and the procedure for an even number of zeros is followed. The n must be reduced by one. Ties occurring in column 3 are assigned the average of the ranks that they would normally occupy. The signs $+$ and $-$ occur one and six times, respectively. The rank associated with the minority sign, which is $+$, is 3.5. The sum of the minority sign ranks is designated as T. For moderate size n's, the sampling distribution of T is approximately normally distributed. Tables contained in Siegel (1956, 254) and Wilcoxon (1949) can be used for small n's. A two-tailed test should be used for *a posteriori* comparisons.

Nemenyi (1963) has proposed an *a posteriori* test for determining which pairwise comparisons among k treatment populations are significant. His test is based on the Friedman two-way analysis of variance by ranks. According to Nemenyi's test, the hypothesis that two samples j and j' were drawn from identically distributed populations is rejected if the absolute difference d for ranks j and j' exceeds dF, where

$$d = | \left(\frac{1}{n} \sum_{i=1}^{n} R_{ij} \right) - \left(\frac{1}{n} \sum_{i=1}^{n} R_{ij'} \right) |$$

and

$$dF = \sqrt{\chi_{r,\alpha}^2} \cdot \sqrt{\frac{k(k+1)}{6n}} .$$

The terms in these formulas are defined in Table 13.3-1. The value of $\chi_{\alpha,k-1}^2$ in Table D.6 can be employed for χ_r^2 in the above formula. According to Friedman (1937), $\chi_{r,\alpha}^2$ has asymptotically ($n \to \infty$) a χ^2 distribution with $k-1$ degrees of freedom. This test statistic can be used to make all pairwise comparisons among k populations with an experimentwise error rate less than α.

Modifications of Nemenyi's test for the case in which (1) n is large or (2) it is desired to make comparisons of $k-1$ treatment populations with a control population are described by Miller (1966, 174).

13.4   OTHER NONPARAMETRIC TESTS
FOR $k \geq 3$ TREATMENT LEVELS

The two nonparametric tests for $k \geq 3$ treatment levels that were described are among the more powerful methods for analyzing data containing ordinal information. If the data contain only nominal information, tests such as the χ^2 test for k independent samples (Cochran; 1952, 1954) and Cochran's Q test (Cochran, 1950) for k related samples can be used. An extensive discussion of partitioning of contingency tables in connection with a chi-square test is given by Castellan (1965), who describes procedures for testing interaction in a contingency table.

A Garner-Hake-McGill multivariate analysis of information method can be used with nominal data and is an analogue of analysis of variance (Garner and Hake, 1951; McGill, 1954). This procedure, which is applicable to a broad range of behavioral research problems, is described in some detail by Attneave (1959).

The median test for k independent samples and an extension of the median test for k related samples were described by Mood (1950). These tests are applicable to data that contain ordinal information. Mood (1950) has also described the use of the median test, with n observations per cell, in evaluating interaction effects. Computational examples of this procedure are contained in Tate and Clelland (1957, 115–119). An extension of the Mann-Whitney test for $k = 3$ independent samples has been described by Whitney (1951). This test is designed to evaluate the hypothesis that three population sums occur in a specified order. A unique test for determining if k populations are ordered in a specific manner was developed by Jonckheere (1954). This test, which is applicable to independent samples, requires an experimenter to specify one rank order out of the many alternatives to the null hypothesis.

A method of analysis for paired comparisons that is an analogue of an incomplete block design has been described by Bradley and Terry (1952). They provide tables for $t = 3$ and 4, $\lambda = 1$, $b = 3$ and 6, $r = 2$ and 3, and $k = 2$, where the letters have the standard definitions given in Chapter 11.

Marascuilo and McSweeney (1967) have described trend analysis procedures for the two nonparametric designs presented in this chapter. A nonparametric test of interaction using orthogonal polynomials has been developed by Still (1967).

An excellent general survey of nonparametric methods appears in a book by Siegel (1956). Other discussions of nonparametric methods can be found in advanced books by Fraser (1957) and Walsh (1965), a book on rank correlation methods by Kendall (1948b), and an introductory book by Tate and Clelland (1957). A variety of nonparametric multiple comparison procedures is described in a book by Miller (1966). A comprehensive bibliography of nonparametric methods covering the period up to 1961 has been prepared by Savage (1962).

13.5   ADVANTAGES AND DISADVANTAGES OF NONPARAMETRIC MULTIGROUP DESIGNS

The major advantages of nonparametric multigroup designs are

1. Require less stringent assumptions than comparable parametric designs.
2. Computational procedures are relatively simple.
3. They are applicable to experimental data for which parametric designs are inappropriate.

The major disadvantages of these designs are

1. They do not provide tests of the same kinds of hypotheses as comparable parametric tests unless assumptions associated with the latter tests are tenable.
2. The power of nonparametric designs is less than that of parametric designs when the assumptions associated with the latter designs are fulfilled.
3. They do not extract as much information from data as comparable parametric designs if the assumptions associated with the latter designs are fulfilled.
4. Nonparametric analogues of complex multitreatment analysis of variance designs are presently not available.

APPENDIX A /
RULES OF
SUMMATION

Statistical notation can be compared to a language that has its own grammatical rules. This appendix describes summation notation and some of the more important rules concerning summation. Let X stand for a numerical variable. The value of this variable is represented by a score. In order to identify specific scores, one or more subscripts are employed. Two commonly used subscripts are i and j. Let us assume that variable X_i (reads as "X sub i") ranges over the set of values

$$X_1, X_2, \ldots, X_n.$$

The sum of these values can be written

$$X_1 + X_2 + \cdots + X_n = \sum_{i=1}^{n} X_i.$$

The symbol Σ (capital Greek sigma) is interpreted as an instruction that says to add up the variable corresponding to the letter which follows the Σ symbol. $\Sigma_{i=1}^{n} X_i$ is read "the sum of i equals one through n values of X_i." The notation is sometimes abbreviated as

$$X_1 + X_2 + \cdots + X_n = \sum_{1}^{n} X_i \text{ or } \sum_{i} X_i \text{ or } \Sigma X_i.$$

Any one of these abbreviated notations is adequate for most situations. If the n values of X_i are 2, 5, and 4, then

$$\sum_{i=1}^{3} X_i = 2 + 5 + 4 = 11.$$

The letter i below the $\Sigma_{i=1}^{3}$ symbol is the *index of summation*. The lower and upper limits of the index of summation are given below and above, respectively, the Σ symbol. In this example i assumes all integral values from 1 to 3 inclusive.

For convenience, the sum of n values of X_i, beginning with $i = 1$ and ending with $i = n$, is often abbreviated as $\Sigma_1^n X$ in this book. In this example, the relevant information is contained in the upper limit of summation. It is understood that summation takes place with respect to the index of summation and variable subscript, which has n as its upper limit.

Consider the following data matrix, which has $n = 4$ rows and $k = 3$ columns.

	Column 1	Column 2	Column 3	
Row 1	4	5	1	$\sum_{j=1}^{3} X_{1j} = 10$
Row 2	3	2	6	$\sum_{j=1}^{3} X_{2j} = 11$
Row 3	1	8	2	$\sum_{j=1}^{3} X_{3j} = 11$
Row 4	7	3	1	$\sum_{j=1}^{3} X_{4j} = 11$

$$\sum_{i=1}^{4} X_{i1} = 15 \qquad \sum_{i=1}^{4} X_{i2} = 18 \qquad \sum_{i=1}^{4} X_{i3} = 10$$

In order to identify a score in this matrix, two subscripts must be used. It is customary to denote a row by the subscript i and a column by the subscript j. Thus X_{ij} denotes a score in the ith row and jth column. For the above data matrix, $X_{12} = 5$ and $X_{23} = 6$. It is important to note the order of the subscripts because $X_{12} \neq X_{21}$. The term $\Sigma_{i=1}^{n} X_{i2}$ refers to the sum of $i = 1$ through n scores in the second column.

$$\sum_{i=1}^{n} X_{i2} = 5 + 2 + 8 + 3 = 18.$$

The term $\Sigma_{j=1}^{k} X_{3j}$ refers to the sum of $j = 1$ through k scores in the third row.

$$\sum_{j=1}^{k} X_{3j} = 1 + 8 + 2 = 11.$$

The sum over all $kn = 12$ scores can be indicated by double summation. For example, $\Sigma_{j=1}^{k}\Sigma_{i=1}^{n} X_{ij}$ indicates that scores are first summed over $i = 1$ through n scores in each of the columns and then summed over $j = 1$ through k columns. Thus

$$\sum_{j=1}^{k} \sum_{i=1}^{n} X_{ij} = (4 + 3 + 1 + 7) + (5 + 2 + 8 + 3) + (1 + 6 + 2 + 1)$$

$$= 15 + 18 + 10 = 43.$$

It should be noted that the innermost summation is ordinarily performed first, followed by the summation closest to the left margin.

The mean of the four scores in the second column of the data matrix can be written

$$\overline{X}_{.2} = \frac{1}{n} \sum_{i=1}^{n} X_{i2} = \frac{1}{4}(5 + 2 + 8 + 3) = \frac{18}{4} = 4.5.$$

The *dot* in the symbol for the mean indicates that summation and averaging over the subscript replaced by the dot have occurred.

The most commonly used summation rules are described below. An understanding of these rules is necessary in order to follow even the most elementary derivations in statistics.

Rule A.1. The sum of a constant c over, for example, $i = 1, \ldots, n$ observations is equal to n times the constant.

$$\sum_{i=1}^{n} c = c_1 + c_2 + \cdots + c_n = nc$$

For example, if $n = 3$ and $c = 2$, then

$$\sum_{i=1}^{3} 2 = 2 + 2 + 2 = (3)(2) = 6.$$

Rule A.2. The sum of a variable X_i over $i = 1, \ldots, n$ observations is equal to the sum of the variable.

$$\sum_{i=1}^{n} X_i = X_1 + X_2 + \cdots + X_n.$$

For example, if $n = 3$ and $X_i = 2, 3$, and 4,

$$\sum_{i=1}^{3} X_i = 2 + 3 + 4 = 9.$$

Rule A.3. The sum of a constant c times a variable X_i over $i = 1, \ldots, n$ observations is equal to the constant times the sum of the variable.

$$\sum_{i=1}^{n} cX_i = c\sum_{i=1}^{n} X_i.$$

For example, if $n = 3$, $c = 2$, and $X_i = 2, 3, 4$,

$$\sum_{i=1}^{3} 2X_i = (2)(2) + (2)(3) + (2)(4) = 2\sum_{i=1}^{3} X_i = 2(2 + 3 + 4) = 18.$$

Rule A.4. If several operations, including summation, are to be performed on a numerical variable, the sequence of operations is determined by the mathematical punctuation. For example,

$$\sum_{i=1}^{n} (X_i)^2 = X_1^2 + X_2^2 + \cdots + X_n^2$$

$$\left(\sum_{i=1}^{n} X_i\right)^2 = (X_1 + X_2 + \cdots + X_n)^2.$$

In the absence of explicit mathematical punctuation, rules concerning the sequence of performance of addition, subtraction, multiplication, and division apply. For example, the operation of multiplication (squaring a score) is performed before the operation of addition (summation). Thus

$$\sum_{i=1}^{n} X_i^2 = X_1^2 + X_2^2 + \cdots + X_n^2$$

$$\sum_{i=1}^{n} X_i^2 \neq (X_1 + X_2 + \cdots + X_n)^2.$$

Consider the example in which two scores X_i and Y_i are associated with each of $i = 1$ through n subjects. Then

$$\sum_{i=1}^{n} X_i Y_i = X_1 Y_1 + X_2 Y_2 + \cdots + X_n Y_n$$

$$\sum_{i=1}^{n} X_i Y_i \neq \left(\sum_{i=1}^{n} X_i \right) \left(\sum_{i=1}^{n} Y_i \right).$$

Rule A.5. If addition and subtraction are the only operations to be performed before summation, the summation can be distributed. For example,

$$\sum_{i=1}^{n} (X_i^2 + 5X_i - 2) = \sum_{i=1}^{n} X_i^2 + \sum_{i=1}^{n} 5X_i - \sum_{i=1}^{n} 2.$$

By using Rules A.1, A.2, A.3, and A.5, this can be written

$$\sum_{i=1}^{n} (X_i^2 + 5X_i - 2) = \sum_{i=1}^{n} X_i^2 + 5\sum_{i=1}^{n} X_i - n2.$$

Rule A.6. If one variable (say, X_j) of a product of two variables $(X_j Y_{ij})$ being summed involves only the outside index of summation, this variable can be factored out of the inside summation sign. For example,

$$\sum_{j=1}^{k} \sum_{i=1}^{n} (X_j Y_{ij}) = \sum_{j=1}^{k} X_j \left(\sum_{i=1}^{n} Y_{ij} \right).$$

This can be shown as follows:

$$\sum_{j=1}^{k} \sum_{i=1}^{n} (X_j Y_{ij}) = \sum_{j=1}^{k} (X_j Y_{1j} + X_j Y_{2j} + X_j Y_{3j} + \cdots + X_j Y_{nj})$$

$$= \sum_{j=1}^{k} X_j (Y_{1j} + Y_{2j} + Y_{3j} + \cdots + Y_{nj})$$

$$= \sum_{j=1}^{k} X_j \left(\sum_{i=1}^{n} Y_{ij} \right).$$

It should be noted that

$$\sum_{j=1}^{k} X_j \left(\sum_{i=1}^{n} Y_{ij} \right) \neq \left(\sum_{j=1}^{k} X_j \right) \left(\sum_{i=1}^{n} Y_{ij} \right). \qquad \text{(Rule A.4)}$$

APPENDIX B /
RULES OF
EXPECTATIONS

Appendix A described rules of summation. Similar kinds of rules apply to the mathematical expectation of a random variable, say, X. The *expected value* of any random variable is defined as the average long-run value of the variable. The average long-run value of a discrete random variable can be found by multiplying each possible value of the variable by its corresponding probability and summing the product. That is,

$$E(X) = \sum_{1}^{N} Xp(X),$$

where E stands for expected value and $\Sigma_1^N p(X) = 1$. For a continuous random variable,

$$E(X) = \int_{-\infty}^{\infty} Xf(X)\, d(X),$$

where

$$\int_{-\infty}^{\infty} f(X)\, d(X) = 1.00.$$

Consider a population containing N elements. Assume that a sample is obtained from this population and that every element X has an equal chance of being selected for the sample. If the sampling process is repeated many, many times, the long-run average value of the X's will be the mean of the population μ. This is expressed as

Rule B.1. $E(X) = \mu.$

The symbol E is similar to Σ in that both are instruction or operator symbols. It says to find the average long-run value of the terms that follow it.

For each random variable X, there is a corresponding squared deviation of X from the population mean μ; that is, $(X - \mu)^2$. If the sampling procedure described above is followed, the long-run average value of $(X - \mu)^2$ is the population variance σ^2. This is expressed as

Rule B.2. $E(X - \mu)^2 = \sigma^2.$

The following rules of mathematical expectation, which are applicable to both discrete and continuous random variables, are widely used in mathematical statistics.

Rule B.3 *Expectation of a constant.* If c is a constant, the expected value of the constant is c.

$$E(c) = c.$$

Rule B.4 *Expectation of a constant times a random variable.* If c is a constant and X is a random variable, the expected value of cX is the constant times the expected value of X.

$$E(cX) = cE(X).$$

According to Rule B.1, this can be written

$$E(cX) = c\mu$$

Rule B.5 *Expectation of a constant plus a random variable.* If c is a constant and X is a random variable, the expected value of $(c + X)$ is the constant plus the expected value of X.

$$E(c + X) = c + E(X).$$

According to Rule B.1, this can be written

$$E(c + X) = c + \mu.$$

Rule B.6 *Expectation of sum of random variables.* If X and Y are random variables, the expected value of $(X + Y)$ or $(X - Y)$ is the sum or difference of the expected values of X and Y.

$$E(X + Y) = E(X) + E(Y)$$

$$E(X - Y) = E(X) - E(Y).$$

This rule holds for any finite number of random variables.

Rule B.7 *Expectation of product of random variables.* If X and Y are random variables that are statistically independent, the expected value of the product of the random variables is the product of their separate expectations.

$$E(XY) = E(X)E(Y).$$

If $E(XY) \neq E(X)E(Y)$, the two random variables are correlated. This rule holds for any finite number of random variables.

Rule B.8 *Expectation of sum of random variables from a common population.* If $X_1, X_2, \ldots, X_n$ are random variables from the same population or from populations with the same mean (μ), the expected value of the sum of the random variables is

$$E\left(\sum_{1}^{n} X_i\right) = E(X_1 + X_2 + \cdots + X_n) = n\mu.$$

Rule B.9 *Expectation of square of random variable.* If X is a random variable, the expected value of X^2 is

$$E(X^2) = \mu^2 + \sigma^2.$$

This follows from Rule B.2, which states that $E(X - \mu)^2 = \sigma^2$. According to this rule,

$$E(X - \mu)^2 = \sigma^2$$

$$E(X^2 - 2X\mu + \mu^2) = \sigma^2$$

$$E(X^2) - 2\mu E(X) + \mu^2 = \sigma^2, \quad \text{(Rules B.3, B.4, B.5, B.6)}$$

but
$$E(X) = \mu. \quad \text{(Rule B.1)}$$

Thus

$$E(X^2) - 2\mu\mu + \mu^2 = \sigma^2$$

$$E(X)^2 = \mu^2 + \sigma^2.$$

Rule B.10 *Expectation of sum of squared random variables from a common population.* If $X_1^2, X_2^2, \ldots, X_n^2$ are random variables from the same population with mean $= \mu$ and variance $= \sigma^2$, the expected value of the sum of the squared random variables is

$$E\left(\sum_1^n X_i^2\right) = E(X_1^2 + X_2^2 + \cdots + X_n^2) = n(\mu^2 + \sigma^2).$$

Rule B.9 showed that $E(X^2) = \mu^2 + \sigma^2$. Because there are n terms, the expected value of the sum of these terms is

$$n(\mu^2 + \sigma^2).$$

Rule B.11 *Expectation of the square of a sum of random variables from a common population.* If $X_1, X_2, \ldots, X_n$ are independent random variables from the same population with mean $= \mu$ and variance $= \sigma^2$, the expected value of the square of the sum of these random variables is

$$E\left(\sum_1^n X_i\right)^2 = E(X_1 + X_2 + \cdots + X_n)^2 = n(n\mu^2 + \sigma^2).$$

This can be shown as follows:

$$E(X_1 + X_2 + \cdots + X_n)^2 = E[X_1(X_1 + X_2 + \cdots + X_n)$$
$$+ X_2(X_1 + X_2 + \cdots + X_n) + \cdots + X_n(X_1 + X_2 + \cdots + X_n)].$$

It is evident from the above expansion that there are n terms of the form X_i^2 and $n(n - 1)$ terms of the form $X_i X_{i'}$, where $i \neq i'$.

According to Rule B.10,

$$E(X_1^2 + X_2^2 + \cdots + X_n^2) = n(\mu^2 + \sigma^2).$$

If the random variables X_i and $X_{i'}$ are independent,

$$E(X_i X_{i'}) = E(X_i)E(X_{i'}) \quad \text{(Rule B.7)}$$

and
$$E(X_i) = \mu, \quad \text{also} \quad E(X_{i'}) = \mu.$$

Thus
$$E(X_i)E(X_{i'}) = (\mu)(\mu) = \mu^2.$$

Because there are $n(n - 1)$ terms of the form $X_i X_{i'}$ their expected value is equal to $n(n - 1)\mu^2$.

Under the assumptions that the X_i's are independent random variables with mean $= \mu$ and variance $= \sigma^2$,

$$E\left(\sum_1^n X_i\right)^2 = n(\mu^2 + \sigma^2) + n(n - 1)\mu^2$$

$$= n\mu^2 + n\sigma^2 + n^2\mu^2 - n\mu^2$$

$$= n^2\mu^2 + n\sigma^2$$

$$= n(n\mu^2 + \sigma^2).$$

APPENDIX C /
ORTHOGONAL
COEFFICIENTS FOR
UNEQUAL INTERVALS
AND UNEQUAL n's

Orthogonal coefficients for $k = 3$ to 10 treatment levels are given in Table D.12 of Appendix D. These coefficients can be used only if the treatment levels are separated by equal intervals and the sample n's are equal. This appendix describes procedures for deriving coefficients for any set of ordered treatment levels. Let us designate the numerical value of the jth treatment level by Y_j. Orthogonal coefficients c_{ij} for the ith trend component are functions of Y_j and have the form

$$c_{1j} = \alpha_1 + Y_j \qquad \text{(linear)}$$

$$c_{2j} = \alpha_2 + \beta_2 Y_j + Y_j^2 \qquad \text{(quadratic)}$$

$$c_{3j} = \alpha_3 + \beta_3 Y_j + \gamma_3 Y_j^2 + Y_j^3 \qquad \text{(cubic)}$$

$$c_{4j} = \alpha_4 + \beta_4 Y_j + \gamma_4 Y_j^2 + \delta_4 Y_j^3 + Y_j^4 \qquad \text{(quartic)}$$

$$\begin{array}{ccccccc} \cdot & \cdot & \cdot & \cdot & \cdot & \cdot \\ \cdot & \cdot & \cdot & \cdot & \cdot & \cdot \\ \cdot & \cdot & \cdot & \cdot & \cdot & \cdot \end{array}$$

$$c_{nj} = \alpha_n + \beta_n Y_j + \gamma_n Y_j^2 + \delta_n Y_j^3 + \varepsilon_n Y_j^4 + \cdots + X_j^n. \qquad (n\text{th power})$$

Derivation of the coefficients c_{ij} will be illustrated for an experiment in which the numerical values of the $k = 4$ treatment levels are as follows: $Y_1 = 0$, $Y_2 = 5$, $Y_3 = 10$, and $Y_4 = 20$. The respective n's for the treatment levels are 5, 5, 4, and 4. For convenience, the values of Y_j can be transformed by dividing each one by five. The transformed values of Y_j' are shown in column 3 of Table C.1-1. This transformation does not affect the ratios among the numerical values.

COEFFICIENTS FOR LINEAR COMPONENT

The procedure that is shown is similar to that described by Gaito (1965). Another version of the same procedure for the case of equal n's

TABLE C.1-1 Computation of Coefficients for Linear Component

(1) Treatment Level	(2) Numerical Value of Treatment Level Y_j	(3) Transformed Value Y'_j	(4) n_j	(5) $c_{1j} = \alpha_1 + Y'_j$	(6) $n_j c_{1j} = n_j \alpha_1 + n_j Y'_j$	(7) Linear Coefficients	(8) Col (7) × 18
b_1	0	0	5	$c_{11} = \alpha_1 + 0$	$5c_{11} = 5\alpha_1 + 5(0)$	$-29/18$	-29
b_2	5	1	5	$c_{12} = \alpha_1 + 1$	$5c_{12} = 5\alpha_1 + 5(1)$	$-11/18$	-11
b_3	10	2	4	$c_{13} = \alpha_1 + 2$	$4c_{13} = 4\alpha_1 + 4(2)$	$7/18$	7
b_4	20	4	4	$c_{14} = \alpha_1 + 4$	$4c_{14} = 4\alpha_1 + 4(4)$	$43/18$	43
					$0 = 18\alpha_1 + 29$		

has been described by Grandage (1958). Both procedures involve solving a series of simultaneous equations. This becomes increasingly laborious for higher-order components. However, it is seldom necessary to go beyond the quartic component because higher-order components are generally not significant. The details of the computational procedure are shown in Table C.1-1. Four simultaneous equations with five unknowns corresponding to the four treatment levels are given in column 5 of Table C.1-1. The product of n_j times each equation is shown in column 6. According to the orthogonality condition, $\Sigma n_j c_{ij} = 0$. Thus

$$0 = 18\alpha_1 + 29.$$

Solving for α_1 gives

$$18\alpha_1 = -29$$

$$\alpha_1 = \frac{-29}{18}.$$

The value of $\alpha_1 = -29/18$ is substituted in the equations in column 5 to obtain column 7. The resulting coefficients for the linear component are fractions. For convenience, the fractions can be multiplied by a constant chosen so as to provide integers reduced to lowest terms. This has been done in column 8. The coefficients for the linear trend are -29, -11, 7, and 43.

COEFFICIENTS FOR QUADRATIC COMPONENT

The quadratic coefficients are derived from $c_{2j} = \alpha_2 + \beta_2 Y'_j + Y'^2_j$. The product of n_j times each of the four simultaneous equations that are based on $c_{2j} = \alpha_2 + \beta_2 Y'_j + Y'^2_j$ is

$$5c_{21} = 5\alpha_2 + 5(0)\beta_2 + 5(0)^2$$

$$5c_{22} = 5\alpha_2 + 5(1)\beta_2 + 5(1)^2$$

$$4c_{23} = 4\alpha_2 + 4(2)\beta_2 + 4(2)^2$$

$$\underline{4c_{24} = 4\alpha_2 + 4(4)\beta_2 + 4(4)^2}$$

$$0 = 18\alpha_2 + 29\beta_2 + 85$$

(1)

According to the orthogonality condition, $\Sigma n_j c_{2j} = 0$ and is so designated in equation (1). This equation contains two unknowns. The orthogonality condition also specifies that $\Sigma n_j c_{1j} c_{2j} = 0$. The value of β_2 can be determined from the four equations that result from the product of n_j, c_{1j}, and c_{2j}. These equations are

$$5(-29)c_{21} = 5(-29)\alpha_2 + 5(0)(-29)\beta_2 + 5(0)^2(-29)$$

$$5(-11)c_{22} = 5(-11)\alpha_2 + 5(1)(-11)\beta_2 + 5(1)^2(-11)$$

$$4(7)c_{23} = 4(7)\alpha_2 + 4(2)(7)\beta_2 + 4(2)^2(7)$$

$$\underline{4(43)c_{24} = 4(43)\alpha_2 + 4(4)(43)\beta_2 + 4(4)^2(43)}$$

(2) $\qquad 0 = 0\alpha_2 + 689\beta_2 + 2809$

Solving for β_2 gives

$$689\beta_2 = -2809$$

$$\beta_2 = \frac{-2809}{689} = -4.0769.$$

The value of $\beta_2 = -4.0769$ can be substituted in equation (1). Solving for α_2 gives

$$18\alpha_2 = -29(-4.0769) - 85$$

$$18\alpha_2 = 33.2301$$

$$\alpha_2 = 1.8461.$$

The values of α_2 and β_2 can be substituted in the original equation $c_{2j} = \alpha_2 + \beta_2 Y'_j + Y'^2_j$ to determine the quadratic coefficients. These coefficients are

$$c_{21} = 1.8461 + (-4.0769)(0) + (0)^2 = 1.8461$$

$$c_{22} = 1.8461 + (-4.0769)(1) + (1)^2 = -1.2308$$

$$c_{23} = 1.8461 + (-4.0769)(2) + (2)^2 = -2.3077$$

$$c_{24} = 1.8461 + (-4.0769)(4) + (4)^2 = 1.5385.$$

The calculations can be checked by determining if, in fact,

$$\Sigma n_j c_{2j} = 0 \quad \text{and} \quad \Sigma n_j c_{1j} c_{2j} = 0.$$

COEFFICIENTS FOR CUBIC AND HIGHER-ORDER COMPONENTS

Cubic coefficients are derived from

(3) $\qquad c_{3j} = \alpha_3 + \beta_3 Y'_j + \gamma_3 Y'^2_j + Y'^3_j.$

This equation involves three unknowns α_3, β_3, and γ_3. We solved for the two unknowns α_2 and β_2 in computing the quadratic coefficients by making use of the relations $\Sigma n_j c_{1j} = 0$ and $\Sigma n_j c_{1j} c_{2j} = 0$. The three unknowns in equation (3) can be calculated from equations based on the orthogonal conditions $\Sigma n_j c_{3j} = 0$, $\Sigma n_j c_{1j} c_{3j} = 0$, and $\Sigma n_j c_{2j} c_{3j} = 0$.

Quartic coefficients are derived from

$$c_{4j} = \alpha_4 + \beta_4 Y_j' + \gamma_4 Y_j'^2 + \delta_4 Y_j'^3 + Y_j'^4.$$

In solving for the four unknowns in this equation, the orthogonal conditions $\Sigma n_j c_{4j} = 0$, $\Sigma n_j c_{1j} c_{4j} = 0$, $\Sigma n_j c_{2j} c_{4j} = 0$, and $\Sigma n_j c_{3j} c_{4j}$ are used. This procedure can be extended to the nth power component.

Computation of orthogonal coefficients is simplified somewhat if the n's are equal. In this case,

$$\Sigma c_{1j} = 0, \quad \Sigma c_{1j} c_{2j} = 0, \quad \Sigma c_{1j} c_{3j} = 0, \text{ etc.}$$

Thus the n's can be dispensed with in all of the computations.

APPENDIX D /
TABLES

TABLE D.1   Squares, Square Roots, and Reciprocals

N	N^2	$\sqrt{N}$	$\sqrt{10N}$	$1/N$	N	N^2	$\sqrt{N}$	$\sqrt{10N}$	$1/N$ .0
					50	2 500	7.071 068	22.36068	2000000
1	1	1.000 000	3.162 278	1.0000000	51	2 601	7.141 428	22.58318	1960784
2	4	1.414 214	4.472 136	.5000000	52	2 704	7.211 103	22.80351	1923077
3	9	1.732 051	5.477 226	.3333333	53	2 809	7.280 110	23.02173	1886792
4	16	2.000 000	6.324 555	.2500000	54	2 916	7.348 469	23.23790	1851852
5	25	2.236 068	7.071 068	.2000000	55	3 025	7.416 198	23.45208	1818182
6	36	2.449 490	7.745 967	.1666667	56	3 136	7.483 315	23.66432	1785714
7	49	2.645 751	8.366 600	.1428571	57	3 249	7.549 834	23.87467	1754386
8	64	2.828 427	8.944 272	.1250000	58	3 364	7.615 773	24.08319	1724138
9	81	3.000 000	9.486 833	.1111111	59	3 481	7.681 146	24.28992	1694915
10	100	3.162 278	10.00000	.1000000	60	3 600	7.745 967	24.49490	1666667
11	121	3.316 625	10.48809	.09090909	61	3 721	7.810 250	24.69818	1639344
12	144	3.464 102	10.95445	.08333333	62	3 844	7.874 008	24.89980	1612903
13	169	3.605 551	11.40175	.07692308	63	3 969	7.937 254	25.09980	1587302
14	196	3.741 657	11.83216	.07142857	64	4 096	8.000 000	25.29822	1562500
15	225	3.872 983	12.24745	.06666667	65	4 225	8.062 258	25.49510	1538462
16	256	4.000 000	12.64911	.06250000	66	4 356	8.124 038	25.69047	1515152
17	289	4.123 106	13.03840	.05882353	67	4 489	8.185 353	25.88436	1492537
18	324	4.242 641	13.41641	.05555556	68	4 624	8.246 211	26.07681	1470588
19	361	4.358 899	13.78405	.05263158	69	4 761	8.306 624	26.26785	1449275
20	400	4.472 136	14.14214	.05000000	70	4 900	8.366 600	26.45751	1428571
21	441	4.582 576	14.49138	.04761905	71	5 041	8.426 150	26.64583	1408451
22	484	4.690 416	14.83240	.04545455	72	5 184	8.485 281	26.83282	1388889
23	529	4.795 832	15.16575	.04347826	73	5 329	8.544 004	27.01851	1369863
24	576	4.898 979	15.49193	.04166667	74	5 476	8.602 325	27.20294	1351351
25	625	5.000 000	15.81139	.04000000	75	5 625	8.660 254	27.38613	1333333
26	676	5.099 020	16.12452	.03846154	76	5 776	8.717 798	27.56810	1315789
27	729	5.196 152	16.43168	.03703704	77	5 929	8.774 964	27.74887	1298701
28	784	5.291 503	16.73320	.03571429	78	6 084	8.831 761	27.92848	1282051
29	841	5.385 165	17.02939	.03448276	79	6 241	8.888 194	28.10694	1265823
30	900	5.477 226	17.32051	.03333333	80	6 400	8.944 272	28.28427	1250000
31	961	5.567 764	17.60682	.03225806	81	6 561	9.000 000	28.46050	1234568
32	1 024	5.656 854	17.88854	.03125000	82	6 724	9.055 385	28.63564	1219512
33	1 089	5.744 563	18.16590	.03030303	83	6 889	9.110 434	28.80972	1204819
34	1 156	5.830 952	18.43909	.02941176	84	7 056	9.165 151	28.98275	1190476
35	1 225	5.916 080	18.70829	.02857143	85	7 225	9.219 544	29.15476	1176471
36	1 296	6.000 000	18.97367	.02777778	86	7 396	9.273 618	29.32576	1162791
37	1 369	6.082 763	19.23538	.02702703	87	7 569	9.327 379	29.49576	1149425
38	1 444	6.164 414	19.49359	.02631579	88	7 744	9.380 832	29.66479	1136364
39	1 521	6.244 998	19.74842	.02564103	89	7 921	9.433 981	29.83287	1123596
40	1 600	6.324 555	20.00000	.02500000	90	8 100	9.486 833	30.00000	1111111
41	1 681	6.403 124	20.24846	.02439024	91	8 281	9.539 392	30.16621	1098901
42	1 764	6.480 741	20.49390	.02380952	92	8 464	9.591 663	30.33150	1086957
43	1 849	6.557 439	20.73644	.02325581	93	8 649	9.643 651	30.49590	1075269
44	1 936	6.633 250	20.97618	.02272727	94	8 836	9.695 360	30.65942	1063830
45	2 025	6.708 204	21.21320	.02222222	95	9 025	9.746 794	30.82207	1052632
46	2 116	6.782 330	21.44761	.02173913	96	9 216	9.797 959	30.98387	1041667
47	2 209	6.855 655	21.67948	.02127660	97	9 409	9.848 858	31.14482	1030928
48	2 304	6.928 203	21.90890	.02083333	98	9 604	9.899 495	31.30495	1020408
49	2 401	7.000 000	22.13594	.02040816	99	9 801	9.949 874	31.46427	1010101
50	2 500	7.071 068	22.36068	.02000000	100	10 000	10.00000	31.62278	1000000

TABLE D.2 Random Numbers

	1 2 3 4 5	6 7 8 9 10	11 12 13 14 15	16 17 18 19 20	21 22 23 24 25
1	10 27 53 96 23	71 50 54 36 23	54 31 04 82 98	04 14 12 15 09	26 78 25 47 47
2	28 41 50 61 88	64 85 27 20 18	83 36 36 05 56	39 71 65 09 62	94 76 62 11 89
3	34 21 42 57 02	59 19 18 97 48	80 30 03 30 98	05 24 67 70 07	84 97 50 87 46
4	61 81 77 23 23	82 82 11 54 08	53 28 70 58 96	44 07 39 55 43	42 34 43 39 28
5	61 15 18 13 54	16 86 20 26 88	90 74 80 55 09	14 53 90 51 17	52 01 63 01 59
6	91 76 21 64 64	44 91 13 32 97	75 31 62 66 54	84 80 32 75 77	56 08 25 70 29
7	00 97 79 08 06	37 30 28 59 85	53 56 68 53 40	01 74 39 59 73	30 19 99 85 48
8	36 46 18 34 94	75 20 80 27 77	78 91 69 16 00	08 43 18 73 68	67 69 61 34 25
9	88 98 99 60 50	65 95 79 42 94	93 62 40 89 96	43 56 47 71 66	46 76 29 67 02
10	04 37 59 87 21	05 02 03 24 17	47 97 81 56 51	92 34 86 01 82	55 51 33 12 91
11	63 62 06 34 41	94 21 78 55 09	72 76 45 16 94	29 95 81 83 83	79 88 01 97 30
12	78 47 23 53 90	34 41 92 45 71	09 23 70 70 07	12 38 92 79 43	14 85 11 47 23
13	87 68 62 15 43	53 14 36 59 25	54 47 33 70 15	59 24 48 40 35	50 03 42 99 36
14	47 60 92 10 77	88 59 53 11 52	66 25 69 07 04	48 68 64 71 06	61 65 70 22 12
15	56 88 87 59 41	65 28 04 67 53	95 79 88 37 31	50 41 06 94 76	81 83 17 16 33
16	02 57 45 86 67	73 43 07 34 48	44 26 87 93 29	77 09 61 67 84	06 69 44 77 75
17	31 54 14 13 17	48 62 11 90 60	68 12 93 64 28	46 24 79 16 76	14 60 25 51 01
18	28 50 16 43 36	28 97 85 58 99	67 22 52 76 23	24 70 36 54 54	59 28 61 71 96
19	63 29 62 66 50	02 63 45 52 38	67 63 47 54 75	83 24 78 43 20	92 63 13 47 48
20	45 65 58 26 51	76 96 59 38 72	86 57 45 71 46	44 67 76 14 55	44 88 01 62 12
21	39 65 36 63 70	77 45 85 50 51	74 13 39 35 22	30 53 36 02 95	49 34 88 73 61
22	73 71 98 16 04	29 18 94 51 23	76 51 94 84 86	79 93 96 38 63	08 58 25 58 94
23	72 20 56 20 11	72 65 71 08 86	79 57 95 13 91	97 48 72 66 48	09 71 17 24 89
24	75 17 26 99 76	89 37 20 70 01	77 31 61 95 46	26 97 05 73 51	53 33 18 72 87
25	37 48 60 82 29	81 30 15 39 14	48 38 75 93 29	06 87 37 78 48	45 56 00 84 47
26	68 08 02 80 72	83 71 46 30 49	89 17 95 88 29	02 39 56 03 46	97 74 06 56 17
27	14 23 98 61 67	70 52 85 01 50	01 84 02 78 43	10 62 98 19 41	18 83 99 47 99
28	49 08 96 21 44	25 27 99 41 28	07 41 08 34 66	19 42 74 39 91	41 96 53 78 72
29	78 37 06 08 43	63 61 62 42 29	39 68 95 10 96	09 24 23 00 62	56 12 80 73 16
30	37 21 34 17 68	68 96 83 23 56	32 84 60 15 31	44 73 67 34 77	91 15 79 74 58
31	14 29 09 34 04	87 83 07 55 07	76 58 30 83 64	87 29 25 58 84	86 50 60 00 25
32	58 43 28 06 36	49 52 83 51 14	47 56 91 29 34	05 87 31 06 95	12 45 57 09 09
33	10 43 67 29 70	80 62 80 03 42	10 80 21 38 84	90 56 35 03 09	43 12 74 49 14
34	44 38 88 39 54	86 97 37 44 22	00 95 01 31 76	17 16 29 56 63	38 78 94 49 81
35	90 69 59 19 51	85 39 52 85 13	07 28 37 07 61	11 16 36 27 03	78 86 72 04 95
36	41 47 10 25 62	97 05 31 03 61	20 26 36 31 62	68 69 86 95 44	84 95 48 46 45
37	91 94 14 63 19	75 89 11 47 11	31 56 34 19 09	79 57 92 36 59	14 93 87 81 40
38	80 06 54 18 66	09 18 94 06 19	98 40 07 17 81	22 45 44 84 11	24 62 20 42 31
39	67 72 77 63 48	84 08 31 55 58	24 33 45 77 58	80 45 67 93 82	75 70 16 08 24
40	59 40 24 13 27	79 26 88 86 30	01 31 60 10 39	53 58 47 70 93	85 81 56 39 38
41	05 90 35 89 95	01 61 16 96 94	50 78 13 69 36	37 68 53 37 31	71 26 35 03 71
42	44 43 80 69 98	46 68 05 14 82	90 78 50 05 62	77 79 13 57 44	59 60 10 39 66
43	61 81 31 96 82	00 57 25 60 59	46 72 60 18 77	55 66 12 62 11	08 99 55 64 57
44	42 88 07 10 05	24 98 65 63 21	47 21 61 88 32	27 80 30 21 60	10 92 35 36 12
45	77 94 30 05 39	28 10 99 00 27	12 73 73 99 12	49 99 57 94 82	96 88 57 17 91
46	78 83 19 76 16	94 11 68 84 26	23 54 20 86 85	23 86 66 99 07	36 37 34 92 09
47	87 76 59 61 81	43 63 64 61 61	65 76 36 95 90	18 48 27 45 68	27 23 65 30 72
48	91 43 05 96 47	55 78 99 95 24	37 55 85 78 78	01 48 41 19 10	35 19 54 07 73
49	84 97 77 72 73	09 62 06 65 72	87 12 49 03 60	41 15 20 76 27	50 47 02 29 16
50	87 41 60 76 83	44 88 96 07 80	83 05 83 38 96	73 70 66 81 90	30 56 10 48 59

Table D.2 is taken from Table 33 of Fisher and Yates, *Statistical Tables for Biological, Agricultural and Medical Research*, published by Oliver and Boyd Ltd., Edinburgh, by permission of the authors and publishers.

TABLE D.2 (Continued)

	1 2 3 4 5	6 7 8 9 10	11 12 13 14 15	16 17 18 19 20	21 22 23 24 25
1	22 17 68 65 84	68 95 23 92 35	87 02 22 57 51	61 09 43 95 06	58 24 82 03 47
2	19 36 27 59 46	13 79 93 37 55	39 77 32 77 09	85 52 05 30 62	47 83 51 62 74
3	16 77 23 02 77	09 61 87 25 21	28 06 24 25 93	16 71 13 59 78	23 05 47 47 25
4	78 43 76 71 61	20 44 90 32 64	97 67 63 99 61	46 38 03 93 22	69 81 21 99 21
5	03 28 28 26 08	73 37 32 04 05	69 30 16 09 05	88 69 58 28 99	35 07 44 75 47
6	93 22 53 64 39	07 10 63 76 35	87 03 04 79 88	08 13 13 85 51	55 34 57 72 69
7	78 76 58 54 74	92 38 70 96 92	52 06 79 79 45	82 63 18 27 44	69 66 92 19 09
8	23 68 35 26 00	99 53 93 61 28	52 70 05 48 34	56 65 05 61 86	90 92 10 70 80
9	15 39 25 70 99	93 86 52 77 65	15 33 59 05 28	22 87 26 07 47	86 96 98 29 06
10	58 71 96 30 24	18 46 23 34 27	85 13 99 24 44	49 18 09 79 49	74 16 32 23 02
11	57 35 27 33 72	24 53 63 94 09	41 10 76 47 91	44 04 95 49 66	39 60 04 59 81
12	48 50 86 54 48	22 06 34 72 52	82 21 15 65 20	33 29 94 71 11	15 91 29 12 03
13	61 96 48 95 03	07 16 39 33 66	98 56 10 56 79	77 21 30 27 12	90 49 22 23 62
14	36 93 89 41 26	29 70 83 63 51	99 74 20 52 36	87 09 41 15 09	98 60 16 03 03
15	18 87 00 42 31	57 90 12 02 07	23 47 37 17 31	54 08 01 88 63	39 41 88 92 10
16	88 56 53 27 59	33 35 72 67 47	77 34 55 45 70	08 18 27 38 90	16 95 86 70 75
17	09 72 95 84 29	49 41 31 06 70	42 38 06 45 18	64 84 73 31 65	52 53 37 97 15
18	12 96 88 17 31	65 19 69 02 83	60 75 86 90 68	24 64 19 35 51	56 61 87 39 12
19	85 94 57 24 16	92 09 84 38 76	22 00 27 69 85	29 81 94 78 70	21 94 47 90 12
20	38 64 43 59 98	98 77 87 68 07	91 51 67 62 44	40 98 05 93 78	23 32 65 41 18
21	53 44 09 42 72	00 41 86 79 79	68 47 22 00 20	35 55 31 51 51	00 83 63 22 55
22	40 76 66 26 84	57 99 99 90 37	36 63 32 08 58	37 40 13 68 97	87 64 81 07 83
23	02 17 79 18 05	12 59 52 57 02	22 07 90 47 03	28 14 11 30 79	20 69 22 40 98
24	95 17 82 06 53	31 51 10 96 46	92 06 88 07 77	56 11 50 81 69	40 23 72 51 39
25	35 76 22 42 92	96 11 83 44 80	34 68 35 48 77	33 42 40 90 60	73 96 53 97 86
26	26 29 13 56 41	85 47 04 66 08	34 72 57 59 13	82 43 80 46 15	38 26 61 70 04
27	77 80 20 75 82	72 82 32 99 90	63 95 73 76 63	89 73 44 99 05	48 67 26 43 18
28	46 40 66 44 52	91 36 74 43 53	30 82 13 54 00	78 45 63 98 35	55 03 36 67 68
29	37 56 08 18 09	77 53 84 46 47	31 91 18 95 58	24 16 74 11 53	44 10 13 85 57
30	61 65 61 68 66	37 27 47 39 19	84 83 70 07 48	53 21 40 06 71	95 06 79 88 54
31	93 43 69 64 07	34 18 04 52 35	56 27 09 24 86	61 85 53 83 45	19 90 70 99 00
32	21 96 60 12 99	11 20 99 45 18	48 13 93 55 34	18 37 79 49 90	65 97 38 20 46
33	95 20 47 97 97	27 37 83 28 71	00 06 41 41 74	45 89 09 39 84	51 67 11 52 49
34	97 86 21 78 73	10 65 81 92 59	58 76 17 14 97	04 76 62 16 17	17 95 70 45 80
35	69 92 06 34 13	59 71 74 17 32	27 55 10 24 19	23 71 82 13 74	63 52 52 01 41
36	04 31 17 21 56	33 73 99 19 87	26 72 39 27 67	53 77 57 68 93	60 61 97 22 61
37	61 06 98 03 91	87 14 77 43 96	43 00 65 98 50	45 60 33 01 07	98 99 46 50 47
38	85 93 85 86 88	72 87 08 62 40	16 06 10 89 20	23 21 34 74 97	76 38 03 29 63
39	21 74 32 47 45	73 96 07 94 52	09 65 90 77 47	25 76 16 19 33	53 05 70 53 30
40	15 69 53 82 80	79 96 23 53 10	65 39 07 16 29	45 33 02 43 70	02 87 40 41 45
41	02 89 08 04 49	20 21 14 68 86	87 63 93 95 17	11 29 01 95 80	35 14 97 35 33
42	87 18 15 89 79	85 43 01 72 73	08 61 74 51 69	89 74 39 82 15	94 51 33 41 67
43	98 83 71 94 22	59 97 50 99 52	08 52 85 08 40	87 80 61 65 31	91 51 80 32 44
44	10 08 58 21 66	72 68 49 29 31	89 85 84 46 06	59 73 19 85 23	65 09 29 75 63
45	47 90 56 10 08	88 02 84 27 83	42 29 72 23 19	66 56 45 65 79	20 71 53 20 25
46	22 85 61 68 90	49 64 92 85 44	16 40 12 89 88	50 14 49 81 06	01 82 77 45 12
47	67 80 43 79 33	12 83 11 41 16	25 58 19 68 70	77 02 54 00 52	53 43 37 15 26
48	27 62 50 96 72	79 44 61 40 15	14 53 40 65 39	27 31 58 50 28	11 39 03 34 25
49	33 78 80 87 15	38 30 06 38 21	14 47 47 07 26	54 96 87 53 32	40 36 40 96 76
50	13 13 92 66 99	47 24 49 57 74	32 25 43 62 17	10 97 11 69 84	99 63 22 32 98

TABLE D.3   Percentiles of the Standardized Normal Distribution

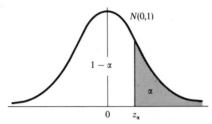

$1 - \alpha$	z_α	$1 - \alpha$	z_α	$1 - \alpha$	z_α
.50	0.00	.75	0.67	.950	1.645
.51	0.03	.76	0.71	.955	1.695
.52	0.05	.77	0.74	.960	1.751
.53	0.08	.78	0.77	.965	1.812
.54	0.10	.79	0.81	.970	1.881
.55	0.13	.80	0.84	.975	1.960
.56	0.15	.81	0.88	.980	2.054
.57	0.18	.82	0.92	.985	2.170
.58	0.20	.83	0.95	.990	2.326
.59	0.23	.84	0.99	.995	2.576
.60	0.25	.85	1.04	.996	2.652
.61	0.28	.86	1.08	.997	2.748
.62	0.30	.87	1.13	.998	2.878
.63	0.33	.88	1.17	.999	3.090
.64	0.36	.89	1.23		
.65	0.39	.90	1.28	.9995	3.291
.66	0.41	.91	1.34	.99995	3.891
.67	0.44	.92	1.41		
.68	0.47	.93	1.48	.999995	4.417
.69	0.50	.94	1.55		
				.9999995	5.327
.70	0.52				
.71	0.55				
.72	0.58				
.73	0.61				
.74	0.64				

This table is abridged from Table 9 in *Biometrika Tables for Statisticians*, vol. 1, 2nd ed. New York: Cambridge, 1958. Edited by E. S. Pearson and H. O. Hartley. Reproduced with the kind permission of the editors and the trustees of *Biometrika*.

TABLE D.4   Percentage Points of Student's *t* Distribution

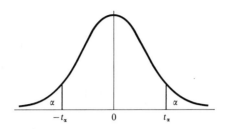

df	α .25 2α .50	.20 .40	.15 .30	.10 .20	.05 .10	.025 .05	.01 .02	.005 .01	.0005 .001
1	1.000	1.376	1.963	3.078	6.314	12.706	31.821	63.657	636.619
2	.816	1.061	1.386	1.886	2.920	4.303	6.965	9.925	31.598
3	.765	.978	1.250	1.638	2.353	3.182	4.541	5.841	12.924
4	.741	.941	1.190	1.533	2.132	2.776	3.747	4.604	8.610
5	.727	.920	1.156	1.476	2.015	2.571	3.365	4.032	6.869
6	.718	.906	1.134	1.440	1.943	2.447	3.143	3.707	5.959
7	.711	.896	1.119	1.415	1.895	2.365	2.998	3.499	5.408
8	.706	.889	1.108	1.397	1.860	2.306	2.896	3.355	5.041
9	.703	.883	1.100	1.383	1.833	2.262	2.821	3.250	4.781
10	.700	.879	1.093	1.372	1.812	2.228	2.764	3.169	4.587
11	.697	.876	1.088	1.363	1.796	2.201	2.718	3.106	4.437
12	.695	.873	1.083	1.356	1.782	2.179	2.681	3.055	4.318
13	.694	.870	1.079	1.350	1.771	2.160	2.650	3.012	4.221
14	.692	.868	1.076	1.345	1.761	2.145	2.624	2.977	4.140
15	.691	.866	1.074	1.341	1.753	2.131	2.602	2.947	4.073
16	.690	.865	1.071	1.337	1.746	2.120	2.583	2.921	4.015
17	.689	.863	1.069	1.333	1.740	2.110	2.567	2.898	3.965
18	.688	.862	1.067	1.330	1.734	2.101	2.552	2.878	3.922
19	.688	.861	1.066	1.328	1.729	2.093	2.539	2.861	3.883
20	.687	.860	1.064	1.325	1.725	2.086	2.528	2.845	3.850
21	.686	.859	1.063	1.323	1.721	2.080	2.518	2.831	3.819
22	.686	.858	1.061	1.321	1.717	2.074	2.508	2.819	3.792
23	.685	.858	1.060	1.319	1.714	2.069	2.500	2.807	3.767
24	.685	.857	1.059	1.318	1.711	2.064	2.492	2.797	3.745
25	.684	.856	1.058	1.316	1.708	2.060	2.485	2.787	3.725
26	.684	.856	1.058	1.315	1.706	2.056	2.479	2.779	3.707
27	.684	.855	1.057	1.314	1.703	2.052	2.473	2.771	3.690
28	.683	.855	1.056	1.313	1.701	2.048	2.467	2.763	3.674
29	.683	.854	1.055	1.311	1.699	2.045	2.462	2.756	3.659
30	.683	.854	1.055	1.310	1.697	2.042	2.457	2.750	3.646
40	.681	.851	1.050	1.303	1.684	2.021	2.423	2.704	3.551
60	.679	.848	1.046	1.296	1.671	2.000	2.390	2.660	3.460
120	.677	.845	1.041	1.289	1.658	1.980	2.358	2.617	3.373
∞	.674	.842	1.036	1.282	1.645	1.960	2.326	2.576	3.291

Table D.4 is taken from Table 3 of Fisher and Yates, *Statistical Tables for Biological, Agricultural and Medical Research*, published by Oliver and Boyd Ltd., Edinburgh, by permission of the authors and publishers.

TABLE D.5 Upper Percentage Points of the *F* Distribution

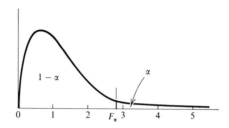

| df for denominator | α | \multicolumn{12}{c}{df for numerator} |
		1	2	3	4	5	6	7	8	9	10	11	12
1	.25	5.83	7.50	8.20	8.58	8.82	8.98	9.10	9.19	9.26	9.32	9.36	9.41
	.10	39.9	49.5	53.6	55.8	57.2	58.2	58.9	59.4	59.9	60.2	60.5	60.7
	.05	161	200	216	225	230	234	237	239	241	242	243	244
2	.25	2.57	3.00	3.15	3.23	3.28	3.31	3.34	3.35	3.37	3.38	3.39	3.39
	.10	8.53	9.00	9.16	9.24	9.29	9.33	9.35	9.37	9.38	9.39	9.40	9.41
	.05	18.5	19.0	19.2	19.2	19.3	19.3	19.4	19.4	19.4	19.4	19.4	19.4
	.01	98.5	99.0	99.2	99.2	99.3	99.3	99.4	99.4	99.4	99.4	99.4	99.4
3	.25	2.02	2.28	2.36	2.39	2.41	2.42	2.43	2.44	2.44	2.44	2.45	2.45
	.10	5.54	5.46	5.39	5.34	5.31	5.28	5.27	5.25	5.24	5.23	5.22	5.22
	.05	10.1	9.55	9.28	9.12	9.01	8.94	8.89	8.85	8.81	8.79	8.76	8.74
	.01	34.1	30.8	29.5	28.7	28.2	27.9	27.7	27.5	27.3	27.2	27.1	27.1
4	.25	1.81	2.00	2.05	2.06	2.07	2.08	2.08	2.08	2.08	2.08	2.08	2.08
	.10	4.54	4.32	4.19	4.11	4.05	4.01	3.98	3.95	3.94	3.92	3.91	3.90
	.05	7.71	6.94	6.59	6.39	6.26	6.16	6.09	6.04	6.00	5.96	5.94	5.91
	.01	21.2	18.0	16.7	16.0	15.5	15.2	15.0	14.8	14.7	14.5	14.4	14.4
5	.25	1.69	1.85	1.88	1.89	1.89	1.89	1.89	1.89	1.89	1.89	1.89	1.89
	.10	4.06	3.78	3.62	3.52	3.45	3.40	3.37	3.34	3.32	3.30	3.28	3.27
	.05	6.61	5.79	5.41	5.19	5.05	4.95	4.88	4.82	4.77	4.74	4.71	4.68
	.01	16.3	13.3	12.1	11.4	11.0	10.7	10.5	10.3	10.2	10.1	9.96	9.89
6	.25	1.62	1.76	1.78	1.79	1.79	1.78	1.78	1.78	1.77	1.77	1.77	1.77
	.10	3.78	3.46	3.29	3.18	3.11	3.05	3.01	2.98	2.96	2.94	2.92	2.90
	.05	5.99	5.14	4.76	4.53	4.39	4.28	4.21	4.15	4.10	4.06	4.03	4.00
	.01	13.7	10.9	9.78	9.15	8.75	8.47	8.26	8.10	7.98	7.87	7.79	7.72
7	.25	1.57	1.70	1.72	1.72	1.71	1.71	1.70	1.70	1.69	1.69	1.69	1.68
	.10	3.59	3.26	3.07	2.96	2.88	2.83	2.78	2.75	2.72	2.70	2.68	2.67
	.05	5.59	4.74	4.35	4.12	3.97	3.87	3.79	3.73	3.68	3.64	3.60	3.57
	.01	12.2	9.55	8.45	7.85	7.46	7.19	6.99	6.84	6.72	6.62	6.54	6.47
8	.25	1.54	1.66	1.67	1.66	1.66	1.65	1.64	1.64	1.63	1.63	1.63	1.62
	.10	3.46	3.11	2.92	2.81	2.73	2.67	2.62	2.59	2.56	2.54	2.52	2.50
	.05	5.32	4.46	4.07	3.84	3.69	3.58	3.50	3.44	3.39	3.35	3.31	3.28
	.01	11.3	8.65	7.59	7.01	6.63	6.37	6.18	6.03	5.91	5.81	5.73	5.67
9	.25	1.51	1.62	1.63	1.63	1.62	1.61	1.60	1.60	1.59	1.59	1.58	1.58
	.10	3.36	3.01	2.81	2.69	2.61	2.55	2.51	2.47	2.44	2.42	2.40	2.38
	.05	5.12	4.26	3.86	3.63	3.48	3.37	3.29	3.23	3.18	3.14	3.10	3.07
	.01	10.6	8.02	6.99	6.42	6.06	5.80	5.61	5.47	5.35	5.26	5.18	5.11

TABLE D.5   (Continued)

					df *for numerator*									df *for de-nomi-nator*
15	20	24	30	40	50	60	100	120	200	500	∞	α	
9.49	9.58	9.63	9.67	9.71	9.74	9.76	9.78	9.80	9.82	9.84	9.85	.25	
61.2	61.7	62.0	62.3	62.5	62.7	62.8	63.0	63.1	63.2	63.3	63.3	.10	1
246	248	249	250	251	252	252	253	253	254	254	254	.05	
3.41	3.43	3.43	3.44	3.45	3.45	3.46	3.47	3.47	3.48	3.48	3.48	.25	
9.42	9.44	9.45	9.46	9.47	9.47	9.47	9.48	9.48	9.49	9.49	9.49	.10	2
19.4	19.4	19.5	19.5	19.5	19.5	19.5	19.5	19.5	19.5	19.5	19.5	.05	
99.4	99.4	99.5	99.5	99.5	99.5	99.5	99.5	99.5	99.5	99.5	99.5	.01	
2.46	2.46	2.46	2.47	2.47	2.47	2.47	2.47	2.47	2.47	2.47	2.47	.25	
5.20	5.18	5.18	5.17	5.16	5.15	5.15	5.14	5.14	5.14	5.14	5.13	.10	3
8.70	8.66	8.64	8.62	8.59	8.58	8.57	8.55	8.55	8.54	8.53	8.53	.05	
26.9	26.7	26.6	26.5	26.4	26.4	26.3	26.2	26.2	26.2	26.1	26.1	.01	
2.08	2.08	2.08	2.08	2.08	2.08	2.08	2.08	2.08	2.08	2.08	2.08	.25	
3.87	3.84	3.83	3.82	3.80	3.80	3.79	3.78	3.78	3.77	3.76	3.76	.10	4
5.86	5.80	5.77	5.75	5.72	5.70	5.69	5.66	5.66	5.65	5.64	5.63	.05	
14.2	14.0	13.9	13.8	13.7	13.7	13.7	13.6	13.6	13.5	13.5	13.5	.01	
1.89	1.88	1.88	1.88	1.88	1.88	1.87	1.87	1.87	1.87	1.87	1.87	.25	
3.24	3.21	3.19	3.17	3.16	3.15	3.14	3.13	3.12	3.12	3.11	3.10	.10	5
4.62	4.56	4.53	4.50	4.46	4.44	4.43	4.41	4.40	4.39	4.37	4.36	.05	
9.72	9.55	9.47	9.38	9.29	9.24	9.20	9.13	9.11	9.08	9.04	9.02	.01	
1.76	1.76	1.75	1.75	1.75	1.75	1.74	1.74	1.74	1.74	1.74	1.74	.25	
2.87	2.84	2.82	2.80	2.78	2.77	2.76	2.75	2.74	2.73	2.73	2.72	.10	6
3.94	3.87	3.84	3.81	3.77	3.75	3.74	3.71	3.70	3.69	3.68	3.67	.05	
7.56	7.40	7.31	7.23	7.14	7.09	7.06	6.99	6.97	6.93	6.90	6.88	.01	
1.68	1.67	1.67	1.66	1.66	1.66	1.65	1.65	1.65	1.65	1.65	1.65	.25	
2.63	2.59	2.58	2.56	2.54	2.52	2.51	2.50	2.49	2.48	2.48	2.47	.10	7
3.51	3.44	3.41	3.38	3.34	3.32	3.30	3.27	3.27	3.25	3.24	3.23	.05	
6.31	6.16	6.07	5.99	5.91	5.86	5.82	5.75	5.74	5.70	5.67	5.65	.10	
1.62	1.61	1.60	1.60	1.59	1.59	1.59	1.58	1.58	1.58	1.58	1.58	.25	
2.46	2.42	2.40	2.38	2.36	2.35	2.34	2.32	2.32	2.31	2.30	2.29	.10	8
3.22	3.15	3.12	3.08	3.04	3.02	3.01	2.97	2.97	2.95	2.94	2.93	.05	
5.52	5.36	5.28	5.20	5.12	5.07	5.03	4.96	4.95	4.91	4.88	4.86	.01	
1.57	1.56	1.56	1.55	1.55	1.54	1.54	1.53	1.53	1.53	1.53	1.53	.25	
2.34	2.30	2.28	2.25	2.23	2.22	2.21	2.19	2.18	2.17	2.17	2.16	.10	9
3.01	2.94	2.90	2.86	2.83	2.80	2.79	2.76	2.75	2.73	2.72	2.71	.05	
4.96	4.81	4.73	4.65	4.57	4.52	4.48	4.42	4.40	4.36	4.33	4.31	.01	

TABLE D.5   (Continued)

df for de-nomi-nator	α	\multicolumn{12}{c}{df for numerator}
		1	2	3	4	5	6	7	8	9	10	11	12
10	.25	1.49	1.60	1.60	1.59	1.59	1.58	1.57	1.56	1.56	1.55	1.55	1.54
	.10	3.29	2.92	2.73	2.61	2.52	2.46	2.41	2.38	2.35	2.32	2.30	2.28
	.05	4.96	4.10	3.71	3.48	3.33	3.22	3.14	3.07	3.02	2.98	2.94	2.91
	.01	10.0	7.56	6.55	5.99	5.64	5.39	5.20	5.06	4.94	4.85	4.77	4.71
11	.25	1.47	1.58	1.58	1.57	1.56	1.55	1.54	1.53	1.53	1.52	1.52	1.51
	.10	3.23	2.86	2.66	2.54	2.45	2.39	2.34	2.30	2.27	2.25	2.23	2.21
	.05	4.84	3.98	3.59	3.36	3.20	3.09	3.01	2.95	2.90	2.85	2.82	2.79
	.01	9.65	7.21	6.22	5.67	5.32	5.07	4.89	4.74	4.63	4.54	4.46	4.40
12	.25	1.46	1.56	1.56	1.55	1.54	1.53	1.52	1.51	1.51	1.50	1.50	1.49
	.10	3.18	2.81	2.61	2.48	2.39	2.33	2.28	2.24	2.21	2.19	2.17	2.15
	.05	4.75	3.89	3.49	3.26	3.11	3.00	2.91	2.85	2.80	2.75	2.72	2.69
	.01	9.33	6.93	5.95	5.41	5.06	4.82	4.64	4.50	4.39	4.30	4.22	4.16
13	.25	1.45	1.55	1.55	1.53	1.52	1.51	1.50	1.49	1.49	1.48	1.47	1.47
	.10	3.14	2.76	2.56	2.43	2.35	2.28	2.23	2.20	2.16	2.14	2.12	2.10
	.05	4.67	3.81	3.41	3.18	3.03	2.92	2.83	2.77	2.71	2.67	2.63	2.60
	.01	9.07	6.70	5.74	5.21	4.86	4.62	4.44	4.30	4.19	4.10	4.02	3.96
14	.25	1.44	1.53	1.53	1.52	1.51	1.50	1.49	1.48	1.47	1.46	1.46	1.45
	.10	3.10	2.73	2.52	2.39	2.31	2.24	2.19	2.15	2.12	2.10	2.08	2.05
	.05	4.60	3.74	3.34	3.11	2.96	2.85	2.76	2.70	2.65	2.60	2.57	2.53
	.01	8.86	6.51	5.56	5.04	4.69	4.46	4.28	4.14	4.03	3.94	3.86	3.80
15	.25	1.43	1.52	1.52	1.51	1.49	1.48	1.47	1.46	1.46	1.45	1.44	1.44
	.10	3.07	2.70	2.49	2.36	2.27	2.21	2.16	2.12	2.09	2.06	2.04	2.02
	.05	4.54	3.68	3.29	3.06	2.90	2.79	2.71	2.64	2.59	2.54	2.51	2.48
	.01	8.68	6.36	5.42	4.89	4.56	4.32	4.14	4.00	3.89	3.80	3.73	3.67
16	.25	1.42	1.51	1.51	1.50	1.48	1.47	1.46	1.45	1.44	1.44	1.44	1.43
	.10	3.05	2.67	2.46	2.33	2.24	2.18	2.13	2.09	2.06	2.03	2.01	1.99
	.05	4.49	3.63	3.24	3.01	2.85	2.74	2.66	2.59	2.54	2.49	2.46	2.42
	.01	8.53	6.23	5.29	4.77	4.44	4.20	4.03	3.89	3.78	3.69	3.62	3.55
17	.25	1.42	1.51	1.50	1.49	1.47	1.46	1.45	1.44	1.43	1.43	1.42	1.41
	.10	3.03	2.64	2.44	2.31	2.22	2.15	2.10	2.06	2.03	2.00	1.98	1.96
	.05	4.45	3.59	3.20	2.96	2.81	2.70	2.61	2.55	2.49	2.45	2.41	2.38
	.01	8.40	6.11	5.18	4.67	4.34	4.10	3.93	3.79	3.68	3.59	3.52	3.46
18	.25	1.41	1.50	1.49	1.48	1.46	1.45	1.44	1.43	1.42	1.42	1.41	1.40
	.10	3.01	2.62	2.42	2.29	2.20	2.13	2.08	2.04	2.00	1.98	1.96	1.93
	.05	4.41	3.55	3.16	2.93	2.77	2.66	2.58	2.51	2.46	2.41	2.37	2.34
	.01	8.29	6.01	5.09	4.58	4.25	4.01	3.84	3.71	3.60	3.51	3.43	3.37
19	.25	1.41	1.49	1.49	1.47	1.46	1.44	1.43	1.42	1.41	1.41	1.40	1.40
	.10	2.99	2.61	2.40	2.27	2.18	2.11	2.06	2.02	1.98	1.96	1.94	1.91
	.05	4.38	3.52	3.13	2.90	2.74	2.63	2.54	2.48	2.42	2.38	2.34	2.31
	.01	8.18	5.93	5.01	4.50	4.17	3.94	3.77	3.63	3.52	3.43	3.36	3.30
20	.25	1.40	1.49	1.48	1.46	1.45	1.44	1.43	1.42	1.41	1.40	1.39	1.39
	.10	2.97	2.59	2.38	2.25	2.16	2.09	2.04	2.00	1.96	1.94	1.92	1.89
	.05	4.35	3.49	3.10	2.87	2.71	2.60	2.51	2.45	2.39	2.35	2.31	2.28
	.01	8.10	5.85	4.94	4.43	4.10	3.87	3.70	3.56	3.46	3.37	3.29	3.23

TABLE D.5   (Continued)

15	20	24	30	40	50	60	100	120	200	500	∞	α	df *for denominator*
				df for numerator									
1.53	1.52	1.52	1.51	1.51	1.50	1.50	1.49	1.49	1.49	1.48	1.48	.25	
2.24	2.20	2.18	2.16	2.13	2.12	2.11	2.09	2.08	2.07	2.06	2.06	.10	10
2.85	2.77	2.74	2.70	2.66	2.64	2.62	2.59	2.58	2.56	2.55	2.54	.05	
4.56	4.41	4.33	4.25	4.17	4.12	4.08	4.01	4.00	3.96	3.93	3.91	.01	
1.50	1.49	1.49	1.48	1.47	1.47	1.47	1.46	1.46	1.46	1.45	1.45	.25	
2.17	2.12	2.10	2.08	2.05	2.04	2.03	2.00	2.00	1.99	1.98	1.97	.10	11
2.72	2.65	2.61	2.57	2.53	2.51	2.49	2.46	2.45	2.43	2.42	2.40	.05	
4.25	4.10	4.02	3.94	3.86	3.81	3.78	3.71	3.69	3.66	3.62	3.60	.01	
1.48	1.47	1.46	1.45	1.45	1.44	1.44	1.43	1.43	1.43	1.42	1.42	.25	
2.10	2.06	2.04	2.01	1.99	1.97	1.96	1.94	1.93	1.92	1.91	1.90	.10	12
2.62	2.54	2.51	2.47	2.43	2.40	2.38	2.35	2.34	2.32	2.31	2.30	.05	
4.01	3.86	3.78	3.70	3.62	3.57	3.54	3.47	3.45	3.41	3.38	3.36	.01	
1.46	1.45	1.44	1.43	1.42	1.42	1.42	1.41	1.41	1.40	1.40	1.40	.25	
2.05	2.01	1.98	1.96	1.93	1.92	1.90	1.88	1.88	1.86	1.85	1.85	.10	13
2.53	2.46	2.42	2.38	2.34	2.31	2.30	2.26	2.25	2.23	2.22	2.21	.05	
3.82	3.66	3.59	3.51	3.43	3.38	3.34	3.27	3.25	3.22	3.19	3.17	.01	
1.44	1.43	1.42	1.41	1.41	1.40	1.40	1.39	1.39	1.39	1.38	1.38	.25	
2.01	1.96	1.94	1.91	1.89	1.87	1.86	1.83	1.83	1.82	1.80	1.80	.10	14
2.46	2.39	2.35	2.31	2.27	2.24	2.22	2.19	2.18	2.16	2.14	2.13	.05	
3.66	3.51	3.43	3.35	3.27	3.22	3.18	3.11	3.09	3.06	3.03	3.00	.01	
1.43	1.41	1.41	1.40	1.39	1.39	1.38	1.38	1.37	1.37	1.36	1.36	.25	
1.97	1.92	1.90	1.87	1.85	1.83	1.82	1.79	1.79	1.77	1.76	1.76	.10	15
2.40	2.33	2.29	2.25	2.20	2.18	2.16	2.12	2.11	2.10	2.08	2.07	.05	
3.52	3.37	3.29	3.21	3.13	3.08	3.05	2.98	2.96	2.92	2.89	2.87	.01	
1.41	1.40	1.39	1.38	1.37	1.37	1.36	1.36	1.35	1.35	1.34	1.34	.25	
1.94	1.89	1.87	1.84	1.81	1.79	1.78	1.76	1.75	1.74	1.73	1.72	.10	16
2.35	2.28	2.24	2.19	2.15	2.12	2.11	2.07	2.06	2.04	2.02	2.01	.05	
3.41	3.26	3.18	3.10	3.02	2.97	2.93	2.86	2.84	2.81	2.78	2.75	.01	
1.40	1.39	1.38	1.37	1.36	1.35	1.35	1.34	1.34	1.34	1.33	1.33	.25	
1.91	1.86	1.84	1.81	1.78	1.76	1.75	1.73	1.72	1.71	1.69	1.69	.10	17
2.31	2.23	2.19	2.15	2.10	2.08	2.06	2.02	2.01	1.99	1.97	1.96	.05	
3.31	3.16	3.08	3.00	2.92	2.87	2.83	2.76	2.75	2.71	2.68	2.65	.01	
1.39	1.38	1.37	1.36	1.35	1.34	1.34	1.33	1.33	1.32	1.32	1.32	.25	
1.89	1.84	1.81	1.78	1.75	1.74	1.72	1.70	1.69	1.68	1.67	1.66	.10	18
2.27	2.19	2.15	2.11	2.06	2.04	2.02	1.98	1.97	1.95	1.93	1.92	.05	
3.23	3.08	3.00	2.92	2.84	2.78	2.75	2.68	2.66	2.62	2.59	2.57	.01	
1.38	1.37	1.36	1.35	1.34	1.33	1.33	1.32	1.32	1.31	1.31	1.30	.25	
1.86	1.81	1.79	1.76	1.73	1.71	1.70	1.67	1.67	1.65	1.64	1.63	.10	19
2.23	2.16	2.11	2.07	2.03	2.00	1.98	1.94	1.93	1.91	1.89	1.88	.05	
3.15	3.00	2.92	2.84	2.76	2.71	2.67	2.60	2.58	2.55	2.51	2.49	.01	
1.37	1.36	1.35	1.34	1.33	1.33	1.32	1.31	1.31	1.30	1.30	1.29	.25	
1.84	1.79	1.77	1.74	1.71	1.69	1.68	1.65	1.64	1.63	1.62	1.61	.10	20
2.20	2.12	2.08	2.04	1.99	1.97	1.95	1.91	1.90	1.88	1.86	1.84	.05	
3.09	2.94	2.86	2.78	2.69	2.64	2.61	2.54	2.52	2.48	2.44	2.42	.01	

TABLE D.5 (Continued)

df *for de-nomi-nator*	α	1	2	3	4	5	6	7	8	9	10	11	12
							df *for numerator*						
22	.25	1.40	1.48	1.47	1.45	1.44	1.42	1.41	1.40	1.39	1.39	1.38	1.37
	.10	2.95	2.56	2.35	2.22	2.13	2.06	2.01	1.97	1.93	1.90	1.88	1.86
	.05	4.30	3.44	3.05	2.82	2.66	2.55	2.46	2.40	2.34	2.30	2.26	2.23
	.01	7.95	5.72	4.82	4.31	3.99	3.76	3.59	3.45	3.35	3.26	3.18	3.12
24	.25	1.39	1.47	1 46	1.44	1.43	1.41	1.40	1.39	1.38	1.38	1.37	1.36
	.10	2.93	2.54	2.33	2.19	2.10	2.04	1.98	1.94	1.91	1.88	1.85	1.83
	.05	4.26	3.40	3.01	2.78	2.62	2.51	2.42	2.36	2.30	2.25	2.21	2.18
	.01	7.82	5.61	4.72	4.22	3.90	3.67	3.50	3.36	3.26	3.17	3.09	3.03
26	.25	1.38	1.46	1.45	1.44	1.42	1.41	1.39	1.38	1.37	1.37	1.36	1.35
	.10	2.91	2.52	2.31	2.17	2.08	2.01	1.96	1.92	1.88	1.86	1.84	1.81
	.05	4.23	3.37	2.98	2.74	2.59	2.47	2.39	2.32	2.27	2.22	2.18	2.15
	.01	7.72	5.53	4.64	4.14	3.82	3.59	3.42	3.29	3.18	3.09	3.02	2.96
28	.25	1.38	1.46	1.45	1.43	1.41	1.40	1.39	1.38	1.37	1.36	1.35	1.34
	.10	2.89	2.50	2.29	2.16	2.06	2.00	1.94	1.90	1.87	1.84	1.81	1.79
	.05	4.20	3.34	2.95	2.71	2.56	2.45	2.36	2.29	2.24	2.19	2.15	2.12
	.01	7.64	5.45	4.57	4.07	3.75	3.53	3.36	3.23	3.12	3.03	2.96	2.90
30	.25	1.38	1.45	1.44	1.42	1.41	1.39	1.38	1.37	1.36	1.35	1.35	1.34
	.10	2.88	2.49	2.28	2.14	2.05	1.98	1.93	1.88	1.85	1.82	1.79	1.77
	.05	4.17	3.32	2.92	2.69	2.53	2.42	2.33	2.27	2.21	2.16	2.13	2.09
	.01	7.56	5.39	4.51	4.02	3.70	3.47	3.30	3.17	3.07	2.98	2.91	2.84
40	.25	1.36	1.44	1.42	1.40	1.39	1.37	1.36	1.35	1.34	1.33	1.32	1.31
	.10	2.84	2.44	2.23	2.09	2.00	1.93	1.87	1.83	1.79	1.76	1.73	1.71
	.05	4.08	3.23	2.84	2.61	2.45	2.34	2.25	2.18	2.12	2.08	2.04	2.00
	.01	7.31	5.18	4.31	3.83	3.51	3.29	3.12	2.99	2.89	2.80	2.73	2.66
60	.25	1.35	1.42	1.41	1.38	1.37	1.35	1.33	1.32	1.31	1.30	1.29	1.29
	.10	2.79	2.39	2.18	2.04	1.95	1.87	1.82	1.77	1.74	1.71	1.68	1.66
	.05	4.00	3.15	2.76	2.53	2.37	2.25	2.17	2.10	2.04	1.99	1.95	1.92
	.01	7.08	4.98	4.13	3.65	3.34	3.12	2.95	2.82	2.72	2.63	2.56	2.50
120	.25	1.34	1.40	1.39	1.37	1.35	1.33	1.31	1.30	1.29	1.28	1.27	1.26
	.10	2.75	2.35	2.13	1.99	1.90	1.82	1.77	1.72	1.68	1.65	1.62	1.60
	.05	3.92	3.07	2.68	2.45	2.29	2.17	2.09	2.02	1.96	1.91	1.87	1.83
	.01	6.85	4.79	3.95	3.48	3.17	2.96	2.79	2.66	2.56	2.47	2.40	2.34
200	.25	1.33	1.39	1.38	1.36	1.34	1.32	1.31	1.29	1.28	1.27	1.26	1.25
	.10	2.73	2.33	2.11	1.97	1.88	1.80	1.75	1.70	1.66	1.63	1.60	1.57
	.05	3.89	3.04	2.65	2.42	2.26	2.14	2.06	1.98	1.93	1.88	1.84	1.80
	.01	6.76	4.71	3.88	3.41	3.11	2.89	2.73	2.60	2.50	2.41	2.34	2.27
∞	.25	1.32	1.39	1.37	1.35	1.33	1.31	1.29	1.28	1.27	1.25	1.24	1.24
	.10	2.71	2.30	2.08	1.94	1.85	1.77	1.72	1.67	1.63	1.60	1.57	1.55
	.05	3.84	3.00	2.60	2.37	2.21	2.10	2.01	1.94	1.88	1.83	1.79	1.75
	.01	6.63	4.61	3.78	3.32	3.02	2.80	2.64	2.51	2.41	2.32	2.25	2.18

TABLE D.5 (Continued)

15	20	24	30	40	50	60	100	120	200	500	∞	α	df *for de-nomi-nator*
				df *for numerator*									
1.36	1.34	1.33	1.32	1.31	1.31	1.30	1.30	1.30	1.29	1.29	1.28	.25	
1.81	1.76	1.73	1.70	1.67	1.65	1.64	1.61	1.60	1.59	1.58	1.57	.10	22
2.15	2.07	2.03	1.98	1.94	1.91	1.89	1.85	1.84	1.82	1.80	1.78	.05	
2.98	2.83	2.75	2.67	2.58	2.53	2.50	2.42	2.40	2.36	2.33	2.31	.01	
1.35	1.33	1.32	1.31	1.30	1.29	1.29	1.28	1.28	1.27	1.27	1.26	.25	
1.78	1.73	1.70	1.67	1.64	1.62	1.61	1.58	1.57	1.56	1.54	1.53	.10	24
2.11	2.03	1.98	1.94	1.89	1.86	1.84	1.80	1.79	1.77	1.75	1.73	.05	
2.89	2.74	2.66	2.58	2.49	2.44	2.40	2.33	2.31	2.27	2.24	2.21	.01	
1.34	1.32	1.31	1.30	1.29	1.28	1.28	1.26	1.26	1.26	1.25	1.25	.25	
1.76	1.71	1.68	1.65	1.61	1.59	1.58	1.55	1.54	1.53	1.51	1.50	.10	26
2.07	1.99	1.95	1.90	1.85	1.82	1.80	1.76	1.75	1.73	1.71	1.69	.05	
2.81	2.66	2.58	2.50	2.42	2.36	2.33	2.25	2.23	2.19	2.16	2.13	.01	
1.33	1.31	1.30	1.29	1.28	1.27	1.27	1.26	1.25	1.25	1.24	1.24	.25	
1.74	1.69	1.66	1.63	1.59	1.57	1.56	1.53	1.52	1.50	1.49	1.48	.10	28
2.04	1.96	1.91	1.87	1.82	1.79	1.77	1.73	1.71	1.69	1.67	1.65	.05	
2.75	2.60	2.52	2.44	2.35	2.30	2.26	2.19	2.17	2.13	2.09	2.06	.01	
1.32	1.30	1.29	1.28	1.27	1.26	1.26	1.25	1.24	1.24	1.23	1.23	.25	
1.72	1.67	1.64	1.61	1.57	1.55	1.54	1.51	1.50	1.48	1.47	1.46	.10	30
2.01	1.93	1.89	1.84	1.79	1.76	1.74	1.70	1.68	1.66	1.64	1.62	.05	
2.70	2.55	2.47	2.39	2.30	2.25	2.21	2.13	2.11	2.07	2.03	2.01	.01	
1.30	1.28	1.26	1.25	1.24	1.23	1.22	1.21	1.21	1.20	1.19	1.19	.25	
1.66	1.61	1.57	1.54	1.51	1.48	1.47	1.43	1.42	1.41	1.39	1.38	.10	40
1.92	1.84	1.79	1.74	1.69	1.66	1.64	1.59	1.58	1.55	1.53	1.51	.05	
2.52	2.37	2.29	2.20	2.11	2.06	2.02	1.94	1.92	1.87	1.83	1.80	.01	
1.27	1.25	1.24	1.22	1 21	1 20	1.19	1.17	1.17	1.16	1.15	1.15	.25	
1.60	1.54	1.51	1.48	1.44	1.41	1.40	1.36	1.35	1.33	1.31	1.29	.10	60
1.84	1.75	1.70	1.65	1.59	1.56	1.53	1.48	1.47	1.44	1.41	1.39	.05	
2.35	2.20	2.12	2.03	1.94	1.88	1.84	1.75	1.73	1.68	1.63	1.60	.01	
1.24	1.22	1.21	1.19	1.18	1.17	1.16	1.14	1.13	1.12	1.11	1.10	.25	
1.55	1.48	1.45	1.41	1.37	1.34	1.32	1.27	1.26	1.24	1.21	1.19	.10	120
1.75	1.66	1.61	1.55	1.50	1.46	1.43	1.37	1.35	1.32	1.28	1.25	.05	
2.19	2.03	1.95	1.86	1.76	1.70	1.66	1.56	1.53	1.48	1.42	1.38	.01	
1.23	1.21	1.20	1.18	1.16	1.14	1.12	1.11	1.10	1.09	1.08	1.06	.25	
1.52	1.46	1.42	1.38	1.34	1.31	1.28	1.24	1.22	1.20	1.17	1.14	.10	200
1.72	1.62	1.57	1.52	1.46	1.41	1.39	1.32	1.29	1.26	1.22	1.19	.05	
2.13	1.97	1.89	1.79	1.69	1.63	1.58	1.48	1.44	1.39	1.33	1.28	.01	
1.22	1.19	1.18	1.16	1.14	1.13	1.12	1.09	1.08	1.07	1.04	1.00	.25	
1.49	1.42	1.38	1.34	1.30	1.26	1.24	1.18	1.17	1.13	1.08	1.00	.10	∞
1.67	1.57	1.52	1.46	1.39	1.35	1.32	1.24	1.22	1.17	1.11	1.00	.05	
2.04	1.88	1.79	1.70	1.59	1.52	1.47	1.36	1.32	1.25	1.15	1.00	.01	

TABLE D.6 Upper Percentage Points of the χ^2 Distribution

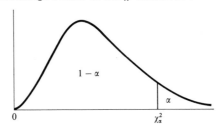

df	.99	.98	.95	.90	.80	.70	.50	.30	.20	.10	.05	.02	.01	.001
1	$.0^3157$	$.0^3628$	.00393	.0158	.0642	.148	.455	1.074	1.642	2.706	3.841	5.412	6.635	10.827
2	.0201	.0404	.103	.211	.446	.713	1.386	2.408	3.219	4.605	5.991	7.824	9.210	13.815
3	.115	.185	.352	.584	1.005	1.424	2.366	3.665	4.642	6.251	7.815	9.837	11.345	16.266
4	.297	.429	.711	1.064	1.649	2.195	3.357	4.878	5.989	7.779	9.488	11.668	13.277	18.467
5	.554	.752	1.145	1.610	2.343	3.000	4.351	6.064	7.289	9.236	11.070	13.388	15.086	20.515
6	.872	1.134	1.635	2.204	3.070	3.828	5.348	7.231	8.558	10.645	12.592	15.033	16.812	22.457
7	1.239	1.564	2.167	2.833	3.822	4.671	6.346	8.383	9.803	12.017	14.067	16.622	18.475	24.322
8	1.646	2.032	2.733	3.490	4.594	5.527	7.344	9.524	11.030	13.362	15.507	18.168	20.090	26.125
9	2.088	2.532	3.325	4.168	5.380	6.393	8.343	10.656	12.242	14.684	16.919	19.679	21.666	27.877
10	2.558	3.059	3.940	4.865	6.179	7.267	9.342	11.781	13.442	15.987	18.307	21.161	23.209	29.588
11	3.053	3.609	4.575	5.578	6.989	8.148	10.341	12.899	14.631	17.275	19.675	22.618	24.725	31.264
12	3.571	4.178	5.226	6.304	7.807	9.034	11.340	14.011	15.812	18.549	21.026	24.054	26.217	32.909
13	4.107	4.765	5.892	7.042	8.634	9.926	12.340	15.119	16.985	19.812	22.362	25.472	27.688	34.528
14	4.660	5.368	6.571	7.790	9.467	10.821	13.339	16.222	18.151	21.064	23.685	26.873	29.141	36.123
15	5.229	5.985	7.261	8.547	10.307	11.721	14.339	17.322	19.311	22.307	24.996	28.259	30.578	37.697
16	5.812	6.614	7.962	9.312	11.152	12.624	15.338	18.418	20.465	23.542	26.296	29.633	32.000	39.252
17	6.408	7.255	8.672	10.085	12.002	13.531	16.338	19.511	21.615	24.769	27.587	30.995	33.409	40.790
18	7.015	7.906	9.390	10.865	12.857	14.440	17.338	20.601	22.760	25.989	28.869	32.346	34.805	42.312
19	7.633	8.567	10.117	11.651	13.716	15.352	18.338	21.689	23.900	27.204	30.144	33.687	36.191	43.820
20	8.260	9.237	10.851	12.443	14.578	16.266	19.337	22.775	25.038	28.412	31.410	35.020	37.566	45.315
21	8.897	9.915	11.591	13.240	15.445	17.182	20.337	23.858	26.171	29.615	32.671	36.343	38.932	46.797
22	9.542	10.600	12.338	14.041	16.314	18.101	21.337	24.939	27.301	30.813	33.924	37.659	40.289	48.268
23	10.196	11.293	13.091	14.848	17.187	19.021	22.337	26.018	28.429	32.007	35.172	38.968	41.638	49.728
24	10.856	11.992	13.848	15.659	18.062	19.943	23.337	27.096	29.553	33.196	36.415	40.270	42.980	51.179
25	11.524	12.697	14.611	16.473	18.940	20.867	24.337	28.172	30.675	34.382	37.652	41.566	44.314	52.620
26	12.198	13.409	15.379	17.292	19.820	21.792	25.336	29.246	31.795	35.563	38.885	42.856	45.642	54.052
27	12.879	14.125	16.151	18.114	20.703	22.719	26.336	30.319	32.912	36.741	40.113	44.140	46.963	55.476
28	13.565	14.847	16.928	18.939	21.588	23.647	27.336	31.391	34.027	37.916	41.337	45.419	48.278	56.893
29	14.256	15.574	17.708	19.768	22.475	24.577	28.336	32.461	35.139	39.087	42.557	46.693	49.588	58.302
30	14.953	16.306	18.493	20.599	23.364	25.508	29.336	33.530	36.250	40.256	43.773	47.962	50.892	59.703

For $v > 30$, the expression $\sqrt{2\chi^2} - \sqrt{2v - 1}$ may be used as a normal deviate with unit variance.

Table D.6 is taken from Table 4 of Fisher and Yates, *Statistical Tables for Biological, Agricultural and Medical Research*, published by Oliver and Boyd Ltd., Edinburgh, by permission of the authors and publishers.

TABLE D.7 Percentage Points of the Studentized Range

Error df	α	\multicolumn{10}{c}{r = number of means or number of steps between ordered means}									
		2	3	4	5	6	7	8	9	10	11
5	.05	3.64	4.60	5.22	5.67	6.03	6.33	6.58	6.80	6.99	7.17
	.01	5.70	6.98	7.80	8.42	8.91	9.32	9.67	9.97	10.24	10.48
6	.05	3.46	4.34	4.90	5.30	5.63	5.90	6.12	6.32	6.49	6.65
	.01	5.24	6.33	7.03	7.56	7.97	8.32	8.61	8.87	9.10	9.30
7	.05	3.34	4.16	4.68	5.06	5.36	5.61	5.82	6.00	6.16	6.30
	.01	4.95	5.92	6.54	7.01	7.37	7.68	7.94	8.17	8.37	8.55
8	.05	3.26	4.04	4.53	4.89	5.17	5.40	5.60	5.77	5.92	6.05
	.01	4.75	5.64	6.20	6.62	6.96	7.24	7.47	7.68	7.86	8.03
9	.05	3.20	3.95	4.41	4.76	5.02	5.24	5.43	5.59	5.74	5.87
	.01	4.60	5.43	5.96	6.35	6.66	6.91	7.13	7.33	7.49	7.65
10	.05	3.15	3.88	4.33	4.65	4.91	5.12	5.30	5.46	5.60	5.72
	.01	4.48	5.27	5.77	6.14	6.43	6.67	6.87	7.05	7.21	7.36
11	.05	3.11	3.82	4.26	4.57	4.82	5.03	5.20	5.35	5.49	5.61
	.01	4.39	5.15	5.62	5.97	6.25	6.48	6.67	6.84	6.99	7.13
12	.05	3.08	3.77	4.20	4.51	4.75	4.95	5.12	5.27	5.39	5.51
	.01	4.32	5.05	5.50	5.84	6.10	6.32	6.51	6.67	6.81	6.94
13	.05	3.06	3.73	4.15	4.45	4.69	4.88	5.05	5.19	5.32	5.43
	.01	4.26	4.96	5.40	5.73	5.98	6.19	6.37	6.53	6.67	6.79
14	.05	3.03	3.70	4.11	4.41	4.64	4.83	4.99	5.13	5.25	5.36
	.01	4.21	4.89	5.32	5.63	5.88	6.08	6.26	6.41	6.54	6.66
15	.05	3.01	3.67	4.08	4.37	4.59	4.78	4.94	5.08	5.20	5.31
	.01	4.17	4.84	5.25	5.56	5.80	5.99	6.16	6.31	6.44	6.55
16	.05	3.00	3.65	4.05	4.33	4.56	4.74	4.90	5.03	5.15	5.26
	.01	4.13	4.79	5.19	5.49	5.72	5.92	6.08	6.22	6.35	6.46
17	.05	2.98	3.63	4.02	4.30	4.52	4.70	4.86	4.99	5.11	5.21
	.01	4.10	4.74	5.14	5.43	5.66	5.85	6.01	6.15	6.27	6.38
18	.05	2.97	3.61	4.00	4.28	4.49	4.67	4.82	4.96	5.07	5.17
	.01	4.07	4.70	5.09	5.38	5.60	5.79	5.94	6.08	6.20	6.31
19	.05	2.96	3.59	3.98	4.25	4.47	4.65	4.79	4.92	5.04	5.14
	.01	4.05	4.67	5.05	5.33	5.55	5.73	5.89	6.02	6.14	6.25
20	.05	2.95	3.58	3.96	4.23	4.45	4.62	4.77	4.90	5.01	5.11
	.01	4.02	4.64	5.02	5.29	5.51	5.69	5.84	5.97	6.09	6.19
24	.05	2.92	3.53	3.90	4.17	4.37	4.54	4.68	4.81	4.92	5.01
	.01	3.96	4.55	4.91	5.17	5.37	5.54	5.69	5.81	5.92	6.02
30	.05	2.89	3.49	3.85	4.10	4.30	4.46	4.60	4.72	4.82	4.92
	.01	3.89	4.45	4.80	5.05	5.24	5.40	5.54	5.65	5.76	5.85
40	.05	2.86	3.44	3.79	4.04	4.23	4.39	4.52	4.63	4.73	4.82
	.01	3.82	4.37	4.70	4.93	5.11	5.26	5.39	5.50	5.60	5.69
60	.05	2.83	3.40	3.74	3.98	4.16	4.31	4.44	4.55	4.65	4.73
	.01	3.76	4.28	4.59	4.82	4.99	5.13	5.25	5.36	5.45	5.53
120	.05	2.80	3.36	3.68	3.92	4.10	4.24	4.36	4.47	4.56	4.64
	.01	3.70	4.20	4.50	4.71	4.87	5.01	5.12	5.21	5.30	5.37
∞	.05	2.77	3.31	3.63	3.86	4.03	4.17	4.29	4.39	4.47	4.55
	.01	3.64	4.12	4.40	4.60	4.76	4.88	4.99	5.08	5.16	5.23

TABLE D.7   (Continued)

12	13	14	15	16	17	18	19	20	α	Error df
\multicolumn{9}{c	}{r = *number of means or number of steps between ordered means*}		
7.32	7.47	7.60	7.72	7.83	7.93	8.03	8.12	8.21	.05	5
10.70	10.89	11.08	11.24	11.40	11.55	11.68	11.81	11.93	.01	
6.79	6.92	7.03	7.14	7.24	7.34	7.43	7.51	7.59	.05	6
9.48	9.65	9.81	9.95	10.08	10.21	10.32	10.43	10.54	.01	
6.43	6.55	6.66	6.76	6.85	6.94	7.02	7.10	7.17	.05	7
8.71	8.86	9.00	9.12	9.24	9.35	9.46	9.55	9.65	.01	
6.18	6.29	6.39	6.48	6.57	6.65	6.73	6.80	6.87	.05	8
8.18	8.31	8.44	8.55	8.66	8.76	8.85	8.94	9.03	.01	
5.98	6.09	6.19	6.28	6.36	6.44	6.51	6.58	6.64	.05	9
7.78	7.91	8.03	8.13	8.23	8.33	8.41	8.49	8.57	.01	
5.83	5.93	6.03	6.11	6.19	6.27	6.34	6.40	6.47	.05	10
7.49	7.60	7.71	7.81	7.91	7.99	8.08	8.15	8.23	.01	
5.71	5.81	5.90	5.98	6.06	6.13	6.20	6.27	6.33	.05	11
7.25	7.36	7.46	7.56	7.65	7.73	7.81	7.88	7.95	.01	
5.61	5.71	5.80	5.88	5.95	6.02	6.09	6.15	6.21	.05	12
7.06	7.17	7.26	7.36	7.44	7.52	7.59	7.66	7.73	.01	
5.53	5.63	5.71	5.79	5.86	5.93	5.99	6.05	6.11	.05	13
6.90	7.01	7:10	7.19	7.27	7.35	7.42	7.48	7.55	.01	
5.46	5.55	5.64	5.71	5.79	5.85	5.91	5.97	6.03	.05	14
6.77	6.87	6.96	7.05	7.13	7.20	7.27	7.33	7.39	.01	
5.40	5.49	5.57	5.65	5.72	5.78	5.85	5.90	5.96	.05	15
6.66	6.76	6.84	6.93	7.00	7.07	7.14	7.20	7.26	.01	
5.35	5.44	5.52	5.59	5.66	5.73	5.79	5.84	5.90	.05	16
6.56	6.66	6.74	6.82	6.90	6.97	7.03	7.09	7.15	.01	
5.31	5.39	5.47	5.54	5.61	5.67	5.73	5.79	5.84	.05	17
6.48	6.57	6.66	6.73	6.81	6.87	6.94	7.00	7.05	.01	
5.27	5.35	5.43	5.50	5.57	5.63	5.69	5.74	5.79	.05	18
6.41	6.50	6.58	6.65	6.73	6.79	6.85	6.91	6.97	.01	
5.23	5.31	5.39	5.46	5.53	5.59	5.65	5.70	5.75	.05	19
6.34	6.43	6.51	6.58	6.65	6.72	6.78	6.84	6.89	.01	
5.20	5.28	5.36	5.43	5.49	5.55	5.61	5.66	5.71	.05	20
6.28	6.37	6.45	6.52	6.59	6.65	6.71	6.77	6.82	.01	
5.10	5.18	5.25	5.32	5.38	5.44	5.49	5.55	5.59	.05	24
6.11	6.19	6.26	6.33	6.39	6.45	6.51	6.56	6.61	.01	
5.00	5.08	5.15	5.21	5.27	5.33	5.38	5.43	5.47	.05	30
5.93	6.01	6.08	6.14	6.20	6.26	6.31	6.36	6.41	.01	
4.90	4.98	5.04	5.11	5.16	5.22	5.27	5.31	5.36	.05	40
5.76	5.83	5.90	5.96	6.02	6.07	6.12	6.16	6.21	.01	
4.81	4.88	4.94	5.00	5.06	5.11	5.15	5.20	5.24	.05	60
5.60	5.67	5.73	5.78	5.84	5.89	5.93	5.97	6.01	.01	
4.71	4.78	4.84	4.90	4.95	5.00	5.04	5.09	5.13	.05	120
5.44	5.50	5.56	5.61	5.66	5.71	5.75	5.79	5.83	.01	
4.62	4.68	4.74	4.80	4.85	4.89	4.93	4.97	5.01	.05	∞
5.29	5.35	5.40	5.45	5.49	5.54	5.57	5.61	5.65	.01	

TABLE D.8 Percentage Points of the Duncan New Multiple Range Test

Error df	Protection Level	r = number of means for range being tested													
		2	3	4	5	6	7	8	9	10	12	14	16	18	20
1	.05	18.0	18.0	18.0	18.0	18.0	18.0	18.0	18.0	18.0	18.0	18.0	18.0	18.0	18.0
	.01	90.0	90.0	90.0	90.0	90.0	90.0	90.0	90.0	90.0	90.0	90.0	90.0	90.0	90.0
2	.05	6.09	6.09	6.09	6.09	6.09	6.09	6.09	6.09	6.09	6.09	6.09	6.09	6.09	6.09
	.01	14.0	14.0	14.0	14.0	14.0	14.0	14.0	14.0	14.0	14.0	14.0	14.0	14.0	14.0
3	.05	4.50	4.50	4.50	4.50	4.50	4.50	4.50	4.50	4.50	4.50	4.50	4.50	4.50	4.50
	.01	8.26	8.5	8.6	8.7	8.8	8.9	8.9	9.0	9.0	9.0	9.1	9.2	9.3	9.3
4	.05	3.93	4.01	4.02	4.02	4.02	4.02	4.02	4.02	4.02	4.02	4.02	4.02	4.02	4.02
	.01	6.51	6.8	6.9	7.0	7.1	7.1	7.2	7.2	7.3	7.3	7.4	7.4	7.5	7.5
5	.05	3.64	3.74	3.79	3.83	3.83	3.83	3.83	3.83	3.83	3.83	3.83	3.83	3.83	3.83
	.01	5.70	5.96	6.11	6.18	6.26	6.33	6.40	6.44	6.5	6.6	6.6	6.7	6.7	6.8
6	.05	3.46	3.58	3.64	3.68	3.68	3.68	3.68	3.68	3.68	3.68	3.68	3.68	3.68	3.68
	.01	5.24	5.51	5.65	5.73	5.81	5.88	5.95	6.00	6.0	6.1	6.2	6.2	6.3	6.3
7	.05	3.35	3.47	3.54	3.58	3.60	3.61	3.61	3.61	3.61	3.61	3.61	3.61	3.61	3.61
	.01	4.95	5.22	5.37	5.45	5.53	5.61	5.69	5.73	5.8	5.8	5.9	5.9	6.0	6.0
8	.05	3.26	3.39	3.47	3.52	3.55	3.56	3.56	3.56	3.56	3.56	3.56	3.56	3.56	3.56
	.01	4.74	5.00	5.14	5.23	5.32	5.40	5.47	5.51	5.5	5.6	5.7	5.7	5.8	5.8
9	.05	3.20	3.34	3.41	3.47	3.50	3.52	3.52	3.52	3.52	3.52	3.52	3.52	3.52	3.52
	.01	4.60	4.86	4.99	5.08	5.17	5.25	5.32	5.36	5.4	5.5	5.5	5.6	5.7	5.7
10	.05	3.15	3.30	3.37	3.43	3.46	3.47	3.47	3.47	3.47	3.47	3.47	3.47	3.47	3.48
	.01	4.48	4.73	4.88	4.96	5.06	5.13	5.20	5.24	5.28	5.36	5.42	5.48	5.54	5.55
11	.05	3.11	3.27	3.35	3.39	3.43	3.44	3.45	3.46	4.46	3.46	3.46	3.46	3.47	3.48
	.01	4.39	4.63	4.77	4.86	4.94	5.01	5.06	5.12	5.15	5.24	5.28	5.34	5.38	5.39
12	.05	3.08	3.23	3.33	3.36	3.40	3.42	3.44	3.44	3.46	3.46	3.46	3.46	3.47	3.48
	.01	4.32	4.55	4.68	4.76	4.84	4.92	4.96	5.02	5.07	5.13	5.17	5.22	5.24	5.26
13	.05	3.06	3.21	3.30	3.35	3.38	3.41	3.42	3.44	3.45	3.45	3.46	3.46	3.47	3.47
	.01	4.26	4.48	4.62	4.69	4.74	4.84	4.88	4.94	4.98	5.04	5.08	5.13	5.14	5.15
14	.05	3.03	3.18	3.27	3.33	3.37	3.39	3.41	3.42	3.44	3.45	3.46	3.46	3.47	3.47
	.01	4.21	4.42	4.55	4.63	4.70	4.78	4.83	4.87	4.91	4.96	5.00	5.04	5.06	5.07
15	.05	3.01	3.16	3.25	3.31	3.36	3.38	3.40	3.42	3.43	3.44	3.45	3.46	3.47	3.47
	.01	4.17	4.37	4.50	4.58	4.64	4.72	4.77	4.81	4.84	4.90	4.94	4.97	4.99	5.00
16	.05	3.00	3.15	3.23	3.30	3.34	3.37	3.39	3.41	3.43	3.44	3.45	3.46	3.47	3.47
	.01	4.13	4.34	4.45	4.54	4.60	4.67	4.72	4.76	4.79	4.84	4.88	4.91	4.93	4.94
17	.05	2.98	3.13	3.22	3.28	3.33	3.36	3.38	3.40	3.42	3.44	3.45	3.46	3.47	3.47
	.01	4.10	4.30	4.41	4.50	4.56	4.63	4.68	4.72	4.75	4.80	4.83	4.86	4.88	4.89
18	.05	2.97	3.12	3.21	3.27	3.32	3.35	3.37	3.39	3.41	3.43	3.45	3.46	3.47	3.47
	.01	4.07	4.27	4.38	4.46	4.53	4.59	4.64	4.68	4.71	4.76	4.79	4.82	4.84	4.85
19	.05	2.96	3.11	3.19	3.26	3.31	3.35	3.37	3.39	3.41	3.43	3.44	3.46	3.47	3.47
	.01	4.05	4.24	4.35	4.43	4.50	4.56	4.61	4.64	4.67	4.72	4.76	4.79	4.81	4.82
20	.05	2.95	3.10	3.18	3.25	3.30	3.34	3.36	3.38	3.40	3.43	3.44	3.46	3.46	3.47
	.01	4.02	4.22	4.33	4.40	4.47	4.53	4.58	4.61	4.65	4.69	4.73	4.76	4.78	4.79
22	.05	2.93	3.08	3.17	3.24	3.29	3.32	3.35	3.37	3.39	3.42	3.44	3.45	3.46	3.47
	.01	3.99	4.17	4.28	4.36	4.42	4.48	4.53	4.57	4.60	4.65	4.68	4.71	4.74	4.75
24	.05	2.92	3.07	3.15	3.22	3.28	3.31	3.34	3.37	3.38	3.41	3.44	3.45	3.46	3.47
	.01	3.96	4.14	4.24	4.33	4.39	4.44	4.49	4.53	4.57	4.62	4.64	4.67	4.70	4.72
26	.05	2.91	3.06	3.14	3.21	3.27	3.30	3.34	3.36	3.38	3.41	3.43	3.45	3.46	3.47
	.01	3.93	4.11	4.21	4.30	4.36	4.41	4.46	4.50	4.53	4.58	4.62	4.65	4.67	4.69
28	.05	2.90	3.04	3.13	3.20	3.26	3.30	3.33	3.35	3.37	3.40	3.43	3.45	3.46	3.47
	.01	3.91	4.08	4.18	4.28	4.34	4.39	4.43	4.47	4.51	4.56	4.60	4.62	4.65	4.67
30	.05	2.89	3.04	3.12	3.20	3.25	3.29	3.32	3.35	3.37	3.40	3.43	3.44	3.46	3.47
	.01	3.89	4.06	4.16	4.22	4.32	4.36	4.41	4.45	4.48	4.54	4.58	4.61	4.63	4.65
40	.05	2.86	3.01	3.10	3.17	3.22	3.27	3.30	3.33	3.35	3.39	3.42	3.44	3.46	3.47
	.01	3.82	3.99	4.10	4.17	4.24	4.30	4.34	4.37	4.41	4.46	4.51	4.54	4.57	4.59
60	.05	2.83	2.98	3.08	3.14	3.20	3.24	3.28	3.31	3.33	3.37	3.40	3.43	3.45	3.47
	.01	3.76	3.92	4.03	4.12	4.17	4.23	4.27	4.31	4.34	4.39	4.44	4.47	4.50	4.53
100	.05	2.80	2.95	3.05	3.12	3.18	3.22	3.26	3.29	3.32	3.36	3.40	3.42	3.45	3.47
	.01	3.71	3.86	3.93	4.06	4.11	4.17	4.21	4.25	4.29	4.35	4.38	4.42	4.45	4.48
∞	.05	2.77	2.92	3.02	3.09	3.15	3.19	3.23	3.26	3.29	3.34	3.38	3.41	3.44	3.47
	.01	3.64	3.80	3.90	3.98	4.04	4.09	4.14	4.17	4.20	4.26	4.31	4.34	4.38	4.41

Abridged from D. B. Duncan, Multiple range and multiple F tests, *Biome..ics*, 1955, **11**, 1–42, with permission of the editor and the author.

TABLE D.9   Percentage Points for the Comparison of
$k - 1$ Treatment Means with a Control

One-tailed comparisons

Error df	α	\(k\) = number of treatment means, including control								
		2	3	4	5	6	7	8	9	10
5	.05	2.02	2.44	2.68	2.85	2.98	3.08	3.16	3.24	3.30
	.01	3.37	3.90	4.21	4.43	4.60	4.73	4.85	4.94	5.03
6	.05	1.94	2.34	2.56	2.71	2.83	2.92	3.00	3.07	3.12
	.01	3.14	3.61	3.88	4.07	4.21	4.33	4.43	4.51	4.59
7	.05	1.89	2.27	2.48	2.62	2.73	2.82	2.89	2.95	3.01
	.01	3.00	3.42	3.66	3.83	3.96	4.07	4.15	4.23	4.30
8	.05	1.86	2.22	2.42	2.55	2.66	2.74	2.81	2.87	2.92
	.01	2.90	3.29	3.51	3.67	3.79	3.88	3.96	4.03	4.09
9	.05	1.83	2.18	2.37	2.50	2.60	2.68	2.75	2.81	2.86
	.01	2.82	3.19	3.40	3.55	3.66	3.75	3.82	3.89	3.94
10	.05	1.81	2.15	2.34	2.47	2.56	2.64	2.70	2.76	2.81
	.01	2.76	3.11	3.31	3.45	3.56	3.64	3.71	3.78	3.83
11	.05	1.80	2.13	2.31	2.44	2.53	2.60	2.67	2.72	2.77
	.01	2.72	3.06	3.25	3.38	3.48	3.56	3.63	3.69	3.74
12	.05	1.78	2.11	2.29	2.41	2.50	2.58	2.64	2.69	2.74
	.01	2.68	3.01	3.19	3.32	3.42	3.50	3.56	3.62	3.67
13	.05	1.77	2.09	2.27	2.39	2.48	2.55	2.61	2.66	2.71
	.01	2.65	2.97	3.15	3.27	3.37	3.44	3.51	3.56	3.61
14	.05	1.76	2.08	2.25	2.37	2.46	2.53	2.59	2.64	2.69
	.01	2.62	2.94	3.11	3.23	3.32	3.40	3.46	3.51	3.56
15	.05	1.75	2.07	2.24	2.36	2.44	2.51	2.57	2.62	2.67
	.01	2.60	2.91	3.08	3.20	3.29	3.36	3.42	3.47	3.52
16	.05	1.75	2.06	2.23	2.34	2.43	2.50	2.56	2.61	2.65
	.01	2.58	2.88	3.05	3.17	3.26	3.33	3.39	3.44	3.48
17	.05	1.74	2.05	2.22	2.33	2.42	2.49	2.54	2.59	2.64
	.01	2.57	2.86	3.03	3.14	3.23	3.30	3.36	3.41	3.45
18	.05	1.73	2.04	2.21	2.32	2.41	2.48	2.53	2.58	2.62
	.01	2.55	2.84	3.01	3.12	3.21	3.27	3.33	3.38	3.42
19	.05	1.73	2.03	2.20	2.31	2.40	2.47	2.52	2.57	2.61
	.01	2.54	2.83	2.99	3.10	3.18	3.25	3.31	3.36	3.40
20	.05	1.72	2.03	2.19	2.30	2.39	2.46	2.51	2.56	2.60
	.01	2.53	2.81	2.97	3.08	3.17	3.23	3.29	3.34	3.38
24	.05	1.71	2.01	2.17	2.28	2.36	2.43	2.48	2.53	2.57
	.01	2.49	2.77	2.92	3.03	3.11	3.17	3.22	3.27	3.31
30	.05	1.70	1.99	2.15	2.25	2.33	2.40	2.45	2.50	2.54
	.01	2.46	2.72	2.87	2.97	3.05	3.11	3.16	3.21	3.24
40	.05	1.68	1.97	2.13	2.23	2.31	2.37	2.42	2.47	2.51
	.01	2.42	2.68	2.82	2.92	2.99	3.05	3.10	3.14	3.18
60	.05	1.67	1.95	2.10	2.21	2.28	2.35	2.39	2.44	2.48
	.01	2.39	2.64	2.78	2.87	2.94	3.00	3.04	3.08	3.12
120	.05	1.66	1.93	2.08	2.18	2.26	2.32	2.37	2.41	2.45
	.01	2.36	2.60	2.73	2.82	2.89	2.94	2.99	3.03	3.06
∞	.05	1.64	1.92	2.06	2.16	2.23	2.29	2.34	2.38	2.42
	.01	2.33	2.56	2.68	2.77	2.84	2.89	2.93	2.97	3.00

Table reproduced from A multiple comparison procedure for comparing several treatments with a control. *Journal of the American Statistical Association*, 1955, **50**, 1096–1121, with permission of the author, C. W. Dunnett, and the editor.

TABLE D.9   (Continued)

Two-tailed comparisons

Error df	α	k = number of treatment means, including control								
		2	3	4	5	6	7	8	9	10
5	.05	2.57	3.03	3.29	3.48	3.62	3.73	3.82	3.90	3.97
	.01	4.03	4.63	4.98	5.22	5.41	5.56	5.69	5.80	5.89
6	.05	2.45	2.86	3.10	3.26	3.39	3.49	3.57	3.64	3.71
	.01	3.71	4.21	4.51	4.71	4.87	5.00	5.10	5.20	5.28
7	.05	2.36	2.75	2.97	3.12	3.24	3.33	3.41	3.47	3.53
	.01	3.50	3.95	4.21	4.39	4.53	4.64	4.74	4.82	4.89
8	.05	2.31	2.67	2.88	3.02	3.13	3.22	3.29	3.35	3.41
	.01	3.36	3.77	4.00	4.17	4.29	4.40	4.48	4.56	4.62
9	.05	2.26	2.61	2.81	2.95	3.05	3.14	3.20	3.26	3.32
	.01	3.25	3.63	3.85	4.01	4.12	4.22	4.30	4.37	4.43
10	.05	2.23	2.57	2.76	2.89	2.99	3.07	3.14	3.19	3.24
	.01	3.17	3.53	3.74	3.88	3.99	4.08	4.16	4.22	4.28
11	.05	2.20	2.53	2.72	2.84	2.94	3.02	3.08	3.14	3.19
	.01	3.11	3.45	3.65	3.79	3.89	3.98	4.05	4.11	4.16
12	.05	2.18	2.50	2.68	2.81	2.90	2.98	3.04	3.09	3.14
	.01	3.05	3.39	3.58	3.71	3.81	3.89	3.96	4.02	4.07
13	.05	2.16	2.48	2.65	2.78	2.87	2.94	3.00	3.06	3.10
	.01	3.01	3.33	3.52	3.65	3.74	3.82	3.89	3.94	3.99
14	.05	2.14	2.46	2.63	2.75	2.84	2.91	2.97	3.02	3.07
	.01	2.98	3.29	3.47	3.59	3.69	3.76	3.83	3.88	3.93
15	.05	2.13	2.44	2.61	2.73	2.82	2.89	2.95	3.00	3.04
	.01	2.95	3.25	3.43	3.55	3.64	3.71	3.78	3.83	3.88
16	.05	2.12	2.42	2.59	2.71	2.80	2.87	2.92	2.97	3.02
	.01	2.92	3.22	3.39	3.51	3.60	3.67	3.73	3.78	3.83
17	.05	2.11	2.41	2.58	2.69	2.78	2.85	2.90	2.95	3.00
	.01	2.90	3.19	3.36	3.47	3.56	3.63	3.69	3.74	3.79
18	.05	2.10	2.40	2.56	2.68	2.76	2.83	2.89	2.94	2.98
	.01	2.88	3.17	3.33	3.44	3.53	3.60	3.66	3.71	3.75
19	.05	2.09	2.39	2.55	2.66	2.75	2.81	2.87	2.92	2.96
	.01	2.86	3.15	3.31	3.42	3.50	3.57	3.63	3.68	3.72
20	.05	2.09	2.38	2.54	2.65	2.73	2.80	2.86	2.90	2.95
	.01	2.85	3.13	3.29	3.40	3.48	3.55	3.60	3.65	3.69
24	.05	2.06	2.35	2.51	2.61	2.70	2.76	2.81	2.86	2.90
	.01	2.80	3.07	3.22	3.32	3.40	3.47	3.52	3.57	3.61
30	.05	2.04	2.32	2.47	2.58	2.66	2.72	2.77	2.82	2.86
	.01	2.75	3.01	3.15	3.25	3.33	3.39	3.44	3.49	3.52
40	.05	2.02	2.29	2.44	2.54	2.62	2.68	2.73	2.77	2.81
	.01	2.70	2.95	3.09	3.19	3.26	3.32	3.37	3.41	3.44
60	.05	2.00	2.27	2.41	2.51	2.58	2.64	2.69	2.73	2.77
	.01	2.66	2.90	3.03	3.12	3.19	3.25	3.29	3.33	3.37
120	.05	1.98	2.24	2.38	2.47	2.55	2.60	2.65	2.69	2.73
	.01	2.62	2.85	2.97	3.06	3.12	3.18	3.22	3.26	3.29
∞	.05	1.96	2.21	2.35	2.44	2.51	2.57	2.61	2.65	2.69
	.01	2.58	2.79	2.92	3.00	3.06	3.11	3.15	3.19	3.22

Table reproduced from New tables for multiple comparisons with a control. *Biometrics*, 1964, **20**, 482–491, with permission of the author, C. W. Dunnett, and the editor.

TABLE D.10   Upper Percentage Points of the F_{max} Statistic

$$F_{max} = (\hat{\sigma}^2_{largest})/(\hat{\sigma}^2_{smallest})$$

df for $\hat{\sigma}^2_j$	α	\multicolumn{11}{c}{k = number of variances}
		2	3	4	5	6	7	8	9	10	11	12
4	.05	9.60	15.5	20.6	25.2	29.5	33.6	37.5	41.4	44.6	48.0	51.4
	.01	23.2	37.	49.	59.	69.	79.	89.	97.	106.	113.	120.
5	.05	7.15	10.8	13.7	16.3	18.7	20.8	22.9	24.7	26.5	28.2	29.9
	.01	14.9	22.	28.	33.	38.	42.	46.	50.	54.	57.	60.
6	.05	5.82	8.38	10.4	12.1	13.7	15.0	16.3	17.5	18.6	19.7	20.7
	.01	11.1	15.5	19.1	22.	25.	27.	30.	32.	34.	36.	37.
7	.05	4.99	6.94	8.44	9.70	10.8	11.8	12.7	13.5	14.3	15.1	15.8
	.01	8.89	12.1	14.5	16.5	18.4	20.	22.	23.	24.	26.	27.
8	.05	4.43	6.00	7.18	8.12	9.03	9.78	10.5	11.1	11.7	12.2	12.7
	.01	7.50	9.9	11.7	13.2	14.5	15.8	16.9	17.9	18.9	19.8	21.
9	.05	4.03	5.34	6.31	7.11	7.80	8.41	8.95	9.45	9.91	10.3	10.7
	.01	6.54	8.5	9.9	11.1	12.1	13.1	13.9	14.7	15.3	16.0	16.6
10	.05	3.72	4.85	5.67	6.34	6.92	7.42	7.87	8.28	8.66	9.01	9.34
	.01	5.85	7.4	8.6	9.6	10.4	11.1	11.8	12.4	12.9	13.4	13.9
12	.05	3.28	4.16	4.79	5.30	5.72	6.09	6.42	6.72	7.00	7.25	7.48
	.01	4.91	6.1	6.9	7.6	8.2	8.7	9.1	9.5	9.9	10.2	10.6
15	.05	2.86	3.54	4.01	4.37	4.68	4.95	5.19	5.40	5.59	5.77	5.93
	.01	4.07	4.9	5.5	6.0	6.4	6.7	7.1	7.3	7.5	7.8	8.0
20	.05	2.46	2.95	3.29	3.54	3.76	3.94	4.10	4.24	4.37	4.49	4.59
	.01	3.32	3.8	4.3	4.6	4.9	5.1	5.3	5.5	5.6	5.8	5.9
30	.05	2.07	2.40	2.61	2.78	2.91	3.02	3.12	3.21	3.29	3.36	3.39
	.01	2.63	3.0	3.3	3.4	3.6	3.7	3.8	3.9	4.0	4.1	4.2
60	.05	1.67	1.85	1.96	2.04	2.11	2.17	2.22	2.26	2.30	2.33	2.36
	.01	1.96	2.2	2.3	2.4	2.4	2.5	2.5	2.6	2.6	2.7	2.7
∞	.05	1.00	1.00	1.00	1.00	1.00	1.00	1.00	1.00	1.00	1.00	1.00
	.01	1.00	1.00	1.00	1.00	1.00	1.00	1.00	1.00	1.00	1.00	1.00

TABLE D.11   Upper Percentage Points of Cochran's Test for Homogeneity of Variance

$$C = \frac{\text{largest } \hat{\sigma}_j^2}{\Sigma \hat{\sigma}_j^2}$$

df for $\hat{\sigma}_j^2$	α	k = number of variances										
		2	3	4	5	6	7	8	9	10	15	20
1	.05	.9985	.9669	.9065	.8412	.7808	.7271	.6798	.6385	.6020	.4709	.3894
	.01	.9999	.9933	.9676	.9279	.8828	.8376	.7945	.7544	.7175	.5747	.4799
2	.05	.9750	.8709	.7679	.6838	.6161	.5612	.5157	.4775	.4450	.3346	.2705
	.01	.9950	.9423	.8643	.7885	.7218	.6644	.6152	.5727	.5358	.4069	.3297
3	.05	.9392	.7977	.6841	.5981	.5321	.4800	.4377	.4027	.3733	.2758	.2205
	.01	.9794	.8831	.7814	.6957	.6258	.5685	.5209	.4810	.4469	.3317	.2654
4	.05	.9057	.7457	.6287	.5441	.4803	.4307	.3910	·.3584	.3311	.2419	.1921
	.01	.9586	.8335	.7212	.6329	.5635	.5080	.4627	.4251	.3934	.2882	.2288
5	.05	.8772	.7071	.5895	.5065	.4447	.3974	.3595	.3286	.3029	.2195	.1735
	.01	.9373	.7933	.6761	.5875	.5195	.4659	.4226	.3870	.3572	.2593	.2048
6	.05	.8534	.6771	.5598	.4783	.4184	.3726	.3362	.3067	.2823	.2034	.1602
	.01	.9172	.7606	.6410	.5531	.4866	.4347	.3932	.3592	.3308	.2386	.1877
7	.05	.8332	.6530	.5365	.4564	.3980	.3535	.3185	.2901	.2666	.1911	.1501
	.01	.8988	.7335	.6129	.5259	.4608	.4105	.3704	.3378	.3106	.2228	.1748
8	.05	.8159	.6333	.5175	.4387	.3817	.3384	.3043	.2768	.2541	.1815	.1422
	.01	.8823	.7107	.5897	.5037	.4401	.3911	.3522	.3207	.2945	.2104	.1646
9	.05	.8010	.6167	.5017	.4241	.3682	.3259	.2926	.2659	.2439	.1736	.1357
	.01	.8674	.6912	.5702	.4854	.4229	.3751	.3373	.3067·	.2813	.2002	.1567
16	.05	.7341	.5466	.4366	.3645	.3135	.2756	.2462	.2226	.2032	.1429	.1108
	.01	.7949	.6059	.4884	.4094	.3529	.3105	.2779	.2514	.2297	.1612	.1248
36	.05	.6602	.4748	.3720	.3066	.2612	.2278	.2022	.1820	.1655	.1144	.0879
	.01	.7067	.5153	.4057	.3351	.2858	.2494	.2214	.1992	.1811	.1251	.0960
144	.05	.5813	.4031	.3093	.2513	.2119	.1833	.1616	.1446	.1308	.0889	.0675
	.01	.6062	.4230	.3251	.2644	.2229	.1929	.1700	.1521	.1376	.0934	.0709

Reprinted from chapter 15 of *Techniques of Statistical Analysis*, edited by C. Eisenhart, M.W. Hastay, and W. A. Wallis, McGraw-Hill Book Company, 1947.

TABLE D.12 Coefficients of Orthogonal Polynomials

k	Polynomial	Coefficients										Σc_{ij}^2
3	Linear	−1	0	1								2
	Quadratic	1	−2	1								6
	Linear	−3	−1	1	3							20
4	Quadratic	1	−1	−1	1							4
	Cubic	−1	3	−3	1							20
	Linear	−2	−1	0	1	2						10
5	Quadratic	2	−1	−2	−1	2						14
	Cubic	−1	2	0	−2	1						10
	Quartic	1	−4	6	−4	1						70
	Linear	−5	−3	−1	1	3	5					70
6	Quadratic	5	−1	−4	−4	−1	5					84
	Cubic	−5	7	4	−4	−7	5					180
	Quartic	1	−3	2	2	−3	1					28
	Linear	−3	−2	−1	0	1	2	3				28
7	Quadratic	5	0	−3	−4	−3	0	5				84
	Cubic	−1	1	1	0	−1	−1	1				6
	Quartic	3	−7	1	6	1	−7	3				154
	Linear	−7	−5	−3	−1	1	3	5	7			168
	Quadratic	7	1	−3	−5	−5	−3	1	7			168
8	Cubic	−7	5	7	3	−3	−7	−5	7			264
	Quartic	7	−13	−3	9	9	−3	−13	7			616
	Quintic	−7	23	−17	−15	15	17	−23	7			2184
	Linear	−4	−3	−2	−1	0	1	2	3	4		60
	Quadratic	28	7	−8	−17	−20	−17	−8	7	28		2772
9	Cubic	−14	7	13	9	0	−9	−13	−7	14		990
	Quartic	14	−21	−11	9	18	9	−11	−21	14		2002
	Quintic	−4	11	−4	−9	0	9	4	−11	4		468
	Linear	−9	−7	−5	−3	−1	1	3	5	7	9	330
	Quadratic	6	2	−1	−3	−4	−4	−3	−1	2	6	132
10	Cubic	−42	14	35	31	12	−12	−31	−35	−14	42	8580
	Quartic	18	−22	−17	3	18	18	3	−17	−22	18	2860
	Quintic	−6	14	−1	−11	−6	6	11	1	−14	6	780

Table D.12 is taken from Table 23 of Fisher and Yates, *Statistical Tables for Biological, Agricultural and Medical Research*, published by Oliver and Boyd Ltd., Edinburgh, by permission of the authors and publishers.

TABLE D.13   Arcsin Transformation

$$\phi = 2 \arcsin \sqrt{X}$$

X	ϕ	X	ϕ	X	ϕ	X	ϕ	X	ϕ
.001	.0633	.041	.4078	.36	1.2870	.76	2.1177.	.971	2.7993
.002	.0895	.042	.4128	.37	1.3078	.77	2.1412	.972	2.8053
.003	.1096	.043	.4178	.38	1.3284	.78	2.1652	.973	2.8115
.004	.1266	.044	.4227	.39	1.3490	.79	2.1895	.974	2.8177
.005	.1415	.045	.4275	.40	1.3694	.80	2.2143	.975	2.8240
.006	.1551	.046	.4323	.41	1.3898	.81	2.2395	.976	2.8305
.007	.1675	.047	.4371	.42	1.4101	.82	2.2653	.977	2.8371
.008	.1791	.048	.4418	.43	1.4303	.83	2.2916	.978	2.8438
.009	.1900	.049	.4464	.44	1.4505	.84	2.3186	.979	2.8507
.010	.2003	.050	.4510	.45	1.4706	.85	2.3462	.980	2.8578
.011	.2101	.06	.4949	.46	1.4907	.86	2.3746	.981	2.8650
.012	.2195	.07	.5355	.47	1.5108	.87	2.4039	.982	2.8725
.013	.2285	.08	.5735	.48	1.5308	.88	2.4341	.983	2.8801
.014	.2372	.09	.6094	.49	1.5508	.89	2.4655	.984	2.8879
.015	.2456	.10	.6435	.50	1.5708	.90	2.4981	.985	2.8960
.016	.2537	.11	.6761	.51	1.5908	.91	2.5322	.986	2.9044
.017	.2615	.12	.7075	.52	1.6108	.92	2.5681	.987	2.9131
.018	.2691	.13	.7377	.53	1.6308	.93	2.6062	.988	2.9221
.019	.2766	.14	.7670	.54	1.6509	.94	2.6467	.989	2.9315
.020	.2838	.15	.7954	.55	1.6710	.95	2.6906	.990	2.9413
.021	.2909	.16	.8230	.56	1.6911	.951	2.6952	.991	2.9516
.022	.2978	.17	.8500	.57	1.7113	.952	2.6998	.992	2.9625
.023	.3045	.18	.8763	.58	1.7315	.953	2.7045	.993	2.9741
.024	.3111	.19	.9021	.59	1.7518	.954	2.7093	.994	2.9865
.025	.3176	.20	.9273	.60	1.7722	.955	2.7141	.995	3.0001
.026	.3239	.21	.9521	.61	1.7926	.956	2.7189	.996	3.0150
.027	.3301	.22	.9764	.62	1.8132	.957	2.7238	.997	3.0320
.028	.3363	.23	1.0004	.63	1.8338	.958	2.7288	.998	3.0521
.029	.3423	.24	1.0239	.64	1.8546	.959	2.7338	.999	3.0783
.030	.3482	.25	1.0472	.65	1.8755	.960	2.7389		
.031	.3540	.26	1.0701	.66	1.8965	.961	2.7440		
.032	.3597	.27	1.0928	.67	1.9177	.962	2.7492		
.033	.3654	.28	1.1152	.68	1.9391	.963	2.7545		
.034	.3709	.29	1.1374	.69	1.9606	.964	2.7598		
.035	.3764	.30	1.1593	.70	1.9823	.965	2.7652		
.036	.3818	.31	1.1810	.71	2.0042	.966	2.7707		
.037	.3871	.32	1.2025	.72	2.0264	.967	2.7762		
.038	.3924	.33	1.2239	.73	2.0488	.968	2.7819		
.039	.3976	.34	1.2451	.74	2.0715	.969	2.7876		
.040	.4027	.35	1.2661	.75	2.0944	.970	2.7934		

TABLE D.14   Power Function for Analysis of Variance

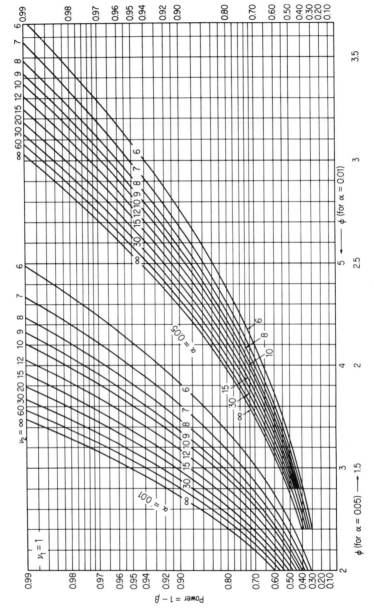

Reproduced with permission from E. S. Pearson and H. O. Hartley, Charts of the power function for analysis of variance tests, derived from the non-central *F*-distribution, *Biometrika,* 1951, **38**, 112–130.

TABLE D.14 (Continued)

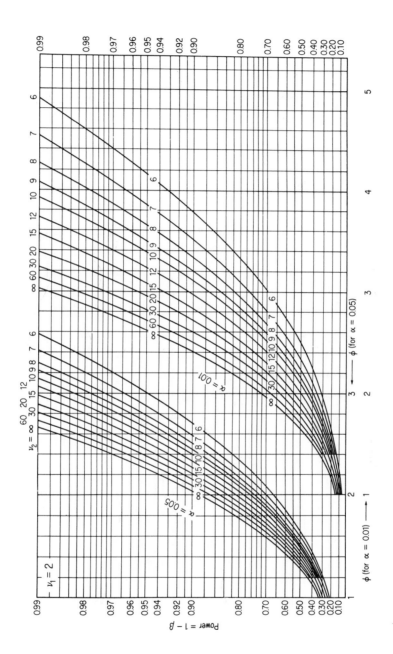

TABLE D.14   (Continued)

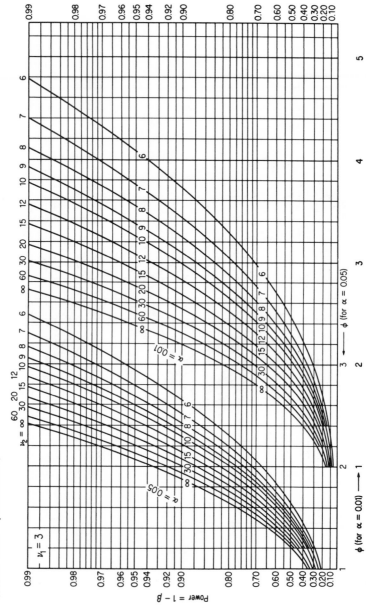

$\nu_1 = 3$

TABLE D.14 (Continued)

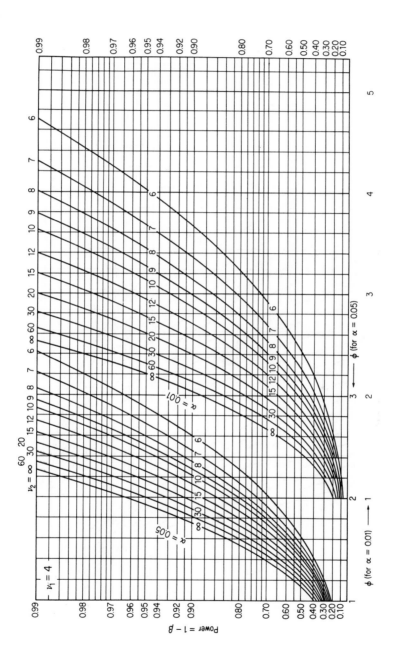

TABLE D.14 (Continued)

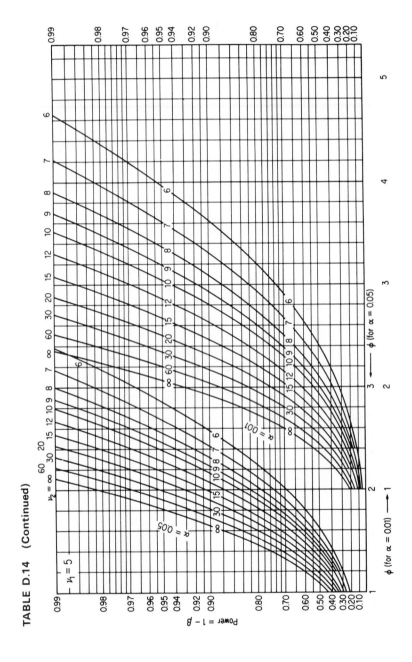

TABLE D.14 (Continued)

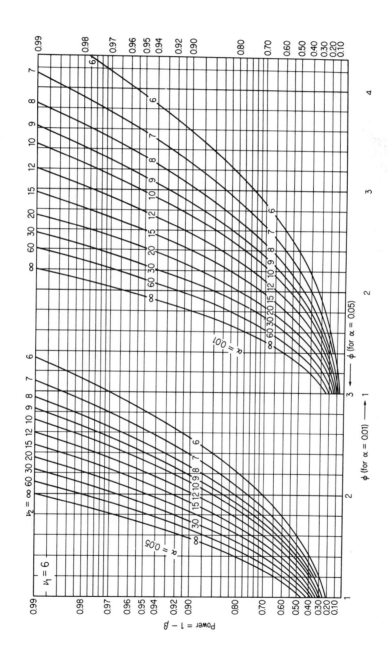

TABLE D.14   (Continued)

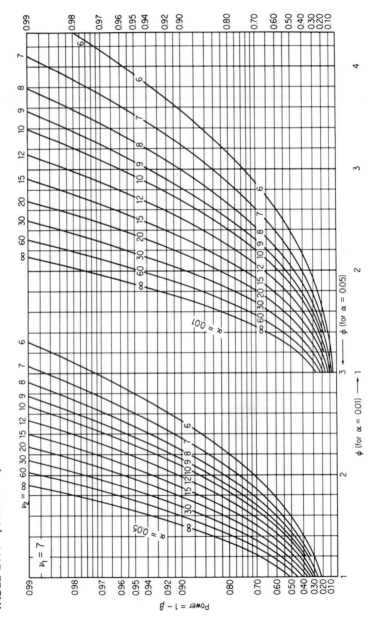

TABLE D.14 (Continued)

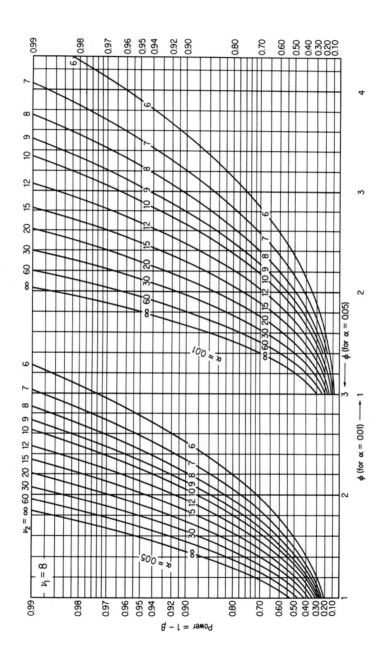

TABLE D.15   Upper Percentage Points of the Mann-Whitney U Test

$n = 3$

U \ n	1	2	3
0	.250	.100	.050
1	.500	.200	.100
2	.750	.400	.200
3		.600	.350
4			.500
5			.650

$n = 4$

U \ n	1	2	3	4
0	.200	.067	.028	.014
1	.400	.133	.057	.029
2	.600	.267	.114	.057
3		.400	.200	.100
4		.600	.314	.171
5			.429	.243
6			.571	.343
7				.443
8				.557

$n = 5$

U \ n	1	2	3	4	5
0	.167	.047	.018	.008	.004
1	.333	.095	.036	.016	.008
2	.500	.190	.071	.032	.016
3	.667	.286	.125	.056	.028
4		.429	.196	.095	.048
5		.571	.286	.143	.075
6			.393	.206	.111
7			.500	.278	.155
8			.607	.365	.210
9				.452	.274
10				.548	.345
11					.421
12					.500
13					.579

$n = 6$

U \ n	1	2	3	4	5	6
0	.143	.036	.012	.005	.002	.001
1	.286	.071	.024	.010	.004	.002
2	.428	.143	.048	.019	.009	.004
3	.571	.214	.083	.033	.015	.008
4		.321	.131	.057	.026	.013
5		.429	.190	.086	.041	.021
6		.571	.274	.129	.063	.032
7			.357	.176	.089	.047
8			.452	.238	.123	.066
9			.548	.305	.165	.090
10				.381	.214	.120
11				.457	.268	.155
12				.545	.331	.197
13					.396	.242
14					.465	.294
15					.535	.350
16						.409
17						.469
18						.531

Table reproduced from On a test of whether one of two random variables is stochastically larger than the other, *Annals of Mathematical Statistics*, 1947, **18**, 50–60, with permission of the authors, H. B. Mann and D. R. Whitney, and the editor.

TABLE D.15   **(Continued)**

$n = 7$

U \ n	1	2	3	4	5	6	7
0	.125	.028	.008	.003	.001	.001	.000
1	.250	.056	.017	.006	.003	.001	.001
2	.375	.111	.033	.012	.005	.002	.001
3	.500	.167	.058	.021	.009	.004	.002
4	.625	.250	.092	.036	.015	.007	.003
5		.333	.133	.055	.024	.011	.006
6		.444	.192	.082	.037	.017	.009
7		.556	.258	.115	.053	.026	.013
8			.333	.158	.074	.037	.019
9			.417	.206	.101	.051	.027
10			.500	.264	.134	.069	.036
11			.583	.324	.172	.090	.049
12				.394	.216	.117	.064
13				.464	.265	.147	.082
14				.538	.319	.183	.104
15					.378	.223	.130
16					.438	.267	.159
17					.500	.314	.191
18					.562	.365	.228
19						.418	.267
20						.473	.310
21						.527	.355
22							.402
23							.451
24							.500
25							.549

TABLE D.15 (Continued)

$$n = 8$$

U \ n	1	2	3	4	5	6	7	8
0	.111	.022	.006	.002	.001	.000	.000	.000
1	.222	.044	.012	.004	.002	.001	.000	.000
2	.333	.089	.024	.008	.003	.001	.001	.000
3	.444	.133	.042	.014	.005	.002	.001	.001
4	.556	.200	.067	.024	.009	.004	.002	.001
5		.267	.097	.036	.015	.006	.003	.001
6		.356	.139	.055	.023	.010	.005	.002
7		.444	.188	.077	.033	.015	.007	.003
8		.556	.248	.107	.047	.021	.010	.005
9			.315	.141	.064	.030	.014	.007
10			.387	.184	.085	.041	.020	.010
11			.461	.230	.111	.054	.027	.014
12			.539	.285	.142	.071	.036	.019
13				.341	.177	.091	.047	.025
14				.404	.217	.114	.060	.032
15				.467	.262	.141	.076	.041
16				.533	.311	.172	.095	.052
17					.362	.207	.116	.065
18					.416	.245	.140	.080
19					.472	.286	.168	.097
20					.528	.331	.198	.117
21						.377	.232	.139
22						.426	.268	.164
23						.475	.306	.191
24						.525	.347	.221
25							.389	.253
26							.433	.287
27							.478	.323
28							.522	.360
29								.399
30								.439
31								.480
32								.520

TABLE D.16 Percentage Points of the Dunn Multiple Comparison Test

Number of Comparisons (C)	α	5	7	10	12	15	Error df 20	24	30	40	60	120	∞
2	.05	3.17	2.84	2.64	2.56	2.49	2.42	2.39	2.36	2.33	2.30	2.27	2.24
	.01	4.78	4.03	3.58	3.43	3.29	3.16	3.09	3.03	2.97	2.92	2.86	2.81
3	.05	3.54	3.13	2.87	2.78	2.69	2.61	2.58	2.54	2.50	2.47	2.43	2.39
	.01	5.25	4.36	3.83	3.65	3.48	3.33	3.26	3.19	3.12	3.06	2.99	2.94
4	.05	3.81	3.34	3.04	2.94	2.84	2.75	2.70	2.66	2.62	2.58	2.54	2.50
	.01	5.60	4.59	4.01	3.80	3.62	3.46	3.38	3.30	3.23	3.16	3.09	3.02
5	.05	4.04	3.50	3.17	3.06	2.95	2.85	2.80	2.75	2.71	2.66	2.62	2.58
	.01	5.89	4.78	4.15	3.93	3.74	3.55	3.47	3.39	3.31	3.24	3.16	3.09
6	.05	4.22	3.64	3.28	3.15	3.04	2.93	2.88	2.83	2.78	2.73	2.68	2.64
	.01	6.15	4.95	4.27	4.04	3.82	3.63	3.54	3.46	3.38	3.30	3.22	3.15
7	.05	4.38	3.76	3.37	3.24	3.11	3.00	2.94	2.89	2.84	2.79	2.74	2.69
	.01	6.36	5.09	4.37	4.13	3.90	3.70	3.61	3.52	3.43	3.34	3.27	3.19
8	.05	4.53	3.86	3.45	3.31	3.18	3.06	3.00	2.94	2.89	2.84	2.79	2.74
	.01	6.56	5.21	4.45	4.20	3.97	3.76	3.66	3.57	3.48	3.39	3.31	3.23
9	.05	4.66	3.95	3.52	3.37	3.24	3.11	3.05	2.99	2.93	2.88	2.83	2.77
	.01	6.70	5.31	4.53	4.26	4.02	3.80	3.70	3.61	3.51	3.42	3.34	3.26
10	.05	4.78	4.03	3.58	3.43	3.29	3.16	3.09	3.03	2.97	2.92	2.86	2.81
	.01	6.86	5.40	4.59	4.32	4.07	3.85	3.74	3.65	3.55	3.46	3.37	3.29
15	.05	5.25	4.36	3.83	3.65	3.48	3.33	3.26	3.19	3.12	3.06	2.99	2.94
	.01	7.51	5.79	4.86	4.56	4.29	4.03	3.91	3.80	3.70	3.59	3.50	3.40
20	.05	5.60	4.59	4.01	3.80	3.62	3.46	3.38	3.30	3.23	3.16	3.09	3.02
	.01	8.00	6.08	5.06	4.73	4.42	4.15	4.04	3.90	3.79	3.69	3.58	3.48
25	.05	5.89	4.78	4.15	3.93	3.74	3.55	3.47	3.39	3.31	3.24	3.16	3.09
	.01	8.37	6.30	5.20	4.86	4.53	4.25	4.1*	3.98	3.88	3.76	3.64	3.54
30	.05	6.15	4.95	4.27	4.04	3.82	3.63	3.54	3.46	3.38	3.30	3.22	3.15
	.01	8.68	6.49	5.33	4.95	4.61	4.33	4.2*	4.13	3.93	3.81	3.69	3.59
35	.05	6.36	5.09	4.37	4.13	3.90	3.70	3.61	3.52	3.43	3.34	3.27	3.19
	.01	8.95	6.67	5.44	5.04	4.71	4.39	4.3*	4.26	3.97	3.84	3.73	3.63
40	.05	6.56	5.21	4.45	4.20	3.97	3.76	3.66	3.57	3.48	3.39	3.31	3.23
	.01	9.19	6.83	5.52	5.12	4.78	4.46	4.3*	4.1*	4.01	3.89	3.77	3.66
45	.05	6.70	5.31	4.53	4.26	4.02	3.80	3.70	3.61	3.51	3.42	3.34	3.26
	.01	9.41	6.93	5.60	5.20	4.84	4.52	4.3*	4.2*	4.1*	3.93	3.80	3.69
50	.05	6.86	5.40	4.59	4.32	4.07	3.85	3.74	3.65	3.55	3.46	3.37	3.29
	.01	9.68	7.06	5.70	5.27	4.90	4.56	4.4*	4.2*	4.1*	3.97	3.83	3.72
100	.05	8.00	6.08	5.06	4.73	4.42	4.15	4.04	3.90	3.79	3.69	3.58	3.48
	.01	11.04	7.80	6.20	5.70	5.20	4.80	4.7*	4.4*	4.5*		4.00	3.89
250	.05	9.68	7.06	5.70	5.27	4.90	4.56	4.4*	4.2*	4.1*	3.97	3.83	3.72
	.01	13.26	8.83	6.9*	6.3*	5.8*	5.2*	5.0*	4.9*	4.8*			4.11

*Obtained by graphical interpolation. Table reproduced from Multiple comparisons among means. *Journal of the American Statistical Association*, 1961, **56**, 52–64, with permission of the author, O. J. Dunn, and the editor.

GLOSSARY OF TERMS

Acceptance region. A set of outcomes of a statistical test that leads to acceptance of the null hypothesis.

Adjusted sum of squares. A sum of squares from which effects associated with a covariate have been removed in analysis of covariance. This sum of squares is also called a reduced sum of squares.

Alias. An effect in a fractionally replicated design that cannot be distinguished from another effect.

Alpha error. Error that occurs when an experimenter rejects the null hypothesis when it is true. This error is usually referred to as a type I error.

Alternative hypothesis (H_1). The hypothesis that remains tenable when the null hypothesis is rejected.

Arcsin transformation. A transformation of a variate, say X, into a variate X' by some relation of the type

$$X' = \arcsin (X + k),$$

where k is chosen for convenience.

Bias. Any effect that systematically distorts the outcome of an experiment so that the results are not representative of the phenomenon under investigation.

Comparison. A linear combination of treatment level sums or means in which the sum of the coefficients, C_j, is equal to zero.

Confidence interval. A range of values that, considering all possible samples, has some designated probability of including the true population value.

Confidence limits. Upper and lower boundaries of confidence interval.

Confounding. A procedure whereby treatments are assigned to subjects so that certain effects cannot be distinguished from other effects. The purpose of confounding is to reduce the number of treatment level combinations that must be assigned to blocks of subjects.

Conjugate squares. Two Latin squares are conjugate if the rows of one are identical to the columns of the other.

Consistent estimator. An estimating procedure is consistent if the estimates it yields tend to approach the parameter more and more closely as the sample size approaches ∞. Such estimates are called consistent estimates.

Consistent test statistic. A statistic provides for a consistent test if the probability of rejecting a false null hypothesis approaches 1 as the sample size approaches ∞.

Critical region. A set of outcomes of a statistical test that leads to the rejection of the null hypothesis.

Critical value. The value of a statistic that corresponds to a given significance level as determined from its sampling distribution. For example, if Prob. $(F > F_{\alpha;v_1,v_2}) = .05$, then $F_{\alpha;v_1,v_2}$ is the critical value of F at the 5% level.

Crossed treatments. An arrangement in which all possible combinations of levels of two or more treatments occur together in an experiment.

Degrees of freedom. The number of independent observations for a source of variation minus the number of independent parameters estimated in computing the variation.

Density function. An expression that gives the frequency of a variate, say X, as a function of X. Unless otherwise specified, the total frequency is taken to be unity, so that the density function represents the proportion of variate-values X.

Distribution free method. A method for testing a hypothesis or setting up a confidence interval, for example, which does not depend on the form of the underlying distribution.

Dummy treatment level. A hypothetical treatment level that is not actually administered but which is conceptually included in an experiment in order to preserve the symmetry of the design.

Efficient estimator. An estimator is asymptotically efficient if the distribution of estimates that it yields tends to normality with the least possible standard deviation of the estimate as the sample size is increased.

Estimator. The particular function of observations in a sample that is chosen to estimate a population parameter. For example, the sample mean is used to estimate the population mean. The numerical value obtained is called an estimate.

Expected value. The long-run average of a random variable over an indefinite number of samplings. The expected value $[E(X)]$ of a discrete random variable X is given by $E(X) = \Sigma X p(X) =$ mean of X. It should be noted from the above definition that an expected value may be a value that the random variable could not actually have.

Experimental error. Measure that includes all uncontrolled sources of variation affecting a particular score.

Fixed-effects model. An experimental design model in which it is assumed that all treatment levels about which inferences are to be made are included in an experiment.

Hypothetical population. A statistical population that has no real existence but is imagined to be generated by repetitions of events of a certain type.

Incomplete block. A block that does not include all treatment levels or combinations of treatment levels contained in an experiment.

Interaction. Two treatments are said to interact if scores obtained under levels of one treatment behave differently under different levels of the other treatment.

Level of significance (α). Probability of rejecting the null hypothesis when it is true.

Likelihood ratio test. A general procedure for finding a test statistic with optimal properties for testing any of a broad class of hypotheses.

Maximum-likelihood estimator. An estimator that, when substituted for the parameter, maximizes the likelihood of the sample result.

Minimax principle.   A decision rule whereby an experimenter minimizes his maximum-expected loss over all possible true situations.

Mixed model.   An experimental design model in which some treatments are fixed effects and other treatments are random effects.

Most powerful test.   A test that has the smallest probability of a type II error when used to evaluate a particular H_0 against some particular true alternative value covered by H_1.

Multivariate normal distribution.   A generalization of a univariate normal distribution to the case of p variates, where $p \geq 2$.

Nested treatment.   A treatment, say B, is nested if each level of treatment B appears in combination with only one level of another treatment.

Nonparametric method.   A method for testing a hypothesis that does not involve an explicit assertion concerning a parameter.

Null hypothesis (H_0).   A statement concerning one or more parameters that is subjected to statistical test.

Orthogonal comparison.   Two comparisons are said to be orthogonal if the products of their corresponding coefficients sum to zero.

Parameter.   A measure computed from all observations in a population. Parameters are designated by Greek letters. For example, the symbols for a population mean and standard deviation are μ and σ, respectively.

Percentage point.   A level of significance (α) that is expressed in the form of a percentage.

Plot.   A set of subjects or materials to which a treatment is administered. The term plot originally referred to a plot of land in agricultural research, but it is now defined more broadly as indicated above.

Population.   A collection of all observations identifiable by a set of rules.

Power of test.   Probability of rejecting the null hypothesis when the alternative hypothesis is true. If β is designated as the probability of committing a type II error, power is equal to $1 - \beta$.

Random-effects model.   An experimental design model in which it is assumed that the treatment levels investigated in an experiment represent a random sample from a population of treatment levels.

Random sample, simple.   A sample drawn from a population in such a way that all possible samples of size n have the same probability of being selected.

Random variable.   A quantity, say X, where X may assume a range of possible values, each having an associated probability $p(X)$.

Relative efficiency of a statistic.   Ratio of experimental error of one statistic to that of another statistic.

Relative information.   The ratio of information concerning an effect relative to the information that would be available concerning the effect if an experimental design involved no confounding.

Replication.   The collection of two or more observations under a set of identical experimental conditions.

Research hypothesis. A tentative theory or supposition provisionally adopted to account for certain facts and to guide in the investigation of others. The terms research hypothesis and scientific hypothesis may be used interchangeably.

Sample. A subset of observations from a population.

Sampling distribution. A theoretical probability distribution that describes the functional relation between possible values of a statistic based on N cases drawn at random and the probability associated with each value over all possible samples of size N.

Standard square. Latin square in which the first row and first column are ordered alphabetically or numerically.

Statistic. A measure computed from observations in a sample. Statistics are designated by Latin letters. For example, the symbols for a sample mean and standard deviation are $\overline{X}$ and S, respectively.

Statistical decision theory. Branch of mathematics concerned with the problem of decision making and the choice of decision rules under uncertain conditions.

Statistical hypothesis. A statement about one or more parameters of a population. Null and alternative hypotheses are two forms of a statistical hypothesis.

Statistical model. A mathematical statement concerning the sampling distribution of random variables that is used in evaluating the outcome of an experiment or in predicting the outcome of future replications of an experiment.

Statistical test. A procedure whereby two mutually exclusive statistical hypotheses are evaluated in the light of sample data. The hypothesis that dictates the sampling distribution against which an obtained sample value is compared is said to be the one tested.

Sufficient estimator. A statistic that contains all the information available in the data concerning a parameter. A statistic is a sufficient or *best* estimator of a parameter if the estimate cannot be improved by utilizing any other aspect of the data not already included in the statistic. For example, the sample mean is a sufficient estimator of the population mean when the distribution is normal.

Test statistic. A statistic whose purpose is to provide a test of some statistical hypothesis. Test statistics such as t and F have known sampling distributions that can be employed in determining the probability of an obtained result under the null hypothesis.

Transformation. A systematic alteration in a set of scores whereby certain characteristics of the set are changed and other characteristics remain unchanged.

Type I error. Error that occurs when the experimenter rejects the null hypothesis when it is true. The probability of committing a type I error is determined by the level of significance (α) which the experimenter adopts.

Type II error. Error that occurs when the experimenter fails to reject the null hypothesis when it is false. The probability (β) of committing a type II error is determined by the magnitude of the experimental effect, size of sample, magnitude of random error, and level of significance.

Unbiased estimator. An estimate of a parameter is said to be unbiased if its expected value is equal to the parameter.

Unbiased test statistic. A statistic provides for an unbiased test of the null hypothesis if it makes the probability of rejecting H_0 a minimum when H_0 is true.

Uniformly most powerful test. A test for which the probability of a type II error is smaller than any other test regardless of the true value covered by the alternative hypothesis.

Variance-covariance matrix. Given n variates $X_{ij} \ldots X_{nj}$ for which the covariance of X_{ij} and $X_{ij'}$ is $\rho\sigma_{jj'}^2$, the square matrix containing σ_j^2 and $\rho\sigma_{jj'}^2$ is called the variance-covariance matrix. The diagonal terms of the square matrix are the variances σ_j^2's, and the off-diagonal terms are the covariances $\rho\sigma_{jj'}^2$'s. A variance-covariance matrix is also called a dispersion matrix and a covariance matrix.

REFERENCES

Ackoff, R. L., S. K. Gupta, and J. S. Minas. *Scientific Method, Optimizing Applied Research Decisions.* New York, John Wiley & Sons, Inc., 1962. [32]*

Addelman, S. Techniques for constructing fractional replicate plans. *Journal of the American Statistical Association,* 1963, **58,** 45–71. [403]

Addelman, S. and S. Bush. A Procedure for Constructing Incomplete Block Designs. Statistics Research Division, *Research Triangle Institute Tech Report No. 4.* Raleigh, North Carolina, 1963. [454]

Allan, F. E. and J. Wishart. A method of estimating yield of a missing plot in field experimental work. *Journal of Agricultural Science,* 1930, **20,** 399–406. [162]

Anderson, N. H. Scales and statistics: parametric and nonparametric. *Psychological Bulletin,* 1961, **58,** 305–316. [492]

Anderson, R. L. Missing-plot techniques. *Biometrics Bulletin,* 1946, **2,** 41–47. [281, 282]

Anderson, R. L. and T. A. Bancroft. *Statistical Theory in Research.* New York, McGraw-Hill Book Co., Inc., 1952. [208, 434]

Anderson, R. L. and E. E. Houseman. Tables of orthogonal polynomial values extended to $N = 104$. *Iowa Agricultural Experiment Station Research Bulletin 297,* 1942. [117]

Anderson, S. L. *see* Box, G. E. P. and…

Anderson, T. W. *Introduction to Multivariate Statistical Analysis.* New York, John Wiley & Sons, Inc., 1958. [5, 257]

Aspin, A. A. Tables for use in comparisons whose accuracy involves two variances separately estimated. *Biometrika,* 1949, **36,** 290–293. [98]

Attneave, F. *Applications of Information Theory to Psychology: A Summary of Basic Concepts, Methods, and Results.* New York, Holt, Rinehart and Winston, Inc., 1959. [502]

Bakan, D. The test of significance in psychological research. *Psychological Bulletin,* 1966, **66,** 423–437. [32, 77]

Bancroft, T. A. *see* Anderson, R. L. and…

Bancroft, T. A. *see also* Bozivich, H.,…, and H. O. Hartley

Bargmann, R. A study of dependence in multivariate normal analysis. *Institute of Statistics Mimeograph Series No. 186.* Raleigh, University of North Carolina, 1957. [247]

Bartlett, M. S. A note on the analysis of covariance. *Journal of Agricultural Science,* 1936, **26,** 488–491. [477]

———————. Properties of sufficiency and statistical tests. *Proceedings of the Royal Society, A901,* 1937, **160,** 268–282. [61]

———————. The use of transformations. *Biometrics,* 1947, **3,** 39–52. [66]

Bechhofer, R. E. A single-sample multiple decision procedure for ranking means of normal populations with known variances. *Annals of Mathematical Statistics,* 1954, **25,** 16–39. [97]

Bechhofer, R. E., C. W. Dunnett, and M. Sobel. A two-sample multiple decision procedure for ranking means of normal populations with unknown variances. *Biometrika,* 1954, **41,** 170–176. [97]

Benjamin, L. S. A special Latin square for the use of each subject "as his own control." *Psychometrika,* 1965, **30,** 499–513. [376]

Bennett, C. A. and N. L. Franklin. *Statistical Analysis in Chemistry and the Chemical Industry.* New York, John Wiley & Sons, Inc., 1954. [208, 217, 275, 392]

Binder, A. Further considerations on testing the null hypothesis and the strategy and tactics of investigating theoretical models. *Psychological Review,* 1963, **70,** 107–115. [23, 77]

——————. Statistical theory. In P. Farnsworth (ed.), *Annual Review of Psychology,* Palo Alto, California, Annual Reviews, Inc., 1964. [32]

Bose, R. C. On the construction of balanced incomplete block designs. *Annals of Eugenics,* 1939, **9,** 353–400. [427]

Bose, R. C., W. H. Clatworthy, and S. S. Shrikhande. Tables of partially balanced designs with two associate classes. *North Carolina, Agricultural Experiment Station Technical Bulletin 107.* West Raleigh, North Carolina, 1954. [454]

Bose, R. C. and K. R. Nair. Partially balanced incomplete block designs. *Sankhyā,* 1939, **4,** 337–372. [454]

Bose, R. C., S. S. Shrikhande, and E. T. Parker. Further results on the construction of mutually orthogonal Latin squares and the falsity of Euler's conjecture. *Canadian Journal of Mathematics,* 1960, **12,** 189–203. [168]

Box, G. E. P. Nonnormality and tests on variances. *Biometrika,* 1953, **40,** 318–335. [61, 142]

——————. Problems in the analysis of growth and wear curves. *Biometrics,* 1950, **6,** 362–389. [258]

——————. Some theorems on quadratic forms applied in the study of analysis of variance problems. I. Effect of inequality of variance in the one-way classification. *Annals of Mathematical Statistics,* 1954a, **25,** 290–302. [61]

——————. Some theorems on quadratic forms applied in the study of analysis of variance problems. II. Effects of inequality of variance and of correlation between errors in the two-way classification. *Annals of Mathematical Statistics,* 1954b, **25,** 484–498. [142, 184]

Box, G. E. P. and S. L. Anderson. Permutation theory in the derivation of robust criteria and the study of departures from assumptions. *Journal of the Royal Statistical Society, Series B,* 1955, **17,** 1–34. [62]

Box, G. E. P. and D. R. Cox. An analysis of transformations. *Journal of the Royal Statistical Society, Series B,* 1964, **26,** 211–252. [67]

Bozivich, H., T. A. Bancroft, and H. O. Hartley. Power of analysis of variance procedures for certain incompletely specified models. *Annals of Mathematical Statistics,* 1956, **27,** 1017–1043. [214, 216]

Bradley, R. A. and M. E. Terry. Rank analysis of incomplete block designs. *Biometrika,* 1952, **39,** 324–345. [502]

Bross, I. Fiducial intervals for variance components. *Biometrics,* 1950, **6,** 136–144. [199]

Bush, H. L. *see* Doxtator, C. W., B. Tolman, C. E. Cormany,..., and V. Jensen

Bush, R. R. *see* Mosteller, F. and...

Bush, S. *see* Addelman, S. and...

Castellan, N. J., Jr. On the partitioning of contingency tables. *Psychological Bulletin,* 1965, **64,** 330–338. [502]

Clark, A. G. *see* Leonard, W. H. and...

Clark, C. A. Hypothesis testing in relation to statistical methodology. *Review of Educational Research,* 1963, **33,** 455–473. [22, 24, 29]

Clatworthy, W. H. *see* Bose, R. C.,..., and S. S. Shrikhande

Clelland, R. C. *see* Tate, M. W. and...

Clem, M. A. and W. T. Federer. Random arrangements for lattice designs. *Iowa Agricultural Experiment Station, Special Report No. 5.* Ames, Iowa, 1950. [453]

Cochran, W. G. Analysis of covariance: its nature and uses. *Biometrics,* 1957, **13,** 261–281. [468, 486]

——————. The analysis of lattice and triple lattice experiments in corn varietal tests. II. Mathematical theory. *Iowa Agricultural Experiment Station Research Bulletin.* Ames, Iowa, 1940a, **281,** 45–66. [486]

——————. The comparison of percentages in matched samples. *Biometrika,* 1950, **37,** 256–266. [502]

——————. The distribution of the largest of a set of estimated variances as a fraction of their total. *Annals of Eugenics,* 1941, **11,** 47–52. [62]

——————. Recent work on the analysis of variance. *Journal of the Royal Statistical Society,* 1938, **101,** 434–449. [151]

——————. Some consequences when the assumptions for the analysis of variance are not satisfied. *Biometrics,* 1947, **3,** 22–38. [60, 61, 63]

——————. Some methods for strengthening the common x^2 tests. *Biometrics,* 1954, **10,** 417–451. [502]

——————. A survey of experimental designs. Mimeographed. U.S. Department of Agriculture, Agricultural Marketing Service, 1940b. [151]

——————. Testing a linear relation among variances. *Biometrics,* 1951, **7,** 17–32. [213]

——————. The x^2 test of goodness of fit. *Annals of Mathematical Statistics,* 1952, **23,** 315–345. [502]

Cochran, W. G. and G. M. Cox. *Experimental Designs,* New York, John Wiley & Sons, Inc., 1957. [8, 60, 78, 98, 267, 334, 339, 346, 365, 373, 374, 380, 394, 403, 427, 437, 443, 452, 453, 454]

Connor, W. S. and S. Young. *Fractional Factorial Designs for Experiments with Factors at Two and Three Levels.* National Bureau of Standards, Applied Mathematics Series 58, 1961. [403]

Connor, W. S. and M. Zelen. *Fractional Factorial Experimental Designs for Factors at Three Levels.* National Bureau of Standards, Applied Mathematics Series 54, 1959. [395]

Cooley, W. W. and P. R. Lohnes. *Multivariate Procedures for the Behavioral Sciences.* New York, John Wiley & Sons, Inc., 1962. [5, 366]

Coons, I. The analysis of covariance as a missing plot technique. *Biometrics,* 1957, **13,** 387–405. [458]

Cormany, C. E. *see* Doxtator, C. W., B. Tolman,..., H. L. Bush, and V. Jensen

Cornfield, J. and J. W. Tukey. Average values of mean squares in factorials. *Annals of Mathematical Statistics,* 1956, **27,** 907–949. [208, 275]

Cornish, E. A. The analysis of covariance in quasi-factorial designs. *Annals of Eugenics,* 1940a, **10,** 269–279. [486]

——————. The estimation of missing values in incomplete randomized block experiments. *Annals of Eugenics,* 1940b, **10,** 112–118. [436]

Cox, D. R. *Planning of Experiments.* New York, John Wiley & Sons, Inc., 1958. [155]

——————. The use of a concomitant variable in selecting an experimental design. *Biometrika,* 1957, **44,** 150–158. [487]

Cox, D. R. *see also* Box, G. E. P. and...

Cox, G. M. Modernized field designs at Rothamsted. *Soil Science Society of America Proceedings,* 1943, **8,** 20–22. [11]

Cox, G. M. *see also* Cochran, W. G. and...

Dalal, S. N. *see* Overall, J. E. and...

Danford, M. B., H. M. Hughes, and R. C. McNee. On the analysis of repeated-measurements experiments. *Biometrics,* 1960, **16,** 547–565. [258]

Daniel, C. Fractional replication in industrial research. *Proceedings of the Third Berkeley Symposium on Mathematical Statistics and Probability,* Berkeley, University of California Press, 1956, **5,** 87. [392]

Das, M. N. Analysis of covariance in two-way classification with disproportionate cell frequencies. *Journal of the Indian Society of Agricultural Statistics,* 1953, **5,** 161–178. [482]

Davies, O. L. (ed.) *The Design and Analysis of Industrial Experiments.* New York, Hafner Publishing Company, Inc., 1956. [365, 392, 394]

DeLury, D. B. The analysis of Latin squares when some observations are missing. *Journal of the American Statistical Association,* 1946, **41,** 370–389. [164]

Dixon, W. J. and F. J. Massey, Jr. *Introduction to Statistical Analysis.* New York, McGraw-Hill Book Company, Inc., 1957. [98]

Doxtator, C. W., B. Tolman, C. E. Cormany, H. L. Bush, and V. Jensen. Standardization of experimental methods. *American Society of Sugar Beet Technology Proceedings,* 1942, **3,** 595–599. [11]

Draper, N. R. and D. M. Stoneman. Estimating missing values in unreplicated two-level factorial and fractional factorial designs. *Biometrics,* 1964, **20,** 443–458. [403]

DuBois, P. H. *An Introduction to Psychological Statistics.* New York, Harper & Row, Publishers, Inc., 1965. [141]

Duncan, D. B. Multiple range and multiple *F* tests. *Biometrics,* 1955, **11,** 1–42. [86, 93, 533]

——————. Multiple range tests for correlated and heteroscedastic means. *Biometrics,* 1957, **13,** 164–176. [94]

Dunn, O. J. Multiple comparisons among means. *Journal of the American Statistical Association,* 1961, **56,** 52–64. [79, 81, 551]

——————. Multiple comparisons using rank sums. *Technometrics,* 1964, **6,** 241–252. [494]

Dunn, O. J. and F. J. Massey, Jr. Estimation of multiple contrasts using *t*-distributions. *Journal of the American Statistical Association,* 1965, **60,** 573–583. [81]

Dunnett, C. W. A multiple comparison procedure for comparing several treatments with a control. *Journal of the American Statistical Association,* 1955, **50,** 1096–1121. [94, 534]

——————. New tables for multiple comparisons with a control. *Biometrics,* 1964, **20,** 482–491. [95, 535]

Dunnett, C. W. *see also* Bechhofer, R. E.,..., and M. Sobel

Dwyer, P. S. *Linear Computations.* New York, John Wiley & Sons, Inc., 1951. [204]

Edgington, E. S. Statistical inference and nonrandom samples. *Psychological Bulletin,* 1966, **66,** 485–487. [13]

Edwards, A. L. *Expected Values of Discrete Random Variables and Elementary Statistics.* New York, John Wiley & Sons, Inc., 1964. [128]

Edwards, W. Tactical note on the relation between scientific and statistical hypotheses. *Psychological Bulletin,* 1965, **63,** 400–402. [23]

Edwards, W., H. Lindman, and L. J. Savage. Bayesian statistical inference for psychological research. *Psychological Review,* 1963, **70,** 193–242. [32]

Eisenhart, C. The assumptions underlying the analysis of variance. *Biometrics,* 1947, **3,** 1–21. [63, 184]

Eisenhart, C., M. W. Hastay, and W. A. Wallis. *Techniques of Statistical Analysis.* New York, McGraw-Hill Book Company, Inc., 1947. [537]

Ellis, D. S. *see* McHugh, R. B. and...

Federer, W. T. Evaluation of variance components from a group of experiments with multiple classifications. *Iowa Agricultural Experiment Station Research Bulletin,* Ames, Iowa, 1951, **380,** 241–310. [146]

——————. *Experimental Design: Theory and Application.* New York, The Macmillan Company, 1955. [9, 11, 155, 169, 203, 283, 327, 338, 339, 346, 365, 367, 370, 374, 380, 452, 453, 477, 479, 482, 485]

Federer, W. T. *see also* Clem, M. A. and...

Feldt, L. S. A comparison of the precision of three experimental designs employing a concomitant variable. *Psychometrika,* 1958, **23,** 335–354. [487]

Finney, D. J. The fractional replication of factorial arrangements. *Annals of Eugenics,* 1945, **12,** 291–301. [385]

——————. *An Introduction to the Theory of Experimental Design.* Chicago, The University of Chicago Press, 1960. [21, 393]

——————. Recent developments in the design of field experiments. III. Fractional replication. *Journal of Agricultural Science,* 1946a, **36,** 184–191. [385]

——————. Standard errors of yields adjusted for regression on an independent measurement. *Biometrics Bulletin,* 1946b, **2,** 53–55. [472]

——————. Stratification, balance, and covariance. *Biometrics,* 1957, **13,** 373–386. [487]

Fisher, R. A. *The Design of Experiments.* Edinburgh, Oliver & Boyd Ltd., 1949. [87]

——————. The fiducial agreement in statistical inference. *Annals of Eugenics,* 1935, **6,** 391–398. [11, 98, 148]

——————. International Mathematical Conference, Toronto, 1924. [39]

Fisher, R. A. and W. A. MacKenzie. The correlation of weekly rainfall. *Quarterly Journal of the Royal Meteorological Society,* 1922, **48,** 234–245. [11]

——————. Studies in crop variation. II. The manurial response of different potato varieties. *Journal of Agricultural Science,* 1923, **13,** 311–320. [11]

Fisher, R. A. and F. Yates. The six by six Latin squares. *Proceedings of the Cambridge Philosophical Society,* 1934, **30,** 492–507. [153, 168]

——————. *Statistical Tables for Biological, Agricultural and Medical Research.* Edinburgh, Oliver & Boyd Ltd., 1963. [117, 152, 154, 155, 168, 427, 520, 523, 530, 538]

Franklin, N. L. *see* Bennett, C. A. and...

Fraser, D. A. S. *Nonparametric Methods in Statistics.* New York, John Wiley & Sons, Inc., 1957. [502]

Freeman, M. F. and J. W. Tukey. Transformations related to the angular and the square root. *Annals of Mathematical Statistics,* 1950, **21,** 607–611. [65]

Friedman, M. The use of ranks to avoid the assumption of normality implicit in the analysis of variance. *Journal of the American Statistical Association,* 1937, **32,** 675–701. [498, 501]

Fryer, H. C. *Concepts and Methods of Experimental Statistics.* Boston, Allyn and Bacon, Inc., 1966. [5]

Gabriel, K. R. A procedure for testing the homogeneity of all sets of means in analysis of variance. *Biometrics,* 1964, **20,** 459–477. [97]

Gaito, J. Repeated measurements designs and counterbalancing. *Psychological Bulletin,* 1961, **58,** 46–54. [248]

──────────. Unequal intervals and unequal *n* in trend analyses. *Psychological Bulletin,* 1965, **63,** 125–127. [513]

Garner, W. R. and H. W. Hake. The amount of information in absolute judgments. *Psychological Review,* 1951, **58,** 446–459. [502]

Geisser, S. and S. W. Greenhouse. An extension of Box's results on the use of the *F* distribution in multivariate analysis. *Annals of Mathematical Statistics,* 1958, **29,** 885–891. [143, 262]

Gosset, W. S. The probable error of the mean. *Biometrika,* 1908, **6,** 1–25. [41]

Gourlay, N. Covariance analysis and its application in psychological research. *British Journal of Statistical Psychology,* 1953, **6,** 25. [487]

Grandage, A. Orthogonal coefficients for unequal intervals. *Biometrics,* 1958, **14,** 287–289. [515]

Grant, D. A. Testing the null hypothesis and the strategy and tactics of investigating theoretical models. *Psychological Review,* 1962, **69,** 54–61. [23, 77]

Green, B. F. and J. Tukey. Complex analysis of variance: general problems. *Psychometrika,* 1960, **25,** 127–152. [214, 216]

Greenhouse, S. W. *see* Geisser, S. and...

Gupta, S. K. *see* Ackoff, R. L.,..., and J. S. Minas

Haggard, E. A. *Intraclass Correlation and the Analysis of Variance.* New York, The Dryden Press, Inc., 1958. [127]

Hake, H. W. *see* Garner, W. R. and...

Hale, R. W. *see* Yates, F. and...

Harshbarger, B. Near balance rectangular lattices. *Virginia Journal of Science, New Series.* 1951, **2,** 13–27. [452]

──────────. Rectangular lattices. *Virginia Agricultural Experiment Station. Memoir,* Blacksburg, Virginia, 1947, **1,** 1–26. [452]

──────────. Triple rectangular lattices. *Biometrics,* 1949, **5,** 1–13. [452]

Harter, H. L. Error rates and sample sizes for range tests in multiple comparisons. *Biometrics,* 1957, **13,** 511–536. [78, 85]

Harter, H. L. and M. D. Lum. An Interpretation and Extension of Tukey's One Degree of Freedom for Nonadditivity. *WADC Technical Report 62-313.* Wright-Patterson AFB, Ohio, 1962. [228]

──────────. Partially hierarchal models in the analysis of variance. *WADC Technical Report 55-33.* Wright-Patterson AFB, Ohio, 1955. [236]

Hartley, H. O. The maximum *F*-ratio as a short-cut test for heterogeneity of variance. *Biometrika,* 1950, **37,** 308–312. [62]

──────────. Testing the homogeneity of a set of variances. *Biometrika,* 1940, **31,** 249–255. [62]

Hartley, H. O. *see also* Pearson, E. S. and..., 1942

Hartley, H. O. *see also* Pearson, E. S. and..., 1943

Hartley, H. O. *see also* Pearson, E. S. and..., 1951

Hartley, H. O. *see also* Pearson, E. S. and..., 1958

Hartley, H. O. *see also* Smith, C. A. B. and...

Hartley, H. O. *see also* Bozivich, H., T. A. Bancroft, and...

Hastay, M. W. *see* Eisenhart, C...., and W. A. Wallis

Hays, W. L. *Statistics for Psychologists.* New York, Holt, Rinehart and Winston, Inc., 1963. [22, 126, 127, 128, 184, 199]

Hazel, L. N. The covariance analysis of multiple classification tables with unequal subclass numbers. *Biometrics,* 1946, **2,** 21-25. [282, 482]

Henderson, C. R. Estimation of variance and covariance components. *Biometrics,* 1953, **9,** 226-252. [282]

Hicks, C. R. *Fundamental Concepts in the Design of Experiments.* New York, Holt, Rinehart and Winston, Inc., 1965. [231, 339]

Horst, P. *Matrix Algebra for Social Scientists.* New York, Holt, Rinehart and Winston, Inc., 1963. [144]

Houseman, E. E. *see* Anderson, R. L. and...

Hughes, H. M. *see* Danford, M. B.,..., and R. C. McNee

Jensen, V. *see* Doxtator, C. W., B. Tolman, C. E. Cormany, H. L. Bush, and...

Johnson. N. L. and F. C. Leone. *Statistics and Experimental Design In Engineering and the Physical Sciences.* Vol. II, New York, John Wiley & Sons, Inc., 1964. [365, 403]

Jonckheere, A. R. A distribution-free k-sample test against ordered alternatives. *Biometrika,* 1954, **41,** 133-145. [502]

Kempthorne, O. *The Design and Analysis of Experiments.* New York, John Wiley & Sons, Inc., 1952. [163, 204, 321, 358, 365, 366, 367, 374, 403, 427, 453, 454]

—————————. A simple approach to confounding and fractional replication in factorial experiments. *Biometrika,* 1947, **34,** 255-272. [385]

Kempthorne, O. *see also* Wilk, M. B. and...

Kendall, M. G. *The Advanced Theory of Statistics,* Vol. II. London, Charles Griffin and Company, Ltd., 1948a. [470]

—————————. *Rank Correlation Methods.* London, Charles Griffin and Company, Ltd., 1948b. [498, 502]

Keuls. M. The use of studentized range in connection with an analysis of variance. *Euphytica,* 1952, **1,** 112-122. [91]

Khargonkar, S. A. The estimation of missing plot value in split-plot and strip trials. *Journal of the Indian Society of Agricultural Statistics,* 1948, **1,** 147-161. [281]

Kishen, K. Symmetrical unequal block arrangements. *Sankhyā,* 1941, **5,** 329-344. [486]

Kramer, C. Y. Extension of multiple range tests to group means with unequal numbers of replications. *Biometrics,* 1956, **12,** 307-310. [94]

Krishna Iyer, P. V. The analysis of simple nonsymmetrical experiments. *Indian Journal of Agricultural Science,* 1940, **10,** 686-690. [282]

Kruskal, W. H. and W. A. Wallis. Use of ranks in one-criterion variance analysis. *Journal of the American Statistical Association,* 1952, **47,** 583-621. [493]

La Forge, R. Confidence intervals or tests of significance in scientific research. *Psychological Bulletin,* 1967, **68,** 446-447. [77]

Lana, R. E. and A. Lubin. The effect of correlation on the repeated measures design. *Educational and Psychological Measurement,* 1963, **23,** 729-739. [143, 247]

Lee, W. Experimental design symbolization and model derivation. *Psychometrika,* 1966, **31,** 397-412. [176]

Leonard, W. H. and A. G. Clark. *Field Plot Techniques.* Minneapolis, Minnesota, Burgess Publishing Co., 1939. [11]

Leone, F. C. *see* Johnson, N. L. and...

Lewis, D. *Quantitative Methods in Psychology*. New York, McGraw-Hill Book Company, Inc., 1960. [116]

Li, C. C. *Introduction to Experimental Statistics*. New York, McGraw-Hill Book Company, Inc., 1964. [453]

Li, J. C. R. Design and statistical analysis of some confounded factorial experiments. *Iowa Agricultural Experiment Station Research Bulletin*, Ames, Iowa, 1944, **333**, 449-492. [367, 374, 375]

Lindman, H. *see* Edwards, W.,..., and L. J. Savage

Lindquist, E. F. *Design and Analysis of Experiments in Psychology and Education*. Boston, Houghton Mifflin Company, 1953. [21, 38, 61, 246]

Lohnes, P. R. *see* Cooley, W. W. and...

Lubin, A. *see* Lana, R. E. and...

Lum, M. D. *see* Harter, H. L. and..., 1955

Lum, M. D. *see also* Harter, H. L. and..., 1962

McGill, W. J. Multivariate information transmission. *Psychometrika*, 1954, **19**, 97-116. [502]

McHugh, R. B. and D. S. Ellis. The "postmortem" testing of experimental comparisons. *Psychological Bulletin*, 1955, **52**, 425-428. [86]

MacKenzie, W. A. *see* Fisher, R. A. and..., 1922

MacKenzie, W. A. *see also* Fisher, R. A. and..., 1923

McNee, R. C. *see* Danford, M. B., H. M. Hughes, and...

McSweeney, M. *see* Marascuilo, L. A., and...

Mann, H. B. and D. R. Whitney. On a test of whether one of two random variables is stochastically larger than the other. *Annals of Mathematical Statistics*, 1947, **18**, 50-60. [495, 548]

Marascuilo, L. A. and M. McSweeney. Nonparametric post hoc comparisons for trend. *Psychological Bulletin*, 1967, **67**, 401-412. [502]

Massey, F. J., Jr. *see* Dixon, W. J., and...

Massey, F. J., Jr. *see also* Dunn, O. J. and...

Mattson, T. B. *see* Olds, E. G.,..., and R. E. Odeh

Merrington, M. and C. M. Thompson. Tables for testing the homogeneity of a set of estimated variances. *Biometrika*, 1946, **33**, 296-304. [62]

Miller, R. G., Jr. *Simultaneous Statistical Inference*. New York, McGraw-Hill Book Company, Inc., 1966. [79, 84, 97, 498, 501, 502]

Minas, J. S. *see* Ackoff, R. L., S. K. Gupta, and...

Mood, A. M. *Introduction to the Theory of Statistics*. New York, McGraw-Hill Book Company, Inc., 1950. [502]

Morrison, D. F. *Multivariate Statistical Methods*, New York, McGraw-Hill Book Company, Inc., 1967. [5, 144]

Mosteller, F. and R. R. Bush. Selected quantitative techniques. In G. Lindzey (ed.), *Handbook of Social Psychology*. Cambridge, Addison-Wesley Publishing Company, Inc., 1954, 289-334. [65]

Nair, K. R. Balanced confounded arrangements for the 5^n type of experiment. *Sankhyā*, 1940, **5**, 57-70. [365]

——————. A note on rectangular lattices. *Biometrics*, 1953, **9**, 101-106. [452]

——————. On a method of getting confounded arrangements in the general symmetrical type of experiments. *Sankhyā*, 1938, **4**, 121-138. [365, 367]

Nair, K. R. *see also* Bose, R. C. and...

National Bureau of Standards. *Fractional Factorial Experiment Designs for Factors at Two Levels.* National Bureau of Standards, Applied Mathematics Series 48, 1957. [394]

Natrella, M. G. The relation between confidence intervals and tests of significance — a teaching aid. *American Statistics,* 1960, **14,** 20–22, 38. [77]

Nemenyi, P. *Distribution-free multiple comparisons.* Unpublished doctoral thesis. Princeton University, Princeton, N.J., 1963. [494, 497, 501]

Newman, D. The distribution of the range in samples from a normal population, expressed in terms of an independent estimate of standard deviation. *Biometrika,* 1939, **31,** 20–30. [91]

Norton, H. W. The 7×7 squares. *Annals of Eugenics,* 1939, **9,** 269–307. [153]

Nunnally, J. The place of statistics in psychology. *Educational and Psychological Measurement,* 1960, **20,** 641–650. [77]

Odeh, R. E. and E. G. Olds. Notes on the analysis of variance of logarithms of variances. *WADC Technical Note, 59–82,* Wright-Patterson AFB, Ohio, 1959. [62]

Odeh, R. E. *see also* Olds, E. G., T. B. Mattson, and...

Olds, E. G., T. B. Mattson, and R. E. Odeh. Notes on the use of transformations in the analysis of variance. *WADC Technical Report 56–308,* Wright-Patterson AFB, Ohio, 1956. [64]

Olds, E. G. *see also* Odeh, R. E. and...

Overall, J. E. and S. N. Dalal. Design of experiments to maximize power relative to cost. *Psychological Bulletin,* 1965, **64,** 339–350. [11]

Parker, E. T. *see* Bose, R. C., S. S. Shrikhande, and...

Paull, A. E. On a preliminary test for pooling mean squares in the analysis of variance. *Annals of Mathematical Statistics,* 1950, **21,** 539–556. [216]

Pearce, S. C. Field experimentation with fruit trees and other perennial plants. *Commonwealth Bureau Horticultural Plantation Crops Technical Communication,* **23,** 1953. [453]

—————————. Some new designs of Latin square type. *Journal of the Royal Statistical Society,* 1952, **14,** 101–106. [453]

Pearson, E. S. The analysis of variance in cases of non-normal variation. *Biometrika,* 1931, **23,** 114–133. [61]

Pearson, E. S. and H. O. Hartley. *Biometrika Tables for Statisticians,* vol. 1, 2nd ed. New York: Cambridge, 1958. [522, 524, 531, 536]

—————————. Charts of the power function for analysis of variance tests, derived from the non-central F-distribution. *Biometrika,* 1951, **38,** 112–130. [540]

—————————. The probability integral of the range in samples of n observations from a normal population. *Biometrika,* 1942, **32,** 301–310. [78]

—————————. Tables of the probability integral of the studentized range. *Biometrika,* 1943, **33,** 89–99. [78]

Preece, D. A. Classifying Youden rectangles. *Journal of the Royal Statistical Society, Series B,* 1966, **28,** 118–130. [443]

Rao, C. R. *Advanced Statistical Methods in Biometric Research.* New York, John Wiley & Sons, Inc., 1952. [5, 208]

—————————. General methods of analysis for incomplete block designs. *Journal of the American Statistical Association,* 1947, **42,** 541–561. [427, 454]

Rozeboom, W. W. The fallacy of the null hypothesis significance test. *Psychological Bulletin,* 1960, **57,** 416–428. [77]

Ryan, T. A. The experiment as the unit for computing rates of error. *Psychological Bulletin,* 1962, **59,** 301–305. [78, 83, 86]

_____. Multiple comparisons in psychological research. *Psychological Bulletin,* 1959, **56,** 26–47. [83, 86, 90]

_____. Significance tests for multiple comparison of proportions, variances, and other statistics. *Psychological Bulletin,* 1960, **57,** 318–328. [86, 97, 494, 495]

Sade, A. An omission in Norton's list of 7x7 squares. *Annals of Mathematical Statistics,* 1951, **22,** 306–307. [153]

Satterthwaite, F. E. An approximate distribution of estimates of variance components. *Biometrics Bulletin,* 1946, **2,** 110–114. [98, 212]

Savage, I. R. *Bibliography of Nonparametric Statistics.* Cambridge, Mass., Harvard University Press, 1962. [502]

Savage, L. J. *see* Edwards, W., H. Lindman, and...

Scheffé, H. *The Analysis of Variance.* New York, John Wiley & Sons, Inc., 1959. [94, 112, 145, 160, 199, 217, 430]

_____. A method for judging all contrasts in the analysis of variance. *Biometrika,* 1953, **40,** 87–104. [81, 90]

Searle, S. R. *Matrix Algebra for the Biological Sciences.* New York, John Wiley & Sons, Inc., 1966. [141, 144]

Seshadri, V. Combining unbiased estimators. *Biometrics,* 1963, **19,** 163–170. [432]

Shrikhande, S. S. *see* Bose, R. C., W. H. Clatworthy, and...

Shrikhande, S. S. *see also* Bose, R. C.,..., and E. T. Parker

Siegel, S. *Nonparametric Statistics for the Behavioral Sciences.* New York, McGraw-Hill Book Company, Inc., 1956. [498, 501, 502]

Smith, C. A. B. and H. O. Hartley. The construction of Youden squares. *Journal of the Royal Statistical Society,* 1948, **10,** 262–263. [442]

Smith, H. F. The problem of comparing the results of two experiments with unequal errors. *Journal of Scientific and Industrial Research,* 1936, **9,** 211–212. [98]

Snedecor, G. W. *Analysis of Variance and Covariance.* Ames, Iowa, Iowa State University Press, 1934. [39]

_____. *Statistical Methods Applied to Experiments in Agriculture and Biology.* Ames, Iowa, Iowa State University Press, 1956. [146, 231, 233, 479]

Sobel, M. *see* Bechhofer, R. E., C. W. Dunnett, and...

Steel, R. G. D. A multiple comparison rank sum test: treatments versus control. *Biometrics,* 1959, **15,** 560–572. [494]

_____. A rank sum test for comparing all pairs of treatments. *Technometrics,* 1960, **2,** 197–208. [494]

_____. Some rank sum multiple comparisons tests. *Biometrics,* 1961, **17,** 539–552. [494]

Still, A. W. Use of orthogonal polynomials with nonparametric tests. *Psychological Bulletin,* 1967, **68,** 327–329. [502]

Stoneman, D. M. *see* Draper, N. R. and...

Student. Errors of routine analysis. *Biometrika,* 1927, **19,** 151–164. [91]

Tang, P. C. The power function of the analysis of variance tests with tables and illustrations of their use. *Statistics Research Memorandum,* 1938, **2,** 126–149. [9, 107]

Tate, M. W. and R. C. Clelland. *Nonparametric and Shortcut Statistics.* Danville, Ill., Interstate Printers and Publishers, Inc., 1957. [502]

Taylor, J. The comparison of pairs of treatments in split-plot experiments. *Biometrika,* 1950, **37,** 443–444. [268]

_____. Errors of treatment comparisons when observations are missing. *Nature,* 1948, **162,** 262–263. [147]

Terry, M. E. *see* Bradley, R. A. and...

Thompson, C. M. *see* Merrington, M. and...

Tolman, B. *see* Doxtator, C. W.,..., C. E. Cormany, H. L. Bush, and V. Jensen

Tukey, J. W. Comparing individual means in the analysis of variance. *Biometrics,* 1949a, **5,** 99–114. [90]

―――――. One degree of freedom for nonadditivity. *Biometrics,* 1949b, **5,** 232–242, [64, 137]

―――――. The problem of multiple comparisons. Ditto, Princeton University, 396 pp., 1953. [81, 85, 88, 112, 145, 199]

―――――. Queries. *Biometrics,* 1955, **11,** 111–113. [160]

Tukey, J. W. *see also* Cornfield, J. and...

Tukey, J. W. *see also* Freeman, M. F. and...

Tukey, J. W. *see also* Green, B. F. and...

Veldman, D. J. *Fortran Programming for the Behavioral Sciences.* New York, Holt, Rinehart and Winston, 1967. [366]

Wallis, W. A. *see* Eisenhart, C., M. W. Hastay, and...

Wallis, W. A. *see also* Kruskal, W. H. and...

Walsh, J. E. *Handbook of Nonparametric Statistics,* Vols. I, II. Princeton, N.J., D. Van Nostrand Company, Inc., 1965. [502]

Welch, B. L. The generalization of Student's problem when several different population variances are involved. *Biometrika,* 1947, **34,** 28–35. [98]

Whitney, D. R. A bivariate extension of the U statistic. *Annals of Mathematical Statistics,* 1951, **22,** 274–282. [502]

Whitney, D. R. *see also* Mann, H. B. and...

Wilcoxon, F. Individual comparisons in ranking methods. *Biometrics Bulletin,* 1945, **1,** 80–83. [500]

―――――. *Some Rapid Approximate Statistical Procedures.* New York, American Cyanamid Company, 1949. [500, 501]

Wilk, M. B. and O. Kempthorne. Nonadditivities in a Latin square design. *Journal of the American Statistical Association,* 1957, **52,** 218–236. [160]

Wilkinson, G. N. The analysis of variance and derivation of standard errors for incomplete data. *Biometrics,* 1958, **14,** 360–384. [437]

Wilson, W. A note on the inconsistency inherent in the necessity to perform multiple comparisons. *Psychological Bulletin,* 1962, **59,** 296–300. [78, 86]

Winer, B. J. *Statistical Principles in Experimental Design.* New York, McGraw-Hill Book Company, Inc., 1962. [21, 208, 246, 365, 366, 374, 400, 406, 454, 484]

Wishart, J. *see* Allan, F. E. and...

Yates, F. The analysis of replicated experiments when field results are incomplete. *Empire Journal of Experimental Agriculture,* 1933, **1,** 129–142. [146, 162, 163]

―――――. The design and analysis of factorial experiments. *Imperial Bureau of Soil Science Technical Communication No. 35,* Harpenden, England, 1937. [321, 333, 362, 363, 367, 374, 375, 380]

―――――. Incomplete Latin squares. *Journal of Agricultural Science,* 1936a, **26,** 301–315. [164, 453]

―――――. A new method of arranging variety trials involving a large number of varieties. *Journal of Agricultural Science,* 1936b, **26,** 424–455. [424, 452]

―――――. The recovery of inter-block information in balanced incomplete block designs. *Annals of Eugenics,* 1940, **10,** 317–325. [434]

Yates, F. *see also* Fisher, R. A. and..., 1934

Yates, F. *see also* Fisher, R. A. and..., 1963

Yates, F. and R. W. Hale. The analysis of Latin squares when two or more rows, columns, or treatments are missing. *Journal of the Royal Statistical Society Supplement,* 1939, **6,** 67–79. [164, 453]

Youden, W. J. Experimental designs to increase accuracy of greenhouse studies. *Boyce Thompson Institute, Contributions,* Yonkers, N.Y., 1940, **11,** 219–228. [441]

Young, S. *see* Connor, W. S. and...

Zelen, M. The analysis of covariance for incomplete block designs. *Biometrics,* 1957, **13,** 309–332. [486]

Zelen, M. *see also* Connor, W. S. and...

INDEX